Keeping Students Safe and Helping Them Thrive

Keeping Students Safe and Helping Them Thrive

A Collaborative Handbook on School Safety, Mental Health, and Wellness

Volume 2

David Osher, Matthew J. Mayer, Robert J. Jagers, Kimberly Kendziora, and Lacy Wood, Editors

PRAEGER™

An Imprint of ABC-CLIO, LLC
Santa Barbara, California • Denver, Colorado

Library of Congress Cataloging-in-Publication Data

Names: Osher, David, editor. | Mayer, Matthew J., editor. | Jagers, Robert J., editor. | Kendziora, Kimberly, editor. | Wood, Lacy, editor.
Title: Keeping students safe and helping them thrive : a collaborative handbook on school safety, mental health, and wellness / David Osher, Matthew J. Mayer, Robert J. Jagers, Kimberly Kendziora, and Lacy Wood, editors.
Description: Santa Barbara, California : Praeger, an Imprint of ABC-CLIO, [2019] | Includes bibliographical references and index.
Identifiers: LCCN 2018043487 (print) | LCCN 2018044317 (ebook) | ISBN 9781440854149 (ebook) | ISBN 9781440854132 (set : alk. paper) | ISBN 9781440854156 (vol. 1 : alk. paper) | ISBN 9781440854163 (vol. 2 : alk. paper)
Subjects: | MESH: Child Health | Adolescent Health | School Health Services | Safety | Schools
Classification: LCC RJ101 (ebook) | LCC RJ101 (print) | NLM WS 440 | DDC 362.19892—dc23
LC record available at https://lccn.loc.gov/2018043487

ISBN: 978-1-4408-5413-2 (set)
978-1-4408-5415-6 (vol. 1)
978-1-4408-5416-3 (vol. 2)
978-1-4408-5414-9 (ebook)

23 22 21 20 19 1 2 3 4 5

This book is also available as an eBook.

Praeger
An Imprint of ABC-CLIO, LLC

ABC-CLIO, LLC
147 Castilian Drive
Santa Barbara, California 93117
www.abc-clio.com

This book is printed on acid-free paper ∞
Manufactured in the United States of America

Contents

PART 1

Comprehensive Approaches to Promotion, Prevention, Intervention, and Support

CHAPTER ONE

Approaches to Promotion and Prevention

Kimberly Kendziora and Trish Shaffer

Every year in the United States, up to 20% of children and youth experience a mental, emotional, or behavioral disorder (Centers for Disease Control and Prevention, 2015; Perou et al., 2013). The most prevalent mental health disorder in children and youth is attention deficit hyperactivity disorder (ADHD), followed by depression, behavioral or conduct problems, anxiety, substance use disorders, Autism spectrum disorders, and Tourette syndrome (Perou et al., 2013). Often these conditions occur together, which can complicate identification and treatment of mental health disorders. The consequences of mental and behavioral health problems can include serious difficulties at home, with peers, and in school; a higher risk for dropping out; and increased risk of engaging in substance use, criminal behavior, and other risk-taking behaviors (Substance Abuse and Mental Health Services Administration [SAMHSA], 2014; Vos et al., 2012).

Despite this need, nearly half of all children with emotional or behavioral difficulties receive no mental health services—only 7.4% of young people report any mental health visits in the past year (Merikangas et al., 2010; Simon, Pastor, Reuben, Huang, & Goldstrom, 2015). Among the relatively few children and youth who do receive mental health services, most do so at school (Substance Abuse and Mental Health Services Administration [SAMHSA], 2017). Indeed, because of compulsory education, the education system has long been recognized as the de facto mental health system for children in the United States (Burns et al., 1995). Schools are an important social field for children and youth and are influential in their development (Osher, Cantor, Berg, Strayer, & Rose, 2018; Osher, Kendziora, Spier, & Garibaldi, 2014), and so any solution to the challenge of improving children's mental and behavioral health outcomes must include schools.

In this chapter, we focus on a set of school-based solutions to the challenges presented by the vast unmet need to address mental, emotional, and behavioral problems using the lens of one district's experience in promoting positive skills and preventing risk and disorder. Because this is a collaborative handbook, the research on promotion and prevention is brought to life by sharing the work of the Washoe County School District (WCSD) in northern Nevada. The chapter begins by defining promotion and prevention, and describing their place in the broader spectrum of interventions. The chapter also addresses the issue of how educators can know whether students may require supports at a higher tier of service and discusses screening and using district data in an early warning system.

What this chapter does *not* do is focus on lists of effective programs. There are many other sources for this information, such as those offered by the Collaborative for Academic, Social, and Emotional Learning (CASEL; https://casel.org/guide/), Blueprints for Healthy Youth Development (https://www.colorado.edu/cspv/blueprints/), or the What Works Clearinghouse (https://ies.ed.gov/ncee/wwc/). What we do offer is a primer on how to think about these important activities and examples from an exemplary district.

About the Washoe County School District

The WCSD is roughly 200 miles north to south and 35 miles wide, bordering California and Oregon; most of the population is concentrated in the city of Reno. The northern half of the county is rural. Washoe County's almost 64,000 students are 45% white, 40% Latino, 4% Asian, and 2% African American; 45% of students qualify for the free or reduced-price lunch program, 14% are students with disabilities, and 17% are English language learners (Washoe County School District [WCSD], 2018a).

Washoe County's strategic plan, Envision 2020, guides improvement efforts focused on five goals: (1) academic growth; (2) effective personnel; (3) strong relationships among family, staff, trustees, and community members; (4) efficient operational systems; and (5) safe, secure, supportive, and welcoming schools. The inclusion of a goal related to safety and support is consistent with an orientation toward social and emotional learning (SEL) that the district adopted in 2012 (Washoe County School District [WCSD], 2018b). After about 10 years of graduation rates stagnating at about 55%, WCSD leaders decided they needed to do something different to put their students on the path to college and careers. Grounded in research that showed that social and emotional skills, such as persistence and empathy, as well as feeling connected to school, can help reduce dropout and other poor outcomes, WCSD launched a districtwide SEL initiative in 2012, adopting a mission statement of "Every Child, by Name and Face, to Graduation." The goal was to have 90% of students graduating by the year 2020, or "90 by '20," a phrase that has become a mantra around the district (Korbey, 2017).

WCSD's SEL efforts were supported by a grant from the NoVo Foundation and participation in the Collaborative for Academic, Social, and Emotional Learning's Collaborating District Initiative (CDI; Kendziora & Osher, 2016; Mart, Weissberg, & Kendziora, 2015), which supports districts in integrating SEL into all students' education. As part of its work related to the CDI, WCSD:

- developed SEL standards with the input of diverse stakeholders
- provided a comprehensive program of professional learning for district and school staff related to SEL
- integrated SEL into academic instruction through the Core Task Project (which was a 3-day class over a 6-week period with 30 implementation specialists on implementing SEL strategies in English and language arts)
- implemented evidence-based SEL programs in all grades
- developed a communications plan.

WCSD's focus has been on SEL as an integrated strategy rather than as a stand-alone program. To date, results have been promising. Figure 1.1 shows that the district's adjusted four-year graduation rate, which was the point of despair that propelled them toward this improvement pathway, has increased 29 percentage points in the past 10 years, from 55% in 2007 to 84% in 2017.

WCSD's many related efforts will be highlighted throughout the chapter as we address each section in turn. Before discussing promotion and prevention in action, we first address where these activities fit in the continuum of interventions.

Levels of Intervention for Mental, Emotional, and Behavioral Problems

The concept of levels of intervention is central to public health. Modern approaches recognize four broad levels of intervention presented in the 2009 Institute of Medicine (IOM) report, *Preventing Mental, Emotional, and Behavioral Disorders among Young People: Progress and Possibilities* (O'Connell, Boat, & Warner, 2009). These levels are:

- **Promotion.** Usually intended for the general public or a whole population, promotive interventions aim to enhance individuals' ability to achieve

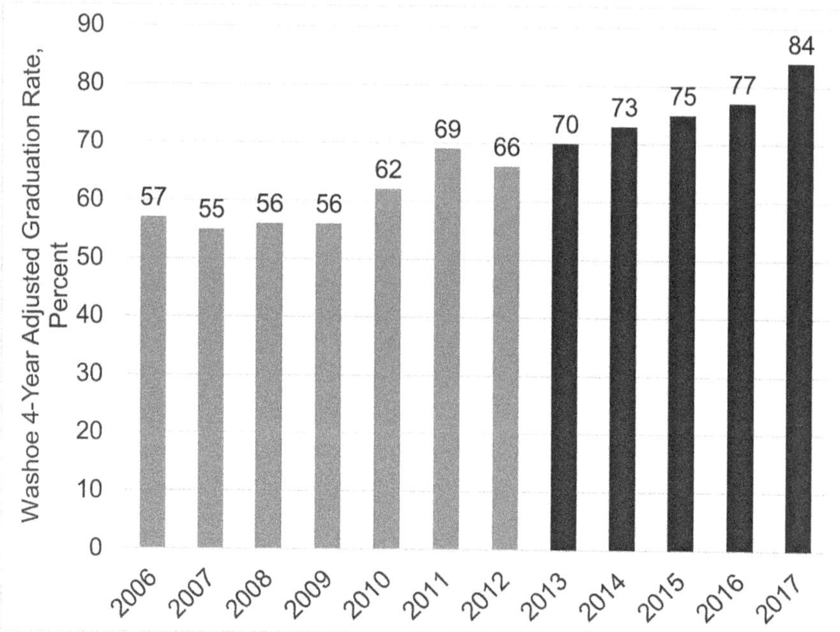

Figure 1.1 Washoe County school district's graduation rates, 2006 to 2017

developmentally appropriate tasks (competence) and a positive sense of mastery, well-being, and social inclusion, and strengthen their ability to cope with adversity.

- **Prevention**. Three levels of prevention are identified. *Universal* interventions target whole groups, such as school-based programs offered to all children to avoid substance abuse. *Selective* interventions address subgroups of people who experience biological, psychological, or social risk factors that are associated with the onset of a mental, emotional, or behavioral disorder. Examples include programs offered to children exposed to abuse, death of a loved one, or academic failure. *Indicated* interventions serve individuals identified as having some signs or symptoms foreshadowing a mental, emotional, or behavioral disorder, but who do not currently meet diagnostic criteria.
- **Treatment** provides benefits, including symptomatic relief, for an already-existing diagnosable condition. Treatment actives are characterized as *case definition* and *standard treatment* for the disorder, which includes interventions to reduce the likelihood of future co-occurring disorders. The optimal treatment protocol aims to reduce the length of time the disorder exists, halt a progression of severity, and halt the recurrence of the original disorder, or if not possible, to increase the length of time between episodes.

- **Maintenance** interventions aim to decrease the disability associated with a disorder. They may be supportive, educational, or pharmacological in nature, and are generally provided on a long-term basis. The two components of maintenance are (1) compliance with long-term treatment to reduce relapse and recurrence; and (2) after-care services, including rehabilitation.

An important advance in the 2009 report was the inclusion of promotion in the spectrum of interventions. Prior IOM work did not include this level of intervention because "health promotion is not driven by an emphasis on illness, but rather by a focus on the enhancement of well-being" and that was seen as being outside the scope of mental health efforts at that time (Mrazek & Haggerty, 1994, p. 27). The 2009 report called on the nation to shift the focus from the *treatment* of mental, emotional, and behavioral disorders to not only their *prevention* but even further, in addition to actively reducing risk prior to any onset of disorders, the nation should also actively promote positive mental health and well-being.

The distinction between promotion and prevention is somewhat fuzzy (Bottiani, Heilbrun, & Bradshaw, 2019). Because of its focus on reducing risk factors, some have characterized prevention as more deficit-focused and promotion as more strengths-focused. Prevention involves helping youth move away from risk, and promotion can be seen as helping them to actively develop competencies (e.g., social skills, emotion regulation, or grit) that enable them to meet role expectations (e.g., being a successful student) and improve well-being. In the 1980s, Karen Pittman of the Forum for Youth investment coined the phrase, "problem-free is not fully prepared" to highlight the fundamental difference between the goals of prevention and promotion, and the practices of working from strengths rather than addressing deficits (Pittman, 1999; Pittman, Irby, Tolman, Yohalem, & Ferber, 2003). In a related line of work, Keyes (2002) and Lamers, Westerhof, Bohlmeijer, ten Klooster, and Keyes (2011) have conceptualized mental health and mental illness as two separate but related continua, and have characterized the positive presence of mental health (defined as emotional, psychological, and social well-being) as *flourishing*. However, the IOM committee stated in the 2009 report that prevention and promotion were so closely related that promotion should be regarded as a component of prevention: both focus on changing common influences on the development young people to help them achieve better life outcomes.

Promotion and Prevention in the Context of Multitiered System of Supports

Although the topic of multitiered systems of support (MTSS) was addressed in its own chapter in Volume 1 of this publication, it is important to provide an overview of this approach to organizing interventions in schools so that the work of promotion and prevention can be well-understood. Like many districts across the country, WCSD uses a multitiered framework to coordinate the delivery of services and supports to students. In short, MTSS organizes a continuum of services at multiple levels of intensity within a school into tiers of service.

On the instructional side, the dominant multitiered model (and the one used in WCSD) is Response to Intervention (RTI). RTI is an approach to the early identification and support of students with learning needs that begins with high-quality instruction and universal screening of all children in the general education classroom, and then provides students who struggle with interventions at increasing levels of intensity.

On the behavioral side of student support, several models of organizing services into tiers exist. The most common approach, Positive Behavioral Intervention and Supports, is in use in 26,370 schools and serves more than 14 million students (Horner, 2018). Services for all students may include teaching behavioral expectations or developing positive character traits. At higher levels of student need, such as those experiencing mental health issues, services may involve providers outside the immediate school setting. The processes of student identification, screening, referral, and care management that are necessary for effective service provision require strong coordination within schools and between schools and community-based providers and families (Barrett, Eber, & Weist, 2012).

MTSS is not a program itself; it is a system of organizing programs or interventions so that they are delivered to appropriate students. Services can be provided to all students in a building (Tier 1), students who are at risk (Tier 2), or students in high need (Tier 3; see figure 1.2).

Tier 1 in MTSS refers to the set of programs, interventions, and overall environments provided to all students in a building. Behavior management, bullying prevention, and family engagement are examples of practices or

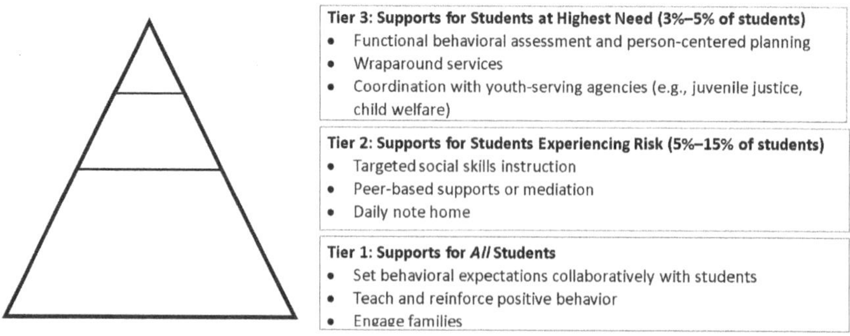

Figure 1.2 Multitiered Systems of Support: Description of levels of support with sample intervention activities

approaches that all students receive. School counselors may visit classes to provide structured lessons in SEL or character education. Schoolwide interventions supporting a positive school climate and promoting positive relationships also belong in Tier 1. Such interventions may include establishing norms; promoting strengths and positive adaptation; and preventing problems such as bullying, suicide, or substance abuse.

At Tier 2, schools provide services to students having some problems functioning successfully in school. Most school systems have counselors, social workers, or school psychologists on staff who can provide these services. Schools generally provide these services to small groups of students outside the regular classroom setting. Tier 2 services include social skills groups, peer mediation, or behavior plans that may involve a daily note home. In some instances, community-based organizations may be contracted to provide Tier 2 services in schools that have a limited capacity for student behavioral support. In these cases, the school and the service provider would engage in some coordination to arrange the logistics for the services, as well as potentially integrating the service plan with the student's schooling.

Tier 3 refers to a more intensive level of services, such as individual therapy, functional behavioral assessment, wraparound services, or supervisory support for youth on probation. A student identified as needing additional supports may receive either Tier 2 or Tier 3 services or both. The level of coordination between school staff and mental health or other agency personnel tends to be higher at Tier 3 (Debnam, Pas, & Bradshaw, 2012). Teachers may receive support or training from a specialist to implement behavioral interventions in the classroom, or teachers may be invited to attend treatment-planning meetings. Therapists may make recommendations to be implemented by school staff regarding behavior support for students at high risk, or counselors may be asked to coordinate in-school visits for youth in juvenile justice diversion programs.

Screening for Mental or Behavioral Health Challenges

Given the multilevel nature of MTSS and public mental health generally, the question of how children access services at the most appropriate level becomes paramount. A regular system of screening is valuable to ensure that all children are receiving the most suitable care. Assessments can be nested within the various levels of interventions to measure children's responses to specific interventions. Because both promotion and the first level of prevention—universal interventions—are delivered to every child within a defined population, screening typically includes all students in a grade. Measurement usually proceeds in a two-stage process: (1) universal screening and (2) more in-depth testing or progress monitoring for students who scored at or below the cut score to verify whether they are truly at risk. Universal screening measures usually consist of brief assessments focused on target skills (e.g., phonological awareness, numeracy, attention, and behavior) that are predictive of future outcomes (Jenkins, Hudson, & Johnson, 2007). Universal screening instruments should be developmentally and culturally appropriate, as well as technically valid (Glover & Albers, 2007). Table 1.1 (adapted from Dymnicki, Kendziora, Williamson, & Osher, 2018) presents some common screening tools for use in MTSS.

Table 1.1 Examples of commonly used mental and behavioral health screening tools

Screener	Applicable Grades	Content	Number of Items, Time Required	Notes
Behavioral and Emotional Screening System (BASC-2/ BESS; Kamphaus & Reynolds, 2007)	PreK–12	Internalizing problems Externalizing problems School problems Adaptive skills	25 items 5 minutes per student	Web-based screening capacity available via AIMSweb Three versions: • Teacher: PreK–12 • Student self-report: Grades 3–12 • Parent: PreK–12
Social Skills Improvement System (SSIS) Performance Screening (Elliott et al., 2017)	Ages 3–18	Prosocial behaviors Motivation to learn Reading skills Math skills	5-point rubric per student 30 minutes per class of 25	Computer and web-based (AIMSweb) administration and scoring available
Strengths and Difficulties Questionnaire (SDQ; Goodman, 1997)	Elementary (ages 3–10) Secondary (ages 11–17)	Emotional symptoms Conduct problems Hyperactivity/ inattention Peer relationship problems Prosocial behavior	25 items per student 60–75 minutes for a classroom of 25	Pencil/paper and online versions available Can be scored online

(continued)

Table 1.1 (continued)

Screener	Applicable Grades	Content	Number of Items, Time Required	Notes
Student Risk Screening Scale (SRSS; Lane et al., 2015, 2016)	K–6; some evidence it may be used in grades 7–12	Externalizing and internalizing behaviors	12 items per student 7 externalizing items 5 internalizing items	Conducted three times per year—fall, winter, and spring No cost
Systematic Screening for Behavior Disorders (SSBD; Walker, Severson, & Feil, 2014)	Grades 1–6	Internalizing and externalizing behaviors	45 minutes for a classroom of 25	A multi-gated system that relies on teacher nominations

Measuring Social and Emotional Skills in the Washoe County School District

Through a Researcher-Practitioner Partnerships in Education Research grant funded by the U.S. Department of Education, WCSD and CASEL worked together to improve the quality of student self-report measures of social and emotional competence. Like many school districts, WCSD included a section on its student-reported school climate surveys in which students could rate their own social and emotional competencies. Existing student measures used in the district had the problem of too many students giving themselves the top ratings across items—the items were, in a psychometric sense, too easy. In addition, the vocabulary on the test was too hard for some students (WCSD, 2015).

In an effort to address these issues, as well as include student voice in the new measure, WCSD conducted focus groups with students to create relevant and understandable questions that would reflect a wider range of difficulty. From a bank of 150 items assessing a range of social competencies, WCSD identified 17 "anchor items" that can be used as a scale on future surveys. WCSD uses these data not for accountability but rather to assess whether its own programs are working as intended.

Washoe County School District's Early Warning System

Other than assessment of students or collecting teacher ratings, another way to monitor whether a student has fallen off track and may benefit from additional supports or interventions involves using district data systems. Examining data about which students may be showing early indicators of trouble, such as frequent absences, atypical discipline events, or sudden changes in grades may allow districts to identify and address problems before they grow into major obstacles. For this reason, many schools and school systems are implementing some form of Early Warning Systems. These systems use a wide range of data to identify students who are at risk, allowing educators to provide timely interventions and supports.

Rigorous research on such systems has documented their promise. For example, Faria and colleagues (2017) examined the use of an early warning system in 73 schools that looked at grade 9 and 10 students' data to identify those at risk for not graduating on time. The study team found that, despite incomplete implementation, using a warning system reduced the percentage of students with risk indicators related to chronic absence and course failure but not related to low grade point averages, suspensions, or insufficient credits to graduate.

WCSD has been developing and refining its early warning system for almost 10 years. Based on both practical experience and research, WCSD identified two clear paths for student disengagement from school: (1) academic failure and struggle; and (2) behavioral reactions to school (misbehavior, school avoidance; Janosz, Le Blanc, Boulerice, & Tremblay, 2000). Based on research showing that attendance, behavior, and course failures in grade 6 predicted 60% of dropouts (Balfanz, Herzog, & Mac Iver, 2007), WCSD developed a system based on five indicators: attendance, transience, retention, credit deficiency, and a history of suspensions (Hayes, 2015). Earlier models included reading and mathematics achievement test scores, but testing and development showed that these factors did not add to the quality of prediction. WCSD has found its Early Warning System to be effective, but not perfect. Of 9th grade students identified as being at low risk in the 2010–2011 school year, 89% graduated on time and 3% dropped out. Conversely, of 9th grade students identified as being at high risk, 31% graduated on time and 39% dropped out (Hayes, 2015). The differences are stark, but there may be room to improve the system.

Perhaps the most crucial element of WCSD's Early Warning System is that the Office of Accountability has used district data platforms to put these data into the hands of both district leaders and teachers. Once credentialed to use the system, educators can examine their students' data, cross-classifying results to identify groups or trends. For example, a teacher may run an Early Warning System Report on her class list and may decide to group students who are at higher risk with those at lower risk for instructional tasks. The Director of MTSS in the district reported that the Early Warning System has allowed schools to be more efficient, strategic, and purposeful.

Washoe County School District's Approaches to Promotion and Prevention

Promotion in Washoe County School District

For its work related to the CDI initiative, WCSD began its journey focusing on establishing standards for what both students and adults in the district should know and be able to do in the areas of self-awareness, self-management, social awareness, relationship skills, and responsible decision-making. Professional learning throughout the district on these standards had the effect of introducing SEL concepts to staff, busting myths that SEL is "soft and fuzzy" content that did not really matter for student outcomes, and establishing a common language for discussing priorities and programs to address needs and goals in these areas.

In 2014, WCSD introduced an evidence-based SEL program for grades K–8, called MindUP. This curriculum features 15 lessons each school year that combine age-appropriate information about the brain with mindfulness-based strategies to help students focus their attention, improve their self-regulation skills, build resilience to stress, and develop a positive mind-set. A quasi-experimental study of MindUP done in Canada found among 146 students in grades 4 and 7, it increased positive social behavior, reduced conduct problems, and reduced emotional distress (Schonert-Reichl & Lawlor, 2010).

In high schools, WCSD implemented School–Connect (Hutson, Beland, & Douglass, 2016). School–Connect is a teacher-facilitated curriculum designed to improve SEL and academic skills of high school students and create supportive relationships among students and between students and their teachers. The School–Connect curriculum consists of 60, 45-minute lessons for each year of high school. These lessons can be delivered during freshman seminars, grade-level advisories, or academic classes. Each year's curriculum is composed of three curriculum modules: Module 1: Creating a Supportive Learning Community, Module 2: Developing Self-Awareness and Self-Management, and Module 3: Building Relationships and Resolving Conflicts. Each module contains 20 lessons and PowerPoints that include research-based content and strategies, interactive activities that foster student engagement, and opportunities for reflection and application (Hutson et al., 2016).

A quasi-experimental evaluation of School–Connect for freshmen conducted in Texas compared a variety of student indicators from the end of grade 8 (baseline), end of grade 9 (post-intervention), and fall of grade 10 (six-month follow-up). Results showed small but significant improvements in discipline referrals and higher math grades (p = .05, d = .13) and average core subject pass rates at the end of grade 9. At six-month follow-up, School–Connect students had significantly fewer discipline referrals and higher average Social Studies grades. There were no effects on attendance. Overall, findings indicated that School–Connect had positive effects on discipline, grades, and pass rates at post-test. Six months after intervention, students who participated in the program still had lower disciplinary rates than those in a matched control group, but the findings for grades did not sustain in the longer term.

In addition, elementary counselors use lessons from the Promoting Alternative THinking Strategies (PATHS) program to teach social and emotional skills directly (Conduct Problems Prevention Research Group, 1999; Kusché, Greenberg, & Conduct Problems Prevention Research Group, 2011). PATHS is one of the most extensively researched and effectively replicated classroom-based SEL programs available to schools. PATHS provides a scope and sequence of lessons that directly teach SEL skills. It also includes practices to promote skill generalization and teaching strategies to create a positive classroom climate. PATHS has been proven effective in numerous randomized trials (Conduct Problems Prevention Research Group, 2011), although use of the lessons alone have not been evaluated.

As of the end of the 2017–2018 school year, every one of the 104 schools in WCSD has some SEL components in place, with about 80%–85% of schools reporting consistent use of their SEL curriculum. Almost all 14 high schools have advisory periods at least for freshmen, and most have it for freshmen, sophomores, and juniors. In addition to the implementation of School–Connect, these periods are used to provide opportunities to engage the student voice, work with students on their leadership abilities, and simply talk about what is happening in the school, community, and country.

Climate and culture activities are carried out throughout the school district, including activities with staff, to ensure that all students feel safe, seen, and celebrated. One activity has included staff gatherings in which either student names are posted on chart paper or rosters are distributed, and staff make marks if they know "Name/Face," "Something Personal," "Personal/Family Story," and "Academic Standing." The goal is to know something more about students than just whether they are enrolled. This exercise can identify not only the students who are well known to staff (to the good or ill) but also what students lack connections to adults in the building. The exercise points out who is "flying under the radar." Data from the student connection exercises are then cross-referenced with Early Warning System data, and students in need of greater connection are assigned to teachers as mentees. This helps ensure that every student has someone who knows how to say their name correctly, and who talks with them about their experiences beyond academic tasks.

Other climate and culture activities are focused on staff experience of connection. For example, professional learning meetings among staff, with families, and between district leaders and school personnel have welcoming rituals and routines, engaging pedagogy, then optimistic closure. These core activities serve to strengthen relationships, build empathy and understanding, and promote connection.

WCSD runs about 60–80 parent universities every school year that focus on fostering resilience, creating self-efficacy through goal-setting, and strengthening social and emotional competencies. At these sessions, parents and educators can learn more about SEL districtwide. At all events for families, translators, childcare, and meals for children are provided.

Prevention in Washoe County School District

Prevention efforts in WCSD build on the foundation created by their significant body of work that promotes social and emotional competencies, student voice, and connection. WCSD's prevention efforts are strongly grounded in its MTSS framework, which the district has been implementing since 2008. All its schools have a functioning MTSS team in place, called an intervention assistance team, or IAT. IATs support Tier 1 and 2 services that are delivered by grade level or department level teacher teams. There is also a school intervention assistance team, which is a multidisciplinary team that sometimes includes external professionals and family members. These school-level teams can work with families at all tiers of service. For the past four years, there has also been a district-level IAT. This highly multidisciplinary team, with representatives from juvenile justice, social services, foster care, the city's children's cabinet, psychological services, MTSS/SEL, counseling, and wraparound services meets every week to review the care plans for students with intensive support needs, including looking at student data. Finally, a behavioral health and management team housed within MTSS trains and coaches district and school staff on functional behavioral assessments, writing and implementing positive behavior support plans, and de-escalation techniques.

Some of the teams established to operate WCSD's MTSS framework also play a role in prevention. For example, the district intervention assistance team plays a significant role in instances when students are placed on emergency suspension and are being considered for expulsion. These occasions present an opportunity to address the entire ecosystem for that child to make adjustments or improvements where possible. On some occasions, the team has managed rent payments, connected family members to counseling or other therapeutic services, and has worked with juvenile justice for students who are on parole.

Overall, promotion and prevention efforts in WCSD are strongly championed at the district level and are taking root in schools. One insight from implementation science has been that belief and commitment often follow behavior (Huberman & Miles, 1984), so communicating the expectation that SEL is not optional and creating conditions in which school staff work together to improve programming can build momentum. Another element that supports progress is "early wins," and WCSD has begun to see some results. According to WCSD's internal data (WCSD, 2018), students who report higher social and emotional competence on the WCSD annual student climate survey have:

- Significantly higher reading and math test scores and weighted high school GPAs
- Lower rates of suspension and absenteeism
- More likelihood that they will graduate on time.

In addition, staff who work at schools with high buy-in for SEL report significantly less work stress and burnout than staff who work at schools where buy-in for SEL is lower.

Future Directions in Promotion and Prevention

One obstacle to districts' and schools' committing to addressing prevention and promotion has been that doing so has required a significant effort and resources. WCSD was one of only eight districts in the country to be awarded a CDI grant to supplement these resources, for example. Other districts have contracted with sometimes-expensive education consultants or technical assistance providers to develop plans and oversee their execution.

One way the field can advance the update of promotion and prevention efforts is by making them easier to implement. On strategy toward this end is to distill common "kernels" from multiple evidence-based SEL programs and offer those active ingredients in their simplest form. Over the last 10–15 years, there has been a growing movement in the prevention and intervention sciences directed toward identifying *evidence-based prevention kernels* (Barth et al., 2012; Embry & Biglan, 2008; Rotheram-Borus, Swendeman, & Chorpita, 2012). Kernels are "fundamental units" of effective promotion or prevention programs that have been shown to effect specific behavior changes (Embry, 2004). Kernels include deep nasal breathing for calming down, or the use of hand signals in the classroom to indicate a change in activities or to send a message to the group. Kernels have promise in affecting a range of outcomes tied to academic achievement and social adjustment, including classroom behavior, discipline, self-control, and the ability to manage emotions effectively (Jones & Bouffard, 2012). Kernels are compelling to educators because they do not have to be tied to a specific manualized curriculum (in fact, they appear in many evidence-based curricula) and because they are typically low cost and relatively simple to use.

One frontier in promotion and prevention is to develop, test, and scale such less-intensive strategies that are easy to implement outside the context of a manualized program, while still achieving meaningful outcomes for students. Teachers, staff, and administrators in all schools need access to evidence-based strategies and activities they can use with students in fairly brief, but ongoing ways, interspersed naturally throughout the day in normal routines, and tailored to the school's unique context, needs, and capacities. The need for such programming is acute, and exemplars such as WCSD's can help inspire other districts and schools to follow suit.

References

Balfanz, R., Herzog, L., & Mac Iver, D. (2007). Preventing student disengagement and keeping students on the graduation path in the urban middle grade schools: Early identification and effective interventions. *Educational Psychologist, 42*(4), 223–235.

Barrett, S., Bradshaw, C. P., & Lewis-Palmer, T. (2008). Maryland Statewide PBIS Initiative: Systems, evaluation, and next steps. *Journal of Positive Behavior Interventions, 10*(2), 105–114.

Barrett, S., Eber, L., & Weist, M. (Eds.). (2012). *Advancing education effectiveness: Interconnecting school mental health and school-wide positive behavior support.* Eugene, OR and Baltimore: Office of Special Education Programs Center on Positive Behavioral Interventions and Supports and the University of Maryland Center for School Mental Health. Retrieved from http://www.pbis.org/common/cms/files/Current%20Topics/Final-Monograph.pdf

Barth, R. P., Lee, B. R., Lindsey, M. A., Collins, K. S., Streider, F., Chorpita, B. F., . . . Sparks, J. A. (2012). Evidence-based practice at a crossroads: The timely emergence of common elements and common factors. *Research on Social Work Practice, 22*, 108–119. doi:10.1177/1049731511408440

Bottiani, J. H., Heilbrun, A., & Bradshaw, C. P. (2019). Models of health promotion and preventive intervention. In M. J. Mayer & S. R. Jimerson (Eds.), *School safety and violence prevention: Science, practice, policy* (pp. 71–94). Washington, DC: American Psychological Association.

Burns, B. J., Costello, E. J., Angold, A., Tweed, D., Stangl, D., Farmer, E. M. Z., & Erkanli, A. (1995). Children's mental health service use across service sectors. *Health Affairs, 14*(3), 147–159. doi:10.1377/hlthaff.14.3.147

Centers for Disease Control and Prevention. (2015). *Web-based injury statistics query and reporting system (WISQARS)*. Atlanta: Author. Retrieved from http://www.cdc.gov/injury/wisqars/index.html

Conduct Problems Prevention Research Group. (1999). Initial impact of the Fast Track Prevention Trial for Conduct Problems II: Classroom effects. *Journal of Consulting and Clinical Psychology, 67*, 648–657.

Conduct Problems Prevention Research Group. (2011). The effects of the Fast Track preventive intervention on the development of conduct disorder across childhood. *Child Development, 82*(1), 331–345. doi:10.1111/j.1467-8624.2010.01558.x

Debnam, K. J., Pas, E. T., & Bradshaw, C. P. (2012). Secondary and tertiary support systems in schools implementing school-wide positive behavioral interventions and supports: A preliminary descriptive analysis. *Journal of Positive Behavior Interventions, 14*(3), 142–152. doi:10.1177/1098300712436844

Dymnicki, A., Kendziora, K., Williamson, S., & Osher, D. (2018). Selective strategies. In D. Osher, D. Moroney, & S. Williamson (Eds.). *Creating safe, equitable, engaging schools: A comprehensive, evidence-based approach to supporting students* (pp. 187–200). Cambridge, MA: Harvard Education Press.

Elliott, S. N., Davies, M. D., Frey, J. R., Gresham, F., & Cooper, G. (2017). Development and initial validation of a social emotional learning assessment for universal screening. *Journal of Applied Developmental Psychology*. Advance online publication. doi:10.1016/j.appdev.2017.06.002

Embry, D. D. (2004). Community-based prevention using simple, low-cost, evidence-based kernels and behavior vaccines. *Journal of Community Psychology, 32*(5), 575–591. doi:10.1002/jcop.20020

Embry, D. D., & Biglan, A. (2008). Evidence-based kernels: Fundamental units of behavioral influence. *Clinical Child and Family Psychology Review, 11*, 75–113. doi:10.1007/s10567-008-0036-x

Faria, A.-M., Sorensen, N., Heppen, J., Bowdon, J., Taylor, S., Eisner, R., & Foster, S. (2017). *Getting students on track for graduation: Impacts of the Early Warning Intervention and Monitoring System after one year* (REL 2017–272). Washington, DC: U.S. Department of Education, Institute of Education Sciences, National Center for Education Evaluation and Regional Assistance, Regional Educational Laboratory Midwest. Retrieved from http://ies.ed.gov/ncee/edlabs

Glover, T. A., & Albers, C. A. (2007). Considerations for evaluating universal screening assessments. *Journal of School Psychology, 45*(2), 117–135. doi:10.1016/j.jsp.2006.05.005

Goodman, R. (1997). The Strengths and Difficulties Questionnaire: A research note. *Journal of Child Psychology and Psychiatry, 38*, 581–586.

Hayes, B. (2015). *Every child, by name and face to graduation: Are my students at risk for negative outcomes? A look at the Early Warning System in WCSD*. Presentation at the Saturday Café, Reno, NV. Retrieved from https://slideplayer.com/slide/7694204/

Horner, R. (2018, March). *Current and future directions for PBS.* Paper presented at the 15th International Conference on Positive Behavior Support, San Diego, CA. Retrieved from http://www.pbis.org/Common/Cms/files/pbis resources/(post)%20APBS%20Featured%20Session%20A-1%202018.pdf

Huberman, M., & Miles, M. B. (1984). *Innovation up close: How school improvement works.* New York: Plenum.

Hutson, A., Beland, K., & Douglass, J. (2016, January). *School-Connect intervention impact on high school students' discipline referrals and academic outcomes* (Unpublished manuscript). Retrieved from http://www.school-connect .net/pdf/School-Connect-Evalaution-Report-1.27.16.pdf

Janosz, M., Le Blanc, M., Boulerice, B., & Tremblay, R. E. (2000). Predicting different types of school dropouts: A typological approach with two longitudinal samples. *Journal of Educational Psychology, 92*(1), 171–190. doi:10.1037/0022-0663.92.1.171

Jenkins, J. R., Hudson, R. F., & Johnson, E. S. (2007). Screening for at-risk readers in a response to intervention framework. *School Psychology Review, 36*, 582–600.

Jones, S. M., & Bouffard, S. M. (2012). Social and emotional learning in schools: From programs to strategies. *Society for Research in Child Development Social Policy Report, 26*, 1–22.

Kamphaus, R. W., & Reynolds, C. R. (2007). *Behavior Assessment System for Children—Second Edition (BASC-2): Behavioral and Emotional Screening System (BESS).* Bloomington, MN: Pearson.

Kendziora, K., & Osher, D. (2016). Promoting children's and adolescents' social and emotional development: District adaptations of a theory of action. *Journal of Clinical Child and Adolescent Psychology. Special Issue: Good enough? Interventions for child mental health: From adoption to adaptation—from programs to systems, 45*, 797–811. doi:10.1080/15374416.2016 .1197834

Keyes, C. L. M. (2002). The mental health continuum: From languishing to flourishing in life. *Journal of Health and Social Behavior, 43*(2), 207–222.

Korbey, H. (2017, October). The power of being seen. *Edutopia.* Web post. Retrieved from https://www.edutopia.org/article/power-being-seen

Kusché, C. A., Greenberg, M. T., & Conduct Problems Prevention Research Group. (2011). *Grade level PATHS (grades 1–2).* South Deerfield, MA: Channing-Bete.

Lamers, S. M. A., Westerhof, G. J., Bohlmeijer, E. T., ten Klooster, P. M., & Keyes, C. L. M. (2011). Evaluating the psychometric properties of the Mental Health Continuum-Short Form (MHC-SF). *Journal of Clinical Psychology, 67*(1), 99–110. doi:10.1002/jcl p.20741

Lane, K. L., Oakes, W. P., Cantwell, E. D., Schatschneider, C., Menzies, H., Crittenden, M., & Messenger, M. (2016). Student risk screening scale for internalizing and externalizing behaviors: Preliminary cut scores to support data-informed decision making in middle and high schools. *Behavioral Disorders, 42*(1), 271–284. doi:https://doi.org/10.17988/BD-16-115.1

Lane, K. L., Oakes, W. P., Swogger, E. D., Schatschneider, C., Menzies, H. M., & Sanchez, J. (2015). Student risk screening scale for internalizing and externalizing behaviors: Preliminary cut scores to support data-informed decision making. *Behavioral Disorders, 40*, 159–170.

Mart, A. K., Weissberg, R. P., & Kendziora, K. (2015). Systemic support for social and emotional learning in school districts. In J. Durlak, C. Domitrovich, R. Weissberg, T. Gullotta, & P. Goren (Eds.), *The handbook of social and emotional learning* (pp. 482–499). New York: Guilford.

Merikangas, K. R., He, J. P., Burstein, M., Swanson, S. A., Avenevoli, S., Cui, L., . . . Swendsen, J. (2010). Lifetime prevalence of mental disorders in U.S. adolescents: Results from the National Comorbidity Survey Replication—Adolescent Supplement (NCS-A). *Journal of the American Academy of Child and Adolescent Psychiatry, 49*, 980–989. doi:10.1016/j.jaac.2010.05.017

Messick, S. (1989). Validity. In R. L. Linn (Ed.), *Educational measurement* (3rd ed., pp. 13–103). New York: Macmillan.

Mrazek, P. J., & Haggerty, R. J. (1994). *Reducing risks for mental disorders: Frontiers for preventive intervention research.* Washington, DC: National Academies Press.

O'Connell, M. E., Boat, T., & Warner, K. E. (2009). *Preventing mental, emotional, and behavioral disorders among young people: Progress and possibilities.* Washington, DC: National Academies Press.

Osher, D., Cantor, P., Berg, J., Strayer, L., & Rose, T. (2018). Drivers of human development: How relationships and context shape learning and development. *Applied Developmental Science.* Advance online publication. doi:10.1080/10888691.2017.1398650

Osher, D., Kendziora, K., Spier, E., & Garibaldi, M. L. (2014). School influences on child and youth development. In Z. Sloboda & H. Petras (Eds.), *Advances in prevention science: Vol. 1. Defining prevention science* (pp. 151–169). New York: Springer. doi:10.1007/978-1-4899-7424-2_7

Perou, R., Bitsko, R. H., Blumberg, S. J., Pastor, P., Ghandour, R. M., & Huang, L. N. (2013). Mental health surveillance among children—United States, 2005–2011. *Morbidity and Mortality Weekly Report, 62*, 1–35. Retrieved from https://www.cdc.gov/mmwr/preview/mmwrhtml/su 6202a1.htm?s_cid=su6202a1_w

Pittman, K. J. (1999, September). *Youth today: The power of engagement.* Web post. The Forum for Youth Investment. Retrieved from http://forumfyi.org/content/youth-today-power-enga

Pittman, K. J., Irby, M., Tolman, J., Yohalem, N., & Ferber, T. (2003). *Preventing problems, promoting development, encouraging engagement: Competing priorities or inseparable goals?* Washington, DC: Forum for Youth Investment. Retrieved from http://citeseerx.ist.psu.edu/viewdoc/download?doi=10.1.1.471.1224&rep=rep1&type=pdf

Rotheram-Borus, M. J., Swendeman, D., & Chorpita, B. F. (2012). Disruptive innovations for designing and diffusing evidence-based interventions. *American Psychologist, 67*, 463–476. doi:10.1037/a0028180

Schonert-Reichl, K. A., & Lawlor, M. S. (2010). The effects of a mindfulness-based education program on pre- and early adolescents' wellbeing and social and emotional competence. *Mindfulness, 1*, 137–151.

Simon, A. E., Pastor, P. N., Reuben, C. A., Huang, L. N., & Goldstrom, I. D. (2015). Use of mental health services by children ages six to 11 with emotional or behavioral difficulties. *Psychiatric Services, 66*(9), 930–937. doi:10.1176/appi.ps.201400342

Substance Abuse and Mental Health Services Administration (SAMHSA). (2014). *Results from the 2013 National Survey on Drug Use and Health: Summary of national findings* (HHS Publication No. SMA 14-4863). Rockville, MD: Author. Retrieved from http://www.samhsa.gov/data/sites/default/files/NSDUHresultsPDFWHTML2013/Web/NSDUHresults2013.pdf

Substance Abuse and Mental Health Services Administration (SAMHSA). (2017). *Results from the 2014 National Survey on Drug Use and Health: Mental health detailed tables.* Rockville, MD: Author. Retrieved from https://www.samhsa.gov/data/sites/default/files/NSDUH-MHDetTabs2014/NSDUH-MHDetTabs2014.htm#tab2-1a

Vos, T., Flaxman, A. D., Naghavi, M., Lozano, R., Michaud, C., Ezzati, M., . . . Murray, C. J. L. (2012). Years lived with disability (YLDs) for 1160 sequelae of 289 diseases and injuries 1990–2010: A systematic analysis for the Global Burden of Disease Study 2010. *The Lancet, 380*, 2163–2196. doi:10.1016/S0140-6736(12)61729-2

Walker, H. M., Severson, H. H., & Feil, E. G. (2014). *Systematic screening for behavior disorders (SSBD) technical manual: Universal screening for pre-K–9* (2nd ed.). Eugene, OR: Pacific Northwest Publishing.

Washoe County School District. (2018a). *2017–18 characteristics and performance.* Retrieved from https://www.washoeschools.net/

Washoe County School District. (2018b). *Washoe SEL one-pager.* Web document. Retrieved from https://www.washoeschools.net/cms/lib/NV01912265/Centricity/Domain/202/Social%20Emotional%20Learning/SEL%20Snapshot/REFINEMENT_WASHOE_SEL_ONEPAGER_F.pdf

CHAPTER TWO

Early Intervention within the School Setting

Heather J. Clawson and Stephanie Wu

The Importance of Early Intervention in Keeping Students on Track

Research has consistently made the case for the importance of early intervention. In essence, early intervention seeks to identify and address significant student needs before the problem escalates. It involves the formulation of *stable relationships with caring and responsive adults*, provision of *safe and supportive environments*, development of *social, emotional, and cognitive skills*, and attention to *nutrition and physical health* to change the life trajectory for children and improve outcomes for children, families, and communities (Center on the Developing Child, 2008). That said, early intervention is not just limited to the early childhood years. Many children and adolescents at some point in their development will experience a period during which they have challenges and begin to show early signs that they are falling off course. For example, one study found that 50% of students that dropped out of high school showed signs of not graduating as early as 6th grade (Balfanz, Herzog, & Mac Iver, 2007). Additionally, studies show that half of people who will develop mental health disorders show symptoms by age 14 (Paus, Keshavan, & Giedd, 2008). And the pathway to juvenile delinquency is not dissimilar; with onset of severe antisocial behavior often in early childhood or adolescents (Silverthorn & Frick, 1999). Yet, we tend to ignore problems until they reach a level of severity that requires more intensive and costly interventions and treatment and not always with success as evident by unacceptable rates of suicide, school dropout, homelessness, and involvement in the juvenile justice system in our society (Mental Health America, n.d.). As children of any age exhibit telltale signs of struggle, whether with academics, behavior, or social and emotional development, the ability to intervene early and help them establish robust personal support networks, as well as provide them access to supports that address the underlying causes of their challenges, becomes an important factor in whether they will be able to get back on track. Intervening early and often, as demonstrated through research, can result in short- and long-term benefits related to academic achievement, behavior, educational progression and attainment, delinquency and crime, and labor market success (Karoly, Kilburn, & Cannon, 2005).

Identifying the right supports at the right time requires a collective effort by the school, community partners, family, and the student. For collaborative partnerships like these to be successful, however, there are several conditions that need to be present. Without the right foundation and resources, schools may miss their students' early signs of trouble and along with it, the opportunity to intervene early and address emerging issues before they become an intractable problem that overwhelms the school, the students, the families, and the community.

This chapter describes three elements that should be in place in schools for early interventions to be effective, along with examples of two organizations that partner with schools and families across the country to provide early intervention services in elementary and secondary schools.

Elements of Effective Early Intervention in Schools

Three elements should be present in schools to adequately identify and address the needs of students early enough to intervene before a problem escalates and requires more intensive interventions and treatment, and to ensure investment and follow-through by all parties. They are: healthy school-community partnerships, early warning and response systems, and developmental relationships.

Healthy School-Community Partnerships

Many schools and districts are drawing on the wealth of research about the practices that can improve students' social, emotional, and academic outcomes as they design their approaches to early intervention. Schools and districts alone, however, do not have the resources (e.g., staffing, access to programming) to address the many challenges faced by its students; in particular, the growing number of students living in poverty, estimated at

15 million or 21% of all children (National Center for Children in Poverty, 2016), attend schools that are underresourced to address the stressors of poverty on learning, many of which can be mitigated with support. The *National Survey of School Counselors* (College Board Advocacy & Policy Center, 2012) provides us some insight. In this survey, counselors in schools with high numbers of students from families with low incomes reported caseloads averaging 427 students, although the American School Counselors Association recommends a caseload of 250 students per counselor. In addition, the roles of these counselors included everything from college and career counseling to mental health counseling and administrative duties. Teachers also felt the pressure on their instruction and classroom environment when too many students were coping with stressors that distracted them from learning. This dynamic is unsurprising given that public schools, in general, were originally designed to provide supplemental services to only 15% of students, but in an average high-poverty school, as many as 54% of students require additional support beyond their daily lesson (Baker, Kamphaus, Horne, & Winsor, 2006). The solution to close the resource gap lies within collaborative partnerships between districts and schools, community and faith-based organizations, local government, businesses, and families and community members and the execution of a tiered system of supports.

We can best understand these needed supports in the context of a Multi-tiered System of Support (MTSS)—the practice of providing high-quality instruction and interventions matched to student need, monitoring progress frequently to make decisions about changes in instruction or goals, and applying student data to important educational decisions (Batsche et al., 2005). Key to MTSS is the ability to provide services and interventions as soon as a student demonstrates a need (Fuchs & Deschler, 2007). Within this framework, there are three tiers of support or intervention as depicted in figure 2.1.

For tiered supports to be most effective, they must be built on a strong foundation of universal or schoolwide instruction and intervention. It is this foundation that provides the conditions and focus of learning for all students and sets the norms, expectations, and climate for the school. A strong foundation should address the social, emotional, and behavioral needs of most students. While most schools are prepared to provide Tier 1, whole school, preventative, and promotive approaches, providing Tier 2 targeted supports (i.e., early interventions) that mitigate the effects of adversity is an unmanageable burden on even the most effective school administrator and personnel in settings with disproportionately high needs. Often, the gap between need and resources leaves students without the social, emotional, and academic supports, relationships, and opportunities they need to get back on track in school. As mentioned above, the lack of adequate resources is more pervasive in schools located in areas of concentrated poverty (National Governors Association for Best Practices, 2011; Winsor, Baker, & Davis, 2001).

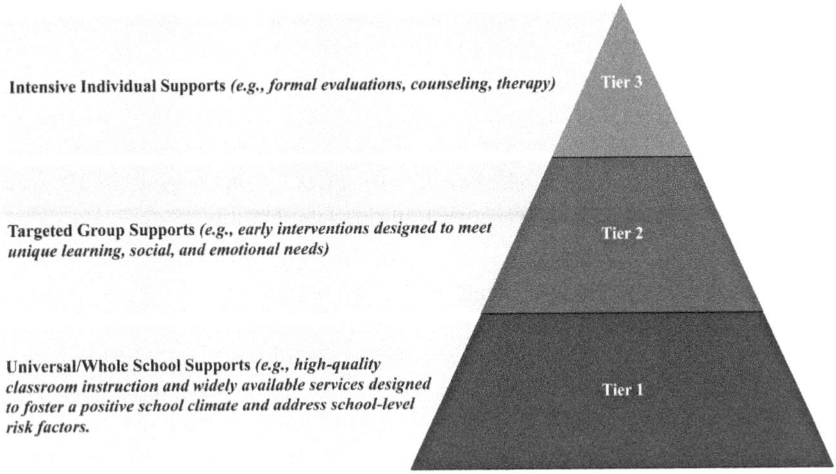

Figure 2.1 Multitiered system of supports

Box 2.1 Key Elements for Effective Implementation of a Tiered Support Framework

1. Comprehensive assessment of student needs, resource availability, and service gaps
2. Availability of data used for early identification of students in need of additional academic and/or nonacademic supports
3. School-based teams to identify students in need and implement the appropriate levels of evidence-based interventions
4. Access to multiple tiers of support
5. Process in place to monitor and assess student progress throughout the course of an intervention

These schools also tend to be more culturally and linguistically diverse than other more affluent schools, which requires schools to develop the capacity to use flexible and responsive strategies that match the needs of their student community. The blend of practices in box 2.1 will support the adults in the school in collectively planning and implementing coherent strategies.

With the right resources, schools can properly implement a tiered framework aligned with the needs of its students, thus, leveraging the talents of their teachers to focus on instruction and creating a healthy classroom environment while other partners provide the necessary noninstructional supports to help combat barriers to learning. It is through school-community partnerships characterized by trust, shared goals that center on the success of students, frequent and honest communication, and systematic sharing about the challenges facing students and the agreed upon roles of each party to respond that we see success. A healthy school-community partnership is the foundation for the other elements to work. Later in this chapter, two organizations, City Year and Communities In Schools, share their approach to being a part of a school's and district's response system. Both organizations apply the evidence-based risk indicator system described below.

Early Warning and Response System

A successful early intervention approach values knowing the student story as holistically as is reasonable and possible. Schooling is a complex and ever-changing experience for a young person. For example, students must manage academic performance across multiple subjects as well as diverse classroom cultures and a variety of teacher relationships. Layer onto this other considerations, such as child and adolescent development, social relations with peers, family issues, or exposure to trauma, and it is easy to understand why it becomes hard for schools to meet the unique needs of their young people. At the same time, it is essential that each student is understood and seen as an individual.

Developed by the Everyone Graduates Center at Johns Hopkins University, early warning systems use readily available data to alert teachers and administrators to students who are at risk of falling so deeply off track that they are at risk of dropping out of school. A key benefit of early warning systems is that they help educators to know what to look for amid the mountains of data about students (Neild, Balfanz, & Herzog, 2007). The Center originally developed the system for primary use in middle and high school levels based on their research that students exhibit signs of risk as early as 6th grade; however, more recent studies have demonstrated the benefits of using these indicators as early as 3rd grade (Rethinam & West, 2012). These early signs or early warning indicators (EWIs) include:

- Attending school less than 80% of the time
- Failing a core academic course (e.g., math, English, below grade level in literacy)
- Experiencing at least one suspension or disciplinary action.

Using these EWIs, the Everyone Graduates Center developed an Early Warning and Response System that enables schools to identify which students need which supports and signal when those students are back on track to graduate, thereby enabling an effective, efficient, and on-demand response to student needs. The testimonial in box 2.2 is one student's experience of the support. The Early Warning and Response System includes five key components:

1. **On-site facilitation.** A key point of contact or coordinator is identified to support school staff and the administration to develop and implement the Early Warning System of support, lead the data analysis process, and provide initial meeting facilitation and coordination of services.
2. **Student data profiles.** The Early Warning System relies on regularly updated student data to ensure timely and accurate identification of students in need in order to intervene early and often. These data generate profiles of students at risk of dropout. EWI data are often available from existing district data systems, with the most common data including measures of attendance, behavior, and course performance. When available, these EWIs should be supplemented by nonacademic data that speaks to noncognitive factors, such as resilience, self-motivation, self-confidence, and so on. Research has shown that these indicators can detect those students at greatest risk of dropping out as early as elementary school.
3. **Student/EWI data review meetings.** Student data profiles are reviewed on a regular basis by a team of school administration, teachers, counselors, school support staff, and others as necessary. During the meetings, members identify students showing EWIs of off track or falling off track behaviors and members share strengths of students, reasons for problematic behaviors, and impact of prior interventions and supports provided to the student. Intervention options are discussed and plans are made to follow up with the student.
4. **Tiered supports or interventions.** To address the varying intensity and needs of students, a "one-size fits all" approach to early intervention is not the solution. Instead, a range of supports must be available that align with the specific needs of the school and its students or a tiered system of support as described previously (see figure 2.1)
5. **Integration of supports.** Existing school resources and needs are identified and additional community-based partnerships are established, coordinated, and integrated into the system of supports. This ensures the right interventions are available at the right time to address the needs of the school and students at risk of academic failure.

Box 2.2

"Before CIS it seemed like every week I was either out of school or in school suspension. I was once an honor student in middle school, then I found myself failing miserably in almost all of my classes as a freshman in high school. But with help from my CIS site coordinator, including tutoring to counseling to parent-teacher conferences, I am now back on track, more focused and determined to do better in my academics and behavior."

—Testimonial from a CIS case-managed student in Atlanta

Developmental Relationships

Early interventions depend upon strong, trusting relationships so that together the student and their supporter or caring adult in the school (e.g., guidance counselor, teacher, school support staff, or mentor) discover the root cause(s) of an issue and tackle it. In addition to issue spotting, developing a web of relationships is also important for young people showing early signs of risk. A report from America's Promise Alliance called *Don't Quit on Me* found that supportive relationships with adults in school can help reduce the likelihood of a student leaving school by 25%. The report also demonstrated that students felt there are different types of relationships with each providing a distinct benefit, including emotional, informational, instrumental, and general guidance (Center for Promise, 2015).

Researchers at Search Institute have also confirmed that relationships in young people's lives matter. Their framework for a developmental relationship approach names key dimensions of a healthy relationship, see box 2.3. Developmental relationships create conditions that help young people attain the psychological and social skills that are essential for success in education and in life. In particular, the number and intensity of this type of relationship in students' lives is linked to a range of positive educational outcomes. Relationships with caring adults and peers can increase student engagement and improve academic motivation. Students who experience developmental relationships get better grades, have higher aspirations for the future, and participate in college-preparatory activities more frequently (Perkins et al., 2016). The student testimonial in box 2.4 expresses how this relationship support felt. An intentional focus on developing positive relationships with students by the adults in the school and the community is essential if we are to intervene early with students and get at the root cause

Box 2.3 The Developmental Relationship Framework

According to Search Institute (2014), students are more likely to be successful in school and life if they experience relationships that do the following:

1. Express care
2. Challenge growth
3. Provide support
4. Share power
5. Expand possibilities

Box 2.4

"He motivates me. He's the best person I ever met . . . I have no other people like him, that's always on me, pushing me. Ever since I met with Justin the first time, it was a big difference for me. I felt like he cared for me."

—Sixth grader speaking about City Year AmeriCorps member, who mentored him during the 2016–2017 school year in Providence, RI.

of their problems. But peer relationships are also important. Encouraging a peer community that fulfills students' relational needs cultivates a proactive mind-set for all students as well as adults. Given the powerful influence of community expectations on human behavior, this group mind-set reinforces the creation of a habit at the individual student level to reflect and take action—basically learning to nip a problem in the bud before it blossoms, which is a valuable life skill.

In sum, when a strong foundation of universal or schoolwide instruction and intervention is established with clear emphasis on preventative and promotive approaches that build social, emotional, and academic or cognitive competencies of students, those who need more support can be identified early and offered what they need. This can happen when formal systems and structures are in place that allow for the use of data to identify students who are heading for academic failure and the ability to connect those students to the appropriate supports and early interventions needed to get them back on track, so they can progress in school, graduate ready for postsecondary education, job training, or a career, and ultimately, succeed in life. And, it is through strong school-community partnerships, these early warning and response systems, and the development and presence of positive relationships between students and school administrators, teachers, providers, parents, and peers that change can happen.

Effective School-Community Partnership Approaches to Early Intervention

Highlighted in this chapter are two national nonprofit organizations that work in public schools—both traditional and charter—across the country to help identify students at risk of dropping out of school and intervene early to provide them the supports they need to address both academic and nonacademic barriers. The two organizations, City Year and Communities In

Schools, are part of an innovative collaboration designed to provide schools a well-integrated set of early intervention supports that include mental health, identity formation, family, and social emotional, academic supports to students with early signs of risk.

The collaboration, known as Diplomas Now, and led by Johns Hopkins University Talent Development Secondary, partners with school districts and schools to: (1) improve teacher practice to ensure students graduate with the academic, social, and emotional skills required for college, career, and life success; and (2) address the scale and intensity of student needs. All three partners share a belief and the ability to execute as a team the three elements of effective early intervention: healthy school-community partnerships, an MTSS approach using the Early Warning and Response System paired with instructional coaching by Talent Development, and student access to developmental relationships from their City Year AmeriCorps members and Communities In Schools site coordinators and the provision of an integrated, tiered system of supports.

In 2010, Diplomas Now received a $30 million Investing in Innovation (i3) grant from the U.S. Department of Education to implement the program in schools across the country and to support one of the largest-ever randomized control trials of secondary schools—62 schools from 11 large urban districts. The latest impact report from the study (Corrin, Sepanik, Rosen, & Shane, 2016) found it is possible to reduce the number of students who are off track on attendance, behavior, and course performance and on the path to dropping out, thereby changing their course and getting these students back on track to high school graduation.

The study also determined the differentiating characteristics of schools that implement the Diplomas Now model, including increased frequency of using data to drive instruction and select struggling students, greater collaboration, and additional support for teachers (e.g., coaching, professional development). For students, Diplomas Now schools showed increased frequency of coordinated academic and nonacademic services, additional academic assistance, and more behavioral supports. Critical to the success of Diplomas Now was the ability to identify students in need and provide early interventions, in particular, for students during the difficult transition years of 6th and 9th grades. The study found that results of a universal approach with embedded early intervention include the following:

- Diplomas Now has a positive, statistically significant impact on increasing the percentage of 6th and 9th graders exhibiting no EWIs. The finding suggests a positive whole school effect that goes beyond students at risk receiving early interventions.
- Diplomas Now had a positive, statistically significant impact on reducing EWIs in middle schools, particularly on reducing chronic absenteeism,

increasing the number of middle school students who attended over 90% of enrolled days.

- Students at Diplomas Now schools were more likely to report a positive relationship with an adult at school who was not a teacher. They also reported participating in more academically focused after-school activities than did their peers at schools without Diplomas Now. This finding bolsters previous research findings that students stay in school, are more engaged, and report they perform better academically when they feel connected to at least one adult who is part of their educational experience.

This study demonstrated the value for students and schools in using a sustained whole school approach to providing early interventions, and the vital role that partners play in helping schools be responsive to the scale of individual student needs in schools serving high-poverty neighborhoods. Below are descriptions of the City Year and Communities In Schools programs.

City Year Overview

City Year is an education-focused AmeriCorps program serving in over 300 public schools where student development is often impeded by significant adverse effects of poverty. Research has found that chronic stress and adversity, often experienced by children growing up in poverty, significantly impacts the development of areas of the brain responsible for foundational skills; examples include controlling for impulses, focusing attention or organizing thinking (Stafford-Brizzard, 2016). Mental health research has also found that the majority of people, of all ages, who experience adversity can heal with the right supports (Noam, 2006). City Year employs evidence-based strategies from multiple sciences such as human development, learning, and mental health to support students from communities of intergenerational poverty.

City Year was founded in 1988 in Boston, Massachusetts, with the goal of bringing together diverse young adults to do one year of intensive full-time service in their communities. The organization invested in an asset-based youth development approach to help develop leadership and civic engagement mind-sets, skills, and behaviors in the young adults who signed up to serve, thus orienting graduates to a lifetime of civic participation. Serving in 29 cities in 19 states, City Year is a member of the AmeriCorps national service network, a federal program that connects individuals of all ages with nonprofit, community-based, and faith-based organizations for a year of service. ("What is AmeriCorps?", n.d.). The Corporation for National and Community Service (CNCS) is an independent federal agency that leverages more than three million Americans in service through its core programs, including AmeriCorps.

Key findings from a longitudinal study of City Year alumni found that at least 90% of alumni, nearly three years after their service, believed their City Year experience contributed to their ability to lead others and to work with people from diverse backgrounds (Anderson, LaGuarda, & Williams, 2007). The lessons learned from supporting the development of its members are now being applied to advance a developmental approach to meeting students' holistic needs in high-need urban schools. Over the past decade, City Year's community service efforts shifted to exclusively partner with urban public schools to counter the toxic levels of chronic stress related to poverty that research has found to impede cognitive and social emotional development (Osher, Cantor, Berg, Steyer, & Rose, 2018a).

City Year's school-based model, known as Whole School Whole Child, provides its intervention services within a broader set of universal engagement strategies in classrooms and the whole school that promote student engagement, identity formation, and community/civic mindedness. Because the model is designed to support whole school improvement, City Year invests in partnerships with key educators at all three levels of the school system: the district leadership and administration, school principals, and classroom teachers. In figure 2.2, City Year's system approach shows its emphasis on districts and school partnerships. For the purposes of this chapter's focus, the description below details City Year's intervention approach.

The City Year program is designed to help schools serving communities in poverty, by deploying a diverse team of trained young adults who serve full time in schools. City Year AmeriCorps members work alongside students throughout the school day and after school, tutoring them in coursework and coaching them in social-emotional skills—in essence, serving as near peer role models, tutors, and mentors. Their services help schools differentiate and personalize according to classroom and student need. Early intervention supports are provided to students exhibiting early signs of disengagement. The research-informed supports build student resiliency, thereby minimizing the effects of their challenges on their school success (Cantor et al., 2018).

City Year Early Intervention Services

School and Student Assignment

City Year's impact model is designed to increase the number of students who reach the 10th grade on track and on time to graduate from high school in the communities it serves. Partner schools are identified by applying research from Johns Hopkins University, which found that only 12% of high schools produced 50% of the nation's dropouts (Balfanz & Letgers, 2004). City Year, working with district and school leaders, found that the same

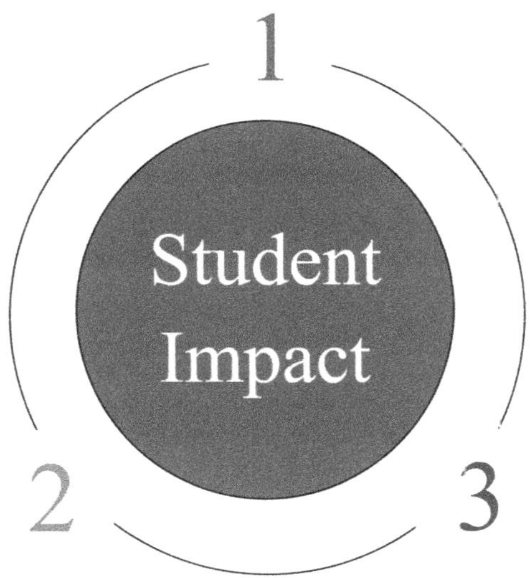

1 School & District Partnership

- Integrated with district and school partners to work collectively toward overall school and student improvement
- Strong school partnerships that ensure conditions for success are in place
- Mutually accountable to short and long term shared impact goals
- Jointly develop strategic deployment plan for multi-year sustainable impact

2 WSWC Model Fidelity

The WSWC model is designed to be fully integrated into a school environment to reinforce school programs. Critical integration points for maximum impact include:

- Use of timely student data
- Intervention time across early warning indicators
- School-wide student engagement approach
- Early warning indicator meetings with teachers and student support specialists
- Extended learning time (before, during, after-school)
- School-wide, classroom, and individualized student support
- Integrated professional development with teachers

3 School Operating Conditions

Evidence-based school operating conditions influencing the effective integration of WSWC include:

- Response to Intervention approach
- Student engagement plan
- Teaching & learning strategy
- Effective school organization

Figure 2.2 City Year's Whole School, Whole Child (WSWC) system focus

pattern exists at a district level. By identifying the elementary and middle schools that feed into struggling high schools, City Year strategically deploys teams of corps members into those feeder schools with the highest concentration of students at risk.

City Year's universal services are designed to promote the school's vision for success, including having a positive impact on whole school climate, as well as on learning environments in classrooms and common areas throughout the school. In classrooms, AmeriCorps members use engagement strategies that create a safe and positive environment, help students meet the teacher expectations and norms, and support the implementation of differentiated instruction by working with small groups. At a whole school level, they welcome students into school, support school transition times, lead school assemblies, coordinate campaigns and family events, and run afterschool activities. Through its whole school services, the City Year team becomes a familiar presence and member of the entire school community.

Nested within by schoolwide Tier 1 services are personalized and responsive Tier 2 interventions, which are available only for identified students in grades 3–9. These intensive services reflect student needs throughout critical transition years during which performance challenges develop and can still be detected early in a student's academic career (Schwerdt & West, 2011). Throughout middle school and into high school, students have to navigate increasing complexity in their school and personal lives, such as more challenging academic requirements, multiple teacher relationships, personal and/or home responsibilities, and the social life of a teenager. City Year AmeriCorps team in schools can support students through their school experiences and help them develop important life skills and habits in the process.

At the beginning of the school year, the City Year supervisor of the team, called an Impact Manager, meets with the principal and teachers to set up City Year's Tier 2 activities. The City Year team and the faculty collaboratively analyze EWI data of student enrollment. The risk indicators used to identify candidates for intervention are poor performance in English and/or Math (evidenced by grades or assessments), low attendance, and disciplinary infractions; these same indicators are described in more detail at the beginning of this chapter. Again, as partners, City Year and the school identify students with one or more EWIs that would benefit from City Year's Tier 2 interventions. The Tier 2 focus areas include supplemental skill-building in the four areas of attendance, behavior, math, and English Language Arts (ELA). Each intervention practice reflects evidence-based strategies. For example, students struggling with attendance participate in a Check In, Check Out program run by AmeriCorps members involving two or three short meetings each week to set goals related to improving attendance and determining the root cause of the challenge. Academic interventions include intervention curricula with evidence-based protocols and are conducted in small groups or individually. Students identified for Tier 2 supports are referred to as Focus List students. Each City Year AmeriCorps member will work with a total of up to 20 Focus List students across all four intervention areas. Social-emotional (SEL) skill development is an element of all four intervention areas. City Year and the school/teachers agree upon dedicated intervention time to develop skills and set goals for the academic interventions.

City Year AmeriCorps teams use a student progress monitoring process that ensures the consistent and timely review of student and intervention data by AmeriCorps members and their partner teachers. The process is supported by a technology platform which City Year teams can use to track the frequency and focus of interventions with student data such as grades, academic assessments, student engagement results, attendance, and SEL skill development. City Year uses SEL assessments that are asset-oriented and specific in their descriptions: one is an observation tool completed by the City Year AmeriCorps member, the DESSA (Apperture), and the other is a student survey, the Holistic Student Assessment (Program for Education and Resilience). City Year members can review these data reports with the principal, teachers, and other adults in the school who work directly with students. City Year also surveys teachers annually to monitor their involvement in progress monitoring. According to its 2016–2017 teacher survey, of the 2,020 respondents, when asked about use of data with their City Year member, 77% of teachers reported that they meet at least once every two weeks to discuss student progress, 64% reported that they use data in their meetings about student progress, and 56% reported that they meet at least once a week.

The holistic set of services that a City Year team provides is visualized in figure 2.3. The services are a blend of whole school, classroom, and targeted early interventions/Tier 2 support delivered throughout the school day and into the extended day setting. Through this holistic approach, the AmeriCorps members gain a full picture of the student experience, increasing their effectiveness to guide, coach, and tutor students in areas of course performance, academic/school routines and habits, and school community membership. To further facilitate a more consistent student school experience, the City Year Impact Manager frequently coordinates with the nonprofit partners in the school, like after-school and student services providers, to minimize redundancy and maximize opportunities for the students. City Year regularly refers students to other programs in the building if and when they learn of needs that those partners are better suited to provide, with a particular emphasis on partnering with the school social workers.

The quality of City Year's student engagement during the supplemental Tier 2 intervention time depends upon its Tier 1/universal service approach;

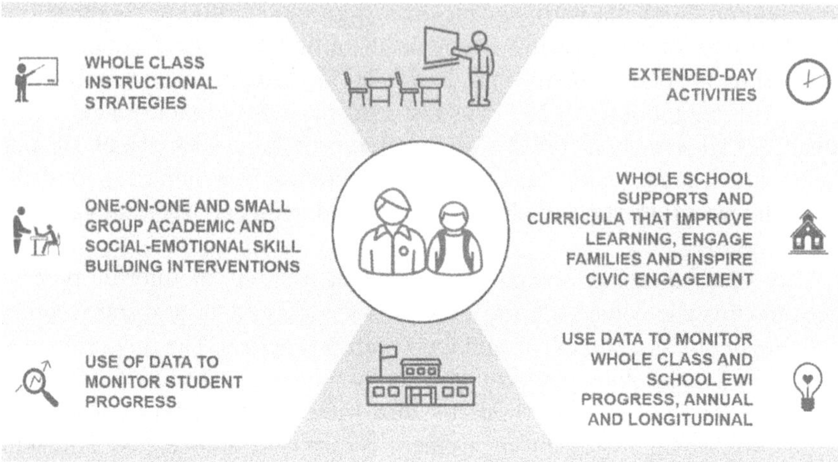

Figure 2.3 Whole School, Whole Child services. (Courtesy of City Year, Inc.)

Tier 2 activities nest within the larger context of the Tier 1 activities. In figure 2.3, one can see that City Year AmeriCorps members support and interact with all students in the school through a variety of settings, such as whole class instruction, school transitions, whole school assemblies and campaigns, evening events for the family, and extended learning. Oftentimes City Year Focus List students are present at those settings, providing more authentic opportunities for the AmeriCorps members to unobtrusively reinforce their student's intervention learning goals. Importantly, the blended Tier 1 and Tier 2 student support approach counters any stigma that might be associated with working with City Year because all students in any school setting are likely to receive some type of just-in-time support from a City Year AmeriCorps member. Students think generally of City Year staff as more mature young persons who are there to help everyone in the school, as they provide school engagement programs as well as support classroom instruction.

Research studies of City Year's services during early years of implementation have found promising yet inconclusive results focused on whole school effects. A Policy Studies Associates (PSA) national study (Meredith & Anderson, 2015) matched City Year schools (elementary, middle, and high schools) to similar schools not implementing City Year to assess City Year's effect on within-year changes in school-level mathematics and ELA state standardized test scores. They found statistically significant positive results on ELA scores for all three years of implementation and on mathematics for the second and third years of implementation. The study found that the City Year model increased a school's likelihood of improving its ELA state test scores by about 11 percentage points (Cohen's $d = 0.22$) and of improving its mathematics state test scores by about 10 percentage points (Cohen's $d = 0.20$). Effect sizes for ELA and mathematics state test scores were low (Cohen's $d = 0.07$ and 0.08, respectively). Although inconclusive, third party evaluations of City Year also offer descriptive evidence that suggests that City Year does positively affect student engagement and the school climate, encouraging future research of the Whole School Whole Child model (Anderson & Mielke, 2012; Billig & Jesse, 2009; Mielke, Butler, Palmiter, & Anderson, 2014; Palmiter, Sanzone, Mielke, & Reisner, 2010; RMC Research Corporation, 2008). Building on this early research of a whole school effect, City Year is now conducting an experimental study of our interventions. In 2017, the Institute of Educational Sciences awarded City Year and the American Institutes of Research a grant to conduct a multiyear randomized control study of Tier 2 services at the student level to begin school year 2018–2019.

Asset-Based Youth Development Strategies

The Power of Near Peer Developmental Relationships

Research has shown that an effective teacher is a critical element for student success (Osher, Cantor, Berg, Steyer, & Rose, 2018a). Even the most skilled teacher, however, would find it difficult to meet each student's unique needs in an environment where more than half of the students struggle to overcome the challenges associated with intergenerational poverty and, thus, require more than just excellent instruction. For example, imagine a teacher working in a middle school with 30 students in the classroom. Many days, 5 different students are absent; 6 have been suspended; 20 are multiple grade levels behind in reading or math; and 4 students require supports from student support specialists.

Now, imagine a principal with 30 classrooms just like that one. Even the most capable teachers, school counselors, and principals would find it difficult to provide all of these struggling students with the necessary individualized instructional and behavioral supports. Educators are understandably overwhelmed by the scale and intensity of student need.

Not only does a City Year team provide additional people power in an under-resourced system, the close age of AmeriCorps member to their students facilitates a powerful near peer connection. City Year AmeriCorps members are young adults ages 18–25—the majority are college graduates and from diverse backgrounds. They are old enough and experienced enough to offer guidance to the younger students, yet young enough to remember similar experiences that the students are going through. In turn, the students are curious about their "City Years" and enjoy being the focus of their attention and in their company. This relatability positions the AmeriCorps members to be effective coaches and role models. One of the theoretical frameworks supporting this near peer approach is Bandura's social-learning theory, which posits that people learn from one another, via observation, imitation, and modeling (Bandura, 1997). Research shows that middle school students are easily influenced by the behavior of individuals they perceive as role models, whether it is prosocial or antisocial behavior (Hurd, Zimmerman, & Reischl, in press). Through their positive relationships with students and modeling of positive interpersonal communication, AmeriCorps members may counteract the negative influence of aggressive and delinquent role models (Kidron & Osher, 2010).

Before entering schools for service, the AmeriCorps members are trained in youth development techniques, group management, student progress monitoring, and tutoring. Throughout their year of service AmeriCorps members receive ongoing support and professional development that includes trainings from City Year, teacher professional development in their schools, observation and coaching from a City Year specialist, and participation in a staff-facilitated community of practice with their City Year peers.

A practitioner who provides a balance of care, support, and challenge in the way that they work with young people is creating opportunities for a young person to learn more about themselves, whether that's through positive risk-taking, overcoming challenges and learning how to become comfortable in different types of situations and with diverse people. When young people experience developmental relationships, they are more likely to be successful adults (Osher et al., 2018a; Roehlkepartain, Pekel, Syvertsen, Sethi, Sullivan, & Scales, 2017).

Resilience-Informed Learning Environments

City Year Impact Managers and teams intentionally create learning environments that meet the developmental needs of young people. The strategy is based on research literature that explains the effects of relationships and environmental context on learning. For example, the context of poverty creates chronic stress that impedes learning, but once acknowledged and understood as a factor, there are strategies that will counteract the stress (Cantor et al., 2018; Osher et al., 2018b). Furthermore, when the strategies are consistently and effectively employed, students develop their innate resiliencies. An example of one such strategy is increasing disadvantaged students' access to positive, consistent, and productive relationships that nurture student voice, meaning-making, and belonging (Noam & Malti, 2009). As near peers, City Year AmeriCorps members are aware of the power of their role modeling and as such, they intentionally model interpersonal, intrapersonal, and leadership skills when working with students. They extend modeling these skills when working with their City Year colleagues and their partner teachers.

AmeriCorps members also use group organizing practices (known as student mobilization at City Year) that encourage peer connections, identity formation, and practicing pro-social skills (Kendziora & Osher, 2010). Playworks is a City Year training partner that specializes in developing engaging strategies for youth practitioners.

The student-facing strategies are rooted in an asset-based, youth development approach. The organization's consistent use of group norms and techniques fosters positive, productive, caring relationships and a joyful learning environment that sets high expectations (Corrin, Sepanik, Rosen, & Shane, 2016). To aid AmeriCorps members and staff in consistently achieving a developmental disposition, City Year uses the Clover Model (Program for Education and Resilience). The Clover Model offers an accessible framework that values meeting human development needs required for social-emotional and academic growth, highlighting four essential elements that young people need to thrive, learn, and grow: active engagement, assertiveness, belonging, and reflection (Malti & Noam, 2009). The easily accessible mental framework includes a training segment on the effects of trauma on a young person's development and the ways in which developing the Clover elements improves resilience. AmeriCorps members use the Clover Model to better understand student behavior and select appropriate strategies based on a student's Clover make-up. AmeriCorps members explicitly name the strategies they use with their students and over time will coach the student to use strategies on their own, gradually releasing them from the City Year sphere of influence so that the student internalizes and transfers the new skill in non-City Year settings. Referred to as positive adaptation in the research literature, this process is part of developing resilience (Cantor et al., 2018; Osher et al., 2018a).

City Year's youth engagement strategies are designed to support both SEL skill development and identity formation. The strategies are referred to as Power Tools within City Year and can be used at any appropriate time throughout the day. They reflect research findings that show the effectiveness of common routines in elementary and secondary schools to establish safe, orderly environments. When intentionally designed, whole school routines and norms support students in developing aspirational and resilient mindsets and behaviors that contribute to the social-emotional development of individuals and the student community (Kidron & Osher, 2010). These four examples of Power Tools illustrate the organization's emphasis on balancing self-management, student meaning-making, and inclusive community.

1. **Strong Circles**. When a large or small group stands together shoulder to shoulder in a circle with "no one inside and no one outside." This circle provides an equal forum for all members of the group to participate fully and share information effectively.

2. **NOSTUESO**. An acronym for "No One Speaks Twice until Everyone Speaks Once." This is a group discussion facilitation technique that helps ensure inclusive input from an entire group or classroom and prevents a few people from dominating a discussion or brainstorm. With students, this helps reinforce taking turns and ensures that every student has a voice.
3. **Check In, Check Out**. A weekly check-in system for AmeriCorps members and students to discuss issues affecting student attendance or academics, followed by problem-solving, and setting goals regarding their attendance. AmeriCorps members check in with students at the beginning of the week (to set goals, discuss potential challenges) and once or twice over the week (to review goals, discuss any concerns or issues). Check In, Check Out provides meaningful support and problem-solving to students while providing an opportunity for AmeriCorps members and students to build relationships.
4. **Morning Greeting**. A daily routine used in the morning before school starts that includes the City Year team at the school entrance welcoming the students and teachers with enthusiasm and personalized greetings that help set the tone and make everyone feel welcome and energized for the day of learning ahead.

A City Year AmeriCorps team employs dozens of such techniques throughout the school day over multiple years in the same school. The consistent use of the techniques builds a distinct culture and shapes the student's experience of school. As students repeatedly use the Power Tools, they recognize the benefits of the behaviors to attaining the goals they set for themselves. It is within this universal environment of learnership and leadership that City Year's early interventions in attendance, behavior, math, and ELA occur.

Communities In Schools

Communities In Schools (CIS) is one of the nation's largest network of nonprofit organizations dedicated to keeping kids in school and helping them succeed in life. Many children, particularly those living in poverty, face enormous challenges both inside and outside the classroom. In fact, students in the low-income communities served by CIS are more likely to be chronically absent from school, three times more likely to repeat a grade, and two times more likely to drop out of school. If not identified early, the challenges for these students can become insurmountable, making it difficult for students to stay on track in school and, for many, dropping out and experiencing more hardships in life becomes their future. By partnering with school districts and schools across 25 states and the District of Columbia, more than 130 local CIS affiliates are able to help schools identify those students at risk for academic failure, intervene early and often, and help get students back on track. It is CIS's mission to surround students with a community of support, empowering them to stay in school and succeed in life.

Figure 2.4 Communities In Schools model of integrated student supports. (Courtesy of Communities In Schools)

How Communities In Schools Works

CIS leverages partnerships to connect students and families with community resources, tailoring them to their specific needs. This is done through a local CIS affiliate that brings the evidence-based CIS model of integrated student supports into a school. Figure 2.4 depicts the key components of the CIS model.

The Communities In Schools Site Coordinator

Key to the CIS model is the site coordinator. This trained professional fills a pivotal role as the single point of contact working inside the school, coordinating and providing integrated student supports. They work with school leadership and staff to connect students and families with community resources that help to address both academic and nonacademic needs, allowing students to show up in the classroom healthy, safe, and prepared to learn.

Working with school leadership and staff, CIS site coordinators identify and prioritize the needs of the schools through a comprehensive needs assessment, determine which supports need to be increased or improved, and identify supports that the schools need but don't currently have (i.e., resource gap). In addition to the school needs assessment, site coordinators work with student support teams consisting of school administrators, teachers, guidance counselors, and other community providers to identify individuals or groups of students at risk of dropping out through the review of EWIs.

Once the needs assessment is complete and students in need of early intervention are identified, the site coordinator meets with their school support team to put together a plan to address the needs and provide supports to the general student population (i.e., Tier 1 supports), and create individual plans for the students presenting with early warning signs of problem behavior, as well as plans for students with more significant needs. Site coordinators then collaborate with local providers to put these plans into action. They attach measurable goals to the school and individual student support plans and track progress against defined metrics to ensure they provide the best possible supports that can yield positive results for schools and students. Key outcomes that CIS helps schools and students address include: attendance, behavior, course performance, college and career readiness, graduation, and social, emotional, and academic development.

Tiers of Support

The CIS site coordinator works with volunteers, partners, and the local community to provide students with the supports they need to succeed both inside and outside the classroom. CIS provides these supports across three different tiers (see figure 2.1). By differentiating supports, CIS is able to serve most students in a school through Tier 1 supports and also focus attention on targeted students who have more significant needs through Tier 2 and 3 supports.

Case Management for Students Who Are at Risk

Those students identified through EWI meetings, parent referrals, or self-referral as being at risk for dropping out are placed on the CIS site coordinator's caseload and are subsequently case managed throughout the year by CIS. The degree of "risk" or number of EWIs present for a student determines the intensity of case management and supports needed. CIS site coordinators are trained to consider where a student falls on a continuum of risk and need as shown in figure 2.5, with the students at the low end or low need

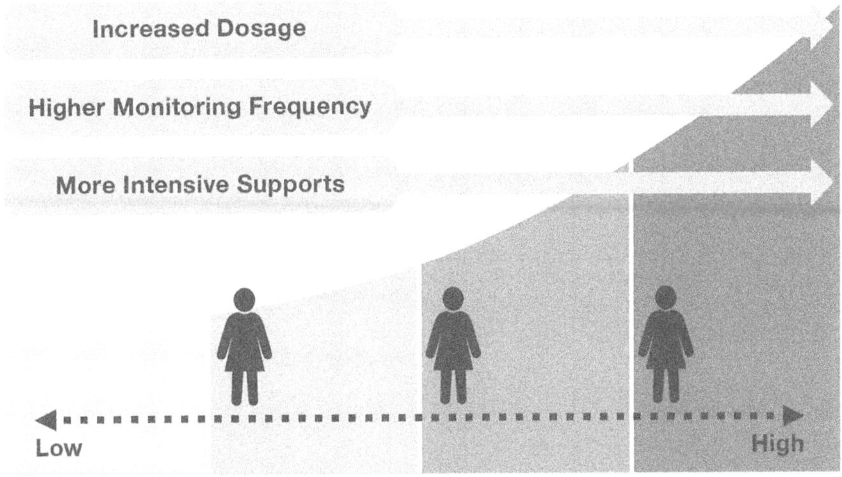

Figure 2.5 CIS case management continuum: From prevention to early intervention to treatment. (Courtesy of Communities In Schools)

being best served by Tier 1 or whole school supports rather than requiring case management and more intensive supports. Students showing moderate levels of risk or need are often those where early interventions or Tier 2 supports are necessary to ensure de-escalation of problems and a focus on getting students on track for success. Students presenting with high levels or significant risk tend to need intensive, individualized Tier 3 supports, such as counseling, therapy, or other forms of remediation.

There is no single way to determine where students fall on this continuum. Through the initial needs assessment process and review of data with student support teams, CIS site coordinators work to identify the following characteristics of each student:

- EWIs, specifically whether a student is on track, sliding, or off track with regards to attendance, behavior, and/or course performance (see Monitoring Guide in table 2.1 used to determine EWI status)
- Presence of other risk factors (e.g., low commitment to school, lack of motivation, unhealthy relationships with peers, early onset of aggression, family disruption)
- Presence of protective factors and assets (e.g., strong family bonds, positive peer associations, engagement in education, positive sense of future)

Based on this information, CIS site coordinators use their best professional judgment to assess where each student falls on the continuum. Over time, each student may move along the continuum in either direction as they

Table 2.1 Example of early warning indicators monitoring guide for off track, sliding, on track status

Monitoring Guidelines for Student Early Warning Indicator Metrics							
	Attendance	Behavior		Course Performance/Academics			
Risk level	**Chronic Absenteeism**	**Suspensions**	**Classroom Conduct (work habit/behavior)**	**Course Grades**	**Credit Completion**	**Standardized Test Scores**	**GPA**
On track	> 90% ADA	No suspensions	O/S (outstanding/ satisfactory)	A, B, C	¼ credits required–1 credit	Proficient/on grade level	2.0 or Above
Sliding	> 85 to ≤ 90% ADA	NA	NA	D	2–4 behind target	1 grade level behind	D Average
Off track	≤ 85% ADA	1 or more suspensions	NI (needs improvement)	1 or more Fs	More than 4 credits behind	Not Proficient/ more than 1 grade level behind	Failing

ADA, average daily attendance.

Component	Student with Moderate Needs	Student with High Intensity Needs
Needs Assessment	• Basic Demographics • Risk Factors/Assets • Baseline Early Warning Indicators (attendance, behavior, course performance, and social, emotional, and academic competencies)	• Additional assessment of risk factors, needs • Family engagement plans
Student Support Plan	• At least one attendance, behavior or course performance goal	• Multiple goals
Tiered Supports	• At least one Tier 2 support or intervention • Monthly check-ins with student	• Comprehensive, wraparound supports – from Tier 2, Tier 3 • Multiple check-ins per week with student • Regular check-ins with providers
Monitor, Adjust, Evaluate	• Review progress toward set goal(s) • Review Early Warning Indicator data • Progress is apparent	• Progress requires additional time, measures

Figure 2.6 Case management process for students with moderate to high needs

achieve goals and develop new protective factors or as they develop additional risk factors and needs.

The overall components of case management are the same for each student regardless of where s/he falls on the continuum. As shown in figure 2.6, these include: conducting a needs assessment, developing a student support plan, connecting students to tiered supports, and monitoring, adjusting, and evaluating against the plan. Identifying a student's level of risk early helps CIS site coordinators intervene with the appropriate intensity of intervention and hopefully avoid students falling off track. It is these students, those beginning to slide off track, that receive early interventions and supports. Throughout the school year, CIS site coordinators will collect, track, and analyze attendance, behavior, and course performance data in collaboration with school personnel to determine whether the early interventions are working. In addition to ongoing monitoring of data, CIS site coordinators continue to meet with students, families, teachers, and providers to make sure the supports are working. If they find out the plan is not working as well as it could, they bring the right people back to the drawing board to adjust or re-create a plan that does.

At the end of the year, the site coordinator determines whether the goals set for the school and each student were met or exceeded, whether goals were unmet but progress was made, or whether the goals were unmet with no progress. Historically, the trends have been positive, with 80% or more of students receiving case management from CIS showing progress or meeting their attendance, behavior, and/or academic/course performance goals. Additionally, according to data obtained annually by CIS National from across its network, more than 90% of the student cases managed by CIS are promoted to the next grade and 90% or more of case-managed seniors graduate. External evaluations have also found that schools that implement the CIS model of integrated student supports as part of their improvement strategies see positive results including improved on-time graduation rates for high schools, lower dropout rates, and higher average daily attendance rates for elementary schools (ICF International, 2008; Somers & Haider, 2017).

Early Intervention in Practice: The Power of Building Relationships and the Development of Social and Emotional Competencies

From its inception more than 40 years ago, CIS has recognized the importance of relationships for young people. Bill Milliken, founder of CIS, is often quoted as saying, "It isn't programs that change people, it is relationships." Central to the work of the CIS site coordinator are the relationships they form with students. The CIS site coordinator builds trusting, long-term relationships with students, parents, teachers, and the school administration. CIS is *in* schools and *in* students' lives, providing a consistent, caring adult who supports students and helps them see their potential. It is through these trusting relationships that CIS site coordinators are able to uncover the underlying causes of problems related to academics and behavior that students are facing and intervene early. Often the root causes cannot be addressed with additional classroom instruction or tutors but instead, require a focus on the social and emotional needs of students.

In recent years, the importance of social and emotional learning (SEL) has received considerable attention among education stakeholders, policy makers, and the general public. Broadly speaking, SEL is defined as "a set of skills that individuals need to succeed in schooling, the workplace, relationships, and citizenships" (Jones & Bouffard, 2012). In other words, SEL refers to managing one's emotions and engaging with people in a positive and healthy manner. A sizable body of research has found that social and emotional competence is critical for academic performance, student well-being, and life success (Goleman, 1995; Hymel & Ford, 2014; Juvonen & Wentzel, 1996; McClelland, Morrison, & Holmes, 2000; Raver, 2002; Wentzel & Asher, 1995).

While many schools are addressing social and emotional development with teacher professional development, implementation of whole school SEL curricula and efforts to improve school and classroom climate, this is often not sufficient for some students, in particular, students living in poverty and students who have experienced trauma. But to help CIS site coordinators identify these students, CIS recognized that using only EWI data was too limiting and did not provide a holistic picture of what was happening with the student. To assist CIS site coordinators to better understand the causes of the presenting problems, CIS developed an assessment of social, emotional,

Box 2.5 SEAD Assessment

SEAD Assessment is a 54-item student self-report survey that assesses students' competencies and needs in a number of social, emotional, and academic domains, including: social support (family, peers); belongingness (school, community); social competence; empathy; emotion regulation; self-regulation; self-compassion; self-worth; growth mindset; academic competence; academic motivation; and academic engagement.

and academic development (SEAD). The results of this assessment are used to determine areas of student need and help the site coordinator identify appropriate supports to promote the development and growth of students' social, emotional, and academic competences.

For students showing room for greater social and emotional development, CIS intervenes early, providing Tier 2 supports, often in small group settings. These range from meditation classes to anger management groups to restorative circles aimed at empowering students to implement solutions to their problems. Examples of early interventions focused on social and emotional development are pervasive across the CIS network. CIS of Central Texas serving the Austin Independent School District (AISD) participates in a Collaborative for Academic, Social, and Emotional Learning (CASEL) pilot program to develop a model to implement SEL programming systematically. In some AISD schools, CIS staff members assist with overall school planning and implementation by training teachers about the effects of trauma on students and how to educate and care for students experiencing trauma. CIS staff also reinforce Tier 1 lessons and concepts with small group interventions. One example is CIS of Central Texas' XY-Zone program; which is used as a Tier 2 support that helps adolescent boys develop social and emotional skills so they can be successful in school and beyond. The program focuses on the 5Rs: respect, responsibility, relationships, role modeling, and reaching out. Students set goals, hold peers accountable, practice their social and emotional skills, and learn how to apply those skills as they transition into manhood. Through CIS of Central Texas, XY-Zone serves 450 adolescent boys per year. The program is also implemented at several other CIS affiliates across the network.

CIS of the Charleston Area implements Second Step, a social and emotional curriculum suitable for students in preschool through 8th grade that utilizes repetition, music, visual stimuli, brain busters, and short, informative lessons to teach students valuable social skills. Second Step is supplemented by Strengthening Families and other parent engagement programming to improve family relationships, parenting skills, and improve social and life skills of children. CIS of Charleston implements these programs with case-managed early learners, as a Tier 2, early intervention for students in preschool through 3rd grade.

Across the CIS network, site coordinators play an important role in delivering early interventions that supplement and enhance the schoolwide efforts in addressing SEL in schools. Through strong relationships, CIS site coordinators are able to work as champions for students, providing support and encouragement in an effort to build important social and emotional skills for young people. A recent evaluation of students receiving case management and early intervention supports from CIS found that these students reported improved relationships with adults, better quality relationships with peers, and improvements in their engagement with school, their educational attitudes, and their belief that education has value for their futures (Parise et al., 2017).

Fostering positive relationships and nurturing the social and emotional development of students has broad implications and long-lasting effects, such as reducing risky behaviors, decreasing dropout rates, and reducing depression and anxiety in adulthood (Aspen Institute, 2016). Schools, educators, policy makers, and youth-serving organizations, like CIS and City Year have integrated SEL—something some have identified as a "missing piece in efforts to reach the array of goals associated with improving schooling in the United States" (Elias et al., 1997, pp. 1–10)—into their practices and into schools.

Summary

From decades of working in elementary, middle, and high schools, City Year and CIS have learned that early intervention efforts make a difference for students of all ages. Using research-based indicators of risk, secondary schools and their partners, can come together with a shared aim and metrics to readily identify students showing early signs of struggle. Even for adolescent age students who have not previously struggled, the changing demands of middle and high school can surface academic or developmental needs. Their early intervention needs will be diverse, for example, academic skill building, support managing home situations, and academic habits and skills development. To customize timely responses to such varied needs, the school will need partners with expertise in providing early intervention supports for both academics and social-emotional development.

Both organizations described in this chapter offer an early intervention approach anchored in a whole school prevention model that includes screening, progress monitoring, and an array of program responses that can be customized to individual students as well as fit in the context of the school environment. In addition to the technical capacity to operate an early intervention model, both organizations recognize the vital role that relationships play in learning and in effective partnerships. It is not enough to bring only tools and systems to make early intervention work. The trust of students is essential for a tutor, mentor, educator, and school to be effective, and students will only give their trust when a developmental relationship is established.

References

Anderson, L. M., LaGuarda, K. G., & Williams, I. J. (2007). The effect of the City Year experience over time: Findings from the longitudinal studies of alumni. Retrieved from http://www.socialimpactexchange.org/sites/www.socialimpactexchange.org/files/PSA%20Longitudinal%20Alumni%20Study_0.pdf

Aspen Institute, The. (2016, September). *National Commission on Social, Emotional, & Academic Development fact sheet.* Retrieved from https://assets.aspeninstitute. org/content/uploads/2016/09/ncsead-fact-sheet.pdf

Baker, J. A., Kamphaus, R. W., Horne, A. M., & Winsor, A. P. (2006). Evidence for population-based perspectives on children's behavioral adjustment and needs for service delivery in schools. *School Psychology Review, 35*(1), 31–46.

Balfanz, R., Herzog, L., & Mac Iver, D. (2007). Preventing student disengagement and keeping students on the graduation path in urban middle-grades schools: Early identification and effective interventions. *Educational Psychologist, 42*(4), 223–235.

Balfanz, R. & Legters, N. (2004). Locating the dropout crisis: Which high schools produce the nation's dropouts? Where are they located? Who attends them? *Center for Research on the Education of Students Places at Risk.* Retrieved from https://files.eric.ed.gov/fulltext/ED484525.pdf

Bandura, A. (1997). *Self-efficacy: The exercise of control.* New York: W. H. Freeman.

Batsche, G., Elliott, J., Graden, J. L., Grimes, J., Kovaleski, J. F., Prasse, D., . . . Tilly III, W. D. (2005). *Response to intervention: Policy considerations and implementation.* Alexandria, VA: National Association of State Directors of Special Education.

Billig, S., & Jesse, D. (2008). *Using service-learning to promote character education in a large urban district.* Retrieved from https://www.researchgate.net/publication/281294442_Billig_S_H_Jesse_D_Grimley_M_2008_Using_servicelearning_to_promote_character_education_in_a_large_urban_district_Journal_of_Research_in_Character_Education_61_21-34

Center for Promise. (2015). *"Don't Quit on Me." Report commissioned by America's promise alliance*, p 7. Retrieved from http://www.americaspromise.org/report/dont-quit-me

Center on the Developing Child at Harvard University. (2008). *InBrief: The science of early childhood development*. Retrieved from https://46y5eh11fhgw3ve3ytpwxt9r-wpengine.netdna-ssl.com/wp-content/uploads/2007/03/InBrief-The-Science-of-Early-Childhood-Development2.pdf

College Board Advocacy & Policy Center. (2012). 2017 National Survey of School Counselors, True North: Charting the course to college and career readiness. Retrieved from https://secure-media.collegeboard.org/digitalServices/pdf/nosca/12b_6629_ACS_Flyer_WEB_120928.pdf

Corrin, W., Sepanik, S., Rosen, R., & Shane, A. (2016). *Addressing early warning indicators: Interim impact findings from the investing in innovation evaluation of diplomas now*. Retrieved from https://www.mdrc.org/publication/addressing-early-warning-indicators

Elias, M. J., Zins, J. E., Weissberg, R. P., Frey, K. S., Greenberg, M. T., Haynes, N. M., . . . Shriver, T. P. (1997). *Promoting social and emotional learning: Guidelines for educators*. Alexandria, VA: Association for Supervision and Curriculum Development.

Fuchs, D., & Deshler, D. D. (2007). What we need to know about responsiveness to intervention (and shouldn't be afraid to ask). *Learning Disabilities Research & Practice, 22*, 129–136.

Goleman, D. (1995). *Emotional intelligence*. New York: Bantam.

Hurd, N. M., Zimmerman, M. A., & Reischl, T. M. (2011). Role model behavior and youth violence: A study of positive and negative effects. *Journal of Early Adolescence. 31*(2).

Hymel, S., & Ford, L. (2014). School completion and academic success: The impact of early social-emotional competence. *Encyclopedia of Early Child Development*. Retrieved from http://www.child-encyclopedia.com/sites/default/files/textes-experts/en/839/school-completion-and-academic-success-the-impact-of-early-social-emotional-competence.pdf

ICF International. (2008). *School-level report: Results from the quasi-experimental study, natural variation study, and typology study*. Retrieved from https://www.communitiesinschools.org/media/uploads/attachments/CIS_School_Level_Report_Volume_1.pdf

ICF International. (2010). *Randomized controlled trial study*. Austin, TX. Retrieved from https://www.communitiesinschools.org/media/uploads/attachments/CIS_RCT_Study_Austin_Volume_5_final.pdf

Jones, S. M., & Bouffard, S. M. (2012). Social and emotional learning in schools: From programs to strategies. In K. L. Maxwell, S. L. Odom, & I. Iruka (Eds.), *Social Policy Report, 26*(4). Retrieved from http://www.srcd.org/sites/default/files/documents/spr_264_final_2.pdf

Juvonen, J., & Wentzel, K. R. (1996). *Social motivation: Understanding children's school adjustment*. New York: Cambridge University Press.

Karoly, L. A., Kilburn, M. R., & Cannon, J. S. (2005). RAND research brief: Proven benefits of early childhood interventions. Retrieved from https://www.rand.org/content/dam/rand/pubs/research_briefs/2005/RAND_RB9145.pdf

Kendziora, K. & Osher, D. (2016). Promoting children's and adolescents' social and emotional development: District adaptations of a theory of action. *Journal of Clinical Child & Adolescent Psychology*, *45*(6), 797–811.

Kidron, Y., & Osher, D. (2010). *The social-emotional learning component of city year's whole school, whole child service model: A focus on the middle grades.* American Institute for Research. Retrieved from http://www.socialimpactexchange.org/files/Osher%20white%20paper%20SEL%20Middle%20Research_0.pdf

Malti, T., & Noam, G. G. (2009). A developmental approach to the prevention of adolescent's aggressive behavior and the promotion of resilience. *International Journal of Developmental Science, 3*(3), 235–246. doi:0.3233/DEV-2009-3303

McClelland, M. M., Morrison, F. J., & Holmes, D. H. (2000). Children at-risk for early academic problems: The role of learning-related social skills. *Early Childhood Research Quarterly, 15*, 307–329.

Mental Health America. (n.d.). Prevention and early intervention in mental health. Retrieved from http://www.mentalhealthamerica.net/issues/prevention-and-early-intervention-mental-health

Meredith, J., & Anderson, L. (2015, June). Analysis of the impacts of city year's whole school whole child model on partner schools' performance. Retrieved from https://www.cityyear.org/psa-study-city-year%E2%80%99s-impact-our-partner-schools

Mielke, M., Butler, A., Palmiter, A., & Anderson, L. (2014). *Year 4 evaluation of city year New York's whole school whole child initiative.* Washington, DC: Policy Studies Associates. Retrieved from https://www.nationalservice.gov/sites/default/files/evidenceexchange/FR_CityYearNewYork_WholeSchoolWholeChild.pdf

National Center for Children in Poverty. (2016). *Child poverty.* Retrieved from http://www.nccp.org/topics/childpoverty.html

National Governors Association for Best Practices. (2011, March 24). *State strategies for fixing state schools and districts.* Retrieved from https://classic.nga.org/cms/home/nga-center-for-best-practices/center-publications/page-edu-publications/col2-content/main-content-list/state-strategies-for-fixing-fail.html

Neild, R. C., Balfanz, R., & Herzog, L. (2007, October). An early warning system. *Educational Leadership, Early Intervention at Every Age, 65*(2), 28–33.

Noam, G., & Malti, T. (2009). Where youth development meets mental health and education: The RALLY approach. *New Directions for Youth Development, 120*, 18–55.

Noam, G. G., Young C.H., & Jilnina, J. (2006). Social cognition, psychological symptoms, and mental health: The model, the evidence, and contribution to ego development. In T. Malti & G. Noam (Eds.), *New Directions For Youth Development No. 120 Winter 2008 Where Youth Development Meets Mental Health and Education* (pp. 33–34). San Francisco, CA: Jossey Bass.

Osher, D., Cantor, P., Berg, J., Steyer, L., & Rose, T. (2018a). Drivers of human development: How relationships and context shape learning and development. *Applied Developmental Science*, 10–18. doi:10.1080/10888691.2017.1398650.

Osher, D., Cantor, P., Berg, J., Steyer, L., & Rose, T. (2018b). Malleability, plasticity, and individuality: How children learn and develop in context. *Applied Developmental Science*, 22(2), 1–31.

Parise, L., Corrin, W., Granito, K., Haider, Z., Somers, M. A., & Cerna, O. (2017). *Two years of case management: Final findings from the Communities In Schools random assignment evaluation*. Retrieved from https://www.mdrc.org/publication/two-years-case-management

Paus, T., Keshavan, M., & Giedd, J. N. (2008). Why do many psychiatric disorders emerge during adolescence? *Nature Reviews Neuroscience, 9*(12), 947–957.

Perkins, D. F., Syvertsen, A. K., Mincemoyer, C., Chilenski, S. M., Olson, J. R., Berrena, E., & Spoth, R. (2016). Thriving in school: The role of sixth-grade adolescent-parent-school relationships in predicting eighth-grade academic outcomes. *Youth & Society, 48*(6), 739–762.

Raver, C. C. (2002). Emotions matter: Making the case for the role of young children's emotional development for early school readiness. *Social Policy Report, 16*, 3–19.

Rethinam, V., & West, T. C. (2012). *Predicting grade 6 marking period one performance using grade 3 semester one indicators*. Rockville, MD: Montgomery County Public Schools.

RMC Research Corporation. (2008). *City Year Philadelphia: Evaluation*. RMC Research Corporation October 2018.

Roehlkepartain, E., Pekel, K., Syvertsen, A., Sethi, J., Sullivan, T., & Scales P. (2017). *Relationships first: Creating connections that help young people thrive*. Retrieved from https://www.search-institute.org/wp-content/uploads/2017/12/2017-Relationships-First-final.pdf

Schwerdt, G., & West, M. (2011). *The impact of alternative grade configurations on student outcomes through middle and high school*. Retrieved from http://ftp.iza.org/dp6208.pdf

Search Institute. (2014). *A research update from Search Institute: Developmental relationships*. Retrieved from http://www.mentoring.org/new-site/wp-content/uploads/2016/03/Handout-2A-SEARCH-INSTITUTE-DEV-RELATIONSHIPS-FRAMEWORK.pdf

Silverthorn, P., & Frick, P. J. (1999). Developmental pathways to antisocial behavior: The delayed-onset pathway in girls. *Development & Psychopathology, 11*(1), 101–126.

Somers, M. A., & Haider, Z. (2017). *Using integrated student supports to keep kids in school: A quasi-experimental evaluation of communities in schools*. Retrieved from https://www.mdrc.org/publication/using-integrated-student-supports-keep-kids-school

Stafford-Brizard, K. N. (2016). *Building blocks for learning: A framework for comprehensive student development*. Retrieved from https://www.turnaroundusa.org/wp-content/uploads/2016/03/Turnaround-for-Children-Building-Blocks-for-Learningx-2.pdf

Wentzel, K. R., & Asher, S. R. (1995). Academic lives of neglected, rejected, popular, and controversial children. *Child Development, 66*, 754–763.

What Is AmeriCorps? (n.d.). Retrieved from https://www.nationalservice.gov/programs/americorps/what-americorps

Winsor, A. P., Baker, J. A., & Davis, S. (2001). *Teaching tough kids: Voices from the classroom*. Paper presented at annual meeting of National Association of School Psychologists, Washington, DC.

CHAPTER THREE

Assuring Strengths- and Evidence-Based Approaches in Child, Adolescent, and School Mental Health

Mark D. Weist, Cheri J. Shapiro, Samantha N. Hartley, Abby A. Bode, Elaine Miller, Scott Huebner, John Terry, Kimberly Hills, and David Osher

Approximately 20% of youth contend with emotional/behavioral (EB) problems that are severe enough to impair their daily functioning (Merikangas et al., 2010). The EB challenges that these youth face increase their risks for negative outcomes across many areas of life. When EB problems remain untreated, youth are at an increased risk for difficulties across several facets of daily life including impaired relationships; increased involvement in high risk behavior; school problems such as suspension, expulsion, and dropout; involvement in the criminal justice system and other problems (Aseltine, Gore, & Gordon, 2000; Currie & Stabile, 2006; Fergusson & Woodward, 2002; Frick & Loney, 1999; McWhirter & Page, 1999; Molina & Pelham, 2003). Students contending with EB problems are more likely to be in special education, and students in special education for EB disorders have the poorest outcomes of all disability categories (Bullis & Cheney, 1999; Office of

Special Education Programs, 1998). Youth with more severe EB problems, especially when untreated, have an increased probability of developing severe mental illness, which is also associated with a range of physical health problems (e.g., high blood pressure, other cardiovascular problems, obesity, diabetes) and early death (Hert et al., 2011). Moreover, these youth are at increased risk for suicide (Gould, Greenberg, Velting, & Shaffer, 2003), which is now in the top 10 causes of death in the United States, with suicide rates progressively increasing in recent years (Heron, 2016), especially in younger individuals (Bridge et al., 2015).

Despite such prevalence, less than half of these youth ever receive mental health services and those who do often receive treatment that is not evidence-based or effective (see Burns et al., 1995; Merikangas et al., 2011). There are many missed opportunities to assist these youth and to promote their positive social, emotional, and behavioral functioning (Green et al., 2013; Merikangas et al., 2011). Barriers to receiving treatment often include lack of transportation, stigma, waiting lists (i.e., lack of organizational capacity), and financial constraints, such as having poor insurance that insufficiently covers mental health care (see Owens, Watabe, & Michael, 2013; Weist, 1997), as well as a lack of cultural and linguistic competence at the system, agency, and practice level (Osher, Cartledge, Oswald, Artilles, & Coutinho, 2004). Such barriers commonly prevent families from seeking or regularly attending treatment sessions in mental health clinics (Reardon et al., 2017). Thus, without effective and evidence-based early intervention, youth presenting more serious EB problems are at risk for a range of problems in their life and represent a significant loss in contribution to society, underscoring the urgency and public health significance of improving approaches to mental health promotion and intervention for children, youth, and their families.

Related to recognition of these barriers to care in traditional settings, there are growing national movements on positive behavioral interventions and supports (PBIS, see http://www.pbis.org), and "expanded" school mental health (SMH) programs, involving community mental health clinicians joining school-employed mental health staff to expand the array of services, provide support to schools, and help the mental health system be more accessible (see Weist, 1997; http://csmh.umaryland.edu). In addition, there is significant momentum to join PBIS and SMH together toward greater depth and quality in prevention (Tier 1), early intervention (Tier 2), and intervention (Tier 3) programs in schools (Barrett, Eber, & Weist, 2013). These combined programs have been referred to as Interconnected Systems Framework (ISF) programs, and there is evidence that when they are done well, they are associated with improved social, emotional, behavioral, and school functioning in students (see Bradshaw, Mitchell, & Leaf, 2010; Durlak, Weissberg, Dymnicki, Taylor, & Schellinger, 2011; Fazel, Hoagwood, Stephan, & Ford, 2014; Stein et al., 2003).

Critique of Mental Health Services for Children and Youth

While the progressive development of PBIS, SMH, and integrated ISF is highly promising, there are still many problems with mental health services for children and adolescents, including significant access problems as presented above (Merikangas et al., 2011), with these access problems worse for youth in poverty or youth of color (Kazak et al., 2010). Further, when services are available, access to high-quality evidence-based interventions is variable. While evidence-based interventions to address behavioral health and substance use challenges for children and adolescents exist, they are not well incorporated into usual services (Park, Chorpita, Regan, & Weisz, Research Network on Youth Mental Health, 2015; Schoenwald, Kelleher, Weisz, & The Research Network on Youth Mental Health, 2008). The primary barrier is that community mental health service organizations and schools are often not well-equipped to support implementation of evidence-based interventions with fidelity. Factors affecting implementation occur at all levels of the social ecology: the client, provider, organization, and larger system of service provision, including policies and fiscal structures (Damschroder & Hagedorn, 2011; Greenhalgh, Robert, MacFarlane, Bate, & Kyriakidou, 2004).

In addition to not receiving quality services, youth and families may have negative experiences with the mental health system, such as feeling stigmatized and blamed, and problems needing to be at crisis levels for any possibility of help (Jacobs et al., 2016). This may particularly be the case for services that are not family- and youth-driven or culturally competent (Osher, Osher, & Blau, 2008). Other families express uncertainty about what mental health services are, and generally perceive them as inaccessible (Bone, O'Reilly, Karim, & Vostanis, 2015). The families that do engage in services commonly drop out prematurely, as soon as after one session (Gopalan et al., 2010; also see Becker et al., 2015).

The Role of Diagnoses, Labeling, and Stigma

Diagnosis is often seen as the first step in the treatment of psychological disorders (Jensen-Doss & Weisz, 2008). In real world settings, diagnostic labels are often necessary for billing purposes and may be linked to the selection of broad intervention protocols. A diagnosis is meant to serve as a heuristic to describe a pattern of symptoms and help the clinician understand presenting problems of the child with the intent of facilitating the rapid and effective implementation of appropriate interventions. In many cases, diagnoses serve this role broadly; however, they rarely provide specific guidance on what specific behaviors, underdeveloped skills, and contextual factors that may be exacerbating the challenges a child or adolescent faces. In reality, diagnostic labels are not only stigmatizing but, most importantly, they ignore the ecological factors and possible compromised social capital impacting the presenting problem. Ultimately, diagnosis fails to acknowledge that most of the youth identified with EB problems are living in conditions that are suboptimal to their development (Osher, Cantor, Berg, Strayer, & Rose, 2018).

A long history of research extending from the late 1970s (Carroll & Reppucci, 1978) documents the iatrogenic effects that such diagnostic labels can have on the youth receiving them. In 2005, Hinshaw emphasized that stigmatization of mental illness may be the most central issue in the mental health field. Diagnosis may lead to stigmatization, even by mental health professionals (Heflinger & Hinshaw, 2010). To understand the nature of childhood mental health stigma, Mukolo, Heflinger, and Wallston (2010) proposed that it is necessary to conceptualize "who" (context) does "what" (dimensions) to "whom" (targets); their Framework Integrating Normative Influences on Stigma (FINIS) model identifies contexts (general public, self, institutional), dimensions (negative stereotypes, devaluation, discrimination), and targets (self/individual, family, mental health services) to understand how stigma influences child and adolescent mental health service use.

Data from the National Stigma Study—Children (NSS-C) in 2002 (Pescosolido et al., 2008) indicated the general public holds negative and condition-specific attitudes toward children with mental health conditions. A large number of adults link children's mental health problems to a potential for violence; this is particularly pronounced for boys with ADHD and depression, who were perceived as somewhat or very likely to be dangerous to themselves or others by 33% and 81% of respondents, respectively (Pescosolido et al., 2008). This fearful perception appears to be linked to stigma associated with mental health; respondents who labeled children as "mentally ill" were twice as likely to judge the child as having a potential for violence and five times more likely to support forced treatment (Pescosolido, Fettes, Martin, Monahan, & McLeod, 2007a). Individuals were two to three times more likely to desire social distance for themselves and for children when adolescents were described as having depression or ADHD than when described as having asthma or "normal troubles" (Martin, Pescosolido, Olafsdottir, & McLeod, 2007). Interestingly, in a related study, participants who endorsed these negative views of mental health problems in children and youth also acknowledged the existence of stigma (45% of participants) and that the negative consequences resulting from such stigma can continue to follow a child into adulthood (43% of participants) (Pescosolido, Perry, Martin, McLeod, & Jensen, 2007b).

Perceived stigma can serve as a barrier to seeking out professional services for childhood mental health concerns. A systematic review of studies on self-reported help-seeking barriers for young people similarly identified stigma and embarrassment about seeking help for mental health problems as the most prominent barriers to seeking treatment (Gulliver, Griffiths, & Christensen, 2010). Another study with parents found that embarrassment, stigma, concerns about their child receiving a diagnosis, and fear of being labeled a poor parent contributed to parents not seeking services for EB problems in their children (Sayal et al., 2010; also see Heflinger & Hinshaw, 2010; Jensen, 2002). Beginning in early adolescence, there is a negative correlation between mental health stigma and willingness to use mental health services. This problem is more severe for racial/ethnic minorities (Chandra & Minkovitz, 2006; Gary, 2005), who are more likely to expect disrespectful treatment and poor quality care from mental health providers (Richardson, 2001).

Among adolescents who do seek help and receive mental health treatment, 20% report significant concerns related to self-stigmatization (Moses, 2010a). According to Corrigan and colleagues (2006), self-stigma is experienced as a result of individuals agreeing with negative stereotypes about their condition (i.e., they believe that stereotypes about mental health held by the general public are true), self-concurrence (i.e., agreeing that that these internalized stereotypes apply to them), and impaired self-esteem. Among adolescents diagnosed with mental health disorders, those who "self-label" by using pathological psychiatric terms to refer to their problems report higher ratings of self-stigma, depression, and perceived public stigma (Moses, 2009). Self-stigma has numerous negative effects on an individual's self-esteem, self-efficacy, psychological well-being, and personal achievement goals (Corrigan, Watson, & Barr, 2006). For example, the perception of stigma has been found to strongly predict decreases in self-esteem, as well as fear of rejection and of being devalued by others (Link, Struening, Neese-Todd, Asmussen, & Phelan, 2001).

There is an additional burden for adolescents with mental health issues because a mental health diagnosis or treatment status is a potentially "hidden" or concealed source of stigma, since the teen may be embarrassed and reluctant to acknowledge these challenges with others or worry about being perceived as "weird" (Heary, Hennessy, Swords, & Corrigan, 2017). The psychological implications of concealing hidden stigma are numerous and include affective (e.g., increased anxiety, helplessness, hopelessness, depression, hostility, demoralization, guilt, shame), behavioral (e.g., social avoidance and isolation, impaired close relationship functioning), and self-evaluative (e.g., negative view of self, lack of access to group-based self-protective attributions, diminished self-efficacy) consequences (Pachankis, 2007). Many of these consequences were confirmed in a study by Kranke, Floersch, Townsend, and Munson (2010) concerning the psychosocial consequences of taking a psychiatric medication: 90% of interviewed adolescents reported experiencing stigma related to their medication status and related secrecy concerns (e.g., not wanting peers to know about their diagnosis or medication for fear of being considered "crazy"), shame (e.g., feeling different or damaged, considering themselves to be "crazy" or abnormal), and intentionally limiting social interactions with peers as a result (also see Moses, 2010b).

Psychiatric diagnostic labels can affect the perceptions and expectations that other people, including teachers, make about children and adolescents (Carroll & Reppucci, 1978; Levin, Arluke, & Smith, 1982), often to the detriment of the child. In the realm of mental health, "labeling bias effects" refer to the expectations that might be placed upon an individual by virtue of their diagnostic label. According to labeling theory, these modified expectations are thought to occur as a result of the label priming negative stereotypes that result in devaluation (Fox & Stinnett, 1996). Youth are aware of this. For example, a study of youth with co-occurring mental health and substance abuse disorders indicated that youth preferred the substance use label to one that focused on mental illness (Federation of Families for Children's Mental Health, 2004). In addition to the diagnostic labels found in the *Diagnostic and Statistical Manual*, 5th edition (DSM-V; American Psychiatric Association, 2013), children with behavioral, social, emotional, and learning problems might receive one of a variety of labels if they are determined eligible for special education services, including Serious Emotional Disturbance (SED), Behavior Disorder (BD), Emotionally Disturbed (ED), Emotionally Conflicted (EC), or Emotional-Behavioral Disorder (EBD). Walker and colleagues (2010) directly assessed youth perceptions of the label "emotionally disturbed" and found the great majority of youth found the term offensive and highly inappropriate. Findings from this study were influential in the passage of a law in Maryland, changing use of this term from emotionally disturbed to student experiencing an "emotional disability" (although the preferred term endorsed by youth was "emotional challenges").

Moreover, the use of these labels has been found to affect the way that teachers and other school staff perceive a child's behavior and potential; this has proven especially to be the case with special education labels of SED and ED. In an investigation of the impact of labels and descriptions of student behavior, Levin and colleagues (1982) found that only the emotionally disturbed label had a significant negative impact on teacher expectations regarding a high school student's potential for academic success and continuation to college. Additionally, Fox and Stinnett (1996) found that school psychologists and teachers judged higher levels of disruptiveness and lower levels of adjustment and quality of peer relationships in children labeled conduct disordered, socially maladjusted, or seriously emotionally disturbed compared to peers with similar behaviors but no label. Labeling effects have also been found to extend to even younger students; for example, Ohan, Visser, Strain, and Allen (2011) found that when elementary teachers reacted to vignettes describing children meeting ADHD symptom criteria, the presence of the ADHD label resulted in greater perceptions of a child's impairment, negative expectations about the severity of the child's problems, more negative emotions, and less confidence in their ability to instruct the child.

In an early study on the relationship between psychiatric diagnostic labels and perceptions of child behavior among nursing students, Critchley (1979) reported that nurses rated behavior as significantly more disturbed when children were given a psychiatric diagnostic label because the label brought with it certain expectations about the child's behavior, which was then evaluated in accordance with the nature of the assigned label (versus without preconception). Researchers have hypothesized that attaching labels to children may help create and sustain negative behavioral patterns (Socall & Holtgraves, 1992) by setting up expectancies that are unconsciously reinforced via the environmental response to the child (Caprara & Zimbardo, 1996). In the presence of labels, Critchley warned that there "tends to be excessive attention to pathology, with its stereotyped descriptions of behavior and prognosis; the focus is upon the weaknesses of the [child] rather than upon the strengths" (Critchley, 1979, p. 160).

For adolescents, there is no setting where labels are more present than in the self-contained special education classroom or "pull-out" resource class. Here, children with conduct problems are frequently referred for qualification as ED or SED and brought together with other students dealing with emotional, behavioral, social, and/or learning disorders that require a modified instructional environment or additional supports. Unfortunately, there is evidence to suggest that aggregating adolescents with problem behaviors can have adverse iatrogenic effects associated with "deviancy training," or adolescents' role modeling, sharing, and glorifying instances of problematic behavior (Gifford-Smith, Dodge, Dishion, & McCord, 2005).

Further, because of fears of social rejection and worries about being perceived as different, youth with EB challenges can experience difficulty integrating into school settings, with special education classrooms (Kranke et al., 2010) and alternative schools presenting their own more serious challenges (e.g., ridiculed for not being able to go the home school, having to ride a separate bus; see Slade et al., 2009). Unfortunately, both externalizing (e.g., aggression, noncompliance) and internalizing EB problems (e.g., depression, anxiety) may be exacerbated in these alternative placements or settings (Dishion, McCord, & Poulin, 1999; Dishion & Tipsord, 2011). In these settings, "peer contagion" influences may occur. Peer contagion is defined by Dishion and Tipsord (2011) as a mutual process of influence that occurs between an individual and a peer involving behaviors and emotions that potentially cause harm to others or undermine positive development. In schools, programs that screen youth at risk for more serious EB problems and deliver intervention to particular groups of students showing elevated problems are among those that "provide the most compelling evidence for peer contagion potentiating iatrogenic effects" (Dishion & Tipsord, 2011), in part because they often serve youth at ages when they are particularly vulnerable to peer influence (Dishion, Poulin, & Burraston, 2001). Consistent with earlier comments regarding "deviancy training," Dodge and Pettit (2003) proposed a number of possible mechanisms by which these iatrogenic effects could occur in adolescent interventions, including the self- and public-labeling effects of being identified as part of a group known to display deviance, the adoption of attitudes and norms based on observational learning, and lack of exposure to the prosocial, tempering influences of normative peers.

The demonstrated possibility that group delivery of prevention and treatment programs in schools may produce iatrogenic effects for youth with problem behavior, and especially for those with initially low levels of problem behavior (Dishion & Dodge, 2005; Poulin, Dishion, & Burraston, 2001), carries with it ethical implications, including active consideration of threats to beneficence (assuring the most helpful approach) and nonmaleficence (avoiding harmful approaches; Rhule, 2005). These considerations also underscore the importance of approaches that focus on positive youth development, nurturant relationships between adults and students, and emphasize enhancing student strengths. These emphases are also consistent with positive psychology, with a review of key dimensions of this subfield presented next.

Lessons from Positive Psychology

Although a positive approach to the delivery of mental health services is not new, Martin Seligman brought it to the foreground of psychology and related disciplines in 2000 by making it one of the cornerstones of his agenda as the President of the American Psychological Association (see Seligman & Csikszentmihalyi, 2000). Seligman and Csikszentmihalyi defined positive psychology as the scientific study of positive subjective experiences, positive individual traits, and institutions that improve humans' quality of life and prevent or ameliorate psychosocial problems. In their seminal article, Seligman and Csikszentmihalyi further pointed to gaps in the existing literature and made recommendations for research to advance the science and applications of positive psychology. The notions of strengths-based assessments and case reformulations fit squarely within their conceptual framework and with positive psychology research with children and adolescents (see Suldo, Huebner, & Furlong, 2016).

Since the call for action from Seligman and Csikszentmihalyi (2000), much research has ensued. We would argue that two major lessons relevant to comprehensive strengths- and evidence-based case reformulation (CSECR) have been learned from such research. The first lesson is that mental health and mental illness have been shown to be clearly distinguishable constructs, which has implications for psychological assessments and interventions, even in children as young as elementary school age (Greenspoon & Saklofske, 2001). For example, Suldo and Shaffer (2008) demonstrated the utility of Greenspoon and Saklofske's dual-factor model of mental health, which incorporates positive indicators of mental health (e.g., high subjective well-being [SWB], such as frequent positive emotions and high life satisfaction) along with the traditional negative or "symptom-based" indicators of mental health challenges (e.g., maladaptive internalizing and externalizing behaviors). Using the dual-factor model, Suldo and Shaffer (2008) identified four groups of adolescents. These groups included one group labeled "complete mental health," comprised of adolescents reporting few behavior problems and high SWB. A second group, labeled as "vulnerable," comprised of adolescents reporting few behavior problems and low SWB. The third group, labeled as "symptomatic but content," comprised of adolescents reporting significant behavior problems but also high SWB. The fourth group, which was labeled "troubled," reported significant behavior problems and low SWB. The groups differed significantly with respect to academic outcomes, physical health, and social functioning. The findings supported the importance of the positive indicators of mental health in that the students with complete mental health (i.e., high SWB, low behavior problems) had better reading skills, school attendance, academic self-perceptions, academic-related goals, social support from classmates and parents, self-perceived physical health, and fewer social problems than the vulnerable group who reported few behavior problems, but also low SWB. Among the two groups of students with high levels of behavior problems, students with high SWB (symptomatic but content youth) reported significantly higher social functioning and physical health than their peers in the troubled group, also illustrating the more nuanced picture of well-being provided by the inclusion of the positive indicators of functioning. Similar findings have been reported by others (e.g., Antaramian, Huebner, Hills, & Valois, 2010; Eklund, Dowdy, Jones, & Furlong, 2011; Venning, Wilson, Kettler, & Eliott, 2013). Such studies underscore the incremental utility of more comprehensive models of psychological assessments.

Beyond the assessment of SWB, in particular, much research has investigated the personal and environmental resources that promote SWB and other indicators of well-being. A considerable body of research has converged to identify personal strengths (e.g., hope, engagement, purpose, character strengths) and environmental assets (e.g., effective parenting, peer support, positive school climates, socioeconomic resources) that promote positive development in youth. Such research includes studies of children and adolescents exposed to numerous adverse experiences, which led Masten as early as 2001 to conclude that resilience in youth is relatively common and emerges from "ordinary" adaptational processes that may be brought into play to promote more positive development and overcome psychosocial challenges. Subsequent research has bolstered the notion that a variety of personal strengths and environmental assets may serve as positive and protective factors in facilitating positive mental health among youth (Lippman et al., 2014). For example, Renshaw and colleagues (2014) include the following malleable assets in their model and associated self-report measure for adolescents: self-awareness, persistence, self-efficacy, peer support, teacher support, family support, empathy, emotional regulation, behavioral self-control, gratitude, zest, and optimism. For an overview of promising strengths-based measures for youth, see Suldo and colleagues (2016).

The second major, pertinent lesson from positive psychology research is that strengths-based information appears to improve the expectations and confidence of professionals working with youth, and possibly client outcomes as well. For example, Donovan and Nickerson (2007) found that adding strengths-based information to a traditional psychological evaluation report for an early adolescent male with behavior problems resulted in increased expectations for positive academic, social, and overall outcomes from multidisciplinary team members. Using fictional case studies, Wellborn, Huebner, and Hills (2012) also reported higher teacher ratings regarding current and future behavioral and academic success for fictional students whose vignettes included strengths compared to students whose vignettes did not include strengths. Furthermore, Cox (2006) observed differing outcomes for youth in therapy for behavioral problems. Specifically, youth whose therapists incorporated strengths-based information in their treatment plans showed decreases in externalizing and internalizing behaviors and missed appointments compared to youth whose therapists did not incorporate strengths-based information in their treatment plans. Additionally, the parents of the youth reported greater satisfaction with therapy when strengths-based information was employed.

Although more research is needed, the burgeoning literature in positive psychology reveals multiple potential benefits to the use of more comprehensive and nuanced strengths-based assessments of the functioning of children and adolescents within their ecological context. Intentional efforts to assess and interpret children's mental health from a more comprehensive framework than the traditional, deficit-based approach promise to yield greater sophistication in the efforts of mental health professionals to identify and bring resources to bear on the development of *all* children, including those with serious mental health challenges. Such a strengths-based perspective should enhance the delivery of mental health services to youth through promoting less stigmatization and greater respect for their individuality and potential. Most important, it communicates to youth that they are more than their problems and that providers are more than those who would ignore youth's contexts and the issues with which they have to struggle.

Altering the Approach: Comprehensive Strength- and Evidence-Based Case Reformulation

Within the Psychology Services Center at the University of South Carolina, many of the authors have begun to implement a protocol that we refer to as Comprehensive Strength- and Evidence-Based Case Reformulation (CSECR) when children and youth present to the center with pathologizing labels and narratives (e.g., prior psychological evaluations) that emphasizes their deficits, problems, and lack of abilities to function positively in key life domains, such as family, peer, and school contexts. Please note that this is not to convey that the authors do not believe in psychological evaluation or that there is no purpose for diagnosis or documenting problems youth are contending with. Instead, CSECR represents a balanced approach that attempts to reduce negative labeling and predictions and instead emphasize strengths and the ability of the child/family to reach a new level of positive functioning. Youth are targeted for the protocol when they present to the center with stigmatizing diagnoses and prior evaluations that place emphasis on pathology to the neglect of strengths. A re-evaluation is conducted emphasizing these perspectives, which forms the foundation for evidence-based intervention and developing a new narrative that is presented to the child, family, school, and other important systems or people in his or her life. Use of CSECR is illustrated through the following case example.

Case Example

"Jordan" is a 6-year-old male. Jordan's guardian, Ms. A, indicated that behavioral difficulties were her primary concern and her goal for treatment. Through her narrative of Jordan's life and development, a number of concerns arose. For instance, Ms. A reported that Jordan was the victim of serious physical and sexual abuse during infancy. Ms. A became Jordan's guardian following removal from the home in which he was abused. In addition, she reported that Jordan was no longer enrolled in school, upon the recommendation of a licensed psychologist and was instead being homeschooled. She stated that she removed Jordan from school after several incidents, which included threats to harm himself and others. Jordan had been hospitalized in an inpatient psychiatric setting on at least one occasion and, at the time of referral for services, was prescribed antipsychotic medications.

Ms. A. stated that her primary concern for him was his behavior, as he often had extreme temper tantrums that involved screaming, crying, kicking, and hitting her when he did not get his way; lack of respect for her; and chronic noncompliance. Ms. A and Jordan were receiving therapeutic services from their community mental health agency and reported a long history of psychological and psychiatric care in an attempt to gain control of his behavior. Although Jordan was prescribed two antipsychotic medications, which Ms. A stated were to help with his sleep and to reduce behavioral problems, she reported that their meetings with a psychiatrist were sporadic, as the agency did not have an in-house psychiatrist due to its rural status. Although there was an established history of psychological care, treatment was disjointed, and there was little to no communication across providers. There were also a number of evaluations including stigmatizing diagnoses (e.g., Oppositional Defiant Disorder, Conduct Disorder), Attention-Deficit Hyperactivity Disorder (ADHD), and a preponderance of negative information in these evaluations emphasizing Jordan's history of abuse, neglect, and problems, with no mention of his strengths. Treatment to date ranged widely in intensity, with Ms. A reporting that Jordan had been hospitalized, sedated, prescribed numerous medications, and involved in various episodes of psychotherapy, with different perspectives and approaches taken by these therapists, and no documented communication between them.

Due to the multiple diagnoses given and the multiple agencies involved, treatment began with an aim to better understand the presentation from Jordan and Ms. A's point of view by conducting a thorough biopsychosocial assessment. Ms. A underwent a thorough clinical interview, as well as completed the Behavioral Assessment Systems for Children-II-Parent Report (BASC-2; Reynolds & Kamphaus, 2004). Jordan received cognitive assessment in order to determine his current level of cognitive functioning as well as to provide information for school placement. In addition, school records (BASC, grades, referrals, qualitative data from reports) and previous health and mental health treatment records were collected. School records indicated that Jordan did not regularly attend school; although he was only in the 1st grade, he had frequent absences and as mentioned was not currently attending school related to the recommendation of another psychologist. His medical and mental health records were sometimes incomplete, but revealed that Ms. A had been seeking help for quite some time, and the disjointed nature of the reports indicated that she was not convinced with previous attempts to explain Jordan's presentation. Ms. A also sought physical examinations to ensure that there were no underlying organic complaints that were contributing to the current symptoms.

During this phase of treatment, Ms. A took Jordan for additional psychodiagnostic testing that was not recommended by our team and returned to us with an evaluation indicating an additional diagnosis of Pediatric Bipolar Disorder (PBD). Ms. A reported feeling discouraged by this evaluation and the label of PBD, with the clinician emphasizing Jordan's functional impairments. Furthermore, the report indicated that Jordan should be treated with additional medications and should refrain from enrolling in school, as the overstimulation could further exacerbate his symptoms. The history with systems focusing on labeling him as problematic and prescribing heavy medications left the family feeling as though they were not able to take control of their lives or to help Jordan progress toward positive developmental trajectories.

However, following careful examination of previous assessments, it was determined that the existing diagnoses mainly overlooked a key aspect of Jordan's history: his exposure to traumatic abuse at an early age. The current conceptualization of Jordan's difficulties was to take the label of the "problem" outside of the child, rather than diagnosing his behaviors; the diagnosis of post-traumatic stress disorder was given. The shift in focus behind the diagnosis communicated that the problem resides outside of the child and his observable behavioral difficulties are a result of his experiences, not because of a deficit within himself. His behavioral outbursts were thought to stem from his experiences with trauma; because he had experienced trauma at such an early age, he was never equipped with the language or capacity to effectively communicate his discomfort to others, and thus, responded with extreme behaviors in an attempt to gain attention from caregivers. In addition, the clinical team identified and emphasized a number of Jordan's strengths, including areas of strength in social skills (e.g., eye contact, interest and ability in developing rapport with others), motor abilities, physical attractiveness, and sense of humor. This reformulation was emphasized to Ms. A, Jordan, his pediatrician, and school staff. A report documenting the CSECR was shared with them, and our team recommended focusing on it going forward and de-emphasizing prior negative and highly pejorative reports.

Through the CSECR, this reconceptualization of Jordan as a boy who had experienced severe trauma at a young age with one operating diagnosis—PTSD—and behavioral concerns stemming from it, as well as emphasizing his numerous strengths, created a new platform for therapy. Ms. A indicated feeling encouraged by this new conceptualization, and it allowed for Jordan to have the space to openly explore his reactions without fear of repercussions or him being labeled as a problematic child. Four treatment goals were selected and pursued together, with active involvement in planning by Ms. A and Jordan: (1) to target Jordan's behavioral outbursts through parent training techniques; (2) increase Jordan's ability to communicate discomfort; (3) re-enroll in school; and (4) reduce psychotropic medications and their sedating impact.

Treatment began with a focus on modeling skills to assist Ms. A in productive parenting skills and linking Jordan's behavior to consequences.

Because Jordan did not have explicit memories of the traumatic event, traditional PTSD therapy was not targeted. Rather, a focus was placed on teaching Jordan to calmly communicate his discomfort and to label his emotional experiences. Once contingency plans were in place and the family had established confidence and skill in managing more appropriate behaviors when Jordan felt distressed, the therapists worked with the family to have Jordan enrolled in an appropriate school placement. Together with the family, meetings took place at school in which Jordan's history and current treatment were discussed, and a clear plan and placement were set in motion. Compared to previous attempts, the current treatment team worked to make a smooth transition, through meeting with the school to discuss concerns, as well as a treatment team member meeting with the family and the teacher to help model behavior management skills in session. With Ms. A's permission, the treatment team shared and emphasized the case conceptualization related to early trauma, PTSD, impacts on social development and communication, and Jordan's numerous strengths. Together with the monitored reduction of psychotropic prescriptions, Ms. A reported a significant reduction of behavioral outbursts and noted an increase of affection shared between her and Jordan. Jordan shared that he was better able to tell others what he felt, and he learned that his behavior was important. He also reported enjoying school and making friends. Jordan received intervention services from our team for about a year. He was able to complete 1st grade successfully, had noticeably improved social connections and friendships, and medications were reduced to just one focusing on helping to improve his attentional functioning. There were also improvements in his EB functioning as documented on the BASC, and Ms. A expressed strong satisfaction with the treatment experience.

Through use of the CSECR approach, the interdisciplinary team working with Jordan and Ms. A changed from the prior treatment planning focused on his multiple disorders and limitations of Ms. A in parenting him to a plan building from both of their strengths, based on a case formulation that many of his difficulties reflected challenges in self-regulation resulting from early traumatic experiences. Soon after implementing this deliberate focus on his strengths and making non-stigmatizing environmental changes, his presenting behaviors improved. Strengths, including his growing capacity for self-expression and ability to improve his functioning, were underscored. Furthermore, in the face of reducing the amount of medication he was taking, behavior- and trauma-informed treatment approaches improved the symptoms as opposed to increasing medications and considering further restricted environments. Once Jordan was weaned from heavy medications, he was better able to interact with his environment, as he was no longer sedated. He was given the opportunity to learn and practice new skills in a safe and supportive environment.

Because Jordan was in infancy when the abuse began, it seems as though his symptoms were masked by other complications—mainly, his behavioral outbursts. However, once he was given the opportunity to identify his emotions and to practice methods of handling those emotions (e.g., relaxation training, practice in talking about strong emotions), his behavioral outbursts decreased. Indeed, once the symptoms related to trauma and emotional dysregulation were targeted and considered underdeveloped skills, those symptoms that were previously labeled as "bipolar" or "psychotic" by other providers disappeared.

Conclusion

Children and youth develop within interlinked bioecological contexts that can contribute to mental wellness as well as mental illness (Bornstein & Leventhal, 2015; Bronfenbrenner & Morris, 2006; Osher et al., 2018). Mental health and wellness and mental illness and ill-being are products of the co-influences of intrapersonal and ecological factors. Intrapersonal factors include neurobiological development; physical health; the development of social, emotional, and cognitive competencies; knowledge about self and the world; mindsets; and identities. Ecological factors include the quality of relationships with family, peers, school staff, and service providers; the qualities of the settings that they encounter (microsystems); and the impacts of macro factors such as stigmatizing belief systems and institutionalized racism, poverty, and privilege (Gay & Kirkland, 2003; Spencer, 2007). These ecological factors can support positive development, buffer adversity, and promote resilience when they foster adults' capacities to attune with and provide developmentally appropriate supports that align with children's social-historical life spaces (Osher et al., 2018; Thompson & Goodvin, 2016). The co-influential effects of individual and ecological factors contribute to multiple pathways to mental illness (equifinality) as compared to resilience (multifinality), and underscore the importance of careful consideration of interventions that are implemented, as in the case here and our example of the CSECR approach (see Cicchetti & Rogosch, 1999; Martinez & Hinshaw, 2016; Spencer, 2007).

The prevailing model of providing mental health services to children, adolescents, and families focuses on deficits and "psychopathology." It identifies problems ("pathology") in children, youth, their families, or communities, then develops treatment plans and delivers services to address these problems that limit or constrain client agency. This approach tends to see the provider and the "treatment" as the solution; ignores the wholeness, ideographic uniqueness, and complex life space of children and youth; and, in so doing, prevents or constrains the voice and agency of the child or youth who reports that "you don't see me" (Osher & Hanley, 1996; Osher & Osher, 2002).

This pathology-driven approach to diagnosis, treatment, research, and policy can hinder the formation of developmental relationships and the provision of social and psychological support from individuals in a child's life space, limit access to and engagement in treatment, and undermine caregiver alliance. Moreover, this approach ignores the youth development critique that a "problem free life" is not a full life (Damon, 2004; Dymnicki, Osher, & Zimmerman, 2017) and can compound problems for children and youth through the effects of negative labels on them. These negative labels affect the child (e.g., contributing to a negative self-perception/identity) and others interacting with him or her (e.g., through negative attributions, lowered expectations, bias) (see Corrigan, 2004).

Critiques of pathology-driven approaches and alternative approaches are not new. For example, the critiques are implicit and explicit in the work of Erving Goffman on stigma (2009) and the "tinkering trades" (1961), and national and federal collaborations focused on improving care for youth presenting more challenging EB problems (e.g., Office of Special Education Programs, 1994; Interagency Working Group on Youth Programs, 2016). Successful alternatives have been developed that include strengths-based and ecological approaches to wraparound planning and services (Bruns et al., 2010; Osher & Hanley, 2001), positive youth development approaches (Kendziora & Osher, 2004), social and emotional learning (Dymnicki, Kendziora, & Osher, 2012; Osher et al., 2016), and the development of valid strengths-based assessment instruments (Hurley, Lambert, Epstein, & Stevens, 2015; Osher & Hanley, 2001). Although promising and, in some cases, efficacious (e.g., Osher et al., 2016), these approaches have still not sufficiently penetrated routine mental health practice.

As presented in this chapter, the Comprehensive Strength- and Evidence-Based Case Reformulation (CSECR) provides an alternative that can reduce negative labeling and predictions and instead emphasize strengths and the ability of the child and family to reach a new level of positive functioning. It is designed for youth with stigmatizing diagnoses and prior evaluations that place emphasis on pathology to the neglect of strengths and can help alter stigma-driven trajectories by changing a child's sense of self, the expectations of those who interact with the child, and the transactions that often contribute to a problematic trajectory. A re-evaluation is conducted emphasizing these perspectives, which forms the foundation for evidence-based intervention and developing a new narrative that is presented to the child, family, school and other important systems and people in his or her life. Jordan's case example is consistent with reports in the literature of successful strengths-based wraparound efforts (Kendziora, Bruns, Osher, Pacchiano, & Mejia, 2001) and illustrates how we can positively alter the life course of children whose trajectories are being pushed in a negative direction by the traditional pathology-driven mental health system paradigm.

References

American Institutes for Research. (2011). *Youth listening sessions*. Retrieved from https://youth.gov/docs/listeningSessions/Youth_Listen_Sessions_Summary.pdf

American Psychiatric Association. (2013). *Diagnostic and statistical manual of mental disorders* (5th ed.). Arlington, VA: American Psychiatric Publishing.

Antaramian, S. P., Huebner, E. S., Hills, K. J., & Valois, R. F. (2010). A dual-factor model of mental health: Toward a more comprehensive understanding of youth functioning. *American Journal of Orthopsychiatry, 80*(4), 462–472.

Aseltine, R. H., Jr., Gore, S., & Gordon, J. (2000). Life stress, anger and anxiety, and delinquency: An empirical test of general strain theory. *Journal of Health and Social Behavior, 41*(3), 256–275.

Barrett, S., Eber, L., & Weist, M. D. (2013). *Advancing education effectiveness: An Interconnected systems framework for Positive Behavioral Interventions and Supports (PBIS) and school mental health*. Center for Positive Behavioral Interventions and Supports (funded by the Office of Special Education Programs, US Department of Education). Eugene: University of Oregon Press.

Becker, K. D., Lee, B. R., Daleiden, E. L., Lindsey, M., Brandt, N. E., & Chorpita, B. F. (2015). The common elements of engagement in children's mental health services: Which elements for which outcomes? *Journal of Clinical Child and Adolescent Psychology, 44*(1), 30–43.

Bone, C., O'Reilly, M., Karim, K., & Vostanis, P. (2015). "They're not witches...": Young children and their parents' perceptions and experiences of child and adolescent mental health services. *Child: Care, Health and Development, 41*(3), 450–458.

Bornstein, M. H., & Leventhal, T. (2015). Children in bioecological landscapes of development. In M. H. Bornstein, T. Leventhal, & R. M. Lerner (Eds.), *Handbook of child psychology and developmental science: Ecological settings and processes* (pp. 1–5). Hoboken, NJ: John Wiley.

Bradshaw, C. P., Mitchell, M. M., & Leaf, P. J. (2010). Examining the effects of schoolwide Positive Behavioral Interventions and Supports on student outcomes: Results from a randomized controlled effectiveness trial in elementary schools. *Journal of Positive Behavior Interventions, 12*(3), 133–148.

Bridge, J. A., Asti, L., Horowitz, L. M., Greenhouse, J. B., Fontanella, C. A., Sheftall, A. H., . . . Campo, J. V. (2015). Suicide trends among elementary school-aged children in the United States from 1993 to 2012. *JAMA Pediatrics, 169*(7), 673–677.

Bronfenbrenner, U., & Morris, P. A. (2006). The bioecological model of human development. In R. M. Lerner, & W. Damon (Eds.), *Handbook of child psychology: Theoretical models of human development* (6th ed., Vol. 1, pp. 793–828). Hoboken, NJ: John Wiley.

Bruns, E. J., Walker, J. S., Zabel, M., Matarese, M., Estep, K., Harburger, D., & Pires, S. A. (2010). Intervening in the lives of youth with complex behavioral health challenges and their families: The role of the wraparound process. *American Journal of Community Psychology, 46*(3–4), 314–331.

Bullis, M., & Cheney, D. (1999). Vocational and transition interventions for adolescents and young adults with emotional or behavior disorders. *Focus on Exceptional Children, 31*(7), 1–24.

Burns, B. J., Costello, E. J., Angold, A., Tweed, D., Stangl, D., Farmer, E. M., & Erkanli, A. (1995). Children's mental health service use across service sectors. *Health Affairs, 14*(4), 147–159.

Caprara, G. V., & Zimbardo, P. G. (1996). Aggregation and amplification of marginal deviations in the social construction of personality and maladjustment. *European Journal of Personality, 10*(2), 79–110.

Carroll, C. F., & Reppucci, N. D. (1978). Meanings that professionals attach to labels for children. *Journal of Consulting and Clinical Psychology, 46*(2), 372–374.

Chandra, A., & Minkovitz, C. S. (2006). Stigma starts early: Gender differences in teen willingness to use mental health services. *Journal of Adolescent Health, 38*(6), 754.e1–754.e8.

Cicchetti, D., & Rogosch, F. A. (1999). Psychopathology as risk for adolescent substance use disorders: A developmental psychopathology perspective. *Journal of Clinical Child Psychology, 28*(3), 355–365.

Corrigan, P. (2004). How stigma interferes with mental health care. *American Psychologist, 59*(7), 614–625.

Corrigan, P. W., Watson, A. C., & Barr, L. (2006). The self-stigma of mental illness: Implications for self-esteem and self-efficacy. *Journal of Social and Clinical Psychology, 25*(8), 875–884.

Cox, K. F. (2006). Investigating the impact of strength-based assessment on youth with emotional or behavioral disorders. *Journal of Child and Family Studies, 15*(3), 287–301.

Critchley, D. L. (1979). The adverse influence of psychiatric diagnostic labels on the observation of child behavior. *American Journal of Orthopsychiatry, 49*(1), 157–160.

Currie, J., & Stabile, M. (2006). Child mental health and human capital accumulation: The case of ADHD. *Journal of Health Economics, 25*(6), 1094–1118.

Damon, W. (2004). What is positive youth development? *Annals of the American Academy of Political and Social Science, 591*(1), 13–24.

Damschroder, L. J., & Hagedorn, H. J. (2011). A guiding framework and approach for implementation research in substance use disorders treatment. *Psychology of Addictive Behaviors, 25*(2), 194–205.

Dishion, T. J., & Dodge, K. A. (2005). Peer contagion in interventions for children and adolescents: Moving towards an understanding of the ecology and dynamics of change. *Journal of Abnormal Child Psychology, 33*(3), 395–400.

Dishion, T. J., McCord, J., & Poulin, F. (1999). When interventions harm: Peer groups and problem behavior. *American Psychologist, 54*(9), 755–764.

Dishion, T. J., Poulin, F., & Burraston, B. (2001). Peer group dynamics associated with iatrogenic effects in group interventions with high-risk young adolescents. *New Directions for Child and Adolescent Development, 91*, 79–92.

Dishion, T. J., & Tipsord, J. M. (2011). Peer contagion in child and adolescent social and emotional development. *Annual Review of Psychology, 62*, 189–214.

Dodge, K. A., & Pettit, G. S. (2003). A biopsychosocial model of the development of chronic conduct problems in adolescence. *Developmental Psychology, 39*(2), 349–371.

Donovan, S. A., & Nickerson, A. M. (2007). Strength-based versus traditional social-emotional reports: Impact on multidisciplinary team members' perceptions. *Behavioral Disorders, 32*(4), 228–237.

Durlak, J. A., Weissberg, R. P., Dymnicki, A. B., Taylor, R. D., & Schellinger, K. B. (2011). The impact of enhancing students' social and emotional learning: A meta-analysis of school-based universal interventions. *Child Development, 82*(1), 405–432.

Dymnicki, A. B., Kendziora, K. T., & Osher, D. M. (2012). Adolescent development for students with learning disabilities and behavioral disorders: The promise of social emotional learning. In B. G. Cook, M. Tankersley, & T. J. Landrum (Eds.), *Classroom management: Advances in learning and behavioral disabilities* (Vol. 25, pp. 131–166). Bingley, UK: Emerald Publishing Group.

Dymnicki, A. B., Osher, D., & Zimmerman, M. (2017). Promoting positive youth development. In P. Sturney (Ed.), *The Wiley handbook of violence and aggression: Vol. 3. Societal interventions* (pp. 1–14). New York: Wiley.

Dymnicki, A., Wandersman, A., Osher, D., & Pakstis, A. (2017). Bringing interventions to scale: Implications and challenges for the field of community psychology. In M. A. Bond, I. Serrano-García, C. B. Keys, & M. Shinn (Eds). *APA handbook of community psychology: Methods for community research and action for diverse groups and issues, Vol. 2* (pp. 297–310). Washington, DC: American Psychological Association.

Eklund, K., Dowdy, E., Jones, C., & Furlong, M. J. (2011). Applicability of the dual factor model of mental health for college students. *Journal of College Student Psychotherapy, 25*(1), 79–92.

Fazel, M., Hoagwood, K., Stephan, S., & Ford, T. (2014). Mental health interventions in schools in high-income countries. *The Lancet Psychiatry, 1*(5), 377–387.

Federation of Families for Children's Mental Health and Keyes for Networking. (2004). *Blamed and ashamed: The treatment experiences of youth with co-occurring substance abuse and mental health disorders and their families.* Alexandria, VA: Federation of Families for Children's Mental Health.

Fergusson, D. M., & Woodward, L. J. (2002). Mental health, educational, and social role outcomes of adolescents with depression. *Archives of General Psychiatry, 59*(3), 225–231.

Fox, J. D., & Stinnett, T. A. (1996). The effects of labeling bias on prognostic outlook for children as a function of diagnostic label and profession. *Psychology in the Schools, 33*(2), 143–152.

Frick, P. J., & Loney, B. R. (1999). Outcomes of children and adolescents with oppositional defiant disorder and conduct disorder. In H. Quay & A. Hogan (Eds.), *Handbook of disruptive behavior disorders* (pp. 507–524). New York: Springer.

Gary, F. A. (2005). Stigma: Barrier to mental health care among ethnic minorities. *Issues in Mental Health Nursing, 26*(10), 979–999.

Gay, G., & Kirkland, K. (2003). Developing cultural critical consciousness and self-reflection in preservice teacher education. *Theory into Practice, 42*(3), 181–187.

Gifford-Smith, M., Dodge, K. A., Dishion, T. J., & McCord, J. (2005). Peer influence in children and adolescents: Crossing the bridge from developmental to intervention science. *Journal of Abnormal Child Psychology, 33*(3), 255–265.

Goffman, E. (1961). *Asylum: Essays on the social situation of mental patients and other inmates.* New York: Penguin Random House.

Goffman, E. (2009). *Stigma: Notes on the management of spoiled identity.* New York: Simon and Schuster.

Gopalan, G., Goldstein, L., Klingenstein, K., Sicher, C., Blake, C., & McKay, M. M. (2010). Engaging families into child mental health treatment: Updates and special considerations. *Journal of the Canadian Academy of Child and Adolescent Psychiatry, 19*(3), 182–196.

Gould, M. S., Greenberg, T. E. D., Velting, D. M., & Shaffer, D. (2003). Youth suicide risk and preventive interventions: A review of the past 10 years. *Journal of the American Academy of Child & Adolescent Psychiatry, 42*(4), 386–405.

Green, J. G., McLaughlin, K. A., Alegría, M., Costello, E. J., Gruber, M. J., Hoagwood, K., . . . Kessler, R. C. (2013). School mental health resources and adolescent mental health service use. *Journal of the American Academy of Child & Adolescent Psychiatry, 52*(5), 501–510.

Greenhalgh, T., Robert, G., MacFarlane, F., Bate, P., & Kyriakidou, O. (2004). Diffusion of innovations in service organizations: Systematic review and recommendations. *Milbank Quarterly, 82*(4), 581–629.

Greenspoon, P. J., & Saklofske, D. H. (2001). Toward an integration of subjective well-being and psychopathology. *Social Indicators Research, 54*(1), 81–108.

Gulliver, A., Griffiths, K. M., & Christensen, H. (2010). Perceived barriers and facilitators to mental health help-seeking in young people: A systematic review. *BMC Psychiatry, 10*(113), 1–9.

Heary, C., Hennessy, E., Swords, L., & Corrigan, P. (2017). Stigma towards mental health problems during childhood and adolescence: Theory, research and intervention approaches. *Journal of Child and Family Studies, 26*(11), 2949–2959. doi:10.1007/s10826-017-0829-y

Heflinger, C. A., & Hinshaw, S. P. (2010). Stigma in child and adolescent mental health services research: Understanding professional and institutional stigmatization of youth with mental health problems and their families. *Administration and Policy in Mental Health and Mental Health Services Research, 37*(1–2), 61–70.

Heron, M. (2016). *Deaths: Leading causes for 2013* (National vital statistics reports; vol. 65 no. 2). Hyattsville, MD: National Center for Health Statistics.

Hert, M., Correll, C. U., Bobes, J., Cetkovich-Baskmas, M., Cohen, D., Asai, I., . . . Newcomer, J. W. (2011). Physical illness in patients with severe mental disorders. I. Prevalence, impact of medications and disparities in health care. *World Psychiatry, 10*(1), 52–77.

Hinshaw, S. P. (2005). The stigmatization of mental illness in children and parents: Developmental issues, family concerns, and research needs. *Journal of Child Psychology and Psychiatry, 46*(7), 714–734.

Hurley, K. D., Lambert, M. C., Epstein, M. H., & Stevens, A. (2015). Convergent validity of the Strength-Based Behavioral and Emotional Rating Scale with youth in a residential setting. *Journal of Behavioral Health Services & Research, 42*(3), 346–354.

Interagency Working Group on Youth Programs. (2016). *Pathways for youth: Strategic plan for federal collaboration.* Retrieved from https://youth.gov/sites/default/files/IWGYP-Pathways_for_Youth.pdf

Jacobs, M., Downie, H., Kidd, G., Fitzsimmons, L., Gibbs, S., & Melville, C. (2016). Mental health services for children and adolescents with learning disabilities: A review of research on experiences of service users and providers. *British Journal of Learning Disabilities, 44*(3), 225–232.

Jensen, P. S. (2002). Closing the evidence-based treatment gap for children's mental health services: What we know versus what we do. *Emotional and Behavioral Disorders in Youth, 2*, 43–50.

Jensen-Doss, A., & Weisz, J. R. (2008). Diagnostic agreement predicts treatment process and outcomes in youth mental health clinics. *Journal of Consulting and Clinical Psychology, 76*(5), 711–722.

Kazak, A. E., Hoagwood, K., Weisz, J. R., Hood, K., Kratochwill, T. R., Vargas, L. A., & Banez, G. A. (2010). A meta-systems approach to evidence-based practice for children and adolescents. *American Psychologist, 65*(2), 85–97.

Kendziora, K., Bruns, E., Osher, D., Pacchiano, D., & Mejia, B. (2001). *Systems of care promising practices in children's mental health* (Vol. 1). Washington, DC: American Institute for Research, Center for Effective Collaboration and Practice.

Kendziora, K. T., & Osher, D. M. (2004). Fostering resilience among youth in the juvenile justice system. In C. S. Clauss-Ehlers & M. D. Weist (Eds.), *Community planning to foster resilience in children* (pp. 177–195). Boston: Springer.

Kranke, D., Floersch, J., Townsend, L., & Munson, M. (2010). Stigma experience among adolescents taking psychiatric medication. *Children and Youth Services Review, 32*(4), 496–505.

Levin, J., Arluke, A., & Smith, M. (1982). The effects of labeling students upon teachers' expectations and intentions. *Journal of Social Psychology, 118*(2), 207–212.

Link, B. G., Struening, E. L., Neese-Todd, S., Asmussen, S., & Phelan, J. C. (2001). Stigma as a barrier to recovery: The consequences of stigma for the self-esteem of people with mental illnesses. *Psychiatric Services, 52*(12), 1621–1626.

Lippman, L. H., Ryberg, R., Terzian, M., Moore, K. A., Humble, J., & McIntosh, H. (2014). Positive and protective factors in adolescent well-being. In A. Ben-Arieh, F. Casas, I. Frones, & J. E. Korbin (Eds.), *Handbook of child well-being: Theories, methods and policies in global perspective* (pp. 2823–2866). New York: Springer.

Martin, J. K., Pescosolido, B. A., Olafsdottir, S., & McLeod, J. D. (2007). The construction of fear: Americans' preferences for social distance from children and adolescents with mental health problems. *Journal of Health and Social Behavior, 48*(1), 50–67.

Martinez, A. G., & Hinshaw, S. P. (2016). Mental health stigma: Theory, developmental issues, and research. In D. Cicchetti (Ed.), *Developmental psychopathology* (3rd ed., Vol 4., pp. 997–1040). Hoboken, NJ: John Wiley.

Masten, A. (2001). Ordinary magic: Resilience processes in development. *American Psychologist, 56*(3), 227–238.

McWhirter, B. T., & Page, G. L. (1999). Effects of anger management and goal setting group interventions on state-trait anger and self-efficacy beliefs among high risk adolescents. *Current Psychology, 18*(2), 223–237.

Merikangas, K. R., He, J. P., Brody, D., Fisher, P. W., Bourdon, K., & Koretz, D. S. (2010). Prevalence and treatment of mental disorders among US children in the 2001–2004 NHANES. *Pediatrics, 125*(1), 75–81.

Merikangas, K. R., He, J. P., Burstein, M., Swendsen, J., Avenevoli, S., Case, B., . . . Olfson, M. (2011). Service utilization for lifetime mental disorders in U.S. adolescents: Results of the National Comorbidity Survey Replication—Adolescent Supplement (NCS-A). *Journal of the American Academy of Child & Adolescent Psychiatry, 50*(1), 32–45.

Miller, S. D., & Duncan, B. L. (2000). *The outcome and session rating scales: Administration and scoring manual.* Chicago: Institute for the Study of Therapeutic Change.

Molina, B. S. G., & Pelham, W. E., Jr. (2003). Childhood predictors of adolescent substance use in a longitudinal study of children with ADHD. *Journal of Abnormal Psychology, 112*(3), 497–507.

Moses, T. (2009). Stigma and self-concept among adolescents receiving mental health treatment. *American Journal of Orthopsychiatry, 79*(2), 261–274.

Moses, T. (2010a). Adolescent mental health consumers' self-stigma: Associations with parents' and adolescents' illness perceptions and parental stigma. *Journal of Community Psychology, 38*(6), 781–798.

Moses, T. (2010b). Being treated differently: Stigma experiences with family, peers, and school staff among adolescents with mental health disorders. *Social Science & Medicine, 70*(7), 985–993.

Mukolo, A., Heflinger, C. A., & Wallston, K. A. (2010). The stigma of childhood mental disorders: A conceptual framework. *Journal of the American Academy of Child & Adolescent Psychiatry, 49*(2), 92–103.

Office of Special Education Programs. (1994). *The national agenda for improving results for children and youth with serious emotional disturbance.* Washington, DC: U.S. Department of Education.

Office of Special Education Programs. (1998). *Twentieth annual report to Congress on the implementation of the Individuals with Disabilities Education Act* (pp. 45–74). Washington, DC: U.S. Department of Education.

Ohan, J. L., Visser, T. A., Strain, M. C., & Allen, L. (2011). Teachers' and education students' perceptions of and reactions to children with and without the diagnostic label "ADHD." *Journal of School Psychology, 49*(1), 81–105.

Osher, D., Cantor, P., Berg, J., Strayer, L., & Rose, T. (2018). Drivers of human development: How relationships and context shape learning and development. *Applied Developmental Science.* DOI: 10.1080/10888691.2017.1398650

Osher, D., Cartledge, G., Oswald, D., Artilles, A. J., & Coutinho, M. (2004). Issues of cultural and linguistic competency and disproportionate representation. In R. Rutherford, M. Quinn, & S. Mather (Eds.), *Handbook of research in behavioral disorders* (pp. 54–77). New York: Guilford.

Osher, D., & Hanley, T. V. (1996). Implications of the national agenda to improve results for children and youth with or at risk of serious emotional disturbance. *Special Services in the Schools, 10*(2), 7–36.

Osher, D., & Hanley, T. V. (2001). Implementing the SED national agenda: Promising programs and policies for children and youth with emotional and behavioral problems. *Education and Treatment of Children, 24*(3), 374–403.

Osher, D., Kidron, Y., Brackett, M., Dymnicki, A., Jones, S., & Weissberg, R. P. (2016). Advancing the science and practice of social and emotional learning: Looking back and moving forward. *Review of Research in Education, 40*(1), 644–681.

Osher, T. W., & Osher, D. (2002). The paradigm shift to true collaboration with families. *Journal of Child and Family Studies, 11*(1), 47–60.

Osher, T. W., Osher, D., & Blau, G. M. (2008). Families matter. In T. P. Gullotta & G. M. Blau (Eds.), *Family influences on child behavior and development: Evidence-based prevention and treatment approaches* (pp. 39–63). New York: Taylor & Francis.

Owens, J. S., Watabe, Y., & Michael, K. D. (2013). Culturally responsive school mental health in rural communities. In C. S. Clauss-Ehlers, Z. N. Serpell,

& M. D. Weist (Eds.), *Handbook of culturally responsive school mental health: Advancing research, training, practice, and policy* (pp. 31–42). New York: Springer Science + Business Media.

Pachankis, J. E. (2007). The psychological implications of concealing a stigma: A cognitive-affective-behavioral model. *Psychological Bulletin, 133*(2), 328–345.

Park, A. L., Chorpita, B. F., Regan, J., Weisz, J. R., & Research Network on Youth Mental Health. (2015). Integrity of evidence-based practice: Are providers modifying practice content or practice sequencing? *Administration and Policy in Mental Health and Mental Health Services Research, 42*(2), 186–196.

Pescosolido, B. A., Fettes, D. L., Martin, J. K., Monahan, J., & McLeod, J. D. (2007a). Perceived dangerousness of children with mental health problems and support for coerced treatment. *Psychiatric Services, 58*(5), 619–625.

Pescosolido, B. A., Jensen, P., Martin, J. K., Perry, B. L., Olafsdottir, S., & Fettes, D. L. (2008). Public knowledge and assessment of child mental health problems: Findings from the National Stigma Study-Children. *Journal of the American Academy of Child and Adolescent Psychiatry, 47*(3), 339–349.

Pescosolido, B. A., Perry, B. L., Martin, J. K., McLeod, J. D., & Jensen, P. S. (2007b). Stigmatizing attitudes and beliefs about treatment and psychiatric medications for children with mental illness. *Psychiatric Services, 58*(5), 613–618.

Poulin, F., Dishion, T. J., & Burraston, B. (2001). 3-year iatrogenic effects associated with aggregating high-risk adolescents in cognitive-behavioral preventive interventions. *Applied Developmental Science, 5*(4), 214–224.

Reardon, T., Harvey, K., Baranowska, M., O'Brien, D., Smith, L., & Creswell, C. (2017). What do parents perceive are the barriers and facilitators to accessing psychological treatment for mental health problems in children and adolescents? A systematic review of qualitative and quantitative studies. *European Child & Adolescent Psychiatry, 26*(6), 623–647. doi:10.1007/s00787-016-0930-6

Renshaw, T. L., Furlong, M. J., Smith, D. C., O'Malley, M. D., Lee, S., & Strom, I. F. (2014). A synergistic conception of adolescents' mental health. In M. J. Furlong, R. Gilman, & E. S. Huebner (Eds.), *Handbook of positive psychology in schools* (2nd ed., pp. 12–32). New York: Routledge.

Reynolds, C. R., & Kamphaus, R. W. (2004). *BASC-2: Behavioral assessment system for children manual* (2nd ed.). Circle Pines, MN: AGS Publishing.

Rhule, D. M. (2005). Take care to do no harm: Harmful interventions for youth problem behavior. *Professional Psychology: Research and Practice, 36*(6), 618–625.

Richardson, L. A. (2001). Seeking and obtaining mental health services: What do parents expect? *Archives of Psychiatric Nursing, 15*(5), 223–231.

Sayal, K., Tischler, V., Coope, C., Robotham, S., Ashworth, M., Day, C., . . . Simonoff, E. (2010). Parental help-seeking in primary care for child and adolescent mental health concerns: Qualitative study. *British Journal of Psychiatry, 197*(6), 476–481.

Schoenwald, S. K., Kelleher, K., Weisz, J. R., & The Research Network on Youth Mental Health. (2008). Building bridges to evidence-based practice: The MacArthur Foundation Child System and Treatment Enhancement Projects (Child STEPs). *Administration and Policy in Mental Health and Mental Health Services Research, 35*(1–2), 66–72.

Seligman, M. E. P., & Csikszentmihalyi, M. (2000). Positive psychology: An introduction. *American Psychologist, 55*(1), 5–14.

Slade, T. J. A., Teesson, M., Whiteford, H., Burgess, P., Pirkis, J., & Saw, S. (2009). *The mental health of Australians 2: Report on the 2007 National Survey of Mental Health and Wellbeing.* Canberra, Australia: Department of Health and Ageing.

Socall, D. W., & Holtgraves, T. (1992). Attitudes toward the mentally ill. *Sociological Quarterly, 33*(3), 435–445.

Spencer, M. B. (2007). Phenomenology and ecological systems theory: Development of diverse groups. In R. M. Lerner (Ed.), *Handbook of child psychology and developmental science: Vol. 1. Theory and method* (6th ed., pp. 829–893). Hoboken, NJ: Wiley.

Stein, B. D., Jaycox, L. H., Kataoka, S. H., Wong, M., Tu, W., Elliott, M. N., & Fink, A. (2003). A mental health intervention for schoolchildren exposed to violence: A randomized controlled trial. *Journal of the American Medical Association, 290*(5), 603–611.

Stinnett, T. A., Bull, K. S., Koonce, D. A., & Aldridge, J. O. (1999). Effects of diagnostic label, race, gender, educational placement, and definitional information on prognostic outlook for children with behavior problems. *Psychology in the Schools, 36*(1), 51–59.

Suldo, S. M., Huebner, E. S., & Furlong, M. J. (2016). Measuring students' wellbeing. In S. Suldo (Ed.), *Promoting students' happiness: Positive psychology intervention strategies in school-based practice* (pp. 15–27). New York: Guilford.

Suldo, S. M., & Shaffer, E. J. (2008). Looking beyond psychopathology: The dual-factor model of mental health in youth. *School Psychology Review, 37*(1), 52–68.

Thompson, R. A., & Goodvin, R. (2016). Social support and developmental psychopathology. In D. Cicchetti (Ed.), *Developmental Psychopathology* (3rd ed., Vol 4., pp. 86–135). Hoboken, NJ: John Wiley.

Venning, A., Wilson, A., Kettler, L., & Eliott, J. (2013). Mental health among youth in South Australia: A survey of flourishing, languishing, struggling, and floundering. *Australian Psychologist, 48*(4), 299–310.

Walker, J., Geddes, A., Lever, N., Andrews, C., & Weist, M. D. (2010). Reconsidering the term 'emotional disturbance': A report from Maryland. *Advances in School Mental Health Promotion, 3*(2), 46–52.

Weist, M. D. (1997). Expanded school mental health services: A national movement in progress. In T. H. Ollendick & R. J. Prinz (Eds.), *Advances in clinical child psychology* (pp. 319–352). New York: Plenum.

Wellborn, J. R., Huebner, E. S., & Hills, K. J. (2012). The effects of strengths-based information on teachers' expectations for diverse students. *Child Indicators Research, 5*(2), 357–374.

CHAPTER FOUR

The Impact of Trauma and Adversities

Kathleen Guarino and Sarah Caverly

The majority of children and youth will be exposed to at least one potentially traumatic event before graduating from high school, and many students face multiple types of adversity within and beyond the school setting. Potentially traumatic experiences come in many forms and include abuse and neglect; family, school, and community violence; war or natural disasters and dislocation; stressors associated with poverty and economic distress; and experiences of racism and discrimination across generations. While many youth demonstrate resilience in the face of adversity, unaddressed trauma can have profound and lasting effects. Exposure to severe, chronic adversity early in life compromises physical health, emotional well-being, quality of relationships, and academic achievement. Schools play a critical role in preventing and addressing child trauma by recognizing the effects of adversity and trauma on students, parents, and staff and embedding policies and practices that foster healing and resilience for all in the learning environment.

In the first part of this chapter, we discuss the prevalence of childhood adversity and trauma, the neurobiology of stress and trauma, and the effects of exposure to potentially traumatic experiences on all members of a school community, including students, parents, and school staff. In part two, we explore the role that schools play in preventing and mitigating the effect of trauma by incorporating a range of trauma-sensitive, resilience-building strategies within a multitiered support framework.

PART ONE: UNDERSTANDING THE EFFECTS OF ADVERSITY AND TRAUMA

Defining Our Terms

The health and social service sectors that address experiences and effects of childhood adversity and trauma have a professional vocabulary. We begin by reviewing common terms and their intersections. Throughout this chapter, we will use these terms as we explore various stressors that youth in schools may experience and the effect of adversity on health, well-being, and school success.

Adverse childhood experiences: First defined by the Adverse Childhood Experiences (ACE) Study, ACEs occur before the age of 18 and fall into three main categories: abuse, neglect, and household dysfunction (Felitti et al., 1998). Recently, experts have expanded the categories and types of ACEs to include additional experiences such as exposure to group and/or community violence, poverty and related stressors, bullying, racism and discrimination, poor health, and involvement with systems such as child welfare and juvenile justice (Cronholm et al., 2015; Ellis & Dietz, 2017; Wade, Shea, Rubin, & Wood, 2014). Although the terms "ACEs" and "trauma" are often used interchangeably, not all ACEs listed as part of the ACE Study are always traumatic for every person.

Trauma: The term "trauma" is used to describe an *event*, series of events, or set of circumstances that is *experienced* as physically or emotionally harmful or life-threatening, overwhelms one's ability to cope, and has *adverse effects* on a person's mental, physical, social, emotional, or spiritual well-being (Substance Abuse and Mental Health Services Administration [SAMHSA], 2014). Experiencing a traumatic event can alter how people view themselves and others by challenging their beliefs that the world is a safe place, that other people can be trusted, and that they are worthy of care and protection. Whether an event is experienced as traumatic is influenced by many factors including one's internal coping resources, external supports, and broader community, cultural, and societal factors that shape how one understands and responds to experiences.

Toxic stress: The term "toxic stress" refers to the strong, frequent, and prolonged activation of a child's stress response system caused by exposure to chronic, severe adversity and trauma without adequate support, such as recurrent abuse, chronic neglect or deprivation, and ongoing exposure to threat and violence within families or communities (National Scientific Council on the Developing Child, 2014).

Resilience: "Resilience" refers to a positive, adaptive response to significant adversity (Center on the Developing Child at Harvard University, 2015). Children and youth who demonstrate resilience are able to adapt successfully to stressful situations and maintain healthy functioning.

Trauma sensitivity: "Trauma sensitivity" refers to a universal approach to addressing trauma adopted by all school staff to have the broadest effect on school culture and climate. The concept of trauma sensitivity at is broadest level is also reflected in the terms "trauma-sensitive approach" or "trauma-sensitive schools" (Cole, Eisner, Gregory, & Ristuccia, 2013). In some contexts, the term "trauma-informed schools" is used to refer to a multitiered approach to addressing trauma. The term "trauma-informed" may also be used to describe clinical interventions for addressing trauma-related mental health issues (see next definition).

Trauma-informed/trauma-specific services: The terms trauma-informed and trauma-specific services are sometimes used interchangeably to refer to evidence-based and promising prevention, intervention, or treatment services that address symptoms of traumatic stress and related challenges that developed during or after trauma (SAMHSA, 2014).

Types and Prevalence of Childhood Adversity and Trauma

Types of Childhood Adversity and Trauma

Children and youth may face a range of adverse childhood experiences over the course of development. Potentially traumatic experiences come in many forms that range from one-time events to experiences that are chronic or even generational. Examples of adverse and potentially traumatic experiences for children and youth in a school community include:

- **Natural disasters:** hurricanes, fires, floods
- **Human-caused disasters**: accidents, wars, environmental disasters, acts of terrorism
- **Community violence:** robberies, shootings, assault, gang-related violence, hate crimes, group trauma affecting a particular community
- **School violence:** threats, fights, school shootings, bullying, loss of a student or staff member
- **Family violence and disruption:** abuse, neglect, experiencing or witnessing domestic violence, incarceration of family members, family substance abuse, sudden or expected loss of a loved one
- **Refugee and war experiences:** exposure to war, political violence, torture, forced displacement
- **Medical issues:** pain, injury, and serious illness; invasive medical procedures or treatments
- **Economic stress:** lack of resources, unemployment, absence of support networks, financial stressors, lack of mobility, homelessness

- **System involvement:** foster care placement, involvement in the justice system, family separation due to system involvement.

Some potentially traumatic experiences are associated with belonging to a particular racial, ethnic, or cultural group. The term "racial trauma" refers to potentially traumatic experiences related to race that include: (1) direct experiences of racial harassment including threats of harm or injury and being humiliated; (2) witnessing racial violence toward others; and (3) experiencing discrimination and institutional racism. This includes "racial microaggressions"—brief, everyday verbal or behavioral exchanges that intentionally or unintentionally communicate hostile, derogatory, or negative racial messages or insults (e.g., racial slurs; being followed in a store; communications that convey rudeness and demean a person's racial identity; and exchanges that negate or deny the thoughts, feelings, or experiential reality of a person of color) (Bryant-Davis & Ocampo, 2005; Carter, 2007; Sue et al., 2007).

Racial trauma in schools may manifest in behaviors that perpetuate conscious or implicit biases against particular groups of students. Examples of racial microaggressions in the classroom include: consistently mispronouncing a student's name; making assumptions about a student's intelligence based on their race or ethnicity; insulting, diminishing, or disregarding a student's cultural background and experiences in a manner that perpetuates a sense of inferior status and negative self-perception; using textbooks and curricula that reflect white, upper-class experiences and overlook experiences of other student groups; and a lack of diversity in the workforce (Kohli & Solorzano, 2012). Youth may also experience microaggressions related to factors such as gender and sexual identity or orientation. For example, among LGBTQ youth of color, trauma may be related to both racial or cultural identity and gender identity or expression. Pervasive "microaggressions" related to gender identity or expression in schools include: using the term "gay" to describe something negative; derogatory looks or comments about someone's gender identity or expression; being told not to "flaunt" one's sexuality; and teachers not enforcing bullying or discrimination policies.

The term "historical trauma" refers to the collective and cumulative trauma experienced by a particular group across generations still struggling with the effects (National Child Traumatic Stress Network, 2013). Examples of historical trauma include: violent colonization and assimilation policies; slavery; segregation; racism; homophobia; and discrimination and oppression. Groups that continue to be affected by historical trauma include communities of color, American Indian and Alaska Native communities, members of the LGBTQ communities, and immigrant populations, many of whom have histories of negative experiences with the educational system (National Child Traumatic Stress Network, 2017). The effects of historical trauma in combination with continued racial trauma are reflected in persistent educational disparities for students of color, such as lower access to preschool, higher rates of suspension, and limited access to advanced courses and college-readiness resources (National Child Traumatic Stress Network, 2017).

As exposure to childhood adversity of all types accumulates, the negative effects on development become more severe. The term "complex trauma" describes exposure to multiple traumatic events from an early age, often interpersonal in nature and that occur within caregiving relationships, and the immediate and long-term effects of these experiences over the course of development (National Child Traumatic Stress Network, 2014). Examples include chronic abuse, neglect, or exposure to family violence, as well as other forms of violent victimization or loss experienced from an early age without adequate adult support to manage the experiences. This type of trauma is particularly devastating because it occurs during critical periods of brain development, before a child has had the chance to develop strong, positive ways to cope with stress.

Prevalence of Childhood Adversity and Trauma

The majority of children and youth in the United States will be exposed to at least one potentially traumatic event before they graduate from high school (see figure 4.1). More than two-thirds of children report experiencing a traumatic event by age 16, such as a serious accident, natural disaster, or experiencing or witnessing violence (Copeland, Keeler, Angold, & Costello, 2007).

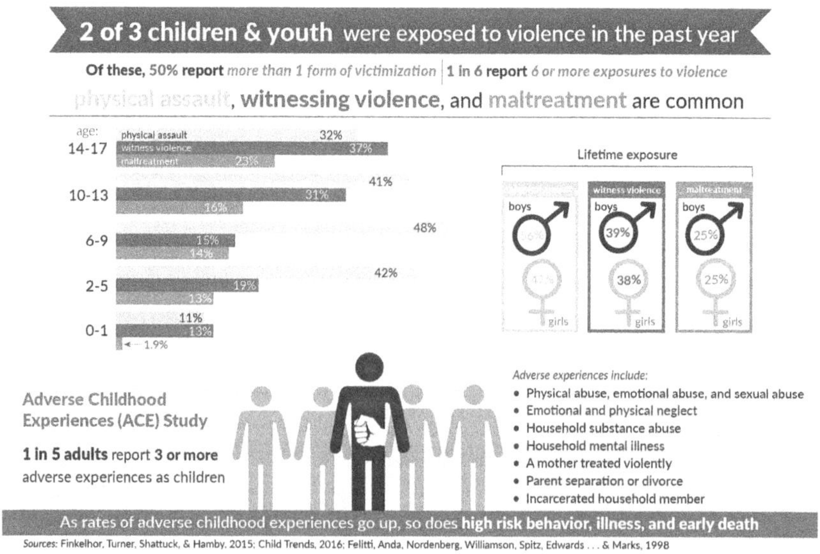

Figure 4.1 Prevalence of childhood adversity and trauma

Exposure to violent trauma in childhood, such as abuse, assault, or family or community violence, is particularly common. Finkelhor and colleagues (2015) reported that approximately 2 out of 3 children and youth ages 17 and younger were exposed to some form of violent victimization at home or in the community in the past year; 50% had more than one exposure; and 1 in 6 had 6 or more exposures to violence (Finkelhor, Turner, Shattuck, & Hamby, 2015).

Adult reports of adverse childhood experiences are also common. The groundbreaking Adverse Childhood Experiences or ACE Study surveyed more than 17,000 middle-class American adults about specific types of adverse experiences in childhood as part of a routine health screening. Adverse events included: physical abuse, emotional abuse, and sexual abuse; emotional and physical neglect; household substance abuse; household mental illness; a mother treated violently; parent separation or divorce; and incarceration of a household member. Nearly two-thirds of adults recalled at least one adverse event, and 1 in 5 adults reported 3 or more adverse childhood experiences (Felitti et al., 1998). Research suggests that as rates of adverse childhood experiences rise, so does the risk for challenges in adulthood such as high-risk behaviors, illness, and even early death (Felitti & Anda, 2010).

It is important to note that while most youth demonstrate resilience in the face of adversity (American Psychological Association, 2008), one's ability to cope with potentially traumatic stressors is directly related to the extent and quality of available supports (Osher, Cantor, Berg, Steyer, & Rose, 2018). Schools can play a critical role in preventing and mitigating the negative effects of adversity and trauma on youth.

A student's risk of exposure to adversity and trauma is influenced by intersecting factors such as race, ethnicity, gender, sexual orientation, immigration status, socioeconomic status, and location. Certain groups of students are more likely to be exposed to overwhelming stressors based on their unique experiences and circumstances. Groups at increased risk of exposure to potentially traumatic events include:

- **Youth of color.** Youth of color, particularly youth living in urban, low-income communities, are at greater risk of being exposed to and affected by various types of potentially traumatic events, including historical and racial trauma, as well as other forms of violent trauma: they are three times as likely to be victims of a robbery and five times more likely to be victims of a homicide (Collins et al., 2010; National Center for Victims of Crime, n.d.; Thomas et al., 2012).
- **American Indian/Alaska Native (AI/AN) children and youth.** AI/AN children and youth are 2.5 times more likely to experience trauma than their peers, including abuse, neglect, and family violence (BigFoot, Willmon-Haque, & Braden, 2008). Experiences of historical trauma, such as such as violence, forced placement in boarding schools, and loss of cultural identity,

continue to affect younger generations of AI/AN students (National Child Traumatic Stress Network, 2013).

- **Lesbian, gay, bisexual, transgender, and questioning (LGBTQ) youth.** LGBTQ youth face adversity in schools and in communities related to their sexual orientation or gender identity that includes bullying, harassment, and violent victimization, and experiences of stigma, discrimination, and social isolation (Coker, Austin, & Schuster, 2010; Institute of Medicine, 2011; Kosciw, Greytak, Giga, Villenas, & Danischewski, 2016).

Other groups at increased risk of exposure to adversity and trauma include children and youth who have disabilities, are refugees, experience homelessness, or who are living in poverty (American Institutes for Research, 2014; Beckerman & Corbett, 2008; Collins et al., 2010; Perez-Foster, 2001; Turner, Vanderminden, Finkelhor, Hamby, & Shattuck, 2011).

Neurobiology of Adversity and Trauma

The Stress Response System

Experiences that threaten our safety and well-being are first registered at a physiological level. The stress response system consists of a series of neural circuits and connections that span all levels of the brain, creating an internal alarm system designed to help us respond effectively to threat. Each of three primary regions of the brain—the brain stem, limbic system, and neocortex—play a distinct role in the stress response (Everly & Lating, 2013; McGill University, n.d.; van der Kolk, 2014; Wilson, Hansen, & Li, 2011).

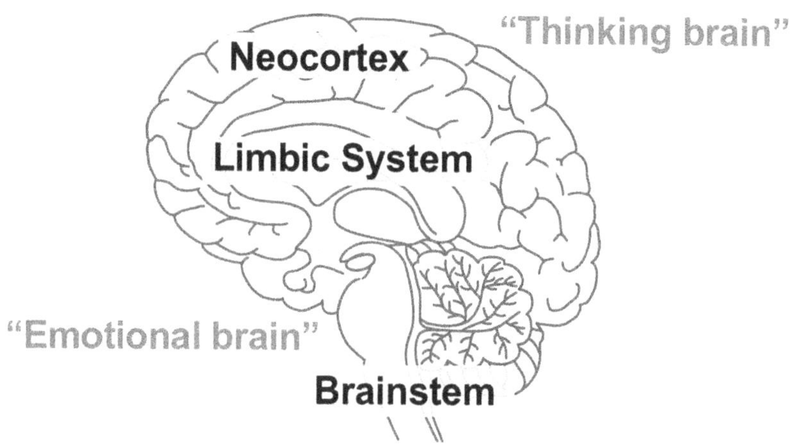

Figure 4.2 Primary regions of the brain

- The **brain stem** controls all of the major systems needed to keep us alive, including heart rate and breathing, and assists in preparing the body to react in a threatening situation.
- The **limbic system**, known as the brain's emotional control center, determines how we feel about an experience (e.g., whether it is pleasurable or frightening), looks out for danger, and sounds the alarm that initiates the stress response. In the face of confirmed threat, key structures in the limbic system, particularly the amygdala and hypothalamus activate the body's survival responses: fight (actively confronting the source of the stress), flight (avoiding the stress), or freeze (shutting down). Together, we can think of the limbic system and the brain stem as the "emotional brain."
- The **neocortex**, or the "thinking brain" is responsible for reasoning, planning, problem-solving, making meaning of our experiences, and regulating our emotions and behaviors. When faced with a threat, this region of the brain contextualizes and evaluates incoming information to determine whether a situation is unsafe and helps us return to a state of calm after the threat has passed.

The stress response involves a complex and dynamic sequencing of events for initiating and shutting down the fight-flight-freeze response. First, the emotional brain senses a threat and sounds the alarm that initiates the stress response. This happens at an automatic and unconscious level. For example, if you hear a loud noise, you immediately jump before you even know whether you are in danger. It is important to remember that when faced with a potential threat we *react first and think second*. The thinking brain assesses the situation and if the threat is confirmed, this part of the brain temporarily goes "offline," and the emotional brain takes over.

Hormones, including adrenaline and cortisol, are released to give the body the energy to flight or flee, and return to a state of calm once the threat has passed—similar to the gas and brake pedals in a car. Changes that happen when the stress response is activated include increased heart rate and blood pressure, rapid breathing, sweating, tunnel vision, and difficulty thinking clearly. When neither fighting nor fleeing is an option in the moment, we may "freeze" or shut down during a threatening situation. For younger children who cannot fight or flee, shutting down may be their best option for dealing with overwhelming stress. Once the threat has passed, the thinking brain helps shut off the alarm, and the body puts the brakes on to allow us calm down and come back into balance.

An experience becomes traumatic when it overwhelms our system for coping with stress and leaves people feeling helpless, vulnerable, out of control, and overly sensitive to reminders of the event (Brewin & Holmes, 2003; Herman, 1992; Macy, Behar, Paulson, Delman, & Schmid, 2004; van der Kolk, 2014; Wilson et al., 2011). Under these circumstances, the emotional brain continues to sound the alarm and send messages to fight or flee, even after the threat has passed, and the emotional brain may become overly sensitive to any potential threat and start reading nonthreatening situations as dangerous (van der Kolk, 2014; Wilson et al., 2011). The body remains in survival mode, resulting in a variety of acute physical, behavioral, emotional, and cognitive symptoms in the immediate aftermath of a traumatic event, including nightmares or flashbacks; increased agitation, irritability, and anxiety; hypervigilance; trouble concentrating; and feeling numb or disconnected. With support, most youth are able to recover from a traumatic experience without risk for long-term challenges. However, as traumatic events accumulate the effects on daily functioning become more pronounced.

Effects of Chronic Stress

Early childhood through adolescence is a period of increased brain plasticity and sensitivity to the effects of environment and experience, either positive or negative. Positive brain development is supported by a healthy physical environment and access to safe, stable relationships with caregivers who are attuned to a child's needs and can respond in caring, consistent, and nurturing ways to protect children from threat and help them to tolerate stress. Under the right conditions, the emotional brain and the thinking brain become more sophisticated and better coordinated as children learn how to use cognitive skills to manage emotional reactions in ways that are critical to learning and academic success.

Exposure to manageable levels of stress, such as being challenged to engage in new experiences and learn new skills, is critical for healthy development. Whether a stress response is deemed *positive*, *tolerable*, or *toxic*, determines its effect on development (National Scientific Council on the Developing Child, 2014). A *positive stress response* refers to a mild or brief stress response activated by experiences such as meeting new people, dealing with challenges, going to the doctor, or overcoming fears. More significant stressors such losing a parent or parent separation or divorce can also be manageable with the right support. A *tolerable stress response* describes serious, temporary stress responses that are buffered by caring adults. Many stressors that are potentially damaging to development can be buffered and addressed in the context of supportive relationships (Osher et al., 2018; Cantor, Osher, Berg, Steyer, & Rose, 2018; Center on the Developing Child at Harvard University, 2015).

Stress becomes damaging when it occurs continuously without adequate adult support. Strong, frequent, and prolonged activation of the stress response without adult support, referred to as a *toxic stress response*, can significantly alter developmental trajectories (National Scientific Council on the Developing Child, 2014). This type of stress response occurs in the context of prolonged, overwhelming adversity that is often interpersonal in nature, such as recurrent abuse, chronic neglect and deprivation, and ongoing exposure to family or community violence—described earlier as *complex trauma*.

Exposure to traumatic events in childhood with inadequate adult support can significantly disrupt positive brain development, placing children at greater risk for adverse emotional, functional, and academic outcomes. A growing body of research suggests chronic exposure to trauma early in life can lead to changes to brain size, structure, and function; alterations in neural pathways including those associated with learning, memory, and ability to self-regulate and cope; heightened baseline state of physiological arousal, including heart rate, body temperature, and anxiety level; and increased sensitivity to internal and external trauma reminders (Center on the Developing Child, 2010; DeBellis & Zisk, 2014; National Scientific Council on the Developing Child, 2010, 2014; Perry, 2001; Perry & Pollard, 1998; Teicher & Samson, 2016). Trauma that continues through adolescence has a profound effect on affect regulation, behavior, cognition, relationships, and self-concept into adulthood (Cook et al., 2005; D'Andrea, Ford, Stolbach, Spinazzola, & van der Kolk, 2012; Felitti et al., 1998; Felitti & Anda, 2010; Putnam, 2006). In both human and economic terms, the cost of not addressing the traumatic stress associated with these adverse experiences is significant: effects are seen in the health care, employment, child welfare, homelessness, criminal/juvenile justice, and education systems.

Effects of Childhood Adversity and Trauma on Schools

A significant percentage of students have been or continue to be exposed to traumatic experiences, including experiencing a traumatic event directly, witnessing an event, or hearing about an event that affects someone a student knows. Whether these experiences happen at home, in the community, or at school, the effects of trauma can be felt at school. As children are exposed to more traumatic experiences, the negative effect on social and academic success becomes more pronounced. In the face of pervasive adversity, all members of the school community—students, families, and school personnel—are affected.

Effects of Adversity and Trauma on Students

Students exposed to adversity and trauma may exhibit a range of responses that can interfere with school success (National Child Traumatic Stress Network, 2010). Physical symptoms include headaches, stomachaches, poor appetite, and a decline in self-care (e.g., poor hygiene). Intense feelings of fear, anxiety, and concern for safety are also common following a traumatic experience. Older students may feel shame, guilt, responsibility, embarrassment, and concern about how others will view them after a traumatic event. Students may have extreme responses to trauma reminders (i.e., triggers) and struggle to calm themselves down and identify and express their emotions in safe ways. For example, youth may over- or under-react to situations or experiences in their environment, such as sudden movements, loud noises, physical contact, or interactions with peers or adults (National Child Traumatic Stress Network Schools Committee, 2008).

Difficulties regulating emotions can lead to behavior problems such as angry or aggressive outbursts, difficulty managing rules and limits, and problems forming and maintaining healthy relationships with peers and adults. Teenagers may have more intense mood swings; withdraw from family, peers, and activities; avoid reminders of the trauma; and engage in risky behaviors such as alcohol or drug use, sexual behaviors, fights, or self-harm as a way to manage feelings related to the trauma (National Child Traumatic Stress Network Schools Committee, 2008). Some students may manage their trauma by "disassociating," or disconnecting from the present moment, to deal with overwhelming feelings or sensations. This may look like daydreaming, not paying attention, or a lack of emotion. The effects of various forms of trauma, including family, community, and racial trauma on identity formation can result in low self-esteem and deeply held feelings of shame and guilt, along with a lack of hope and control over the future that makes goal-setting seem pointless. Students may also develop more significant, long-term mental health issues related to traumatic experiences, such as post-traumatic stress disorder, anxiety, or depression (Putnam, 2006).

Exposure to trauma can lead to difficulties with concentration, learning, and memory that directly affect academic performance. Youth may struggle with learning difficulties and challenges in planning and anticipating during the course of the day. Emotional and behavioral issues and trouble trusting adults and building relationships only further exacerbate these challenges, leading to more time out of class, increased absences, and more frequent suspensions and expulsions, which further disconnect students from their school community (Cole et al., 2013; Perfect, Turley, Carlson, Yohanna, & Saint Gilles, 2016; Wolpow, Johnson, Hertel, & Kincaid, 2009). The effects on academic achievement are profound. Traumatized students have more learning difficulties, are referred more often to special education, score lower on standardized tests, and are more likely to fail a grade (Perfect et al., 2016).

Trauma Reminders

Trauma reminders or "triggers" are related to aspects of previous traumatic experiences that automatically cause the body to react as if the traumatic event is happening again in that moment (National Child Traumatic Stress Network, 2014; van der Kolk, 2014). Trauma reminders include people, places, sights, sounds, smells, feelings, or situations that are associated with a previous traumatic event. When faced with a trauma reminder, the emotional brain assumes the danger is real without having the thinking brain check things out. This allows individuals to move quickly into action, which can be critical to survival in some circumstances. For example, if a child is living in a violent environment, reacting automatically to signs of danger like a slammed door, a raised voice, or a threatening tone or gesture, may help that child stay safe. This automatic response may be less helpful during the school day when an environment becomes loud or chaotic and that same child has an intense fight or flight response. In these moments, the thinking brain is offline, and the body does not always know whether it is reacting to an actual threat or a false alarm.

Potential trauma reminders for children and youth include:

- Loud noises
- Physical touch
- Threatening gestures
- Authority figures and limit-setting
- Chaos or uncertainty
- Particular spaces, such as bathrooms or areas that are dimly lit or less monitored
- Changes in routine
- Hand or body gestures perceived as threatening
- Witnessing violence between others, such as peers fighting
- Emergency vehicles and police or fire personnel
- Certain smells
- Weather
- Particular times of year.

Trauma reminders set off responses that can appear confusing and out of place to others and are easily misunderstood when taken at face value. Common fight responses include yelling, swearing, posturing, and other aggressive behavior; flight responses include running away, refusing to talk, avoidance, or possibly behaviors such as substance abuse; freeze responses may look like spacing out and appearing numb, disconnected, confused, or unresponsive.

Box 4.1 Recognizing Student Trauma

Students exposed to trauma—particularly, chronic trauma from an early age—develop survival strategies to manage traumatic experiences that can be easily misunderstood in the moment. Trauma-related behaviors can be frustrating for adults, especially when they jeopardize a student's success. However, these behaviors often make sense in the context of a youth's experiences.

Without an awareness of the trauma and its effects, there is a greater likelihood of misunderstanding, mislabeling, and even misdiagnosing students, causing further harm (Cook et al., 2005; D'Andrea, Ford, Stolbach, Spinazzola, & van der Kolk, 2012).

Consider how our ways of understanding and talking about students may shift when we put on our "trauma glasses" and examine what may be at the root of difficult behaviors.

Trauma glasses off	Trauma glasses on
Manipulative	*Getting needs met in ways that have worked in the past. Doing whatever is necessary to survive.*
Lazy	*Overwhelmed. Underdeveloped executive functioning skills.*
Resistant	*Mistrustful of others due to history of being hurt by others. Scared to make progress and then lose everything.*
Unmotivated	*Depressed. Fearful. Overwhelmed. "Frozen."*
Disrespectful	*Feeling threatened, unsafe, out of control.*
Attention-seeking	*Feeling disconnected, alone, or unheard by others. Looking for connection.*

Effects of Adversity and Trauma on Caregivers

Parents and other adult caregivers with their own histories of adversity and trauma, particularly chronic exposure to traumatic stress, may have their own difficulties managing emotions and controlling behaviors, forming relationships, and managing stress related to their child's difficult behaviors. Adults with histories of trauma are at increased risk for challenges such as substance abuse, depression, and post-traumatic stress disorder that negatively affect parenting and can affect their children's behaviors at school (Cohen, Hien & Batchelder, 2008; Kistin et al., 2014). In addition, parents with negative or traumatic experiences related to school may be distrustful of educators and the education system and have trouble forming relationships with school staff.

Parents and caregivers with trauma histories likely have their own trauma reminders. Depending on what a parent's experience of school was like, just entering the building may trigger a fight or flight response. Other triggers may include feelings of shame or embarrassment about a child who is struggling, confusion in meetings, and fear of other system involvement. Situations that leave adults feeling ashamed, helpless, frightened, or out of control may remind them of past trauma and lead to intense reactions. Triggered responses one may witness when working with parents include extreme anger, defensiveness, avoidance, or shutting down. These behaviors are challenging and can be easily misunderstood by staff, leading to negative interactions that interfere with parent engagement and relationship-building. Not every parent has a trauma history, and not all intense responses are signs of a trauma. However, the more schools become aware of trauma and its effects, the more staff are able to recognize and minimize potentially triggering situations.

Effects of Adversity and Trauma on School Staff and the Learning Environment

School staff may bring their own histories of trauma to their work or experience trauma on the job, for example, being threatened or assaulted or witnessing violence in school. In addition to direct experiences of trauma, teachers who work with highly traumatized students are at risk of being indirectly traumatized as a result of hearing about their students' trauma and witnessing its negative effects. Symptoms of *secondary traumatic stress* for staff may include: increased anxiety and concern about their own safety; intrusive, negative thoughts and images related to their students' traumatic stories; and a desire to avoid people or situations that trigger these difficult thoughts and emotions (Hoydon, Wong, Langley, Stein, & Kataoka, 2015; National Child Traumatic Stress Network, Secondary Traumatic Stress Committee, 2011). Over time, the cumulative effect of working with traumatized students and their families, commonly referred to as *vicarious trauma*, can lead to negative changes in how staff view themselves and others, including increased difficulty leaving work at work, increased irritability with co-workers and students, diminished energy and patience, and doubts about professional capabilities and effectiveness (National Child Traumatic Stress Network, Secondary Traumatic Stress Committee, 2011).

High rates of trauma among students and staff can have significant, negative effects on school culture and conditions for learning. Students struggling with trauma responses are more likely to escalate and act out in ways that can compromise their safety and the safety of other students and staff (National Child Traumatic Stress Network, Schools Committee, 2017; Perfect et al., 2016). When school environments become increasingly chaotic or unsafe, adults under stress may be quick to threaten students with negative consequences, escalate with students, and use more punitive discipline strategies in an attempt to regain control. Under these circumstances, schools risk retraumatizing students by creating environments and situations that replicate the events or dynamics of a previous trauma. Retraumatizing practices may include: employing harsh or shaming discipline practices that mimic abuse experiences for youth; allowing environments to become chaotic, disorganized, unpredictable, or unsafe; treating students or caregivers disrespectfully and minimizing their voice; and using practices like seclusion or restraint (SAMHSA, 2014). When students and school staff are affected by trauma, safety, engagement, and sense of community may be compromised.

PART TWO: PROMOTING RESILIENCE WITHIN THE SCHOOL CONTEXT

Resilience

The effects of unaddressed childhood adversity and trauma can be profound. However, many children and adolescents who are exposed to potentially traumatic events are able to cope with and adapt to these experiences without significant disruption to their daily lives. Resilience refers to a *positive, adaptive response to significant adversity* (Center on the Developing Child at Harvard University, 2015). Resilience is best understood as a bio-psychological-ecological process influenced by internal and external systems to facilitate the potential for positive outcomes (Cantor, et al., 2018; Masten & Obradovic, 2008). It is defined locally and is a shared, common phenomenon that is culturally, socially, and historically embedded (Bethell, Newacheck, Hawes, & Halfon, 2014; Masten, 2014).

Resilience is influenced early in life through biological and contextual supports that help establish patterns of reactions (Yates, Egeland, & Sroufe, 2003). However, it is important to note that resilience is not fixed and can be supported throughout the life span, especially during times of transition. At times, resilience may be situationally based, meaning that a child may demonstrate resilience in the face of one type of situation but not another. How youth respond to adversity is influenced by the complex interaction between individual and environmental risk and protective factors, including genetic make-up, internal coping resources, environmental conditions, external supports, and broader community, cultural, and societal factors that shape how they understand and respond to their experiences (Brom, Pat-Horenczyk, & Ford, 2009; Layne, Briggs, & Courtois, 2014; Masten, 2014; SAMHSA, 2014).

Schools play a significant role in supporting the health and well-being of children and youth, including those affected by trauma (Osher et al., 2018). Given the plasticity of resilience and its individual experience, interventions with the goal of increasing students' resilience have become increasingly

Box 4.2 Internal and External Resilience Assets

Internal

Internal assets that contribute to children's adaptive responses include social and emotional competencies, self-regulation, growth mindsets, cognitive functioning, self-regulation, self-efficacy, agency, internal perceptions of control, and perceptions of stress (Benson, Scales, & Sylvertsen, 2011; Center on the Developing Child at Harvard University, 2015; Layne et al., 2014; Masten, 2014; Merikangas et al., 2010; Pat-Horenczyk, Rabinowitz & Tucker-Levin, 2009).

External

External assets also contribute to children's adaptive responses and include the availability of at least one stable, caring, and supportive relationship with an adult; affirming faith or cultural traditions; adequate resources and social support networks; positive peer relationships; and healthy, safe environments, communities, and systems (Center on the Developing Child at Harvard University, 2015; Collins et al., 2010; Masten, 2014; Pat-Horenczyk et al., 2009).

common. Each is built upon the premise that multiple systems may contribute to the development of resilience, and no two individuals draw from the same combination and experience of these systems (Masten, 2014). The school context lends itself to strategies targeting both internal (e.g., social and emotional competence, growth mindset, and perceptions of stress) and external (e.g., school culture, staff-child relationships, teaching practices, and cultural resources) assets to bolster resilience (Osher, Kendziora, Spier, & Garibaldi, 2014). This has led resilience researchers to recommend policies and programs to better support both students and the adults in children's lives (Luthar, 2015).

School-Based Interventions to Promote Resilience

In schools with high rates of student trauma and adversity, including those in socioeconomically disadvantaged communities, there is a recognized need for fortified teaching and learning environments that consider the effect of childhood adversity, and work to reduce barriers to success (Farrington et al., 2012). Environments can be fortified to promote universal social and emotional competencies; provide individualized services that address students emotional and behavioral needs; ensure consistent, safe, motivating, student-centered classrooms; and establish mechanisms for sustaining these types of learning environments at the leadership level (Cantor, 2016; Osher, Kidron, DeCandia, Kendziora, & Weissberg, 2016). The movement to create trauma-sensitive schools further supports and augments these efforts to cultivate optimal learning conditions for all students.

The term "Multitiered Systems of Support" (MTSS) refers to a comprehensive, whole-school prevention and intervention framework that integrates and aligns a continuum of evidence-based practices and systems for improving learning outcomes for all students. Within a multitiered prevention framework, universal (Tier 1) strategies for supporting trauma-sensitive and resilience-building approaches are adopted schoolwide to have the broadest effect on culture and climate. Targeted (Tier 2 and 3) interventions for addressing trauma-related challenges are also made available to both students and teachers to foster safe and supportive environments.

Universal Strategies

This section begins by discussing schoolwide trauma sensitivity as a universal approach designed to prevent and mitigate the potentially damaging effects of adversity and trauma and foster healing and resilience for all in the school environment. Additional universal approaches that align with and support trauma sensitivity discussed in this section include: positive behavioral interventions and supports (PBIS); restorative practices; and universal strategies for supporting social and emotional learning. It is important to note that many of these approaches include targeted interventions for select students in need of additional support and skills-building. Later in this section, we will discuss targeted interventions for addressing trauma-related mental health issues and building key skills for resilience among students at increased risk for being exposed to and affected by trauma.

Trauma Sensitivity

In a trauma-sensitive school, all aspects of the educational environment—from workforce training to engagement with students and families to procedures and policies—are grounded in an understanding of trauma and its effects and are designed to promote resilience for all. Within a multitiered prevention framework, trauma sensitivity is a universal approach, embedded into the schoolwide foundation (see figure 4.3). Schoolwide trauma sensitivity maximizes support for all students, including those whose history of adversity is unknown to school staff, and helps staff members recognize those who need more intensive services. This fosters an environment in which targeted and intensive interventions for trauma are more likely to be

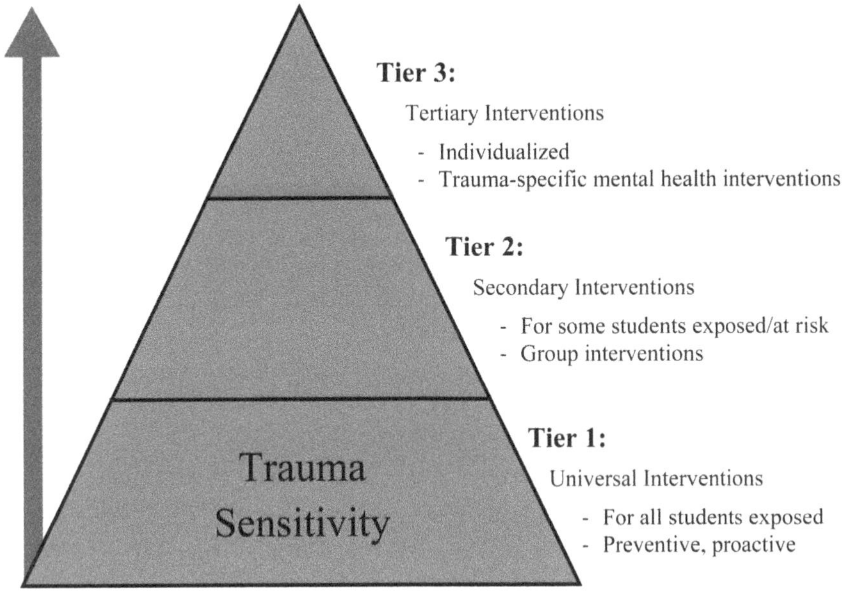

Figure 4.3 Trauma sensitivity and Multitiered Systems of Support

successful. A trauma-sensitive approach also addresses negative effects of trauma on families and school staff. Schools with an awareness and understanding of trauma and its effects can create environments where all students, including those affected by trauma, feel safe, connected, and supported, and the skills critical to resilience building are modeled and taught.

Adopting a universal approach to addressing trauma requires modifications to school practices, policies, and culture. Here we offer a framework for adopting trauma-sensitive strategies across six core domains commonly identified in the field: (1) support staff development; (2) create a safe and supportive environment; (3) assess needs and provide support; (4) build social and emotional skills; (5) collaborate with students and families; and (6) adapt policies and procedures (see table 4.1). Trauma-sensitive strategies in each domain reflect common key elements of a trauma-sensitive school (Cole et al., 2013; Guarino & Chagnon, 2018; Wolpow et al., 2009).

Adopting a trauma-sensitive approach includes acknowledging and addressing the effects of historical and racial trauma and working to create environments that are culturally responsive. Schools integrate culturally responsive practices for addressing and mitigating trauma across all domains within a trauma-sensitive school. Key recommendations for educators include:

- Educate staff about the effects of historical and systemic racism on students
- Establish "brave" environments where students feel safe taking risks to be themselves and share their experiences
- Be aware of one's own beliefs and biases and model honest and authentic communication
- Incorporate materials and references that are culturally relevant to students
- Demonstrate respect in the day-to-day, such as correctly pronouncing students' names, using preferred pronouns, using the preferred language to share information with families, and being curious about and honoring students' cultural stories and experiences
- Consider cultural factors when meeting with families (e.g., how to greet them, what topics may be difficult to address, cultural norms/values/practices, and their experiences with the educational system)
- Adopt and uphold policies related to cultural sensitivity and empowerment
- Consider the use of discipline practices that are culturally informed (e.g., restorative practices)
- Explore how students can be part of addressing racial and social justice issues (Kohli & Solorzano, 2012; National Child Traumatic Stress Network, 2017; U.S. Department of Health and Human Services & U.S. Department of Education, 2016).

Table 4.1 Trauma-sensitive practices across core domains

Support staff development	Educate all school staff on trauma and its effects on students, families, and staff; assess staff understanding and use of trauma-sensitive strategies; integrate expectations related to trauma sensitivity into job expectations, reviews, team meetings, and new hire practices; address the effects of secondary traumatic stress and support staff resilience.
Create a safe and supportive environment	Create a safe physical and emotional environment using positive, strengths-based approaches; recognize and reduce trauma-related triggers in the school environment; incorporate trauma-sensitive crisis prevention and intervention practices; reflect the culturally relevant norms and practices of students, families, and staff.
Assess needs and provide support	Consider potential effect of trauma in all assessment protocol and behavior plan templates. Ensure students have access to trauma-specific mental health services as needed (in school or

(continued)

Table 4.1 *(continued)*

	community settings). Tailor interventions to reflect the experiences and needs of particular groups (e.g., youth of color, immigrant populations, youth who are LGBTQ).
Build social and emotional skills	Integrate universal strategies for teaching and modeling social and emotional skills. Educate students and families about stress and traumatic stress and its effects. Embed formal strategies for helping students cope with adversity.
Collaborate with students and families	Provide opportunities for students and families to have input into programming and voice concerns. Treat students and families as partners. Include students and families in schoolwide efforts to adopt a trauma-sensitive approach (e.g., work groups, training activities, action planning).
Adapt policies and procedures	Include a commitment to trauma sensitivity in school mission; adopt positive and restorative approaches to discipline; ensure communication practices are trauma-sensitive; review policies and procedures to ensure continued alignment with a trauma-sensitive approach.

Positive Behavioral Interventions and Supports

Positive Behavioral Interventions and Supports, or PBIS, is a systemic approach for improving school climate, student behavior, and academic achievement by applying behavioral systems and interventions to achieve positive behavior change in schools (Bradshaw, Mitchell, & Leaf, 2010; Horner, Sugai, & Anderson, 2010; Sugai et al., 2000). PBIS is implemented based on the Response to Intervention model that includes a three-tiered framework to provide a continuum of behavioral and academic supports. PBIS at the universal level is referred to as Schoolwide PBIS. Universal strategies that represent broader systems change include teaching social skills, positively reinforcing behaviors that the school wishes to promote, and structuring learning environments to prevent undesirable behaviors (Sugai & Horner, 2006). For students who require more than these universal supports, Tiers 2 and 3 offer intensive and specialized interventions to groups of students or individuals who are at higher risk for behavioral difficulties.

The aim and approach of PBIS can be bolstered by understanding trauma and its effects and aligning these efforts with a trauma-sensitive approach. An understanding of trauma and its effects supports school personnel in

Table 4.2 Intersection between PBIS and trauma sensitivity

PBIS	Trauma Sensitivity
• Fosters a positive school culture for all students, including those affected by trauma	• Supports a positive school culture by adopting trauma-sensitive responses
• Focuses on teaching social skills and positively reinforces prosocial behaviors that are resilience-building	• Considers trauma-related connections to problem behaviors and reinforces need for social and emotional skill development
• Structures the environment to prevent undesirable behaviors	• Reduces trauma-related triggers or reminders in the environment that contribute to problem behaviors

recognizing potential trauma-related connections to behaviors and reinforces the need for safe and secure environments and a positive school climate. Schools that are already making the cultural shifts needed to adopt PBIS are well positioned to implement trauma-sensitive practices. At a universal level, both approaches share a commitment to helping children achieve success through systems change; both emphasize strengths over deficits, the creation of safe and supportive environments for all, a child-centered approach, and a commitment to adopt universal strategies to ensure support for all and identification of students with more intensive needs (see table 4.2) (Carr et al., 2002; Guarino & Chagnon, 2018; Sugai & Horner, 2006). Trauma-sensitive strategies aimed at identifying and reducing trauma-related triggers and traumatizing practices can also be part of a proactive approach to understanding and preventing particular behaviors.

Restorative Practices

A school's disciplinary environment and culture affects students' sense of safety and connectedness and can traumatize or retraumatize students. Problematic disciplinary practices include harsh exclusionary policies and inconsistently enforced disciplinary policies, including suspensions and expulsions (and how they are employed), corporal punishment, restraint, and exclusion. These practices contribute to a more negative school climate, undermine academic achievement, and may become potential sources of trauma for students. Many school leaders are giving attention to creating a safe and supportive community based upon equity, transparency, and fair rules (Fronius, Persson, Guckenburg, Hurley, & Petrosino, 2016). This often includes strong, positive relationships between students and adults with a focus on promoting student growth.

Restorative practices (RP) or restorative justice programs encompass a growing social movement to build a school context that is peaceful and non-punitive for addressing conflicts and problem-solving through challenging situations (e.g., violations of student rights and harmful situations). RP often serves as an alternative to the traditional discipline models, such as suspension or expulsion. For students who have experienced trauma, RP provides a landscape of support through teachers, administrators, and peers. Both the classroom and school culture shifts to become more supportive and inclusive for students who may otherwise be shamed, isolated and/or minimized by teachers and peers. RP shows promise as an approach that supports improvements in school climate and culture (Mirsky, 2007), a greater sense of community, improved academic achievement (Gonzalez, 2012; Gregory, Clawson, Davis, & Gerewitz, 2014), and decreases in disciplinary referrals (Suvall, 2009). Restorative practices, for example, may improve teachers' and students' positive attitudes and reduce teacher use of exclusionary discipline and student problem behaviors, while improving school climate (Gregory et al., 2014).

Restorative and trauma-sensitive approaches are grounded in a similar set of core principles so that cultural shifts and skills associated with one approach support the other (see table 4.3). Both frameworks emphasize the need to establish a safe physical and emotional learning environment where students and staff are seen, heard, and respected. Trauma-sensitive and restorative practices support student choice and control and opportunities to build skills that enhance connection. This focus on choice, control, and empowerment extends to the entire school community including students, staff, families, and other members of the broader community. Ensuring respect for and integration of cultural protocols and values is also a key principle for both approaches. Trauma-sensitive and restorative practices approaches are collaborative and strengths-based and view students, staff, and families as partners. Finally, these approaches see relationships as central to well-being and to healing and repair.

Similar to the intersection with PBIS, trauma-sensitivity offers an important rationale for why schools are adopting or considering adopting restorative practices. The trauma-informed perspective helps educators see the importance of responding in a restorative manner. This is not only because the misbehaving student may be a victim of trauma but also because helping the child affected by trauma will be more effective if she or he feels safe and secure when being disciplined. For schools that have adopted a restorative approach, understanding trauma and its effects adds a new lens through which to view student behavior that can inform practice. This may involve incorporating trauma education into restorative dialogue to better understand why particular behaviors happened and the effects of these behaviors on the individual and on others in the community who may also be survivors of trauma.

Table 4.3 Intersection between restorative practices and trauma sensitivity

Restorative Practices	Trauma Sensitivity
• Provides an empathic and compassionate space for understanding behavior, including trauma-related responses	• Seeks to Identify and reduce trauma-related triggers that can result in negative behaviors and harm to others
• Fosters relationship and connection that is often compromised for students exposed to trauma	• Provides another lens through which to view underlying reasons for problem behaviors
• Reduces likelihood of retraumatizing students	• Encourages using restorative practices approach to discipline
• Creates an environment where trauma-sensitive practices are more likely to be adopted and sustained	• Fosters an environment where restorative practices are more likely to be adopted and sustained

Social and Emotional Learning

Educators are increasingly aware that a student's academic success is influenced by a number of individual and environmental factors that must be addressed in school settings. An emphasis on social and emotional learning (SEL) reflects the importance of integrating processes for building individual social-emotional competencies that lay the foundation for resilience, agency, and success in school and life. Parallel efforts to create supportive school environments are driven by a growing understanding of the relationship between positive school climate and student well-being and achievement. Universal SEL programming improves student skills, attitudes, behaviors, and academic performance, which in turn, supports a positive school climate (Durlak, Weissberg, Dymnicki, Taylor, & Schellinger, 2011). The number of SEL programs has rapidly expanded over the past 15 years. Many programs focus on enhancing students' SEL skills to reduce behavior problems and promote positive, supportive interactions (Jones & Bouffard, 2012; Wilson, Lipsey, & Derzon, 2003).

Supporting universal processes for social and emotional development is itself a core component of trauma-sensitive schools. Exposure to traumatic stress in childhood with inadequate adult support can significantly disrupt the development of core social-emotional competencies such as emotional and behavioral regulation, problem-solving, planning, and prosocial skills, and place children at greater risk for adverse emotional, functional, and academic outcomes (Cook et al., 2005; National Scientific Council on the Developing Child, 2010, 2014; Perfect et al., 2016). Building social-emotional skills is seen as critical for all students, but particularly for students exposed to traumatic events that may have compromised the development of these skills.

Given that the most common challenge to the successful implementation of SEL programs is lack of teacher and administrator support (Durlak et al., 2011), viewing SEL as essential to resilience-building for students exposed to trauma has the potential to increase staff buy-in. Establishing a formal connection between SEL and trauma sensitivity further unites these efforts and increases the likelihood that SEL will be embedded and sustained successfully as part of the overall mission to support children and youth exposed to trauma. Adopting a trauma-sensitive approach also supports a positive school climate, which is associated with a number of improved academic and social-emotional outcomes for students and influences the effectiveness of SEL programs (Durlak et al., 2011; Osher & Kendziora, 2010; Osher & Berg, 2017; Thapa, Cohen, Guffey, & Higgins-D'Alessandro, 2013; Zins & Elias, 2006).

Targeted Interventions

Mental Health Services

Although significant, the effects of chronic trauma on children are often overlooked or misunderstood (Cook et al., 2005; D'Andrea et al., 2012). Most children who experience distress related to trauma are not identified and do not get the help that they need, particularly children from ethnic and racial minority groups (American Psychological Association, 2008). Children who have experienced trauma have specific needs that may be misidentified or misinterpreted if their history of trauma is not considered during the assessment process. Trauma-related symptoms like those discussed earlier in this chapter can mimic other disorders such as ADHD, bipolar disorder, oppositional-defiant disorder, and reactive attachment disorder (Cook et al., 2005; D'Andrea et al., 2012). Without a thorough assessment that includes a history of trauma, school professionals may mislabel or misdiagnose children on the basis of presenting behaviors and miss the traumatic experiences that may be the source of the symptoms and the primary focus of treatment.

Historically, school-based efforts to address trauma centered on providing intensive, specialized interventions for students with the most significant challenges. While the growing movement to adopt a schoolwide, trauma-sensitive approach focuses on universal strategies, targeted access to mental health supports remains a critical component. In schools, the terms "trauma-informed" or "trauma-specific" services may be used to refer to evidence-based and promising prevention, intervention, or treatment services that address traumatic stress as well as any co-occurring disorders, such as substance use and other mental health issues that are trauma-related (SAMHSA, 2014). Advances in the science of traumatic stress have enhanced the field's ability to assess, diagnose, and treat post-trauma responses. Research has demonstrated that various empirically supported treatment interventions are effective in addressing post-traumatic stress disorder (PTSD) in children and adolescents.

The following trauma-specific interventions have been developed specifically for use in schools and have empirical support for reducing trauma-related symptoms.

- **Cognitive Behavioral Intervention for Trauma in Schools (CBITS)** is a skills-based, group intervention that is aimed at relieving symptoms of post-traumatic stress disorder (PTSD), depression, and general anxiety among children exposed to multiple forms of trauma (Jaycox, Stein, & Amaya-Jackson, 2009); National Child Traumatic Stress Network, n.d.).
- **Bounce Back** is a cognitive-behavioral, skills-based, group intervention aimed at relieving symptoms of child traumatic stress, anxiety, depression, and functional impairment among elementary school children (ages 5–11) who have been exposed to traumatic events. Developed as an adaptation for elementary-aged students of the CBITS program, Bounce Back contains many of the same therapeutic elements but is designed with added elements and engagement activities and more parental involvement to be developmentally appropriate for 5- to 11-year-olds (National Child Traumatic Stress Network, n.d.).
- **Support for Students Exposed to Trauma (SSET)** is a cognitive-behavioral, skills-based, support group aimed at relieving symptoms of child traumatic stress, anxiety, depression, and functional impairment among middle school children (ages 10–16) who have been exposed to traumatic events. Developed as an adaptation of the Cognitive-Behavioral Intervention for Trauma in Schools program, SSET contains many of the same therapeutic elements but is designed to be implemented by school staff members without clinical training, including school teachers or counselors with back-up clinical support (National Child Traumatic Stress Network, n.d.).
- **Multimodality Trauma Treatment-Focused Coping or Trauma-Focused Coping in Schools (TFC)** is a skills-oriented, cognitive-behavioral treatment (CBT) approach for children exposed to single incident trauma and targets PTSD and collateral symptoms. It is designed as a peer-mediating group intervention in schools (Jaycox et al., 2009; National Child Traumatic Stress Network, n.d.).
- **Trauma and Grief Component Therapy for Adolescents (TGCT-A)** is a manualized group or individual intervention for trauma-exposed or traumatically bereaved older children and adolescents that can be implemented in schools (National Child Traumatic Stress Network, n.d.).

In addition to the interventions highlighted here, there are numerous therapeutic interventions for child trauma that can be implemented at an individual level. The National Child Traumatic Stress network (http://www.nctsn.org) offers guidance for mental health professionals related to quality trauma-informed screening and assessment tools and treatment interventions.

Culturally Responsive Interventions

The stress response is universal, but cultural norms inform how children and adults understand and talk about their experiences, express distress, and heal (Kirmayer, Groleau, Guzder, Blake, & Jarvis, 2003; Wilson & So-Kum Tang, 2007). For example, physical or "somatic" responses to traumatic experiences are common in many non-Western cultures, and suffering is sometimes described in spiritual versus medical terms that may not match Western-based diagnostic criteria for PTSD (Hinton & Lewis-Fernández, 2011; Scheeringa, Wright, Hunt, & Zeanah, 2006; Wilson & So-Kim Tang, 2007). A particular cultural group's historical experience with the mental health system, as well as norms regarding help-seeking behaviors, will also influence whether and how people access services. These issues are often overlooked in Western therapies and may contribute to high drop-out rates or poor response to treatment (Haan, Boon, de Jong, & Vermeiren, 2018; Nicolas, DeSilva, Grey & Gonzalez-Eastep, 2006; World Health Organization, 2010).

Being culturally aware implies having the capacity to function effectively as an individual and organization or school within the context of the cultural beliefs, behaviors, and needs presented by survivors and their communities (Wilson & So-Kum Tang, 2007). Helping youth and families stay connected to what is meaningful and relevant to them, within their cultural framework, may protect against future mental and physical stress-related illness (Wilson & So-Kum Tang, 2007). Additional research on cultural adaptations to evidence-based, trauma-specific treatments is critical to provide culturally and linguistically competent treatment for diverse populations. Some of the therapeutic interventions discussed in this chapter, including CBITS and TFC, include information related to how the intervention has been adapted for different cultural groups.

Creative Arts and Mindfulness Interventions

The growing science related to the effect of trauma at the neurobiological level has led to a greater need for therapeutic interventions that address the body-based symptoms associated with trauma. People who have experienced trauma sometimes disconnect from emotions and physical sensations in an attempt to cope. Body-oriented, nonverbal activities serve as a way for trauma survivors to reconnect to their bodies, manage their feelings, and communicate in nontraditional ways; for younger children, who have fewer words to express how they feel, the use of play and body-based activities helps manage stress and strengthen coping skills (Goodman, Chapman, & Gantt, 2009). Creative Arts Therapies (CATs) such as art, movement, dance, yoga, and music, hold promise; however, additional research is needed to support the evidence base for these therapies as effective treatments for PTSD (Goodman et al., 2009).

One opportunity for more body-oriented intervention in schools is the use of mindfulness programs, which promote an increased awareness of one's emotional, social, and physical reactions to environmental stressors. Mindfulness programs may be implemented universally or used as part of targeted therapeutic interventions for addressing trauma-related symptoms. Evidence suggests that mindfulness programs help reduce stress and can result in reduced symptoms of depression and anxiety (Goyal, Singh, Sibinga, et al., 2014). Mindfulness programs teach individuals to attend to the present moment in a nonjudgmental, accepting manner. Engaging in mindful activities increases the likelihood that individuals will take the time to consider a situation and consider response options instead of being reactive to the context.

In addition, rigorous research has demonstrated that teachers also benefit from engaging in activities that build mindfulness. When teachers learn mindfulness, they have more emotionally supportive classrooms (Jennings et al., 2017) and better classroom organization (Flook, Goldberg, Pinger, Bonus, & Davidson, 2013). Teachers report reduced stress and burnout (Flook et al., 2013). These teacher factors could contribute to a safer and more supportive classroom environment for children who have experienced trauma.

Aligning Interventions and Approaches

As we have discussed in this chapter, schools are often integrating many different approaches simultaneously, and rather than implementing each in isolation, it is helpful to consider how these efforts align and support each other. Using a multitiered prevention framework, schools may consider how various approaches fit together to form a broader trauma-sensitive and resilience-focused vision school and districtwide. Because the core principles of these approaches are similar and require similar cultural shifts and complementary practices, joint training sessions help staff to see the commonalities across approaches rather than separate things to learn and implement. There may be similar skills-building needed to support staff in making the cultural and behavioral shifts needed to adopt PBIS, restorative practices, SEL strategies, and trauma sensitivity. Aligning implementation efforts helps to avoid duplication and minimize burden, and to promote a collective understanding of the commonalities and relationships between multiple approaches. The following strategies can be used to integrate the interventions and approaches discussed in this chapter.

- **Align work groups and teams.** It is helpful for staff to view related universal approaches, such as trauma sensitivity, PBIS, and restorative practices, as part of a larger effort to support a safe, respectful, and inclusive environment.
- **Develop a shared vision.** Integrated teams can develop a shared, holistic vision for the school that goes beyond one particular intervention or approach.
- **Integrate professional development activities.** The core principles of the universal strategies discussed in this chapter are similar and require similar cultural shifts, and joint training sessions may help staff to see the commonalities. Similar skill-building may be necessary to support staff in making the cultural and behavioral shifts needed to adopt each approach successfully.

Conclusion

All youth-serving systems share a common mission to support positive youth development and future success. This mission is achieved in many different ways, including fostering academic achievement, providing quality health care, ensuring access to behavioral health services, and supporting family and community safety and stability. As health and social service systems and schools learn more about the negative consequences of childhood trauma, the need to address this public health issue is growing. Enhancing the capacity of schools to consistently identify and respond to adversity and trauma in the lives of their students will not only improve lives for many children and youth but also help school staff feel more able and competent to respond. Schools are part of a larger whole, and no one system can address trauma alone. Efforts to embed trauma-sensitive and resilience-focused approaches in schools align with and support cross-sector efforts to prevent and address child trauma. Schools play a key role in contributing to a larger vision of a fully integrated system of care that supports all youth to lead their healthiest, happiest, most fulfilled lives.

References

American Institutes for Research. (2014). *America's youngest outcasts: A report card on child homelessness.* Waltham, MA: Author.

American Psychological Association. (2008). *Children and trauma: Update for mental health professionals.* APA Presidential Task Force on Posttraumatic Stress Disorder and Trauma in Children and Adolescents. Washington, DC: Retrieved from http://www.apa.org/pi/families/resources/update.pdf

Beckerman, N. L., & Corbett, L. (2008). Immigration and families: Treating acculturative stress from a systemic framework. *Family Therapy, 35*(2), 63–81.

Benson, P. L., Scales, P. C., & Syvertsen, A. K. (2011). The contribution of the developmental assets framework to positive youth development theory and practice. In R. M. Lerner, J. V. Lerner, & J. B. Benson (Eds.), *Advances in child development and behavior: Positive youth development research and applications for promoting thriving in adolescence* (pp. 195–228). London: Elsevier.

Bethell, C. D., Newacheck, P., Hawes, E., & Halfon, N. (2014). Adverse childhood experiences: Assessing the impact on health and school engagement and the mitigating role of resilience. *Health Affairs, 33*, 2106–2115.

BigFoot, D. S., Willmon-Haque, S., & Braden, J. (2008). *Trauma exposure in American Indian/Alaska Native children*. Oklahoma City: Indian Country Child Trauma Center. Retrieved from http://www.theannainstitute.org/American%20Indians%20and%20Alaska%20Natives/Trauma%20Exposure%20in%20AIAN%20Children.pdf

Bradshaw, C. P., Mitchell, M. M., & Leaf, P. J. (2010). Examining the effects of schoolwide positive behavioral interventions and supports on student outcomes: Results from a randomized controlled effectiveness trial in elementary schools. *Journal of Positive Behavioral Interventions, 12*(3), 133–148.

Brewin, C. R., & Holmes, E. A. (2003). Psychological theories of posttraumatic stress disorder. *Clinical Psychology Review, 23*, 339–376.

Brom, D., Pat-Horenczyk, R., & Ford, J. (Eds.). (2009). *Treating traumatized children: Risk, resilience and recovery*. London: Routledge.

Bryant-Davis, T., & Ocampo, C. (2005). Racist incident-based trauma. *Counseling Psychologist, 33*, 479–500.

Cantor, P. (2016). Confronting barriers to learning to help all children succeed. Retrieved from http://www.advanc-ed.org/source/confronting-barriers-learning-help-all-children-succeed

Cantor, P., Berg, J., Strayer, L., & Rose, T. (2018). Drivers of human development: How relationships and context shape learning and development. *Applied Developmental Science*. doi:10.1080/10888691.2017.1398650

Cantor, P., Osher, D., Berg, J., Steyer, L., & Rose, T. (2018). Malleability, plasticity, and individuality: How children learn and develop in context. *Applied Developmental Science*. doi:10.1080/10888691.2017.1398649

Carr, E. G., Dunlap, G., Horner, R. H., Koegel, R. L., Turnbill, A. P., Sailor, W., . . . Fox, L. (2002). Positive behavior support: Evolution of an applied science. *Journal of Positive Behavior Interventions, 4*(1), 4–16.

Carter, R. T. (2007). Racism and psychological and emotional injury: Recognizing and assessing race-based traumatic stress. *Counseling Psychologist, 35*(1), 13–105.

Center on the Developing Child. (2010). The foundations of lifelong health are built in early childhood. Retrieved from https://developingchild.harvard.edu/resources/the-foundations-of-lifelong-health-are-built-in-early-childhood/

Center on the Developing Child at Harvard University. (2015). *Supportive relationships and active skill-building strengthen the foundations of resilience* (Working Paper No. 13). Retrieved from https://developingchild.harvard.edu/resources/supportive-relationships-and-active-skill-building-strengthen-the-foundations-of-resilience/

Child Trends. (2016). Children's exposure to violence. Retrieved from http://www.childtrends.org/?indicators=childrens-exposure-to-violence

Cohen, L. R., Hien, D. A., & Batchelder, S. (2008). The impact of cumulative maternal trauma and diagnosis on parenting behavior. *Child Maltreatment, 13*(1), 27–38.

Coker, T. R., Austin, S. B., & Schuster, M. A. (2010). The health and healthcare of lesbian, gay, and bisexual adolescents. *Annual Review of Public Health, 31*, 457–477.

Cole, S. F., Eisner, A., Gregory, M., & Ristuccia, J. (2013). *Creating and advocating for trauma-sensitive schools: Helping traumatized children*, Vol. 2. Boston: Massachusetts Advocates for Children. Retrieved from https://traumasensitiveschools.org/tlpi-publications/download-a-free-copy-of-a-guide-to-creating-trauma-sensitive-schools

Collins, K., Connors, K., Donohue, A., Gardner, S., Goldblatt, E., Hayward, A., . . . Thompson, E. (2010). *Understanding the impact of trauma and urban poverty on family systems: Risks, resilience, and interventions.* Baltimore: Family Informed Trauma Treatment Center at http://nctsn.org/nccts/nav.do?pid=ctr_rsch_prod_ar.

Cook, A., Spinazzola, J., Ford, J., Lanktree, C., Blaustein, M., Cloitre, M., . . . van der Kolk, B. (2005). Complex trauma in children and adolescents. *Psychiatric Annals, 35*(5), 390–398.

Copeland, W. E., Keeler, G., Angold, A., & Costello, E. (2007). Traumatic events and posttraumatic stress in children. *Archives of General Psychiatry, 64*(5), 577–584.

Cronholm, P. F., Forke, C. M., Wade, R., Bair-Merritt, M. H., Davis, M., Harkins-Schwarz, M. . . . Fein, J. A. (2015). Adverse childhood experiences: Expanding the concept of adversity. *American Journal of Preventative Medicine, 49*(3), 354–361.

D'Andrea, W. D., Ford, J., Stolbach, B., Spinazzola, J., & van der Kolk, B. A. (2012). Why we need a developmentally appropriate trauma diagnosis. *American Journal of Orthopsychiatry, 82*(2), 187–200.

DeBellis, M. D., & Zisk, A. (2014). The biological effects of childhood trauma. *Child and Adolescent Psychiatric Clinics of North America, 23*(2), 185–222.

Durlak, J. A., Weissberg, R. P., Dymnicki, A. B., Taylor, R. D., & Schellinger, K. B. (2011). The impact of enhancing students' social and emotional learning: A meta-analysis of school-based universal interventions. *Child Development, 82*(1), 405–432.

Ellis, W., & Dietz, W. (2017). A new framework for addressing adverse childhood and community experiences: The building community resilience (BCR) model. *Academic Pediatrics, 17*, S86–S93.

Everly, G. S., & Lating, J. M. (2013). *A clinical guide to the treatment of the human stress response.* New York: Springer Science & Business Media.

Farrington, C. A., Roderick, M., Allensworth, E., Nagaoka, J., Keyes, T. S., Johnson, D. W., & Beechum, N. O. (2012). *Teaching adolescents to become learners: The role of noncognitive factors in shaping school performance: A critical literature review.* Chicago: University of Chicago Consortium on Chicago School Research.

Felitti, V. J., & Anda, R. F. (2010). The relationship of adverse childhood experiences to adult health, well-being, social function, and health care. In R. Lanius, E. Vermetten, & C. Pain (Eds.), *The effects of early life trauma on health and disease: The hidden epidemic.* New York: Cambridge University Press (pp. 77–87).

Felitti, V. J., Anda, R. F., Nordenberg, D., Williamson, D. F., Spitz, A. M., Edwards, V., . . . Marks, J. S. (1998). The relationship of adult health status to childhood abuse and household dysfunction. *American Journal of Preventive Medicine, 14*(4), 245–258.

Finkelhor, D., Turner, H. A., Shattuck, A., & Hamby, S. L. (2015). Prevalence of childhood exposure to violence, crime, and abuse: Results from the National Survey of Children's Exposure to Violence. *JAMA Pediatrics, 169*(8), 746–754.

Flook, L., Goldberg, S. B., Pinger, L., Bonus, K., & Davidson, R. J. (2013). Mindfulness for teachers: A pilot study to assess effects on stress, burnout, and teaching efficacy. *Mind, Brain, and Education, 7*(3), 182–195.

Fronius, T., Persson, H., Guckenburg, S., Hurley, N., & Petrosino, A. (2016). *Restorative justice in U.S. Schools: A research review.* San Francisco: WestEd.

González, T. (2012). Keeping kids in schools: Restorative justice, punitive discipline, and the school to prison pipeline. *Journal of Law and Education, 41*(2), 281–335.

Goodman, R. F., Chapman, L. M., & Gantt, L. (2009). Creative arts therapies for children. In E. B. Foa, T. M. Keane, M. J. Friedman, & J. A. Cohen (Eds.), *Effective treatments for PTSD: Practice guidelines from the International Society for Traumatic Stress Studies* (2nd ed., pp. 491–507). New York: Guilford.

Goyal, M., Singh, S., Sibinga, E. M., Gould, N. F., Rowland-Seymour, A., Sharma, R, . . . Haythornthwaite, J. A. (2014). Meditation programs for psychological stress and well-being: a systematic review and meta-analysis. *JAMA Internal Medicine, 174*(3), 357–368.

Gregory, A., Clawson, K., Davis, A., & Gerewitz, J. (2014). The promise of restorative practices to transform teacher-student relationships and achieve equity in school discipline. *Journal of Educational and Psychological Consultation, 26*(4), 325–353.

Guarino, K., & Chagnon, E. (2018). *Trauma-sensitive schools training package.* Washington, DC: National Center on Safe Supportive Learning Environments.

Guckenberg, S., Hurley, N. Pearson, H., Fronius, T., & Petrosino, A. (2015). *Restorative justice in U.S. schools; Summary findings from interviews with experts*. San Francisco: WestEd.

Haan, A. M., Boon, A. E., de Jong, J. T. V. M., & Vermeiren, R. R. J. M. (2018). A review of mental health treatment dropout by ethnic minority youth. *Transcultural Psychiatry, 55*(1), 3–30.

Herman, J. (1992). *Trauma and recovery*. New York: Basic Books.

Hinton, D. E., & Lewis-Fernández, R. (2011). The cross-cultural validity of post-traumatic stress disorder: Implications for DSM-5. *Depression and Anxiety, 28*(9), 783–801.

Horner, R. H., Sugai, G., & Anderson, C. M. (2010). Examining the evidence base for school-wide positive behavior support. *Focus on Exceptional Children, 42*(8), 1–14.

Hoydon, S., Wong, M., Langley, A. K., Stein, B. D., & Kataoka, S. H. (2015). Preventing secondary traumatic stress in educators. *Child and Adolescent Psychiatric Clinics of North America, 24*(2), 319–333.

Institute of Medicine. (2011). *The health of lesbian, gay, bisexual, and transgender people: Building a foundation for better understanding*. Washington, DC: National Academies Press.

Jaycox, L. H., Stein, B. D., & Amaya-Jackson, L. (2009). School-based treatment for children and adolescents. In E. B. Foa, T. M. Keane, M. J., Friedman, & J. A. Cohen (Eds.), *Effective treatments for PTSD: Practice guidelines from the International Society for Traumatic Stress Studies* (2nd ed., pp. 327–345). New York: Guilford.

Jennings, P. A., Brown, J. L., Frank, J. L., Doyle, S. L., Tanler, R., Rasheed, D., . . . Greenberg, M. T. (2017). Impacts of the CARE for Teachers Program on teachers' social and emotional competence and classroom interactions. *Journal of Educational Psychology, 109*(7), 1010–1028.

Jones, S. M., & Bouffard, S. M. (2012). Social and emotional learning in schools: From programs to strategies. *Social Policy Report, 26*(4), 1–33.

Kirmayer, L. J., Groleau, D., Guzder, J., Blake, C., & Jarvis, E. (2003). Cultural consultation: A model of mental health service for multicultural societies. *Canadian Journal of Psychiatry, 48*(3), 145–153.

Kistin, C. J., Radesky, J., Diaz-Linhart, Y., Tompson, M. C., O'Connor, E., & Silverstein, M. (2014). A qualitative study of parenting stress, coping, and discipline approaches among low-income traumatized mothers. *Journal of Developmental and Behavioral Pediatrics, 35*(3), 189–196.

Kohli, R., & Solorzano, D. G. (2012). Teachers, please learn our names!: Racial microaggressions and the K–12 classroom. *Race Ethnicity and Education, 15*(4), 441–462.

Kosciw, J. G., Greytak, E. A., Giga, N. M., Villenas, C., & Danischewski, D. J. (2016). *The 2015 National School Climate Survey: The experiences of lesbian, gay, bisexual, transgender, and queer youth in our nation's schools*. New York: Gay, Lesbian and Straight Education Network.

Layne, C. M., Briggs, E. C., & Courtois, C. A. (2014). Introduction to the special section: Using the trauma history profile to unpack risk factor caravans and their consequences. *Psychological Trauma: Theory, Research, Practice, and Policy, 6*(Suppl. 1), S1–S8.

Luthar, S. S. (2015). Mothering mothers. *Research in Human Development, 12*(3–4), 295–303.

Macy, R. D., Behar, L. B., Paulson, R., Delman, J., & Schmid, L. (2004). Community based acute post-traumatic stress management: A description and evaluation of a psychosocial intervention continuum. *Harvard Rev Psychiatry, 12*(4), 217–228.

Masten, A. S. (2014). *Ordinary magic: Resilience in development*. New York: Guilford Press.

Masten, A. S., & Obradovic, J. (2008). Disaster preparation and recovery: Lessons from research on resilience in human development. *Ecology and Society, 13*(1), 9.

McGill University. (n.d.). The brain from top to bottom. Retrieved from http://thebrain.mcgill.ca/avance.php

Merikangas, K. R., He, J., Burstein, M., Swanson, S. A., Avenevoli, S., Cui, L., . . . Swendsen, J. (2010). Lifetime prevalence of mental disorders in U.S. adolescents: Results from the National Comorbidity Survey Replication—Adolescent Supplement (NCS-A). *Journal of the American Academy of Child and Adolescent Psychiatry, 49*, 980–988.

Mirsky, L. (2007). SaferSanerSchools: Transforming school cultures with restorative practices. *Reclaiming Children and Youth, 12*(2), 5–12.

National Center for Victims of Crime. (n.d.). Black children exposed to violence and victimization. Retrieved from http://victimsofcrime.org/our-programs/other-projects/youth-initiative/interventions-for-black-children%27s-exposure-to-violence/black-children-exposed-to-violence

National Child Traumatic Stress Network. (n.d.). Treatments that work. Retrieved from https://www.nctsn.org/treatments-and-practices/treatments-that-work/interventions

National Child Traumatic Stress Network. (2010). Age-related reactions to a traumatic event. Retrieved from https://www.nctsn.org/resources/age-related-reactions-traumatic-event

National Child Traumatic Stress Network. (2013). Conversations about historical trauma. Retrieved from http://www.nctsn.org/resources/topics/culture-and-trauma

National Child Traumatic Stress Network. (2014). *Complex trauma: Facts for educators*. Los Angeles and Durham, NC: National Center for Child Traumatic Stress.

National Child Traumatic Stress Network, Justice Consortium, Schools Committee, and Culture Consortium. (2017). *Addressing race and trauma in the classroom: A resource for educators*. Los Angeles and Durham, NC: National Center for Child Traumatic Stress.

National Child Traumatic Stress Network, Schools Committee. (2008). *Child trauma toolkit for educators*. Los Angeles and Durham, NC: National Center for Child Traumatic Stress.

National Child Traumatic Stress Network, Schools Committee. (2017). *Creating, supporting, and sustaining trauma-informed schools: A system framework*. Los Angeles and Durham, NC: National Center for Child Traumatic Stress.

National Child Traumatic Stress Network, Secondary Traumatic Stress Committee. (2011). *Secondary traumatic stress: A fact sheet for child-serving professionals*. Los Angeles and Durham, NC: National Center for Child Traumatic Stress.

National Scientific Council on the Developing Child. (2010). *Persistent fear and anxiety can affect young children's learning and development* (Working Paper No. 9). Retrieved from https://developingchild.harvard.edu/resources/persistent-fear-and-anxiety-can-affect-young-childrens-learning-and-development/

National Scientific Council on the Developing Child. (2014). *Excessive stress disrupts the architecture of the developing brain* (Working Paper No. 3). Updated Edition. Retrieved from https://developingchild.harvard.edu/resources/wp3/

Nicolas, G., DeSilva, A. M., Grey, K. S., & Gonzalez-Eastep, D. (2006). Using a multicultural lens to understand illness among Haitians living in America. *Professional Psychology: Research and Practice, 37*(6), 702–707.

Osher, D., & Berg, J. (2017). *School Climate and Social and Emotional Learning: The Integration of Two Approaches*. Edna Bennet Pierce Prevention Research Center, Pennsylvania State University.

Osher, D., & Kendziora, K. (2010). Building conditions for learning and healthy adolescent development: Strategic approaches. In B. Doll, W. Pfohl, & J. Yoon (Eds.), *Handbook of youth prevention science* (pp. 121–140). New York: Routledge.

Osher, D., Kendziora, K., Spier, E., & Garibaldi, M. L. (2014). School influences on child and youth development. In Z. Sloboda & H. Petras (Eds.), *Advances in prevention science: Vol. 1. Defining prevention science* (pp. 151–169). New York: Springer.

Osher, D., Kidron, Y., DeCandia, C. J., Kendziora, K., & Weissberg, R. P. (2016). Interventions to promote safe and supportive school climate. In K. R. Wentzel & G. B. Ramani (Eds.), *Handbook of Social Influences in School Contexts* (pp. 384–404). New York, NY: Routledge.

Pat-Horenczyk, R., Rabinowitz, R. G., Rice, A., & Tucker-Levin, A. (2009). The search for risk and protective factors in childhood PTSD. In D. Brom, R. Pat-Horenczyk, & J. D. Ford (Eds.), *Treating traumatized children: Risk, resilience and recovery* (pp. 51–71). New York: Routledge.

Perez-Foster, R. (2001). When immigration is trauma: Guidelines for the individual and family clinician. *American Journal of Orthopsychiatry, 71*, 153–170.

Perfect, M. M., Turley, M. R., Carlson, J. S., Yohanna, J., & Saint Gilles, M. P. (2016). School-related outcomes of traumatic event exposure and traumatic stress symptoms in students: A systemic review of research from 1990 to 2015. *School Mental Health, 8*, 7–43.

Perry, B. D. (2001). The neurodevelopmental impact of violence in childhood. In D. Schetky & E. Benedek (Eds.), *Textbook of child and adolescent forensic psychiatry* (pp. 221–238). Washington, DC: American Psychiatric Press.

Perry, B. D., & Pollard, R. (1998). Homeostasis, stress, trauma, and adaptation: A neurodevelopmental view of childhood trauma. *Child and Adolescent Psychiatric Clinics of North America, 7*(1), 33–51.

Putnam, F. (2006). The impact of trauma on child development. *Juvenile and Family Court Journal, 57*(1), 1–11.

Scheeringa, M. S., Wright, M. J., Hunt, J. P., & Zeanah, C. H. (2006). Factors affecting the diagnosis and prediction of PTSD symptomatology in children and adolescents. *American Journal of Psychiatry, 163*, 644–651.

Substance Abuse and Mental Health Services Administration (SAMHSA). (2014). *Trauma-informed care in behavioral health services* (Treatment Improvement Protocol [TIP] Series 57, HHS Publication No. [SMA] 14-4816). Rockville, MD: Author.

Sue, D. W., Capodilupo, C. M., Torino, G. C., Bucceri, J. M., Holder, A. M. B., Nadal K. L., & Esquilin, M. (2007). Racial microaggressions in everyday life. *American Psychologist, 62*(4), 271–286.

Sugai, G., & Horner, R. H. (2006). A promising approach for expanding and sustaining school-wide positive behavior support. *School Psychology Review, 35*(2), 245–259.

Sugai, G., Horner, R. H., Dunlap, G., Hieneman, M., Lewis, T. J., Nelson, C. M., . . . Ruef, M. (2000). Applying positive behavior support and functional behavioral assessment in schools. *Journal of Positive Behavior Interventions, 2*, 131–143.

Suvall, C. (2009). Restorative justice in schools: Learning from Jena High School. *Harvard Civil Rights-Civil Liberties Law Review, 44*, 547–569.

Teicher, M. H., & Samson, J. A. (2016). Annual research review: Enduring neurobiological effects of childhood abuse and neglect. *Journal of Child Psychology and Psychiatry, and Allied Disciplines, 57*(3), 241–266. doi:10.1111/jcpp.12507

Thapa, A., Cohen, J., Guffey, S., & Higgins-D'Alessandro, A. (2013). A review of school climate research. *Review of Educational Research, 83*(3), 357–385.

Thomas, A. J., Carey, D., Prewitt, K., Romero, E., Richards, M., & Velsor-Friedrich, B. (2012). African American youth and exposure to community violence: Supporting change from the inside. *Journal for Social Action in Counseling and Psychology, 4*(1), 54–68.

Turner, H. A., Vanderminden, J., Finkelhor, D., Hamby, S., & Shattuck, A. (2011). Disability and victimization in a national sample of children and youth. *Child Maltreatment, 16*, 275–286.

U.S. Department of Health and Human Services and U.S. Department of Education. (2016). Policy statement on family engagement from the early years to the early grades. Retrieved from https://www2.ed.gov/about/inits/ed/earlylearning/files/policy-statement-on-family-engagement.pdf

van der Kolk, B. A. (2014). *The body keeps the score: Brain, mind, and body in the healing of trauma.* New York: Viking.

Wade, R., Jr., Shea, J. A., Rubin, D., & Wood, J. (2014). Adverse childhood experiences of low-income urban youth. *Pediatrics, 134*(1), 13–20.

Wilson, J. P., & So-Kum Tang, C. C. (Eds.). (2007). *Cross-cultural assessment of psychological trauma and PTSD.* New York: Springer US.

Wilson, K. R., Hansen, D. J., & Li, M. (2011). *The traumatic stress response in child maltreatment and resultant neuropsychological effects* (Faculty Publications Paper 549). Lincoln: University of Nebraska, Department of Psychology.

Wilson, S. J., Lipsey, M. W., & Derzon, J. H. (2003). The effects of school-based intervention programs on aggressive behavior: A meta-analysis. *Journal of Consulting and Clinical Psychology, 71*(1), 136–149.

Wolpow, R., Johnson, M. M., Hertel, R., & Kincaid, S. (2009). *The heart of learning and teaching: Compassion, resiliency, and academic success.* Olympia, WA: Washington State Office of the Superintendent of Public Instruction (OSPI) Compassionate Schools.

World Health Organization. (2010). *Mental health in Haiti: A literature review.* Geneva, Switzerland: World Health Organization.

Yates, T. M., Egeland, L. B., & Sroufe, A. (2003). Rethinking resilience: A developmental process perspective. In S. S. Luthar (Ed.), *Resilience and vulnerability: Adaptation in the context of childhood adversities* (pp. 243–266). New York: Cambridge University Press.

Zins, J. E., & Elias, M. J. (2006). Social and emotional learning. In G. G. Bear & K. M. Minke (Eds.), *Children's needs III: Development, prevention, and intervention* (pp. 1–13). Bethesda, MD: National Association of School Psychologists.

CHAPTER FIVE

Students with School Failure Trajectories

Terry Salinger and Matthew J. Mayer

Students who struggle academically are at risk for many challenges that initially may seem unrelated to their achievement. These can include exclusionary discipline and restraint, premature exits from school, and for some, involvement with the juvenile justice system, often at a very young age. Risks arise because far too often teachers and other school staff may simplistically conflate academic difficulties, especially in core subjects such as mathematics and reading, with behavior issues (Learned, 2016a, b, c). Further, educators and researchers seeking to reform schools often look at these two constellations of issues—academics and behaviors—as representing separate risk factors, without thoroughly examining the social and institutional contexts in which teachers and students interact (Berkowitz, Moore, Astor, & Benbenishty, 2017). Close examination of the contexts that envelop students provides insight into the interrelated set of problems that contribute to the "school-to-prison pipeline," a term referring to a trend where students over time experience increased academic and social-emotional-behavioral challenges and become entangled in the juvenile and criminal justice systems.

The intent of this chapter is not to discuss the school-to-prison pipeline per se but the ramifications of school environments that have exacerbated even the most common disciplinary issues beyond the control of classroom teachers and school administrators. Although the social and political contexts that have spawned the conditions that make the school-to-prison pipeline so common are widespread, the phenomenon exists more frequently in schools that are overcrowded and under-resourced, schools where absenteeism, truancy, and student and teacher turnover are highest, and parental involvement is likely lowest (Musu-Gillette et al., 2018). This chapter highlights basic and applied research that points to factors that minimize school failure and prepare these students to assume responsible adult roles in family, work, and community contexts.

Academic and Social-Emotional Trajectories Begin Early

Wide acceptance exists that students' school trajectories are shaped in their early years—the consequences of children's early experiences establish their attitudes toward school and toward themselves as learners, even before school entry. There are strong links between factors in the home environment and the likelihood that children will get off to a good start in school. These factors include the amount and nature of the conversations preschoolers hear and engage in, the extent to which they are supported as they explore and learn about their environments, and the ways in which adults and older siblings model and explain social and emotional behaviors such as self-regulation, persistence, and problem-solving, all of which are essential for school success (Hart & Risley, 1995; Holtz, Fox, & Meurer, 2015).

One of the most critical and well-studied factors in the home is family income, and the evidence is strong that the income level of one's family is highly predictive of children's academic achievement (Duncan & Brooks-Gunn, 1997; Reardon, 2011). Fortunately, *predictive* does not mean *causal*, and Reardon poses the question of the extent to which the correlation of family income and subsequent low academic achievement might be an artifact of social conditions surrounding the family; policy choices affecting families, their communities, and their schools; and the educational practices of the schools children enter. In this case, educational practices include more than curriculum choices and class size; in that, they may encompass a school's attitude toward parents and the ways in which teachers and schools make parents feel welcome and valued as partners in their child's learning, regardless of their income status (Alexander et al., 1994).

Preschools, along with home environment, can help shape students' early academic trajectories and bolster students' social-emotional growth; in many cases, they can even help mitigate less-than-ideal home conditions. Investments in preschool education continue to prove their worth (Gormley, Phillips, & Anderson, 2017; Heckman, Moon, Pinto, Savelyev, & Yavitz, 2009; Kirp, 2017), with participating children gaining invaluable background knowledge, academically, socially, and culturally. Further, the best preschool experiences introduce children to the norms, expectations, and language of school, familiarizing them with behaviors like lining up, participating in story time, handling books and materials, cleaning up after activities, and sharing the teacher's time and attention with fellow students. In short, quality preschools acknowledge that academic and social-emotional trajectories begin early and that sound early experiences contribute to students' preparation for successful participation in the collaborative environments that schools should be (Kirp, 2013, 2017).

Alienation Can Begin Early Too

Children differ in many ways; and the more that is known about them as they first come to school, the more school personnel can be successful in meeting their needs. This is true so long as information about students is used appropriately, not to contribute to stereotyping and not to stymie the usual enthusiasm for learning that young children bring with them at school entry. Formally or informally, most schools channel their students into different "tracks" or bands, often beginning in the lower grades (Burris & Garrity, 2008). Early tracking can happen because of scores on screening or "readiness" tests, children's lack of prior school experience, or other factors, such as disabilities or home languages other than English. Tracking can also occur because of other less concrete factors, sometimes termed "identity contingencies," seen as the social identities that individuals "have to deal with in a situation" because of who they are and how others perceive them (Steele, 2010, p. 3). Features such as race, ethnicity, family composition and income, home language, or early identification of a disability can feed into adults' existing stereotypes for young learners and contribute to the set of expectations schools and teachers create for entering students. The reverse is true as well, in that having gone to preschool or being socially at ease and talkative can correctly or incorrectly label young learners as "ready" for school. Those who are considered "not ready" are often made to feel different, especially as they are consigned to classes to "catch them up" academically or socially. Soon, they can feel alienated from the mainstream of school (Upadyaya & Salmela-Aro, 2015). Even at this young age, students can begin to attribute challenges they experience in school to insufficiencies over which they have no control (Abramson, Metalsky, & Alloy, 1989; Abramson, Seligman, & Teasdale, 1978). This conviction that they are powerless in the face of academic challenges often leads to maladaptive behaviors such as passivity, inattention, or deliberate class disruption; seeing their peers making academic progress in content that they find difficult blinds students to the reality that challenges and obstacles are inherent in most learning and dissuades them from asking for help (Dweck & Leggett, 1988). Teachers, focusing primarily on their instructional goals, see students "falling farther behind" but may not recognize behavior linked to students' social and emotional reactions.

The idea of children's readiness for school can, of course, be easily flipped on its conceptual end when we recognize that far too many schools are themselves not "ready" for all students (Pianta, Cox, Taylor, & Early, 1999). Schools that are in fact "not ready" fail to meet entering students "where *they* are," that is, as individuals with their own expectations for school as challenging but positive environments.

Mechanisms That Continue Students' Alienation

Even in seemingly informed, warm, and nurturing classroom cultures, early-grade teachers can communicate that there are "good" and "poor" students, especially in key subjects like reading and mathematics. As demonstrated in a seminal qualitative study, students who are at risk and who struggle recognize early on that they are somehow "different" (McDermott, Goldman, & Varenne, 2006). Approaches as well-intentioned as the current "tiered instruction" or Response to Intervention (RTI) model can exacerbate this risk and result in tracking, especially if students' needs are not well understood and the interventions they receive do not provide focused instruction in areas of real weakness (Klinger & Edwards, 2006). Further, an RTI approach at the higher tier levels often includes removing students from class, thereby replacing, rather than supplementing, their teachers' core or Tier 1 instruction. An example of this might be providing second graders with intense phonics instruction at the cost of their learning that phonetic analysis to decode words is one of the myriad strategies they need to use to comprehend even the simplest extended texts (Klinger & Edwards, 2006). During their time drilling phonics rules, these students might also miss important math instruction or a discussion about social studies or science concepts that would build background knowledge and vocabulary.

Gutiérrez and colleagues (2009) write of the "discourse of remediation," which RTI models can engender, pointing out that this is especially true for students "from nondominant communities [who] have been socialized to and through their participation in remedial courses" (p. 225). Intervention or remedial classes or placement in the "bottom" reading or math group can reinforce such feelings early on. Students who decide in elementary school that there is no way for them to overcome their struggles will internalize their identity as academically struggling or learning disabled, and for some students, these identities will continue no matter how much "remediation" they are given (Walton, 2014).

RTI is not a panacea; but rather, it is a promising, but still unproven, approach to learning disability (LD) identification and prevention of early reading problems. Using early screening and intervention for emerging reading problems, avoiding a "wait-to-fail" approach (Fuchs, Mock, Morgan, & Young, 2003, p. 158), RTI has the potential to change the learning trajectory for many early elementary students for the better. But as suggested by Fuchs, Fuchs, and Compton (2012, p. 2), and the National Joint Committee on Learning Disabilities (2005), to do this well would require a massive commitment of financial and human resources, involvement of specialists, professional development for classroom and special education teachers, staff buy-in, administrative leadership, and data management systems in schools that are already operating on bare-bones budgets (National Joint Committee on Learning Disabilities (2005, pp. 4, 8, 9–10). This points to much needed major infrastructure development nationally across school districts in 50 states and the District of Columbia.

RTI use is most common in elementary grades, and models for supporting students who struggle academically change in middle school and high school (Mancini-Marshall, 2014). In these grades, students whose scores on state accountability assessments in reading and math or on other standardized tests are seen as problematic, may be assigned to intervention classes that use either a commercially available program or one developed at the school or district level (Mancini-Marshall, 2014). All too often, these programs follow a prescriptive curriculum that does not provide the levels of individualization needed to address students' specific academic needs (Burns, 2010).

Enrollment for middle and high school students usually lasts at least a full year, as students and teachers work their way through the curriculum. Class periods can range from 45 to 90 minutes, and classes usually meet every day. Further, these classes often deprive students of elective courses such as gym, music, art; may limit their eligibility for participation in after-school sports; and usually carry no credit toward graduation (Allington, 2013). Thus, grouping students together in intervention classes often deepens negative feelings, where peer-to-peer dynamic reinforces negative feelings. Students recognize that somehow being in these classes makes them "different," perhaps even "deviant," even though, as Learned (2016c) found that many students enrolled in a reading intervention thought of themselves as readers and could not understand why they had been enrolled in intervention classes.

There is still much to learn about how to make implementation of RTI successful (Allington, 2009, 2010, 2013). For example, concerns over the varying approaches to measuring and determining responsiveness under an RTI approach further complicate efforts to address students' needs. Fuchs and Deschler (2007) cite research demonstrating that multiple methods used by leading researchers to identify responsiveness ended up classifying somewhat different, yet overlapping, groups of students. This research review suggests that there is no agreed upon evidence-based way to measure sustainable responsiveness to intervention leading to a special education classification decision.

Questions remain about students who have received remediation through multiple RTI tiers and who have subsequently been referred, evaluated, and classified as having an LD. Most of these students are educated in the Tier 1 general education classroom, where they likely receive fewer accommodations and supports than would be available in the most intensively supported tier of RTI that preceded their classification as having an LD. Fuchs, Fuchs, and Compton (2012) compared the types and intensities of academic services provided to students with LDs in their Tier I classes with those they had been receiving in their small RTI groups and concluded that students receive an identification that should lead to specialized support for their needs may actually decrease the intensity of services students receive.

How Schools Are Organized to Fail Students

With their abilities seeming to remain relatively static, struggling students cannot compete academically; and some resort to behaviors that allow them to influence how their teachers and schools perceive them. Essentially, they redirect adult attention away from academic performance to disorderly conduct that can range from being a class clown to much more serious infractions (Learned, 2016c). A recent compilation of data about school crime and safety begins: "Our nation's schools should be safe havens for teaching and learning, free of crime and violence" (Musu-Gillette et al., 2018, p. iii). It goes on to detail the extent to which schools are not the safe havens they should be and the factors that contribute to this situation. For example, it reports the causes of disruption to learning and the percentage of 15-year-olds attending schools where these disruptions were common: student truancy was reported as a hindrance to learning to some extent or a lot in 46% of the responding schools; use of alcohol or illegal drugs was present in 19%; and student intimidation or bullying of other students was common in 14% (Musu-Gillette et al., 2018). Percentages are highest in secondary schools, but the same disruptions were reported to be present in at least some of the earlier grades.

Behaviors such as those reported are often clear signs that schools are not addressing the social and emotional needs of many of their students. Educational policies and attitudes about students who struggle academically can communicate to these students that there is little or no tolerance for not meeting their school or state's "standards." These "standards" often equate primarily to scores on state accountability tests, even though, as Walton (2014) has pointed out, improving students' achievement test scores in math or reading does not necessarily alleviate the years of low self-esteem that have hindered their abilities to succeed. Consciously or unconsciously, successful students set goals for themselves, regulate their progress, and apply mastery-oriented strategies to achieve their goals; weaker students often give up, convincing themselves that they will never be "good readers" or "math is just too hard" for them (Molden, Plaks, & Dweck, 2006). Teachers, support staff, and administrators often recognize that students have adopted these negative attitudes but often do not—or cannot—address the causes. Learned (2016a) quoted a reading intervention teacher who described a grade 9 African American girl who had tested as reading at a 5th grade level as "unengaged . . . a behavior . . . and dangerous," largely because of the student's refusal to participate in the different instructional "cycles" the program required (p. 370). Although the same teacher also acknowledged that the girl was undoubtedly frustrated at spending her fourth year in a pull-out reading class, she had no tolerance for the behavior the girl exhibited and never explored whether the understandable frustration might be contributing to both the behaviors and the failure to progress in the reading program. Learned, who studied her subjects for a full year, went on to say that this girl was subsequently suspended for 3.5 days; her GPA for grade 9 was 1.0; and by the end of the year she appeared to have stopped coming to school completely (Learned, 2016a, b).

Zero Tolerance Discipline Policies

In many schools, lack of tolerance also plays out in terms of discipline, most notably in the "zero tolerance" practices in schools that have created a clear tracking system, one that deprives students of precious class time through suspension, expulsion, and even arrests (Musu-Gillette et al., 2018). Data from the School Survey on Crime and Safety indicate that during the 2015–2016 school year, 37% of all public schools—31,100 schools—took at least one serious disciplinary action such as out-of-school suspension lasting five days or more or removal from all academic and social services for the remainder of the school year, or transfers to specialized schools (Musu-Gillette et al., 2018). Teachers and school administrators rarely seek the roots of students' behavior, even though health, environmental, and social challenges outside of school, consequences of childhood trauma, and the side effects of poverty may all play causal roles in students' behavior (Government Accountability Office, 2018). When students who struggle academically and experience out-of-classroom disciplinary actions return to their classes, their alienation often increases: not only are they not meeting academic standards but they are also stigmatized as behavior problems (Weissman, 2015). Once formed, adults' negative behaviors toward and attitudes about students are difficult to change.

The original intent of "zero tolerance" policies was to demonstrate very firm and fixed disciplinary consequences for the most serious offences, such as those involving a gun or inflicting bodily harm on teachers or peers. Consequences ranged from suspension for some period of time to expulsion, regardless of the situational context and any mitigating factors surrounding a transgression. The policy was part of a broader movement to create "safe" schools that included updating the Guns Free School Act in 1996 (Heitzeg, 2009). Increasingly, the policy has applied to minor or nonviolent issues, including disorderly conduct or "talking back" to teachers. Interestingly, the actual percentage of teachers who feel threatened or have actually been attacked in their schools is relatively low, with more elementary teachers (9%) than middle or secondary teachers (2%) reporting these conditions (Musu-Gillette, 2018). Nonetheless, the possibility of such interactions with students can certainly minimize teachers' effectiveness and add to what for many is already a stressful job.

The motivations for enforcing "zero tolerance" have expanded, but the negative effects have not changed at all. Numerous research studies clearly show associations between expulsions from class and out-of-school suspension and subsequent negative consequences, among them retention in grade, failure to graduate, and entry into the juvenile and criminal justice systems (Fabelo et al., 2011; Losen & Martínez, 2013; Losen, Ee, Hodson, & Martínez, 2015; Noguera, 2003; Skiba et al., 2011; Verdugo, 2002). Alarming statistics show that enforcement of zero tolerance often starts early, even in preschools, where the youngest and most vulnerable students are at times subjected to an inflexible behavior standard, in the very period of their lives when they should be supported in learning the culture and language of school (Kirp, 2017). What is even more disturbing is that this early application of zero tolerance shows the beginnings of inequitable treatment for males, students of color, and those with disabilities (Musu-Gillette et al., 2018). Until a 2016 mayoral initiative on school climate specifically prohibited the policy, teachers and school personnel in New York City could suspend students in kindergarten to grade 2 with impunity (Zimmer, 2016). At the national level, suspensions and other exclusionary discipline tactics in preschool have prompted the Office of Child Care in the Administration for Children and Families (2016) to issue federal guidelines for establishing age-appropriate social-emotional behavioral policies to prevent suspension, expulsion, and denial of services to students aged five and younger. A further recommendation is provision of additional training for preschool teachers on identifying students' needs and on their social and emotional development.

Racial Disparities and Cultural Responsiveness

When students do not seem to understand or conform to the behavioral norms of the schools they attend, teachers and school support staff may act upon unrecognized stereotypes and implicit bias in judging students' behaviors and imposing disciplinary action. This is especially true for students of color, those who are poor, and those with disabilities, and frequently males (Government Accountability Office, 2018). The schools these students attend are often ones that have been labeled as "failing," as determined by poor scores on standardized tests and high school completion rate; they are more often than not in economically disadvantaged neighborhoods and serve diverse student bodies (Duncan & Murname, 2011). Even in elementary grades, these schools may well be placing their students on academic failure trajectories, but a parallel trajectory toward social-emotional dysfunction is also often at play. The academic failure trajectory may be easier to understand because academic outcomes—grades, promotion, graduation, college entry—are quantifiable; but understanding students' social and emotional trajectories is equally important if schools are to serve all students, including those consigned to what has been called the "mismatch" group (Deschenes, Cuban, & Tyack, 2001).

Students in the "mismatch" group are often the ones who find themselves falling into the so-called school-to-prison pipeline that leads to brief stays in juvenile detention centers or confinement in prison. Data show that progress toward this "pipeline" is hardly random, in that students of color and those who are poor or have disabilities are disproportionally represented in the statistics documenting the phenomenon (U.S. Department of Education Office of Civil Rights, 2014). Black students account for 16% of the total student enrollment in schools nationwide, but a disproportionate number of black students experience the risks leading to the "school-to-prison pipeline" (Smith & Harper, 2015). The following percentages show the dimensions of this problem:

- 32–42% of students who are suspended from class are black
- 20% of boys and 12% of girls who are expelled from school are black
- 27% of students are referred to law enforcement are black.

Statistics on students with disabilities parallel these findings. Students with disabilities are more than twice as likely to be given one or more out-of-school suspensions as those without disabilities (Losen et al., 2015). Within the total population of individuals with disabilities, the rates, across all grades, are:

- 17% and 10% of Latino/a boys and girls are suspended once or more
- 10% and 6% of Asian American boys and girls are suspended once or more
- 25% and 20% of black boys and girls are suspended once or more.

Nationally, one in three black and one in six Latino boys born in 2001 are at risk of imprisonment during their lifetime, and even though boys are five times as likely to be incarcerated as girls, girls are at increasing risk. This rate of incarceration is endangering children at younger and younger ages (Children's Defense Fund, 2007).

Table 5.1 Comparison of the prison and household samples of individuals aged 16–24 on PIAAC tests of literacy and numeracy

	Percentage below Average: Literacy		Percentage below Average: Numeracy	
Race/ Ethnicity	Prison Sample	Household Sample	Prison Sample	Household Sample
White	18	11	36	19
Black	36	33	65	57
Hispanic	35	41	57	52
Other	29	29	52	28

The probability is high that many students who enter the juvenile justice and prison systems are academically low skilled. In 2014, the Program for International Assessment of Adult Competencies (PIAAC) administered literacy and numeracy tests to an incarcerated population and compared resulting data to data obtained from the national sample of adults who took PIAAC (Rampey et al., 2016). Table 5.1 contrasts data from the prison and the national samples for the youngest cohort of individuals, those who were 16 to 24 years old in 2014.

Unhealthy Schools Syndrome

For decades, researchers have tried to pinpoint the factors that separate schools that serve all their students well from those that seem to be the most prone to create environments that foster discrimination, alienation, and the ultimate inability of many students of color and those with disabilities to thrive academically and socially. Many researchers have accepted the premise that school climate is influenced by factors both within schools and external to them. Lee, Bryk, and Smith (1993) suggested that external factors include the levels of parental involvement and the type and numbers of students, for example, the number of English learners, students with special needs, and students achieving below grade level expectations. Internal factors include the organization or chains of authority and work responsibilities and the social organization of schools. Lee, Bryk, and Smith also emphasize the importance of educational values and normative understandings, saying that good schools had an "autonomous" character meaning primarily that "faculty have 'a sense of ownership' and adults and students share an 'organizational saga' . . . [which] breed organizational excellence" (p. 230). These researchers recommended downsizing schools at all levels and argued against the large, "factory model" of many high schools. Smaller sizes could, they contend, be especially beneficial for students who struggle academically and behaviorally so that their needs are recognized and met before their sense of engagement in school is totally destroyed.

Other researchers have looked more deeply at the environments created when practices such as zero tolerance pervade a school environment. For example, Verdugo's (2002) research on zero tolerance connects these practices with a lack of cultural responsiveness on the part of school staff; he concluded that such policies deny students, particularly those of color, of two fundamental rights: free education and equitable treatment. Verdugo cites as tangible artifacts of zero tolerance the presence of security officers, metal detectors at school entries, unannounced locker searches, and even the insistence on students' wearing school uniforms, supposedly to create a more "businesslike" environment. None of these factors alone deprives students of their education or represent inequitable treatment. Yet, their presence and the threat of zero tolerance create an environment in which the critical connectedness between the student and school is damaged, especially as zero tolerance disciplinary practices are enforced disproportionately against ethnic or racial minority students, particularly males. Students who are expelled or suspended miss out on school, causing them to fall farther and farther behind academically and diminishing any motivation to continue in school. The equity issues in zero tolerance concern not just the numbers of students against whom it is enforced but also the causes. Minority students, especially black males, are likely to receive, humiliating harsh in-classroom punishments or to be suspended or expelled for infractions such as appearing threatening to teachers, staff, or peers or behaving in ways that are construed as disrespectful. Conversely, white students who are suspended have brought guns or other weapons into school or have committed serious drug violations (Skiba et al., 2002; Skiba et al., 2011; Smith & Harper, 2015). The differences in what prompts severe disciplinary steps and in the actual disciplinary procedures provide clear evidence of inequitable treatment for minority students, especially males. Writing about school suspension rates, Skiba pointed out that "racial disproportionality . . . originates at the classroom level" and can seem arbitrary. It is not surprising, then, that "[i]f black students are more likely to be sent to the office for reasons requiring subjective judgment, it might well be expected that they will come to view disparities in discipline as intentional and biased" (Skiba et al., 2002, p. 335).

Just as academic struggles in the early grades can lead to assignment to "pull-out" classes that remove young students from their peers, even brief periods of suspension or expulsion lead to isolation that deprives students of access to content knowledge and to the socializing nature of student-to-student interactions. These actions can also propel students into a vicious and destructive cycle of failure. In essence, there is a cultural disconnect between schools and minority or poor students, fostering an adversarial relationship.

Other strands of research have demonstrated the complex links among environmental factors—community stress and violence, socioeconomic status, hunger, bullying—and students' academic achievement and social and emotional well-being (Berkowitz et al., 2017; Ozer & Weinstein, 2004). The links start early. For example, preschool students from Head Start programs and others from economically impoverished communities have been found to have higher ranges of prevalence of externalizing behavioral problems, compared to age peers in the general population (Holtz, Fox, & Meurer, 2015; Qi & Kaiser, 2003). Economically impoverished communities are known to have generally fewer educational resources such as libraries, less well trained teachers, and greater turnover in school staff, all contributing to longer term difficulties for children's development. A recent comprehensive review of research has shown that these links persist throughout the school years (Berkowitz et al., 2017).

Adverse environmental factors both in school and in surrounding communities can affect students at all levels and cause them to externalize behaviors that result in immediate disciplinary action. It is true, however, that in less stressful settings, teachers and other staff enforcing school discipline policies might recognize the students' actions as signs of treatable behavior disorders (Rosenwasser & Axelrod, 2001) or the results of other factors as personal as parental discord, family stressors, or even boredom or frustration. At the same time, data suggest that teachers are far more inclined to refer white students who misbehave for counseling and treatment than they are for students of color, males, and students with disabilities (Government Accountability Office, 2018).

Regardless of the differential referral rate, much needed support structures and personnel resources are generally limited, and far too many schools have too few guidance counselors to serve their student populations. The American School Counselor Association recommends a ratio of 250 students to one counselor, but the average across the country is actually 428 to one (U.S. Department of Education, 2014). An example of this lack of support for students can be found in New York City, where school personnel and police work together to enforce a harsh discipline policy that includes zero tolerance for truancy, bringing alcohol or drugs into schools, and some other infractions. A report published in 2017 states that in New York City in the previous year, full-time guidance counselors numbered about 2,100, with about 1,250 full-time social workers supporting them, while during the same period there were over 5,500 members of the New York Police Department School Safety contingent (Terenzi & Foster, 2017).

One irony here is that, according to data gathered by the National Center for Education Statistics, about 93% of the schools responding to a national survey reported having training sessions for teachers to recognize signs of potential safety or discipline issues and mental health disorders, such as "depression, mood disorders, and ADHD . . . characterized by alternations in thinking, mood or behavior" (Musu-Gillette, 2018, p. 16). While this is encouraging, recognizing a need does not mean that a school has the means to support or treat that need.

Faced with large classes consisting of students with wide-ranging academic and social needs and sensing that they can get limited help from counselors or other support staff, teachers may well consider some form of zero tolerance as the best option for gaining control over their classrooms; but this attitude of pushing students out is highly problematic and reveals systemic issues within teacher training and professional development and the scarcity of social services for students. Teachers whose school environments are stressful because of large class sizes, scarcity of resources, and little time for planning experience understandable tension and burnout that in turn can negatively impact their interactions with students (Duncan & Murname, 2011). For example, in schools that have adopted a definition of "zero tolerance" that extends beyond disruptive behavior and school violence, some teachers may be less inclined to assume the role of problem solver, where they may not think it is their responsibility to (even) try to meet the needs of students who do not conform to their particular model for student conduct or performance. Teachers may not seek out extra help for students who are struggling (as in a "tiered" instructional setting), may not probe to determine student understanding and work to correct misunderstandings, further emphasizing that teachers need support to be the best conveyers of academics they can be (Lampert, 2017) and to feel comfortable and satisfied in the work. Duckworth, Quinn, and Seligman (2009) found positive relationships between teachers' sense of satisfaction with their work and their effectiveness instructionally, so it is logical to deduce that teachers who feel threatened enough by students to enforce a policy as clearly detrimental and discriminatory as zero tolerance are not experiencing high levels of professional fulfillment.

Addressing These Disparities by Focusing on the School Environment

Students of color and those with learning disabilities can be marginalized through academic tracking and placement in pull-out intervention classes and in special education, and less directly through a lack of a supportive environment and creation of adversarial relationships with adults or other students in school. School practices that lead to disproportionate discipline of minorities, combined with minimal or no academic and social supports for either students or teachers, even though both are greatly needed, can maintain, or even exacerbate the downward trajectory of many at-risk students. Finally, a negative school climate can interfere with positive social development, with incivility, intimidation, racial tensions, and harsh discipline further damaging the student bond to school.

Research continually demonstrates strong connections between education attainment and individuals' likelihood of entering the juvenile-justice system. Keeping students in school as long as possible is essential. For example, increases in compulsory school attendance ages seem to lower the likelihood that youth will commit punishable offenses (Lochner, 2011). There is also some evidence that investments in early education, such as Head Start or Perry Preschool programs, may pay off in fewer encounters with the law in adolescents or young adulthood (Heckman et al., 2009; Lochner, 2011). In addition to bolstering young learners' preparedness for school, programs like these usually include outreach to parents, screening for risk factors such as hearing or vision problems, and general health care (Raphael & Stoll, 2013).

At the same time, it is clear that providing quality preschool experiences at one end of the educational span and requiring students to stay in school longer at the other end are not enough to plug the school-to-prison pipeline and it is essential to look deeply into the many factors that contribute to or hinder creation of strong, safe schools that can counter the potentially negative effects of unsafe communities, poverty, and other factors that put students at risk.

As evidenced in the Every Student Succeeds Act (Gayl, 2017), educational researchers and policy makers have begun to focus more attention on school climate, students' social and emotional well-being, and the inequalities that accrue from a laissez-faire approach to students' needs. Among the focal areas has been the "mindset" of both teachers and students. Indeed, in 2013, David Yeager and colleagues proposed a national research agenda describing the potential benefits of cultivating "growth mindsets" in students (Yeager, Paunesku, Walton, & Dweck, 2013) and emphasizing that "research has increasingly shown that there is more to student success than cognitive ability, curriculum and instruction. Students' mindsets—their beliefs about themselves and the school setting—can powerfully affect whether students learn and grow in school" (Yeager et al., 2013, p. 2). The paper, grounded in a review of extensive research, compares "growth mindsets" and "fixed mindsets," the two contrasting personal attributes mentioned previously as differentiating students who experience themselves as capable academically and those who recognize that they struggle and often cease trying to learn. Individuals displaying the former believe their intelligence is malleable and can be developed and increased at any time through personal effort; the latter term is applied to individuals who believe their intelligence is so finite and unchangeable that there is little use in expending effort when faced with difficult tasks. The term "mindset," long familiar to researchers (Dweck, 2015; Dweck & Leggett, 1988), quickly made its way into popular educational parlance. Packaged instructional programs began to bill themselves as building growth mindsets, and professional development programs to acclimate teachers to the tenets of mindset became common (Sisk, Burgoyne,

Sun, & Butler, 2018). At the same time, subsequent research and a recent meta-analysis of relevant research (Sisk et al., 2018) have investigated the extent to which interventions with a deliberate focus on improving mindset can either directly change or moderate academic success. Results of the meta-analyses showed weak relationships for the student population as a whole, but results confirmed the promise of such interventions when delivered to students who came from low-income homes or who were academically at risk (Sisk et al., 2018).

Although extensive research on noncognitive factors such as self-efficacy and motivation exists, attempts to apply the findings of Dweck and others in the classroom have at times been met with skepticism (e.g., Kohn, 2015) and oversimplification. Dweck (2015) pushed back against critics, stating that "perhaps the most common misconception is simply equating growth mindset with effort. Certainly, effort is key for students' achievement, but it's not the only thing . . . they need [a] *repertoire of approaches*—not just sheer effort—to learn and improve" (italics added).

The key question here is the source of the "repertoire of approaches," and the obvious answer is that it is teachers from whom students most often learn different approaches or strategies and the importance of being flexible in their application. These are teachers who thoroughly understand their content and the pedagogy needed to teach effectively and who give students opportunities to try out and master these approaches (Noguera, Darling-Hammond, & Friedlaender, 2017; see also Gandara, 2017; Vaughn, Danielson, Edmonds, & Holdheide, 2017). Addressing inequities in schools must include a direct focus on teachers, including how their behaviors contribute to inequities.

Only teachers with a positive mindset toward their all their students can interrupt inequitable practices, and, of course, they need the support of like-minded counselors and administrators. Less mindset research has focused on teachers than on students, although it seems reasonable to hypothesize that teachers' own growth or fixed mindset contributes to variance in their teaching practice. For example, Duckworth, Quinn, and Seligman (2009) assessed the "grit" or perseverance and "explanatory style" of almost 400 novice teachers, then studied correlations among these traits and students' academic gains (as a proxy for teacher effectiveness). Analyses of data showed that students of teachers who tended to persist in trying different instructional strategies with struggling learners and those who did not "explain" those struggles only in terms of students' efforts or intelligence scored higher on academic measures. What can be deduced from such research is that teachers with a more fixed mindset are more likely to focus instruction for lower-achieving students on mastery of low-level skills and content and ultimately to consign them to remedial or intervention classes that isolate them from more "normal" school experiences.

In the same vein, many teachers may lack the strategies to meet the needs of all their students, including those who struggle; they may know the "scope and sequence" of their content area from a textbook perspective and across a limited number of grades, but they struggle to work with students who are far behind or who need acceleration. Additionally, they cannot recognize and capitalize on the inherent value of students' curiosity as a motivating force. Yet, to make schools really effective so that all students can learn deeply, schools nationwide will need to commit to providing all students with opportunities to learn and high-level skills such as solving complex problems; all students will have to be given opportunities to conduct research, write and speak in various contexts, and use the most current technologies to find, analyze, and evaluate information. Such learning environment do exists, but it is all too clear that schools serving low-income students and students of color tend to be the ones least able to meet these goals (National Academies of Sciences, Engineering, and Medicine, 2016; Noguera et al., 2017).

Thus, improved and intensive professional development (PD) for teachers and other school personnel must be part of the efforts to address the conditions in schools that create inequities and that often contribute to students' early departure from school, including into the juvenile justice system. But to be effective, the PD must address the realities of teachers' classrooms, where students' diversity spans racial and ethnic identity, academic abilities, and social-emotional well-being. Darling-Hammond and colleagues (2017) point out that effective PD can take many forms, including technology-facilitated approaches that expand teachers' access to collaboration with others so that teachers can share ideas and support each other as they work to strengthen their teaching practice and to identify and overcome their potential negative attitudes toward and about some of their students. They also point out that the Every Student Succeeds Act encourages states and districts not just to integrate increases in content area knowledge into their PD plans but also to attend to methods for creating positive and inclusive school and classroom environments (Gayl, 2017).

But no matter how it is delivered or how well it is planned, PD must be relevant to teachers and their situations. Teachers who participated in lengthy cognitive interviewing about their elementary reading instruction used the term "atypical" as a placeholder for their students who were English learners, received special education services, came from low-income homes, were behind academically, or were difficult to engage. They faulted their PD for presenting strategies for students who met none of these criteria and who (perhaps) always behaved well (Salinger, Thomas, & Martin, 2017). In short, the PD did not create situations in which they, the teachers of "atypical" students, actually learned anything new.

Providing high-quality PD is only one means through which schools can improve their environment for teachers and students, but it must be part of a larger, comprehensive effort on the part of schools or indeed whole districts to change how they do business. Although many educational policy experts and critics have chronicled the failure of decades of school reform efforts (Elmore, 2004; Payne, 2010), Kirp (2013) offers a different narrative, that of districts that have been successful through "slow and steady" progress toward change (p. 196). The primary focus of Kirp's research was Union City, a highly urbanized community in northern New Jersey, but he also studied the reform efforts of several other successful districts, including Sanger, a small, rural district in the California Central Valley. The population of these two communities is highly Latino; and both were, in the recent past, counted among the lowest districts academically in their states (Kirp, 2013; David & Talbert, 2012).

Union City, Sanger, and other districts that Kirp provides as examples of "slow and steady" progress seemed to epitomize what Lee, Bryk, and Smith (1993, p. 230) meant when they mentioned that schools need to be organizations where "faculty have 'a sense of ownership' and adults and students share an 'organizational saga' . . . [which] breed[s] organizational excellence" (p. 230). Administrators wanted improvement across all levels of their system and across both academic and environmental factors but knew that changed had to be both external and tangible, as in the establishment of a strong preschool program for all students, and internal, as in the creation of trust that permeates central office and school-based personnel. Kirp found several "core principles" undergirding the changes in Union City and discovered the same principles operating in Sanger and other districts he studied. Some of these principles differ from empty slogans in that they are completely actionable; they include:

1. Investing in quality preschool for all students
2. Developing and relying on rigorous, consistent, and integrated curriculum
3. Using aggregate data extensively to diagnose problems within the system and pinpoint whatever is required to solve them
4. Involving teams of teachers and administrators from all levels in a continuous process of planning, doing, and reviewing to create unity across the districts' schools.

Other core principles are less directly actionable because they speak to aspects of school and district climate, such as the importance of "put[ting] the needs of students, not the preferences of the staff, at the center of decision making" and "valu[ing] stability and avoid[ing] political drama" (Kirp, 2013, p. 209) These two go hand-in-hand and epitomize the importance of the collaborative approach to teams of teachers and administrators who are committed to their schools and districts and to calling out the problems they see beyond headline-producing low scores on state accountability tests.

Educators in many schools and districts are reluctant or unable to call out and attempt to fix the potentially overwhelming problems related to the toxic conditions that drive students, especially those who are minority, poor, and often disabled, into negative spirals leading to severe disciplinary actions, premature departures from school, and often the juvenile justice system (Government Accountability Office, 2018; Musu-Gillette, 2018). One of the core principles Kirp identified alludes to another problem that is often not addressed: lack of staff stability due to high teacher and administrator turnover. Not surprisingly, turnover tends to be higher in schools that serve low-income and minority students. These are environments where the professional staff often tends to be new to the profession or their role and are often poorly trained, where support for teachers is weakest, and where low test scores and other accountability measures garner more attention than the well-being of students or teachers (Carver-Thomas & Darling-Hammond, 2017). High teacher turnover in such schools is exacerbated by shortages of trained, experienced special education teachers; and attrition among this group of teachers is even higher than among other teachers.

Carver-Thomas and Darling-Hammond (2017) include among the reasons for teacher turnover their dissatisfaction with accountability measures (25%) and administrators (21%), intrusions on teaching time (18%), discipline issues (17%), lack of autonomy for their work in their classrooms (14%), and dissatisfaction with their lack of influence over school policies and practice (13%). What is interesting is that dissatisfaction *with one's students* is not mentioned as a reason for teacher attrition.

A lesson to be gained from Kirp and other researchers who have studied positive changes in districts like Union City and Sanger is that change starts with clear articulations of what may well be a myriad of challenges, not just low test scores. Additionally, change will happen only over time and through collaborative, open communication across all levels of stakeholders. Losing students to severe discipline measures such as suspension and expulsion and to the school-to-prison pipeline is likely only one of the serious problems educators face, and in some districts the total number of students "lost" in this way may be relatively small. But recognizing this loss of even one student as a critically important indictment of the entire school system and serious equity issue is a good place to start the process of change. Addressing this phenomenon makes actionable Kirp's core principle of putting students' needs first, above the preferences of administrators and teachers.

But the biggest challenge, as most district and school administrators, policy makers, and the public will all attest, is often the question of the cost of funding change. Like other low-income, low-performance districts in New Jersey, Union City benefited from extra funding provided through a statewide initiative that increased per student allotments to needy districts. The $18,000 that could be spent on each Union City student gave administrators and teachers a real advantage over their peers in Sanger, where the per pupil allotment during the same time period was about $8,000. However, the similarities in their approach to bringing about change—establishing preschools, addressing school climate and environmental issues as well as academic problems, and creating inclusiveness in planning and decision making—eclipsed the differential in the districts' available funds because it was their methods and determination to effect change that motivated the effort.

The rejoinder to those who question the costs of eradicating toxic conditions in schools is the simple fact that not making changes ultimately results in higher costs to the social fabric of communities and to the taxpayers who live there. Heckman and colleagues' (2009) extensive research on the long-term benefits of preschool education justifies investments in such programs, especially in low-income and minority communities, but some of his work (2001) is often used to argue against expenditures on programs to address the academic and social needs of older students and low-skilled adults. In the most simplistic terms, his data show that expenditures on adolescents and young adults are not as justifiable as expenditures on younger learners because many troubled teenagers and young adults will never "pay back" the investment through taxes on their earnings. What is missing from this argument is that investments through the full pre-kindergarten to grade 12 span have the potential to accomplish two important goals. First, investments have the potential to interrupt the inequitable cycles of academic failure and social dysfunction that endanger far too many students, especially males who are minority, low-income, or disabled. Further, investments also have the potential to block or impede entry into the school-to-prison pipeline, and as such their cost-benefit ratio is high. According to the Center for Popular Democracy (Terenzi & Foster, 2017), in New York City alone, the estimated cost of the school-to-prison pipeline can top $746.8 million per year. This staggering amount breaks down into $397.6 million in direct costs for enforcing and following through on harsh disciplinary actions and another $349.1 million for social costs, including the lost tax revenue when older adolescents and young adults are incarcerated rather than being able to finish school or being able to find work to support themselves. These staggering figures represent the costs in the largest school district in the country, but they can serve as reminders for all districts of the vast sums of money that could be better spent on programs to identify, address, and change the conditions that give rise to toxic school environments.

Conclusion

Policy briefs, reports of student achievement, and accounts of students who get in trouble in school frequently discuss specific categories of students, including minority students, students from low-income homes, students with disabilities, struggling learners, or so-called "troublemakers" who are suspended, expelled, or who disappear into the juvenile justice system. Such categorizations can obscure the complexity of this nation's student population by not acknowledging the dynamic interplay of students' individual characteristics and the environments in which they live and learn. For far too many students, especially those who are minority or from low-income families, their homes and neighborhoods fail to nourish and support academic, social, and behavioral development; instead, even as young children, they are exposed to hunger, stress, violence, and various forms of marginalization. They enter schools that are unprepared to meet the needs of all their students, where "remediation," rather than a love of learning, shapes the attitudes of those who struggle academically, extinguishes their motivation, and essentially drives students toward negative behaviors. Discipline meted out to students displaying negative behaviors is often harsh; and there is conclusive evidence that such discipline is applied disproportionately toward students who are black, brown, disabled, and male (Government Accountability Office, 2018).

Realizing the interconnections of academic struggles and negative behaviors can provide a start for districts and schools to examine the often toxic environments they may create for students who do not meet expected "standards." The next step for districts and schools that want to change is to realize and acknowledge the extent to which students who do not meet expectations are most often minority, poor, disabled, and male. These are the students who often find themselves removed physically from the "mainstream" flow of their peers through school, first in intervention classes and in the most extreme cases, through suspensions, expulsion, and entry into the juvenile justice system. This process of removal and alienation from school deprives students of their right to education and in far too many ways leaves them ill-prepared to enter the workforce. Addressing disproportionality by improving schools comes with a hefty price tag, but such costs are minimal when compared to the long-term costs to society incurred by students whom schools fail. These social costs include possible incarceration, welfare, job training, and health costs. Additionally, as mentioned previously, parents who have themselves felt alienated from schools, often pass on the results of their own bad experiences to their children, thereby perpetuating cycles of disproportionality.

References

Abramson, L. Y., Metalsky, G. I., & Alloy, L. B. (1989). Hopelessness depression: A theory-based subtype of depression. *Psychological Review, 96*, 358–372.

Abramson, L. Y., Seligman, M. E. P., & Teasdale, J. D. (1978). Learned helplessness in humans: Critique and reformulation. *Journal of Abnormal Psychology, 87*, 49–74.

Alexander, P. A., Jetton, T. L., White, S. H., Parsons, J. L., Cotropia, K. K., Lui, H. C., & Ackerman, C. M. (1994). Young children's creative solutions to realistic and fanciful story problems. *Journal of Creative Behavior, 28*, 89–106.

Allington, R. L. (2009). *What really matters in response to intervention: Research-based designs.* Boston: Pearson.

Allington, R. L. (2010, April 9). Responding to RTI [Interview by A. Rebora]. Retrievedfromhttp://www.edweek.org/tsb/articles/2010/04/12/02allington.h03.html

Allington, R. L. (2013). What really matters when working with struggling readers? *The Reading Teacher, 66*(7), 520–530. doi:10.1002/TRTR.1154

Berkowitz, R., Moore, H., Astor, R. A., & Benbenishty, R. (2017). A research synthesis of the associations between socioeconomic background, inequality, school climate, and academic achievement. *Review of Educational Research, 87*(2), 425–469. doi:10.3102/0034654316669821

Burns, M. K. (2010). Response-to-intervention research: Is the sum of the parts as great as the whole? Perspectives on Language and Literacy. Retrieved from http://www.rtinetwork.org/learn/research/response-to-intervention-research-is-the-sum-of-the-parts-as-great-as-the-whole

Burris, C. C., & Garrity, D. T. (2008). *Detracking for excellence and equity.* Alexandria, VA: ASCD.

Carver-Thomas, D., & Darling-Hammond, L. (2017). *Teacher turnover: Why it matters and what we can do about it.* Palo Alto, CA: Learning Policy Institute. Retrieved from https://learningpolicyinstitute.org/product/teacher-turnover

Children's Defense Fund. (2007). *The cradle to prison pipeline,* Washington, DC: Children's Defense Fund.

Darling-Hammond, L., Barron, B., Pearson, P. D., Schoenfeld, A. H., Stage, E. K., Zimmerman, T. D., & Tilson, J. L. (2017). *Powerful learning: What we know about teaching for understanding.* New York: John Wiley.

David, J. L., & Talbert, J. E. (2012). *Turning around a high-poverty school district: Learning from Sanger Unified's success.* Palo Alto, CA: Bay Area Research Group & Stanford, CA: Center for Research on the Context of Teaching.

Davis-Kean, P. E. (2005). The influence of parent education and family income on child achievement: The indirect role of parent expectations and the home environment. *Journal of Family Psychology, 19*(2), 294–304. doi:10.1037/0893-3200.19.2.294

Deschenes, S., Cuban, L., & Tyack, D. (2001). Mismatch: Historical perspectives on schools and students who don't fit them. *Teachers College Record, 103*(4), 525–547.

Duckworth, A. L., Quinn, P. D., & Seligman, M. E. P. (2009). Positive predictors of teacher effectiveness. *Journal of Positive Psychology, 4*, 540–547.

Duncan, G. J., & Brooks-Gunn, J. (1997). *Consequences of growing up poor.* New York: Russell Sage Foundation.

Duncan, G. J., & Murname, R. J. (2011). Introduction: The American dream then and now. In G. J. Duncan & R. J. Murname (Eds.), *Rising inequality, schools, and children's life chances* (pp. 3–27). New York: Russell Sage Foundation.

Dweck, C. (2015, September 22). Carol Dweck revisits the growth mindset. *Education Week*. Retrieved from http://www.edweek.org/ew/articles/2015/09/23/carol-dweck-revisits-the-growth-mindset.html

Dweck, C. S., & Leggett, E. L. (1988). A social-cognitive approach to motivation and personality. *Psychological Review, 95*(2), 256–273. doi:10.1037/0033-295X.95.2.256

Elmore, R. (2004). *School reform from the inside out*. Cambridge, MA: Harvard Education Press.

Fabelo, T., Thompson, M. D., Plotkin, M., Carmichael, D., Marchbanks, M. P., III, & Booth, E. A. (2011). *Breaking schools' rules: A statewide study of how school discipline relates to students' success and juvenile justice involvement.* New York: Council of State Governments Justice Center.

Foster, M. A., Lambert, R., Abbott-Shim, M., McCarty, F., & Franze, S. (2005). A model of home learning environment and social risk factors in relation to children's emergent literacy and social outcomes. *Early Childhood Research Quarterly, 20*, 13–36.

Fuchs, D., & Deshler, D. D. (2007). What we need to know about responsiveness to intervention (and shouldn't be afraid to ask). *Learning Disabilities Research and Practice*. 22(2), 129–136. DOI: 10.1111/j.1540-5826.2007.00237.x

Fuchs, D., Fuchs, L. S., & Compton, D. L. (2012). Smart RTI: A next-generation approach to multilevel prevention. *Exceptional Children, 78*, 263–279.

Fuchs, D., Mock, D., Morgan, P. L., & Young, C. L. (2003). Responsiveness-to-intervention: Definitions, evidence, and implications for the learning disabilities construct. *Learning Disabilities Research and Practice, 18*, 157–171.

Gandara, P. (2017). Deeper learning for English language learners. In R. Heller, R. E. Wolfe, & A. Steinberg (Eds.), *Rethinking readiness: Deeper learning for college, work, and life* (pp. 123–144). Cambridge, MA: Harvard University Press.

Gayl, C. L. (2017, April). *How state planning for the Every Student Succeeds Act (ESSA) can promote academic, social, and emotional learning: An examination of five strategies*. Chicago: CASEL.

Gormley, W. T., Jr., Phillips, D., & Anderson, S. (2017). The effects of Tulsa's pre-K program on middle school student performance. *Journal of Policy Analysis and Management*, 1–25. doi:10.1002/pam.22023

Government Accountability Office. (2018, March). *K–12 education: Discipline disparities for black students, boys, and students with disabilities* (GAO-18-258). Washington, DC: Author.

Gutiérrez, K. D., Morales, P. Z., & Martinez, D. C. (2009). Re-mediating literacy: Culture, difference, and learning for students from nondominant communities. *Review of Research in Education, 33*, 212–245.

Hart, B., & Risley, T. R. (1995). *Meaningful differences in the everyday experience of young American Children*. Baltimore: Brookes.

Heckman, J. J., Moon, S. H., Pinto, R., Savelyev, P. A., & Yavitz, A. (2009). *The rate of return to the High/Scope Perry Preschool Program*. Cambridge, MA: National Bureau of Economic Research Working Paper No. 15471 JEL No. D62.

Heckman, J. J., & Rubenstein, Y. (2001). The importance of noncognitive skills: Lessons from the GED testing program. *American Economic Review, 91*, 145–149.

Heitzeg, N. A. (2009). Education or Incarceration: Zero Tolerance Policies and the School to Prison Pipeline. *Forum on Public Policy Online, 2009*(2), EJ 870076. Retrieved from https://eric.ed.gov/?id=EJ870076

Hill, N. E., & Taylor, L. C. (2004). Parental school involvement and children's academic achievement: Pragmatics and issues. *Current Directions in Psychological Science, 13*, 161–164.

Holtz, C. A., Fox, R. A., & Meurer, J. R. (2015). Incidence of behavior problems in toddlers and preschool children living in poverty. *Journal of Psychology, 149*(2), 161–174.

Kirp, D. L. (2013). *Improbably scholars: The rebirth of a great American school system and a strategy for America's schools*. New York: Oxford University Press.

Kirp, D. L. (2017, December 14). What pre-school means for your pre-teenager. *New York Times*.

Klinger, J. K., & Edwards, P. A. (2006). Cultural considerations with response to intervention models. *Reading Research Quarterly, 41*, 108–117.

Kohn, A. (2015, August 16). The perils of "Growth Mindset" education: Why we're trying to fix our kids when we should be fixing the system. Retrieved from http://www.salon.com/2015/08/16/the_education_fad_thats_hurting_our_kids_what_you_need_to_know_about_growth_mindset_theory_and_the_harmful_lessons_it_imparts/

Lampert, M. (2017). Ambitious teaching: A deep dive. In R. Heller, R. E. Wolfe, & A. Steinberg (Eds.), *Rethinking readiness: Deeper learning for college, work, and life* (pp. 147–175). Cambridge, MA: Harvard Education Press.

Learned, J. E. (2016a). "Feeling like I'm slow because I'm in this class": Secondary school contexts and the identification and construction of struggling readers. *Reading Research Quarterly, 51*, 367–371.

Learned, J. E. (2016b). Becoming "eligible to matter": How teachers' interpretations of struggling readers' stress can disrupt deficit positioning. *Journal of Adolescent and Adult Literacy, 59*, 665–674.

Learned , J. E. (2016c). "The behavior kids": Examining the conflation of youth reading difficulty and behavior problem positioning among school institutional contexts. *American Educational Research Journal, 53*, 1271–1309.

Lee, V. E., Bryk, A. S., & Smith, J. B. (1993). The organization of effective secondary schools. *Review of Research in Education, 19*, 171–267.

Lochner, L. (2011). *Non-production benefits of education: Crime, health, and good citizenship*. Report #16722. Cambridge, MA: National Bureau of Economic Research.

Losen, D. J., Ee, J., Hodson, C., & Martinez, T. E. (2015). Disturbing inequities: Exploring the relationship between racial disparities in special education identification and discipline. In D. J. Losen (Ed.), *Closing the school discipline gap: Equitable remedies for excessive exclusion* (pp. 89–106). New York: Teachers College Press.

Losen, D. J., & Martínez, T. E. (2013). *Out of school & off track: The overuse of suspensions in American middle and high schools*. Los Angeles: UCLA Center for Civil Rights Remedies, The Civil Rights Project.

Mancini-Marshall, A. (2014). *A new approach to middle school reading intervention balancing self-determination and achievement*. Theses, Student Research, and Creative Activity: Department of Teaching, Learning and Teacher Education. 46. Retrieved from http://digitalcommons.unl.edu/teachlearnstudent/46

McDermott, R., Goldman, S., & Varenne, H. (2006). The cultural work of learning disabilities. *Educational Researcher, 35*(6), 12–17.

Molden, D. C., Plaks, J. E., & Dweck, C. S. (2006). "Meaningful" social inferences: Effects of implicit theories on inferential processes. Journal of Experimental Social Psychology, 42, 738-752. https://doi.org/10.1016/j.jesp.2005.11.005

Musu-Gillette, L., Zhang, A., Wang, K., Zhang, J., Kemp, J., Diliberti, M., & Oudekerk, B. A. (2018). *Indicators of school crime and safety: 2017* (NCES 2018-036/NCJ 251413). Washington, DC: National Center for Education Statistics, U.S. Department of Education, and Bureau of Justice Statistics, Office of Justice Programs, U.S. Department of Justice. Retrieved from https://nces.ed.gov/pubs2018/2018036.pdf

National Academies of Sciences, Engineering, and Medicine. (2016). *Advancing the power of economic evidence to inform investments in children, youth, and families*. Washington, DC: National Academies Press. doi:10.17226/23481Retrievable from https://www.nap.edu/login.php?record_id=23481&page=https%3A%2F%2Fwww.nap.edu%2Fdownload%2F23481

National Joint Committee on Learning Disabilities. (2005). *Responsiveness to intervention and learning disabilities*. Retrieved from http://www.ldonline.org/?module=uploads&func=download&fileId=461

Noguera, P. A. (2003). Schools, prisons, and social implications of punishment: Rethinking disciplinary practices. *Theory into Practice, 42*(4), 341–350.

Noguera, P. A., Darling-Hammond, L., & Friedlaender, D. (2017). Equal opportunity for deeper learning. In R. Heller, R. E. Wolfe, & A. Steinberg (Eds.), *Rethinking readiness: Deeper learning for college, work, and life* (pp. 81–104). Cambridge, MA: Harvard University Press.

Office of Child Care, Administration for Children and Families. (2016, November). *Expulsion and suspension policy statement.* Retrieved from https://www.acf.hhs.gov/occ/resource/im-2016-03

Ozer, E. J., & Weinstein, R. S. (2004). Urban adolescents' expose to community violence: The role of support, school safety, and social constraints in a school-based sample of boys and girls. *Journal of Clinical Child and Adolescent Psychology, 33*(3), 463–476.

Payne, C. M. (2010). *So much reform, so little change: The persistence of failure in urban schools.* Cambridge MA: Harvard University Press.

Pianta, R. C., Cox, M. J., Taylor, L. C., & Early, D. M. (1999). Kindergarten teachers' practices related to the transition into school: Results of a national survey. *Elementary School Journal, 100*, 71–86.

Qi, C. H., & Kaiser, A. P. (2003). Behavior problems of preschool children from low-income families: Review of the literature. *Topics in Early Childhood Special Education, 23*, 188–216.

Rampey, B. D., Keiper, S., Mohadjer, L., Krenzke, T., Li, J., Thornton, N., & Hogan, J. (2016). *Highlights from the U.S. PIAAC Survey of Incarcerated Adults: Their Skills, Work Experience, Education, and Training: Program for the International Assessment of Adult Competencies: 2014* (NCES 2016-040). U.S. Department of Education. Washington, DC: National Center for Education Statistics. Retrieved from https://nces.ed.gov/pubs2018/2018036.pdf

Raphael, S., & Stoll, M. A. (2013). *Why are so many Americans in prison?* New York: Russell Sage Foundation.

Reardon, S.F. (2011). *The widening academic achievement gap between the rich and the poor: New evidence and possible explanations.* Palo Alto: Stanford University Press.

Rosenwasser, B., & Axelrod, S. (2001). The contributions of applied behavioral analysis to the education of people with autism. *Behavior Modification, 25*(5), 671–677. doi:10.1177/0145445501255001

Salinger, T., Thomas, M., & Martin, A. (2017, March). *Scholastic balanced literacy tools development and pilot testing.* Washington, DC: American Institutes for Research.

Sisk, V. F., Burgoyne, A. P., Sun, J., & Butler, J. L. (2018). To what extent and under what circumstances are growth mindsets important for academic achievement? Two meta-analyses. *Psychological Sciences, 29* (4), 549–571.

Skiba, R. J., Horner, R. H., Chung, C.-G., Rausch, M. K., May, S. L., & Tobin, T. (2011). Race is not neutral: A national investigation of African American and Latino disproportionality in school discipline. *School Psychology Review, 40*, 85–107.

Skiba, R. J., Michael, R. S, Nardo, A. C., & Peterson, R. C. (2002). The color of discipline: Sources of racial and gender disproportionality in school punishment. *The Urban Review, 34*(4), 317–342.

Smith, E. J., & Harper, S. R. (2015). *Disproportionate impact of K–12 school suspensions and expulsions on black students in southern states*. Philadelphia: Penn Graduate School Center for Study of Race and Equity in Education.
Steele, C. M. (2010). *Whistling Virvaldi: How stereotypes affect us and what we can do*. New York: W. W. Norton.
Taylor, L. C., Clayton, J. D., & Rowley, S. J. (2004). Academic socialization: Understanding parental influences on children's school-related development in the early years. *Review of General Psychology, 8*, 163–178.
Terenzi, K., & Foster, K. (2017). *The $746 million a year school-to-prison pipeline: The ineffective, discriminatory, and costly process of criminalizing New York City schools*. New York: Center for Popular Democracy.
Upadyaya, K., & Salmela-Aro, K. (2015). Development of school engagement in association with academic success and well-being in varying social contexts. *European Psychologist, 18*, 136–147. doi:10.1037/h0034823
U.S. Department of Education, National Center for Education Statistics, Common Core of Data (CCD). (n.d.). State Nonfiscal Public Elementary/Secondary Education Survey, 2014–15 v.1a. Retrieved from https://nces.ed.gov/ccd/pub_snf_report.asp
U.S. Department of Education, Office of Civil Rights. (2014). *Issue Brief No. 1. Civil rights data collection*. Washington, DC: Author. Retrieved from https://ocrdata.ed.gov/downloads/crdc-school-discipline-snapshot.pdf
Vaughn, S., Danielson, L., Edmonds, R. Z., & Holdheide, L. (2017). Deeper learning for students with disabilities. In R. Heller, R. E. Wolfe, & A. Steinberg (Eds.), *Rethinking readiness: Deeper learning for college, work, and life* (pp. 105–122). Cambridge, MA: Harvard University Press.
Verdugo, R. R. (2002). Race-ethnicity, social class, and zero-tolerance policies. *Education and Urban Society, 35*(1), 50–75.
Walton, G. M. (2014). The new science of wise psychological interventions. *Current Developments in Psychological Sciences, 23*, 73–82.
Weissman, M. (2015). *Prelude to prison: Student perspectives on school suspension*. Syracuse, NY: Syracuse University Press.
Yeager, D. S., Paunesku, D., Walton, G. M., & Dweck, C. S. (2013). *How can we instill productive mindsets at scale? A review of the evidence and an initial R&D agenda*. Washington, DC: Carnegie Foundation for the Advancement of Teaching.
Zimmer, A. (2016, July 21). City ends suspension for K-2 students and issues other discipline reforms. Retrieved from https://www.dnainfo.com/new-york/20160721/civic-center/city-ends-suspension-for-k-2-students-issues-other-discipline-reforms

Supporting Students with Intensive Intervention Needs in Comprehensive, Integrated, Three-Tiered Models of Prevention

Considerations for the Field

Frank M. Gresham and Kathleen Lynne Lane

From preschool through 12th grade, students represent an increasingly diverse group of individuals with a wide range of academic, behavioral, and social competencies. Some students have persistent learning and behavioral challenges for which primary intervention efforts are simply insufficient (Gresham, Hunter, Corwin, & Fisher, 2013). Moreover, for these students, typical instructional practices are falling short (Lane, Oakes, & Menzies, 2014).

The prevalence of students experiencing challenges is larger than one might expect. For example, the National Assessment of Education Progress (2015) reported that 64% of 4th grade students and 66% of 8th grade students scored below proficient on reading skills. This is a serious concern given reading is a keystone skill needed to access new information and skills (Fuchs, Fuchs, & Compton, 2012).

Educators are also confronted with similar statistics in terms of behavioral and social-emotional performance. For example, Forness, Freeman, Paparella, Kauffman, and Walker (2012) reported 20% of school-age youth experienced a mild-to-severe emotional or behavior disorder (EBD), with approximately 12% demonstrating moderate-to-severe challenges. These challenges included externalizing (e.g., aggressive, noncompliant) and internalizing (e.g., anxious, socially withdrawn) behaviors, with the latter often difficult to detect in the absence of systematic screening (Gresham et al., 2013; McIntosh & Goodman, 2016).

It is not uncommon for students to have co-occurring academic, behavior, and social-emotional challenges. For example, ample evidence suggests many students with EBD also have pronounced challenges in reading, math, and writing (Lane, Barton-Arwood, Nelson, & Wehby, 2008). In terms of reading skills, many students with EBD perform two years behind grade level (Ciullo, Ortiz, Al Otaiba, & Lane, 2016; Trout, Nordness, Pierce, & Epstein, 2003). These challenges appear to begin early, with students with EBD reading more slowly, and oral reading fluency rates progressing more slowly than typically developing peers (Wanzek, Al Otaiba, & Petscher, 2014).

Although some may contend students will outgrow these challenges, this is simply not the case—academically, behaviorally, or socially (National Center on Intensive Intervention, 2017). Left unchecked, students requiring intensive interventions often experience a host of negative outcomes including limited academic achievement, peer rejection, school failure, unemployment and underemployment, as well as ongoing mental health challenges (Gresham, 2015; Nelson, Benner, Lane, & Smith, 2004; Walker, Ramsey, & Gresham, 2004). These long-term negative outcomes are well-documented through the contributions of the Special Educational Elementary Longitudinal Study-2 (SEELS) and National Longitudinal Transition Study-2 (NLTS2).

Fortunately, practitioners, researchers, and policy makers continue to prioritize the importance of supporting students with intensive needs in an integrated fashion using a systems-level approach to early detection, prevention, and remediation (Gresham & Elliott, 2014; McIntosh & Goodman, 2016; Walker, Forness, & Lane, 2014). This national priority is evident with the establishment of the National Center on Intensive Intervention (http://intensiveintervention.org/) as well as the recent request for applications from the Institute of Education (Institute of Education Sciences, 2017, p. 15) soliciting inquiry regarding tiered systems:

> Researchers are increasingly advocating for the thoughtful integration of these tiered support systems into a single, coherent framework that is more efficient and provides optimal support to address the academic,

> social, emotional, and behavioral needs of all students, including those with or at risk for disabilities. . . . [Such a] framework may have several advantages over separate tiered support systems, including more efficient service delivery and use of resources. An integrated system also has the potential to more seamlessly address students' interrelated academic and behavior problems and ensure that academic and behavioral supports are aligned without counteracting one another (McIntosh & Goodman, 2016). . . . may be especially beneficial for students with or at risk for disabilities who often struggle in both the academic and behavioral realm and whose difficulties in one domain are often related to difficulties in the other (e.g., Nelson, Benner, Lane, & Smith, 2004).

This priority represents an important shift; namely, it reflects a movement away from reactive, exclusionary, and punitive approaches to responding to learning and behavioral challenges and toward a proactive approach emphasizing prevention. This shift is refreshing and encouraging as it is essential to avoid alienating students, families, and educators we seek to support (Walker, Ramsey, & Gresham, 2004). For the last 20 years, the fields of education and school psychology have shifted toward proactive, systems-based approaches to creating collaborative structures to meet students' academic, behavioral, and social needs (Gresham, 2015; Lane, Kalberg, & Menzies, 2009). Examples of such tiered systems include response to intervention (RTI, which focuses largely on academics; Fuchs, Fuchs, & Compton, 2012), positive behavior intervention and supports (PBIS, which focuses largely on behavior; Horner & Sugai, 2015), multitiered system of supports (MTSS, which focuses on both academics and behavior), interconnected systems framework (which has a behavior and social-emotional focus; Weist, Lever, Bradshaw, & Owens, 2014), and comprehensive, integrated, three-tiered models (Ci3T, which has an academic, behavior, and social-emotional focus; Lane, Oakes, Cantwell, & Royer, 2016). Each system uses a data-informed approach to connect students to needed supports across a cascade of research-based supports according to students' needs.

Purpose

In this chapter, we focus on the utility of Ci3T models in meeting the multiple needs of students requiring intensive interventions. We focus on Ci3T models in particular because the structure is designed to focus on three broad domains: academic, behavioral, and social, providing a coordinated continuum of evidence-based practices. We provide an overview of Ci3T models and describe both how these models are designed and implemented and how they use data-informed decision-making and data-informed professional learning. We illustrate how Ci3T models hold promise for students requiring intensive interventions, as this model facilitates collaboration among key stakeholders. Next, we introduce research-based, low-intensity supports that teachers can incorporate classwide followed by intensive, individualized supports. We offer considerations for advancing research, policy, and practice to support a systems approach for meeting these students' multiple needs. We close with a list of related resources.

About Comprehensive, Integrated, Three-Tiered Models

When distinguishing between the various tiered systems in place in school systems, Ci3T is a broadening of MTSS. Specifically, Ci3T is one comprehensive, integrated system explicitly designed to address academic (principles of RTI), behavior (principles of PBIS), and social-emotional learning with the use of validated curricula selected at the district and/or school-site level (e.g., Positive Action; Flay, Allred, & Ordway, 2001). Districts and schools implementing Ci3T models used a team-based process for building a Ci3T model to enable all stakeholders (e.g., administrators, general educators, special educators, families, and students) to use system- and student-level data to inform instructional practices and attain educational goals—including meeting the multiple needs of students requiring intensive intervention supports (Gresham, 2015; Lane, Oakes, Buckman, & Menzies, 2017).

As part of the manualized professional learning series (Lane, Oakes, Cantwell, & Royer, 2016), schools assemble a Ci3T leadership team that includes an administrator (typically the principal), one to two general educators, a special educator, one to two other leaders (e.g., school psychologist, instructional or behavioral coach, or social worker), a parent, and the parent's child. The Ci3T leadership team actively participates in a year-long, six-part professional learning that involves a data-informed, iterative processes involving input on teacher expectations for students' success as well as social validity input from faculty and staff views using validated measures (e.g., Primary Intervention Rating Scale, PIRS; Lane et al., 2009). At the end of the Ci3T Professional Learning Series, each school has a Ci3T implementation manual depicting (a) roles and responsibilities at Tier 1 for stakeholders (students, faculty and staff, parents, and administrators), (b) procedures for teaching, reinforcing, and monitoring Tier 1 components, (c) an assessment schedule for student measures (e.g., academic and behavior screening tools) as well as programmatic measures (e.g., assessing treatment integrity and social validity of Tier 1 practices), (d) a secondary (Tier 2) intervention grid specifying all strategies, practices, and programs available for students requiring more than primary prevention has to offer, and (e) a tertiary (Tier 3) intervention grid specifying supports for students with the most intensive intervention needs.

Primary (Tier 1) Prevention Efforts: Core Elements

In districts or schools implementing Ci3T models of prevention, general and special educators collaborate to implement primary prevention efforts with a high level of integrity. For the *academic domain*, roles and responsibilities are defined for students, faculty and staff, parents, and administrators. For example, in an elementary setting, students might be asked to arrive on time, stay all day, and engage in all instructional activities. For faculty and staff, some of their roles and responsibilities might be to provide 90 minutes of uninterrupted English and Language Arts using an evidenced-based, district-adopted curriculum (e.g., Reading Street; Pearson Education, 2011), use a variety of low-intensity supports to increase engagement (e.g., providing instructional choices; Royer, Lane, Cantwell, & Messenger, 2017), and use data from benchmarks (e.g., AIMSweb; Pearson Education, 2008) to inform instruction. Parents' responsibilities might to be follow attendance policies to maximize student attendance and communicate regularly to learn about students' academic progress. Administrators' responsibilities might be to provide a range of high-quality professional learning opportunities to support implementation as well as provide access to needed materials, all with a goal of providing a high-quality educational experience for all students.

For the *behavior domain*, the focus is on positive behavior intervention and supports (PBIS; Horner & Sugai, 2015). As part of the behavior domain, faculty and staff used a data-informed approach to build an expectation matrix specifying expectations for success in all key settings (e.g., classrooms, hallways, restrooms, buses) as well as a clearly articulated reactive plan to list and define minor and major rule infractions that specify how adults will respond when challenging behaviors occur. Stakeholders share responsibilities. Students might be asked to follow expectations delineated in an expectation matrix (e.g., Be Respectful, Be Responsible, and Be Safe) as defined for each key setting in the building. Faculty and staff are typically charged with explicitly teaching expectations as well as giving students' opportunities to practice and receive reinforcement for meeting expectations (e.g., tickets or tokens paired with behavior-specific praise). Staff are also taught to respond to challenging behaviors with respectful and instructive consequences: show empathy, keep instruction moving forward, offer choices, and give praise when desired behavior follows (Colvin, 2004, 2010). Parents may be encouraged to be aware of the expectations and communicate concerns respectfully to faculty, staff, and administrators. Administrators might be charged with providing ongoing professional learning and identifying areas in need of additional support (e.g., understanding the rationale for moving away from punishment-based approaches).

Finally, in the *social-emotional domain*, students engage in regularly scheduled lessons taught schoolwide and use these new skill sets during instructional (e.g., during cooperative learning) and noninstructional (e.g., lunch-time, recreational) activities throughout the day (e.g., Elliott & Gresham, 2007). Faculty and staff typically teach the lessons according to the instructional schedule as well as prompting the use of these new skill sets throughout the day. These responsibilities are critical for programming for generalization. Parents are given resources to know the instructional objectives of these lessons so they, too, can acknowledge their children as they engage in these skills beyond the school setting. Administrators are responsible for ensuring faculty and staff have the needed curricular materials as well the professional learning to become knowledgeable and comfortable with not only teaching these lessons but also weaving these new skills into the fabric of daily instruction.

Secondary (Tier 2) and Tertiary (Tier 3) Intervention Grids

Even with high-quality instruction in academic, behavior, and social domains, primary prevention (Tier 1) efforts will not be adequate to meet all students' multiple needs. As such, it is imperative for schools to be prepared to support students for whom primary prevention efforts are insufficient (Lane, Oakes, & Menzies, 2014). School leaders need to be clear as to which evidence-based practices are available for students requiring enrichment and remediation supports—either for targeted (secondary, Tier 2) or intensive (tertiary, Tier 3) needs. The Ci3T models include secondary (Tier 2) and tertiary (Tier 3) *intervention grids* to make these supports transparent to all stakeholders (for examples, see http://www.ci3t.org/PL).

Each intervention grid includes a master list of all available strategies, practices, and programs available for students requiring low-intensity (Tier 2) and high-intensity (Tier 3) supports. Each intervention grid includes five components. First the name of the support is listed, understanding a support is not person, but what the person does. For example, the support would not be "school psychologist," but rather Cognitive Behavior Therapy (CBT). Second, each support (strategy, practice, or program) is described. The description is concise, but clearly indicating who is doing what to whom and under what conditions (Wolery & Dunlap, 2001). For example, the school psychologist will meet 30 minutes per session, three days a week in the office conference room during intervention block. This level of detail is provided to facilitate transparent communication between families, students, and educators. Third, the intervention grid defines schoolwide data used to determine for whom this additive support may be useful: inclusion criteria. For example, inclusion criteria may specify students scoring in the high-risk range for internalizing behavior patterns according to the Student Risk Screening Scale for Internalizing and Externalizing (SRSS-IE; Drummond, 1994; Lane & Menzies, 2009) and below benchmark in oral reading fluency according to AIMSweb (Pearson

Education, 2008). Fourth, the intervention grid includes three types of data to monitor progress including a measure of student performance, treatment integrity (to ensure the intervention is implemented as intended; Gresham, 1989), and social validity (to gather input from teachers, students, and often parents regarding intervention goals, procedures, and outcomes; Wolf, 1978). These sources of information are critical to fully understanding the scope of the support and being able to draw definitive conclusions as to how this supplemental support is impacting student performance (Oakes et al., 2014). Fifth, the intervention grid includes explicit exit criteria to define when the intervention should be concluded or faded if desired outcomes are achieved or when an alternative intervention may be warranted. Examples of completed intervention grids are available on http://www.ci3t.org/PL.

The Ci3T implementation manual depicts what is expected at each level of prevention and how data are used to guide movement between tiers. This is important because students' needs are fluid. Namely, a student may have Tier 2 needs in computation that are swiftly addressed with an evidenced-based intervention, but may have persistent Tier 3 needs to manage acting out behavior (Colvin, 2004). The Ci3T implementation manual is similar to a constitution for the school, creating transparency for administrators, faculty and staff, parents, and students to be fully aware of all district initiatives, programs, strategies, and practices. The intent of secondary (Tier 2) and tertiary (Tier 3) intervention grids is to facilitate transparency and clear communication between stakeholders as to what validated supports are available to support students for whom primary prevention efforts are insufficient (Lane, Menzies, Ennis, & Bezdek, 2013).

Implementation Efforts: Data-Informed Processes

During implementation, Ci3T leadership teams from each school work with district leaders to collect and use systems-level data to inform practices. For example, Ci3T team members collect treatment integrity data in fall and spring each year to determine the extent to which Tier 1 efforts are implemented as designed. Typically these data are collected using direct observations as well as teacher self-report data to examine multiple perspectives (Lane, 2009a, 2009b). During this same data collection window, social validity data are collected from faculty and staff to examine their perspectives regarding goals, procedures, and outcomes of Tier 1 efforts. These programmatic data are examined along with student-level data to examine student performance. These measures typically include academic screening, behavior screening, state achievement tests, office disciplinary referrals (ODR), attendance, and credit accrual at the high school level.

A hallmark characteristic of Ci3T models is data-informed decision-making, including data-informed professional learning. By examining these multiple sources of data in tandem, Ci3T leadership teams and professional learning committees can answer questions such as:

1. To what degree are Tier 1 efforts in place as designed? What facets are challenging for faculty and staff? Where is additional professional learning needed? (data sources: treatment integrity and social validity data)
2. How are students performing over time academically and behaviorally? (data sources: academic and behavior screening data)
3. Are there teachers who might benefit from additional support by learning how to implement low-intensity, teacher-delivered strategies such as incorporating instructional choice (Royer et al., 2017) or increasing opportunities to respond (Common, Lane, Cantwell, Brunsting, & Oakes, 2018)? (data sources: academic and behavior screening data aggregated by classrooms)
4. Which students may require Tier 2 and Tier 3 interventions, despite high-fidelity implementation of Tier 1 efforts (Oakes et al., 2014)?

While many educators, technical assistance providers, and researchers have a shared goal of effectively and efficiently meeting the multiple needs of students with intensive intervention needs, it is imperative the context be considered. Under ideal conditions, primary (Tier 1) prevention efforts would be comprised of evidence-based strategies (Cook & Tankersley, 2013), practices, and programs as would secondary (Tier 2) supports. Prior to connecting students to a Tier 3 support, the Ci3T Leadership Team would have clear evidence previous supports were implemented with high-fidelity, but sufficient shifts in student performance were not obtained according to reliable data. Treatment integrity data are absolutely critical to drawing accurate conclusions regarding intervention outcomes at every level of prevention. It would be unwise to suggest students require intensive interventions (Tier 3) without reliable, valid evidence to suggest less intensive interventions (e.g., Tier 1 or Tier 1 and 2 supports) were ineffective.

In addition to data-informed decision-making processes to inform instruction across the tiers, another critical component of Ci3T models is the use of data-informed professional development for faculty and staff (Lane, Menzies, & Oakes, 2014). As part of this approach, treatment integrity and social validity provided by faculty and staff are used to inform professional development offerings for faculty and staff. For example, teams can review treatment integrity data (e.g., Ci3T Treatment Integrity: Direct Observation [Ci3T TI: DO]; Lane, 2009b) and social validity data collected using the Primary Intervention Rating Scale (PIRS; Lane et al., 2009) to determine topics (e.g., managing acting out behavior, interpreting data).

In addition, states and districts have also conducted statewide and districtwide surveys to glean information from administrators and certificated (e.g., teachers) and classified staff (e.g., paraprofessionals) to determine the additional knowledge and skill sets needed to support full installation (Lane, Carter, Jenkins, Magill, & Germer, 2015). Typically these large-scale surveys also included questions as to how they want to access this professional learning: during districtwide professional learning days, faculty and staff meetings, practice guides, webinars, web-based, supports, articles, and the like. The key is to create a range of opportunities for individuals to access the needed information (knowledge and skill sets) to build their confidence and readiness to support high-fidelity implementation.

Meeting the Needs of Students with Intensive Intervention Needs

This rich, data-informed, collaborative tiered system provides the structure necessary to meet the academic, behavioral, and social needs of students who require intensive interventions. As part of daily instruction, teachers learn a range of low-intensity supports such as how to incorporate teachers' use of instructional choice (Royer et al., 2017), increase students' opportunities to respond during instruction (Common et al., 2018), and use precorrection to prompt desired behavior (Ennis et al., 2017) to increase engagement and consequently limit behaviors that distract from instruction (see table 6.1 for definitions). The effectiveness and ease of these (as well as other) strategies has been well-documented in the referenced systematic reviews, with many successful applications with students with EBD and often embedded as part of traditional instruction (e.g., Messenger et al., 2017).

Under optimal conditions, these strategies would be used as a Tier 1 support with all students as well as in a Tier 2 capacity offered as a targeted

Table 6.1 Low-intensity strategies to increase engagement and limit challenging behavior

Strategy	Definition
Instructional choice	Instructional choice involves providing students with two or more options, allowing students to independently select and receive the option they choose
Increasing opportunities to respond (OTR)	OTR involves high rates of questions (3–5 per minute), swift student responding, and prompt feedback
Precorrection	Precorrection involves determining environments or circumstances where challenging behaviors often occur. Then, defining and teaching desired expectations, providing prompts and reinforcement when they engaged in the expected behaviors

intervention for students with moderate levels of risk. For example, a teacher might offer instructional choice classwide, but provide more focused choices for one or two students in the class while collecting data to determine how implementation of instructional choices influences academic engagement and work completion during a 90-minute English and Language Arts instructional block.

As part of a tiered approach, data are used to determine accurately those students requiring the most intensive interventions. These problem-solving models create a context in which educators, administrators, and parents partner to ensure students have access to the level of support they need to progress academically, behaviorally, and socially. Such tiered approaches have been associated with improvements in teachers' sense of self-efficacy, as they embrace a positive, productive, collaborative structure (e.g., Oakes et al., 2014; Ross et al., 2012).

To illustrate, if instructional choices mentioned above proved insufficient in increasing engagement and minimizing disruptions, it could be attempted with greater intensity as a Tier 3 support. Or, perhaps an entirely different type of intensive intervention might be warranted to address academic as well as behavioral and social skill sets.

Academic Skills

In terms of academic performance, students may require highly intensive reading interventions to address persistent challenges in phonemic awareness, phonics, vocabulary, fluency, or comprehension (Ciullo et al., 2014). Students may also have more intensive needs in math (Fuchs, Fuchs, Craddock, Hollenbeck, Hamlett, & Schatschneider, 2008) or written expression (Harris et al., 2012). Typically screening data are used to determine which students are resistant to universal instruction and targeted interventions, with diagnostic tools used to determine specific intervention targets for Tier 3 supports.

The National Center on Intensive Intervention (NCII) at the American Institutes for Research offers a tools chart depicting information regarding academic intervention programs. This "tools chart" examines the technical rigor of studies conducted, providing information on the study quality, study results, intervention intensity, as well as additional inquiry. For example, a study of small-group tutoring (Fuchs et al., 2008) provided convincing evidence that using a two-tiered approach, in this case, tutoring, was more influential than validated classroom instruction in reducing the prevalence of math difficulty among students at risk. This intervention took place in small groups (n = 2–4 students), in 20–30 minute sessions, 3 times a week for 16 weeks, yielding strong effects on academic performance in mathematics (effect sizes = 1.15).

In addition, the NCII's tools chart features several studies ($n = 5$) of READ 180 (see Kim, Capotosto, Hartry, & Fitzgerald, 2011; Sprague, Zaller, Kite, & Hussar, 2011). Using resources such as the NCII tool chart, researchers and practitioners can easily access reliable information as to how to meet the academic needs of students requiring the most intensive intervention needs. The availability of this resource as well as comparable resources such as What Works Clearinghouse can enable educators with multiple task demands to access current information as to "what works" for whom and in what context.

Behavior and Social Skills

The value of using tiered approaches also applies to meeting students' behavioral and social needs (Gresham, 2015; Hawken, Vincent, & Schumann, 2008). For example, there are multiple programs and strategies featured on the NCII site such as the Behavior Education Program (BEP) or Check-in/Check-out (CICO; Hawken & Horner, 2003), the Incredible Years (Webster-Stratton & Hammond, 1997), video modeling, daily report cards, classwide function-related intervention teams, offering choice, differential reinforcement of other behavior (DRO), increasing opportunities to respond (OTR), self-management, and noncontingent reinforcement to name a few. Some of these options are commercially available resources (e.g., Incredible Years), whereas other options are free-access strategies theoretically grounded in applied behavior analytic principles with decades of evidence to support their effectiveness (e.g., DRO and OTR; Cooper, Heron, & Heward, 2007). Although it is beyond the scope of this chapter to provide a detailed description of each support, we note the knowledge is available and implementation is feasible.

In addition to these resources, we highlight the utility of functional assessment-based interventions (FABI) given these are mandated in certain circumstances and recommended in others (Cox et al., 2011; Umbreit, Ferro, Liaupsin, & Lane, 2007). FABI are interventions based on the reason *why* (function) a challenging behavior occurs. In brief, behavior is maintained by positive (to get something) and/or negative (to stop or get out of something) reinforcement (Umbreit et al., 2007). Students may access positive reinforcement in the form of attention from others (e.g., adults or peers), preferred activities or items, or sensory stimulation. In addition, students may escape (negative reinforcement) attention, task demands or items, or sensory stimulation. A range of direct and indirect methods can be used to determine the function of students' target (undesirable) behavior. For example, A-B-C data collection involves conducting direct observations of what happens before (antecedents) and after (consequences) to determine what is setting the stage for the behavior to occur as well as the maintaining consequences (with all learning shaped by consequences; Cooper, Heron, & Heward, 2007). In addition, there are indirect measures such as interviews (teacher, parent, and student; e.g., Student Functional Behavioral Assessment Interview; Crone & Horner, 2003), systematic reviews of school records (e.g., the School Archival Record Search; Walker, Block-Pedago, Todis, & Severson, 1991) and standardized rating scales to distinguish between acquisition and performance deficits (e.g., the Social Skills Intervention System Rating Scales; Gresham & Elliott, 2008). These multiple sources of direct and indirect data are used to determine the function(s) maintaining the target behavior.

After determining (and ideally testing) the function of the students' target behavior, the next step is to develop an intervention linked to the function. As part of a team-based process, an intervention is designed to (a) teach the student a replacement behavior (often a functionally equivalent replacement behavior, meaning the student learns a new way to access or avoid attention, a preferred task, or tangible and/or sensory experiences); (b) modify the environment to set the stage for the replacement behavior; and (c) shift the rate of reinforcement by withholding reinforcement the target behavior and providing reinforcement when the replacement behavior occurs (Umbreit et al., 2007).

Conclusion

Students with intensive intervention needs represent a large percentage of school-age youth (Forness et al., 2012). Often these students are exposed to multiple risk factors presented with many challenges including academic underachievement, impaired social relationships, and behavioral excesses and deficits that make life difficult for them and those around them (Gresham, 2015; Walker et al., 2005). We appreciate the increased attention for advancing research efforts to better serve this often difficult to teach population. The U.S. Department of Education's focus on the issue of tiered frameworks acknowledges the systems-level priorities placed on supporting students with intensive intervention needs.

As lessons are learned from current and future inquiry, we encourage researcher and practitioners to share their journeys. To shape public policy and shape practices in schools, it will be critical for dissemination activities to be broader than traditional outlets such as peer-reviewed journals and professional conferences. While these are indeed important and should be retained, there is also a need to reach a broader audience. It is imperative for faculty and staff, administrators, parents, and even students themselves have the knowledge available and access to high-quality professional learning needed to install evidence-based practices to keep students safe and help them thrive. As such, we applaud the intent of this collaborative handbook for education, safety, and justice professionals, families, and communities. To support this work, we offer a list of related resources to help this endeavor (see table 6.2).

Table 6.2 Related resources

Ci3T Website

http://ci3T.org

Common, E. A., Lane, K. L. Menzies, H. M., Oakes, W. P., & Ennis, R. P. (2015). Low-intensity strategies: Using opportunities to respond to support instruction. A comprehensive, integrated, three-tiered model of prevention professional learning module. Web-based resource available at http://www.ci3t.org/pl.

Johl, L. E., Lane, K. L., Menzies, H. M., Ennis, R. P., & Oakes, W. P. (2015). Low-intensity strategies: A look at instructional choice. A comprehensive, integrated, three-tiered model of prevention professional learning module. Web-based resource available at http://www.ci3t.org/pl.

Royer, D. J., Lane, K. L., Cantwell, E. D., Ennis, R. P., Oakes, W. P., & Menzies, H. M. (2015). Low-intensity strategies: A look at precorrection. A comprehensive, integrated, three-tiered model of prevention professional learning module. Web-based resource available at http://www.ci3t.org/pl.

The Iris Center™

https://iris.peabody.vanderbilt.edu/

Modules

Addressing Disruptive and Noncompliant Behaviors (2-part series)

(Part 1): Understanding the Acting-Out Cycle

(Part 2): Behavioral Interventions

https://iris.peabody.vanderbilt.edu/module/bi1/#content

Early Childhood Environments: Designing Effective Classrooms https://iris.peabody.vanderbilt.edu/module/env/

PBIS National Center

http://pbis.org

Freeman, J., Simonsen, B., Goodman, S., Mitchell, B., George, H., Swain-Bradway, J., Lane, K., Sprague, J., & Putnam, B. (2017, January). PBIS technical brief on systems to support teachers' implementation of positive classroom behavior support. Retrieved from http://www.pbis.org/Common/Cms.

Simonsen, B., Freeman, J., Goodman, S., Mitchell, B., Swain-Bradway, J., Flannery, B., Sugai, G., George, H., & Putman, B. (2015, October). Supporting and responding to behavior: Evidence-based classroom strategies for teachers. Retrieved from http://www.pbis.org/common/cms.

Swain-Bradway, J., Putnam, B., Freeman, J., Simonsen, B., George, H., Lane, K., & Goodman, S. (2017, August). PBIS technical brief on using data to support teachers' implementation of positive classroom behavior support.

References

Ciullo, S., Ortiz, M., Al Otaiba, S., & Lane, K. L. (2016). Advanced reading comprehension expectations in secondary schools: Considerations for students with emotional or behavioral disorders. *Journal of Disabilities and Policy Studies, 27*, 54–64. doi:10.1177/1044207315604365

Colvin, G. (2004). *Managing the cycle of acting-out behavior in the classroom.* Eugene, OR: Behavior Associates.

Colvin, G. (2010). *Defusing disruptive behavior in the classroom.* Thousand Oakes, CA: Corwin Press.

Common, E. A., Lane, K. L., Cantwell, E. D., Brunsting, N., & Oakes, W. P. (2018). Teacher-delivered strategies to increase students' opportunities to respond: A systematic methodological review. Manuscript in review.

Cook, B., & Tankersley, M. (Eds.). (2013). *Effective practices in special education.* Boston: Pearson.

Cooper, J. O. H., Heron, T. E., & Heward, W. L. (2007). *Applied behavior analysis.* Upper Saddle River, NJ: Pearson.

Council for Exceptional Children. (2014). *Council for Exceptional Children standards for evidence-based practices in special education.* Arlington, VA: Author.

Cox, M., Griffin, M. M., Hall, R., Oakes, W. P., & Lane, K. L. (2011). Using a functional assessment-based intervention to increase academic engaged time in an inclusive middle school setting. *Beyond Behavior, 20*, 44–54.

Crone, D. A. , & Horner, R. H. (2003). *Building positive behavior support systems in schools: Functional behavioral assessment.* New York: Guilford.

Drummond, T. (1994). *The Student Risk Screening Scale (SRSS).* Grants Pass, OR: Josephine County Mental Health Program.

Elliott, S. N., & Gresham, F. M. (2007). *Social skills improvement system: Classwide intervention program guide.* Bloomington, MN: Pearson Assessments.

Ennis, R. P., Royer, D., J., Lane, K. L., & Griffith, C. E. (2017). A systematic review of precorrection in PK-12 settings. *Education and Treatment of Children, 40*, 465–496.

Flay, B. R., Allred, C. G., & Ordway, N. (2001). Effects of the Positive Action program on achievement and discipline: Two matched-control comparisons. *Prevention Science, 2*, 71–89.

Forness, S. R., Freeman, S. F. N., Paparella, T., Kauffman, J. M., & Walker, H. M. (2012). Special education implications of point and cumulative prevalence for children with emotional or behavioral disorders. *Journal of Emotional and Behavioral Disorders, 20*, 4–18.

Fuchs, D., Fuchs, L. S., & Compton, D. L. (2012). Smart RTI: A next-generation approach to multilevel prevention. *Exceptional Children, 78*, 263–279.

Fuchs, L. S., Fuchs, D., Craddock, C., Hollenbeck, K. N., Hamlett, C. L., & Schatschneider, C. (2008). Effects of small-group tutoring with and without validated classroom instruction on at-risk students' math problem solving: Are two tiers of prevention better than one? *Journal of Educational Psychology, 100*, 491–509. NIHMS62377; PMID 19122881.

Gresham, F. M. (1989). Assessment of treatment integrity in school consultation and prereferral intervention. *School Psychology Review, 18*, 37–50.

Gresham, F. M. (2015). Evidence-based social skills interventions for students at risk for EBD. *Remedial and Special Education, 36*, 100–104. doi:10.1177/0741932514556183

Gresham, F. M., & Elliott, S. N. (2008). *Social skills improvement system: Rating scales*. Bloomington, MN: Pearson Assessments.

Gresham, F. M., & Elliott, S. N. (2014). Social skills assessment and training in emotional behavioral disorders. In H. M. Walker & F. M. Gresham (Eds.), *Handbook of evidence-based practices in emotional and behavioral disorders: Applications in schools* (pp. 152–172). New York: Guilford Press.

Gresham, F. M., Hunter, K., Corwin, E., & Fisher, A. (2013). Screening, assessment, and outcome evaluation of serious behavioral difficulties in an RTI model. *Exceptionality, 21*, 19–33.

Harris, K. L., Lane, K. L., Graham, S. Driscoll, S., Wilson, K., Sandmel, K., . . . Schatschneider, C. (2012). Practice-based professional development for self-regulated strategies instruction in writing: A randomized controlled study. *Journal of Teacher Education, 63*, 103–119. doi:10.1177/0022487111429005

Hawken, L. S., & Horner, R. H. (2003). Evaluation of a targeted intervention within a schoolwide system of behavior support. *Journal of Behavioral Education, 12*, 225–240.

Hawken, L. S., Vincent, C. G., & Schumann, J. (2008). Response to intervention for social behavior: Challenges and opportunities. *Journal of Emotional and Behavioral Disorders, 16*(4), 213–225.

Horner, R. H., & Sugai, G. (2015). School-wide PBIS: An example of applied behavior analysis implemented at a scale of social importance. *Behavior Analysis in Practice, 8*, 80–85. doi:10.1007/s40617-015-0045-4

Institute of Education Sciences. (2017). Research for Application 84.324N. Retrieved from https://ies.ed.gov/funding/doc/2018_84324N.docx

Kim, J. S., Capotosto, L., Hartry, A., & Fitzgerald, R. (2011). Can a mixed-method literacy intervention improve the reading achievement of low-performing elementary school students in an after-school program? Results from a randomized controlled trial of READ 180 enterprise. *Educational Evaluation and Policy Analysis, 33*(2), 183–201.

Lane, K. L. (2004). Academic instruction and tutoring interventions for students with emotional/behavioral disorders: 1990 to present. In R. B. Rutherford, M. M. Quinn, & S. R. Mathur (Eds.), *Handbook of research in emotional and behavioral disorders* (pp. 462–486). New York: Guilford Press.

Lane, K. L. (2009a). Treatment integrity: Teacher self-report form. www.ci3t.org/measures.

Lane, K. L. (2009b). Treatment integrity: Comprehensive, integrated three-tiered model of prevention direct observation tool. Retrieved from www.ci3t.org/measures.

Lane, K. L. (2017). Building strong partnerships: Responsible inquiry to learn and grow together TECBD-CCBD keynote address. *Education and Treatment of Children, 40*, 597–618.

Lane, K. L., Barton-Arwood, S. M., Nelson, J. R., & Wehby, J. H. (2008). Academic performance of students with emotional and behavioral disorders served in a self-contained setting. *Journal of Behavioral Education, 17*, 43–62.

Lane, K. L., Barton-Arwood, S. M., Rogers, L. A., & Robertson, E. J. (2007). Literacy interventions for students with and at-risk for emotional or behavioral disorders: 1997 to present. In J. C., Crockett, M. M. Gerber, & T. J. Landrum. (Eds.), *Achieving the radical reform of special education: Essays in honor of James M. Kauffman* (pp. 213–241). Mahwah, NJ: Lawrence Erlbaum.

Lane, K. L., Carter, E., Jenkins, A., Magill, L., & Germer, K. (2015). Supporting comprehensive, integrated, three-tiered models of prevention in schools: Administrators' perspectives. *Journal of Positive Behavior Interventions, 17*, 209–222. doi:10.1177/1098300715578916

Lane, K. L., Harris, K., Graham, S., Driscoll, S. A., Sandmel, K., Morphy, P., . . . Schatschneider, C. (2011). Self-regulated strategy development at tier-2 for second-grade students with writing and behavioral difficulties: A randomized control trial. *Journal of Research on Educational Effectiveness, 4*, 322–353.

Lane, K. L., Kalberg, J. R., Bruhn, A. L., Driscoll, S. A., Wehby, J. H., & Elliott, S. (2009). Assessing social validity of school-wide positive behavior support plans: Evidence for the reliability and structure of the Primary Intervention Rating Scale. *School Psychology Review, 38*, 135–144.

Lane, K. L., Kalberg, J. R., Bruhn, A. L., Mahoney, M. E., & Driscoll, S. A. (2008). Primary prevention programs at the elementary level: Issues of treatment integrity, systematic screening, and reinforcement. *Education and Treatment of Children, 31*, 465–494.

Lane, K. L., Kalberg, J. R., & Menzies, H. M. (2009). *Developing schoolwide pro grams to prevent and manage problem behaviors: A step-by-step approach.* New York: Guilford Press.

Lane, K. L., & Menzies, H. M. (2009). Student risk screening scale: Internalizing and externalizing (SRSS-IE). Unpublished rating scale. Retrieved from http://www.ci3t.org/screening

Lane, K. L., Menzies, H. M., Ennis, R. P., & Bezdek, J. (2013). School-wide systems to promote positive behaviors and facilitate instruction. *Journal of Curriculum and Instruction, 7*, 6–31.

Lane, K. L., Menzies, H. M., Ennis, R. P., & Oakes, W. P. (2015). *Supporting behavior for school success: A step-by-step guide to key strategies.* New York: Guilford Press.

Lane, K. L., Oakes, W. P., Buckman, M. M., & Menzies, H. M. (in press). Comprehensive, integrated, three-tiered (Ci3T) models of prevention: Considerations for the field. In D. Bateman, J. Cline, & M. Yell (Eds.), *Current trends and legal issues in special education*. Thousand Oaks, CA: Corwin.

Lane, K. L., Oakes, W. P., Cantwell, E. D., & Royer, D. J. (2016). *Building and installing comprehensive, integrated, three-tiered (Ci3T) models of prevention: A practical guide to supporting school success*. Phoenix: KOI Education (Interactive eBook).

Lane, K. L., Oakes, W. P., & Menzies, H. M. (2014). Comprehensive, Integrated, Three-Tiered (CI3T) models of prevention: Why does my school—and district—need an integrated approach to meet students' academic, behavioral, and social needs? *Preventing School Failure, 58*, 121–128.

McIntosh, K., & Goodman, S. (2016). *Integrating multi-tiered systems of support: Blending RTI and PBIS*. New York: Guilford Press.

Messenger, M., Common, E. A., Lane, K. L., Oakes, W. P., Menzies, H. M., Cantwell, E. D., & Ennis, R. P. (2017). Increasing opportunities to respond for students with internalizing behaviors: The utility of choral and mixed responding. *Behavioral Disorders, 42*, 170–184. doi:10.1177/0198742917712968

National Assessment of Educational Progress. (2015). N.P. Retrieved from https://nces.ed.gov/nationsreportcard/

National Center on Intensive Intervention. (2017). N. P. Retrieved from https://intensiveintervention.org/

Nelson, J. R., Benner, G. J., Lane, K., & Smith, B. W. (2004). An investigation of the academic achievement of K–12 students with emotional and behavioral disorders in public school settings. *Exceptional Children, 71*, 59–73.

Oakes, W. P., Lane, K. L., Cox, M., & Messenger, M. (2014). Logistics of behavior screenings: How and why do we conduct behavior screenings at our school? *Preventing School Failure, 58*, 159–170.

Pearson Education. (2008). *AIMSweb*. San Antonio: Author.

Pearson Education. (2011). *Reading street*. San Antonio: Author.

Ross, S. W., Romer, N., & Horner, R. H. (2012). Teacher well-being and the implementation of School-Wide Positive Behavior Interventions and Supports. *Journal of Positive Behavior Interventions, 14*, 118–128. doi:10.1177/1098300711413820

Royer, D. J., Lane, K. L., Cantwell, E. D., & Messenger, M. L. (2017). A systematic review of the evidence-base for instructional choice in K–12 settings. *Behavioral Disorders, 42*, 89–107. doi:10.1177/0198742916688655

Sprague, K., Zaller, C., Kite, A., & Hussar, K. (2011, June). Springfield-Chicopee School Districts Striving Readers (SR) Program Year 4 Report: Evaluation of implementation and impact. Grantee: Springfield and Chicopee, MA Public Schools. Submitted to the U.S. Department of Education, Office of Elementary and Secondary Education and the Institute of Education Sciences. Providence, RI: Education Alliance at Brown University.

Trout, A., Nordness, P. D., Pierce, C. D., & Epstein, M. H. (2003). Research on the academic status of children with emotional and behavioral disorders:

A Review of the literature from 1961 to 2000. *Journal of Emotional and Behavioral Disorders, 11*(4), 198-210. doi:10.1177/10634266030110040201

Umbreit, J., Ferro, J., Liaupsin, C., & Lane, K. (2007). *Functional behavioral assessment and function-based intervention: An effective, practical approach.* Upper Saddle River, NJ: Prentice-Hall.

Walker, H. M., Block-Pedago, A., Todis, B., & Severson, H. (1991). *School archival records search.* Longmont, CO: Sopris West.

Walker, H. M., Forness, S. R., & Lane, K. L. (2014). Design and management of scientific research in applied school settings. In B. Cook, M. Tankersley, & T. Landrum (Eds.), *Advances in learning and behavioral disabilities* (Vol. 27, pp. 141–169). Bingley, UK: Emerald.

Walker, H. M., Ramsey, E., & Gresham, F. M. (2004). *Antisocial behavior in school: Evidence-based practices* (2nd ed.). Belmont, CA: Wadsworth.

Wanzek, J., Al Otaiba, S. A., & Petscher, Y. (2014). Oral reading fluency development for children with emotional disturbance or learning disabilities. *Exceptional Children, 80*(2), 187–204.

Webster-Stratton, C., & Hammond, M. (1997). Treating children with early-onset conduct problems: A comparison of child and parent training interventions. *Journal of Consulting and Clinical Psychology, 65*, 93–109.

Weist, M. D., Lever, N., Bradshaw, C., & Owens, J. S. (2014). Further advancing the field of school mental health. In M. Weist, N. Lever, C. Bradshaw, & J. Owens (Eds.), *Handbook of school mental health: Research, training, practice, and policy* (2nd ed., pp. 1–16). New York: Springer.

What Works Clearinghouse. (2017). Standards handbook, version 4.0. Retrieved from https://ies.ed.gov/ncee/wwc/Docs/referenceresources/wwc_standards_handbook_v4.pdf

Wolery, M., & Dunlap, G. (2001). Reporting on studies using single-subject experimental methods. *Journal of Early Intervention, 24*, 85–89.

Wolf, M. M. (1978). Social validity: The case for subjective measurement or how applied behavior analysis is finding its heart. *Journal of Applied Behavior Analysis, 11*, 203–214.

Yudin, M. (2014). PBIS: Providing opportunity. A keynote address presented at the National PBIS Leadership Forum: PBIS Building Capacity & Partnerships to Enhance Educational Reform, Rosemont, IL.

PART 2

Creating Emotionally and Physically Safe Schools and Communities

CHAPTER SEVEN

Emotional and Physical Safety

Shannon B. Wanless, Dewey G. Cornell, and Dwight Davis

When students feel safe at school, they are free to engage in academic and social interactions that optimize learning and development (Wanless, 2016). Safety should be a top priority for schools so that students can grapple with academic challenges, express themselves freely and creatively, and apply what they have learned, without having to keep a wary eye out for possible threats. Safety is also a top priority for teachers so they can be free to engage with their students authentically and experience their own professional growth and development. Often, safety is framed as protection from physical injury, but emotional safety is equally necessary and should not be overlooked. Emotional safety includes protection from threats to one's social status, identity, and sense of well-being (Osher & Dwyer, 2006). Each type of safety takes different strategies to maintain, and those efforts may complement one another as integral components of a larger approach for a safe school climate. In this chapter, we describe the importance of physical and emotional safety for students and teachers, threats to safety in schools, and steps schools might take to enhance their overall safety climate.

Physical Safety

Threats to physical safety include fear of physical bullying, assault, and other physically dangerous situations with peers or adults. There is abundant evidence that school order and safety are fundamental conditions for learning (Cornell & Mayer, 2010). For example, threats of peer aggression lead to adjustment problems such as depression, anxiety, impaired attention, and social withdrawal, which in turn lead to school avoidance and reduced engagement in learning activities (Buhs, Ladd, & Herald, 2006; Flannery, Wester, & Singer, 2004; Nansel et al., 2001; Nishina, Juvonen, & Witkow, 2005; Schwartz, Gorman, Nakamoto, & Toblin, 2005). Physical threats can have immediate effects of anxiety, diminished ability to concentrate, and irritability, followed by behaviors such as avoidance and emotional state changes such as chronic apprehension. Threats can produce hormonal changes that can stress the nervous system and influence brain development, leading to a cascade of longer-term outcomes. For example, changes in the brain include impaired development of the prefrontal cortex, which is responsible for executive functions such as managing attention, making plans, persisting on tasks, controlling impulsive behaviors, and making decisions (Arsten, 2009). Perceived physical threats can also impair a student's ability to recognize and interpret others' emotions. Struggling with these skills would make it difficult to form healthy relationships with peers and teachers, which are critical to learning at school (Fox & Shonkoff, 2012; Wismer et al., 2005). This means that when students are worried that they are not physically safe, they are left to struggle with basic learning-related skills and are thus less able to be curious, creative, or persistent when teachers present learning opportunities. Their primary need is to attend to the physical threat, and it is unlikely that even a highly engaging teacher could, or should, convince a student to do otherwise. In the end, learning, development, and academic test scores may all suffer (Lacoe, 2016). It is also important to note that when students feel physically unsafe, they are more prone to hostile attribution bias and may use aggression and violence as a defense against fear (e.g., Anderson, 2000). In other words, a perceived lack of physical safety not only has negative consequences for learning, it can also create a vicious circle of escalating tension and aggression.

Everyone does not, however, experience the same reaction to potential threats to their physical safety. What is considered a threat? And how big of a threat is it? School factors trigger varying degrees of fear for different individuals, and that fear can manifest in different ways depending on what the students have experienced in the past. For example, researchers have found that students with previous experiences with victimization felt less safe at school, than their peers (Bachman, Randolph, & Brown, 2011). They also found that some school security measures actually made all students more fearful. There can be complex reactions that interact with student characteristics. For example, the presence of security guards in schools increased the likelihood of feeling afraid for white adolescents, but not for African American adolescents. Further, African American students were more fearful in suburban and rural schools than urban schools, and white students were more fearful in urban schools than suburban and rural ones. A national survey study found that visible school security measures such as cameras, metal detectors, and security personnel, did not increase student academic performance or attendance, and may have had detrimental effects in some schools (Tanner-Smith & Fisher, 2016). These findings are illustrative of an important issue: there is not a one-size-fits-all approach that schools can take to help everyone feel physically safe. In creating a school plan for physical safety, it is important to know the students, families, and teachers served and to individualize the approach in order to meet their specific needs. Although some efforts may be universally effective, physical safety is also cultivated when teachers and administrators are able to notice and interpret the emotional and behavioral cues of their students, allowing them to detect perceived threats. Addressing physical safety is important, and when doing so, ensuring that students, families, and teachers are attuned to such safety issues, is a critical additional layer.

As an example, we describe the case of a 5th grade boy, Tyrone. Tyrone came to school and began physically threatening another student. This behavior was uncharacteristic for Tyrone, who was normally a good-humored child who was able to laugh at his own mistakes and was known for his love of reading. In this situation, however, he ended up assaulting and biting the teacher who attempted to gracefully remove him from the classroom. Once Tyrone was safe in the school's de-escalation room, the teacher took a breath, and returned to the class to complete the period, and ultimately deliver his lessons for the rest of the day. In this process, the teacher experienced his own decreased physical safety and had to work hard to keep his stress and anger in control. Importantly, the teacher had to approach Tyrone and his family, and figure out how to address the issue so that Tyrone could safely re-enter the classroom and continue to be part of the classroom community. At that point, the teacher came to understand that Tyrone had felt physically unsafe at home the previous night and was responding to his own sense of being physically threatened. In fact, his threats in the classroom closely mimicked what he had heard and seen the night before. The teacher knew he must approach this situation without judgment of the child and the family. Fortunately, the teacher had previously established a relationship with Tyrone and his family, and based all of his interactions on the assumption that "all parents do the best they can." Ultimately, the teacher was successful in bringing Tyrone back into the classroom. He met with Tyrone to discuss the situation and reflect on the connection between his experiences at home and school. When re-entering the classroom, the teacher took the opportunity to address the situation with the class and close out the hostile interaction with a facilitated conversation between Tyrone and the other students that were involved. As was the case in this situation, when a child behaves in a way that is out of character, it is most productive to become curious and responsive, and not to make assumptions.

In some instances, threats to physical safety can be quite serious. Gun violence is a frightening prospect that has had a tremendous impact on perceptions of school safety (Borum, Cornell, Modzeleski, & Jimerson, 2010; Cornell, 2006). School authorities should be mindful that the statistical risk of a school shooting is extraordinarily low; one estimate is that the average school can expect a student homicide every 6,000 years (Borum et al., 2010). Gun violence, including multiple casualty homicide, is many times lower in schools than in other settings such as restaurants, stores, and residences (Nekvasil, Cornell, & Huang, 2015).

Nevertheless, the public fear of school shootings has generated widespread changes in school policies and practices, especially the adoption of excessively punitive zero tolerance discipline that has led to high rates of school suspension, transfer, and expulsion (American Psychological Association Zero Tolerance Task Force, 2008). Exclusionary school discipline has been widely criticized as an ineffective practice that fails to improve student behavior or deter other students from misbehavior, and results in higher rates of school failure and dropout (Morgan, Salomen, Plotkin, & Cohen, 2014). Moreover, the large racial and ethnic disparities in the use of exclusionary discipline have raised criticisms by the U.S. Department of Justice (USDOJ) and the Office for Civil Rights of the U.S. Department of Education (USDOE) that they are discriminatory practices (USDOJ and USDOE, 2014). Exclusionary discipline practices are unlikely to be part of an effective plan for creating a safe school climate. A report by the Council of State Governments Justice Center presents a series of recommendations to help schools move away from exclusionary discipline and adopt more effective and equitable practices (Morgan et al., 2014).

Emotional Safety

In addition to physical safety, students also worry about their interpersonal relationships and threats to their sense of identity such as rejection, criticism, and ridicule. In previous literature, this has been referred to as emotional safety, social-emotional safety, or psychological safety (Edmondson & Lei, 2014; Thapa, Cohen, Guffey, & Higgins-D'Alessandro, 2013). In general, when students feel this type of safety they feel secure, respected, and valued. As a result, they are not afraid that taking interpersonal and academic risks will lead to embarrassment, shame, or loss of face. Primary threats to emotional safety may vary across grades, but the implications of feeling emotionally unsafe are similar (Wanless, 2016). For example, for young children, feeling emotionally safe may mean assurance that their primary caregiver will return for them at the end of the school day. As they get a bit older and begin focusing more on comparing themselves to their peers, emotional safety may mean a positive sense of self. They also become more understanding of their strengths and weaknesses, and accepting of differences between themselves and their peers. For adolescents, in particular, feeling emotionally safe means that there is less concern that their identity could be damaged or taken into question if they take a risk in front of their peers or teachers. Schools are a central cultural context in which adolescents can experience positive growth and develop a sense of identity and self-efficacy (Eccles & Roeser, 2011).

Throughout schooling and across these developmental phases, when students feel emotionally unsafe, they are less able to manage their thoughts and feelings so that they can engage in school. Beyond limiting healthy engagement and risk-taking, feeling emotionally unsafe can also result in increased levels of physical and psychological danger at school. Specifically, students who feel disrespected, rejected, or threatened are more likely to engage in physical aggression, bullying, and other unhealthy behaviors. This can be the result of frustration or a way to restore a sense of self-worth or status (Belmi, Barragan, Neale, & Cohen, 2015; DeBono & Muraven, 2014). Physical and emotional safety can be intertwined, and effective teachers become skilled at reading the interplay between the two. When schools are able to help students feel emotionally safe, the impact can be immediate and long-lasting.

Emotional safety can vary based on social and demographic aspects of identity. For example, race, culture, language, gender, and sexuality all have implications for safety based on implicit and explicit biases in the sociopolitical context, and the degree to which being part of these groups aligns students with the majority of others in the school and community. When students belong to marginalized groups, they are already primed to scan the environment and be hypersensitive to threats to their emotional safety. An example of this can be seen when students detect microaggressions, which are, "subtle, everyday verbal and nonverbal slights, snubs, or insults which communicate hostile, derogatory, or negative messages to people of color based solely on their marginalized group membership" (Hammond, 2014, p. 47). This concept does not only apply to students who are marginalized based on their race but also any stigmatization for other reasons, such as language, gender identity, or sexual orientation. Another related threat is stereotype threat, in which a student may fear that his or her behavior could be interpreted as reflective of a stereotype of a group to which they belong. When there is any sense that microaggressions, stereotype-based threats, or other identity-related threats are present, these students may feel unsafe and less welcome in the classroom community, and as a result, experience lowered aspirations and confidence (Spencer, Logel, & Davies, 2016). As a result, they are less able to take the academic, social, and intrapersonal risks that are needed for learning and development to occur.

Teachers' Sense of Safety in Schools

In general, school leaders who are thinking about safety focus their attention on their students' sense of physical and emotional safety. It is vital, however, for the teachers in schools to feel safe. Teachers must feel safe in order to be fully effective as instructors and mentors. Teachers who do not feel safe at school are more likely to feel burned out, be less engaged with their students, and leave their jobs (Brouwers, Evers, & Tomic, 2001). High teacher turnover has an especially detrimental impact on schools serving a high proportion of low-income students (Johnson, Kraft, & Papay, 2012). Nevertheless, there is evidence that many teachers do not feel safe in their schools. Although there is increasing awareness of the importance of teachers' well-being and safety at work, efforts in this area are just beginning (Berg & Cornell, 2016; Espelage et al., 2013; Jennings & Greenberg, 2009).

Previous research has shown that a sense of trust among teachers in a school, which is related to emotional safety, cultivates an environment that allows innovation and professional learning and development to flourish. In fact, schools with high relational trust are better able to implement school-wide reform in a meaningful and sustained way (Bryk & Schneider, 2002). Like students, however, teachers may be more or less at risk to feel unsafe at school based on their background, skills, and previous experiences. In fact, one study suggests that the extent to which teachers have developed their own social-emotional skills may play a role in their sense of safety at school. Specifically, teachers who were observed to have more emotionally supportive classrooms, were more likely to engage in professional development—considered a positive risk that requires a sense of safety—and use new teaching practices over time (Wanless, Rimm-Kaufman, Abry, Patton, & Larson, 2015). This line of study suggests social-emotional skills may be a malleable precursor to emotional safety that may deserve more focus during preservice teachers' higher education.

School climate, however, may influence teachers' sense of safety, above and beyond any individual factors. In fact, two studies found that when the school climate was more authoritative, meaning more structured and supportive, teachers reported less student aggressive behavior directed at them and less distress at work (Berg & Cornell, 2016; Gregory, Cornell, & Fan, 2012). It is likely that when teachers, like students, feel their schools provide them with a structured and supportive climate that can be trusted, they feel more psychologically safe, and thus more able to engage in working to improve and develop their teaching practices (Wanless & Domitrovich, 2015). Cultivating a climate for safety that rests on trust may be one way to increase physical and emotional safety for students and adults, alike.

School Climate as a Foundation for Safety

There is abundant evidence that school climate is a necessary foundation for school safety. Students have better social and emotional adjustment in schools with a positive school climate, and they report less bullying, fighting, and other forms of peer aggression (Bradshaw, Koth, Thornton, & Leaf, 2009; Gage, Larson, Sugai, & Chafouleas, 2016; Gottfredson, Gottfredson, Payne, & Gottfredson, 2005; Gregory, Cornell, Fan, Sheras, Shih, & Huang, 2010; Thapa, Cohen, Guffey, & Higgins-D'Alessandro, 2013). School-based programs to promote social-emotional competence have beneficial effects on many aspects of student adjustment, from academic motivation to prosocial behavior (Domitrovich, Durlak, Staley, & Weissberg, 2017).

The voluminous research on the benefits of a positive school climate has made it a national priority to assess school climate and find ways to improve it. The 2015 Every Student Succeeds Act (ESSA, Public Law 114-95) encourages schools to measure "school climate and safety" as a nonacademic indicator of school quality or student success. However, the definition of school climate is excessively inclusive. A review of school climate research found that definitions of school climate "encompass just about every feature of the school environment that impacts cognitive, behavioral, and psychological development" (Wang & Degol, 2016, p. 3). The U.S. Department of Education (2013, p. 2) described school climate as "a multi-faceted concept that describes the extent to which a school community creates and maintains a safe school campus, a supportive academic, disciplinary, and physical environment, and respectful, trusting, and caring relationships throughout the school community." Although broad definitions of school climate are comprehensive, they make it difficult for educators to identify the key school conditions that should be targets for improvement.

Authoritative School Climate Model

The authoritative school climate model provides a conceptual framework that can help to identify key features of school climate and their association with positive student outcomes. This model is derived from child development research on effective parenting by Baumrind (1968) and others (Larzelere, Morris, & Harrist, 2013). This research has found that authoritative parents provide a combination of high expectations (also called "demandingness") and emotional warmth or support (also called "responsiveness") for their children. Parents are less effective when they have high expectations but are not supportive (authoritarian), emotionally supportive but lacking high expectations (permissive), or lacking in both expectations and support (disengaged or neglectful). Although the concept of an authoritative school climate is not fully parallel to authoritative parenting, there are some useful similarities that can guide efforts to improve school climate.

Authoritative school climate theory posits that there are two key domains that promote a safe and supportive environment conducive to learning (Gill, Ashton, & Algina, 2004; Gregory & Cornell, 2009; Pellerin, 2005). The first domain is high disciplinary and academic expectations for students, which has been described as the demandingness or *structure* of the school climate. Do teachers and other school staff members enforce discipline in a strict but fair manner, and do they have high academic expectations for all students to learn and achieve? The second domain concerns the responsiveness or *supportiveness* of teacher-student relationships. Do teachers and other school staff members interact with students in a respectful, caring, and helpful manner? Although these two domains do not encompass all aspects of school climate, there is considerable evidence that they are consistently linked to student engagement, academic achievement, and positive behavior.

Many studies support the idea that school structure and support deserve a central role in research on school climate. For example, Johnson's (2009) review of 25 studies concluded that "schools with less violence tend to have students who are aware of school rules and believe they are fair" and "have positive relationships with their teachers" (p. 451). Studies using nationally representative samples found that schools using authoritative practices—a combination of high expectations (structure or demandingness) and high support (also termed responsiveness)—have higher levels of student engagement, less truancy, and fewer dropouts, than schools using an authoritarian approach (Gill, Ashton, & Algina, 2004; Pellerin, 2005).

Cornell and colleagues developed the Authoritative School Climate Survey to measure school climate and safety (Cornell et al., 2016). There is a body of peer-reviewed research supporting the reliability and validity of both student and staff versions of this survey (Huang & Cornell, 2016; Huang et al., 2015; Konold & Cornell, 2015a, 2015b; Konold et al., 2014; Konold et al., 2016), and they are listed as vetted surveys in the federal compendium of school climate measures (National Center on Safe Supportive Learning Environments, 2016).

Using the Authoritative School Climate Survey, three studies found that an authoritative school climate (characterized by high scores on scales measuring structure and support) was associated with positive student behavioral adjustment. A middle school study found that higher disciplinary structure and student support were associated with lower levels of the prevalence of teasing and bullying, as well as fewer self-reports of being victimized in general (Cornell, Shukla, & Konold, 2015). A second study of high school students found that schools with an authoritative school climate had lower levels of student-reported alcohol and marijuana use; bullying, fighting, and weapon carrying at school; interest in gang membership; and suicidal thoughts and behavior (Cornell & Huang, 2016). A third study reported that teachers felt safer and experienced lower levels of student hostility and aggression in authoritative climate schools (Berg & Cornell, 2016). These findings were found across statewide samples of schools and were not attributable to student demographic variables of gender, race, grade, or parent education level; nor were they attributable to school demographics of enrollment size, racial or ethnic minority composition, or percentage of low-income students.

Other studies with the Authoritative School Climate Survey found that higher disciplinary structure and student support were associated with positive academic outcomes, including higher student engagement in school, higher course grades, and higher educational aspirations in both middle school and high school samples (Cornell, Shukla, & Konold, 2016). Studies also found that an authoritative climate was associated with higher grades for students not living with their parents (Huang, Eklund, & Cornell, 2016), and lower high school dropout rates (Jia, Konold, & Cornell, 2016).

Creating Physically and Emotionally Safe Schools

How can a school cultivate a safe school climate and ultimately increase safety? Physical and emotional safety are both critical components of the climate, and, in both cases, schools must attend to perceived threats and overt threats to students' and teachers' sense of safety. First, we offer recommendations for physical safety. One promising strategy to prevent school shootings and other forms of violence is the use of multidisciplinary threat assessment teams to help students resolve conflicts and problems before they escalate into violence (Borum et al., 2010). A threat assessment team usually consists of a school administrator, law enforcement officer, and one or more mental health professionals such as a school psychologist, counselor, and social worker (Cornell & Sheras, 2006). Threat assessment is a systematic approach to distinguish serious threats, defined as behaviors or communications in which a person poses a threat of violence, from cases in which the threat is not serious. Unlike a zero-tolerance approach that applies a strict and punitive consequence to all cases, threat assessment is a more flexible and supportive process. The goal of threat assessment is to prevent violence by planning a response based on the seriousness of the threat and the unique risk and protective factors associated with the case. In many cases, a student's threat is an indication of frustration or conflict that is amenable to resolution.

A series of controlled studies found that schools using the Virginia Student Threat Assessment Guidelines had lower suspension rates and less bullying, and that their students perceived the school climate as safer and more supportive climates than schools not using this approach (Cornell, Allen, & Fan, 2012; Cornell, Gregory, & Fan, 2011; Nekvasil & Cornell, 2015). A study of 1,865 threat assessment cases (using a variety of threat assessment models) in Virginia public schools found that nearly all threats were resolved without a physical act of violence (Cornell, Maeng, et al., in press) and that there were no disparities between black, Hispanic, and white students in disciplinary or legal consequences (Cornell, Maeng, Huang, Shukla, & Konold, in press).

Programs and Strategies for Increasing Students' Sense of Safety

Many popular school improvement programs show promise for increasing students' sense of safety and have goals that are consistent with the authoritative school climate model. For example, Schoolwide Positive Behavioral Interventions and Supports (SW-PBIS) is a school climate transformation program designed to teach and reinforce positive behaviors in order to reduce discipline problems and support student learning needs (OSEP Technical Assistance Center on Positive Behavioral Interventions and Supports, 2017). Restorative Justice (also called Restorative Discipline) is another approach increasingly used in schools to replace traditional punitive disciplinary methods (Wachtel, Costello, & Wachtel, 2009). Restorative practices are intended to help a student recognize and take responsibility for the harm caused by his or her misbehavior and to place an emphasis on fairness and mutual respect in relationships. Both authoritative school climate theory and restorative discipline stress that students will be most responsive to school authorities when they feel respected and supported, and perceive that school rules are fair and equitable (Gregory, Clawson, Davis, & Gerewitz., 2016). Schoolwide programs are helpful in creating an organized and concerted change in school discipline, but the creation of an authoritative school climate fundamentally rests on individual interactions and relationships.

A positive school climate is the culmination of many daily interactions between the adults at school, their students, and families. To have positive daily interactions, teachers should be present, aware, and able to check their own implicit and explicit biases. A case example that illustrates this point is from a 5th year teacher who had siblings in the classroom that were arguing and starting to fight. Another student, Jamilla, was often at the root of difficult situations, and she instigated the argument by saying that one sister was speaking negatively about the other sister's mother. At the end of the day, the teacher decided to visit Jamilla's home, where she lived with her grandmother. Approaching the house, the teacher realized that he had strong biases about this family. He expected the house to be unkempt and the grandmother to be too strict and uncaring, but found that neither was the case. In retrospect, the teacher had recalled training about the importance of home visits, but did not realize until this situation how important they really were. In that walk, up to the front door, he became aware of his biases and shifted his attitude toward Jamilla and her family. During the conversation, the teacher learned that Jamilla's mother was dealing with a difficult situation that was traumatizing for the entire family. He also learned that despite her propensity to disrupt the classroom, Jamilla was a very loving granddaughter. This visit led to a greater appreciation for Jamilla's context and her strengths detailed by her grandmother. In this case, the intervention was a home visit that led to the teacher's deep self-reflection, and ultimately a more authentic and supportive teacher-student relationship.

Example programs that may promote a sense of safety are also emerging with younger children, such as one program called Banking Time, which trains preschool teachers to strengthen relationships with the children in their class that are particularly challenging (i.e., not engaged in classroom activities). In a randomized controlled trial of this prevention program, Hatfield and her colleagues found that when children experienced warmer relationships with their teachers, they showed healthier stress responses, laying the foundation for a greater ability to manage moments when they feel unsafe (Hatfield & Williford, 2017). It is worth noting that the successful implementation of this approach depends in part on the teachers' own social-emotional skills, which we have mentioned as an important factor in cultivating teachers' feeling of safety. Not only can social-emotional skills help teachers to create safe classroom climates, they can also help teachers regulate their emotions in the face of potentially threatening situations. This understudied role of teacher social-emotional skills suggests that more preservice teacher education programs may want to directly teach social-emotional skills. Unfortunately, higher education institutions rarely make social-emotional learning a priority (Schonert-Reichl, Kitil, & Hanson-Peterson, 2017).

Programs for Increasing Teachers' Sense of Safety

In general, programs designed to support teachers' sense of safety aim to decrease stress and improve interactions with students and colleagues (Jennings, Minnici, & Yoder, this volume). These efforts tend to be relatively new and are in a more preliminary stage of establishing evidence for their utility. Teacher programs are developing for inservice and preservice teachers. Three inservice examples that have been the focus of research are Cultivating Awareness and Resilience in Educators (CARE; Jennings, Frank, Snowberg, Coccia, & Greenberg, 2013), Mindfulness Training (Roeser et al., 2013), and Leading Together (Rimm-Kaufman, Leis, & Paxton, 2014). Notably, all three of these programs incorporate mindfulness practices for teachers. In other words, part of their theory of change suggests that when teachers are able to intentionally focus their attention, without judgment, they are more likely to be aware of their own signals of unsafety as well as cues that their students are feeling unsafe, and be able to address them more clearly without being clouded by impulsive and judgmental reactions. In previous research on one of these programs, teachers across grade levels that were randomly assigned to participate in CARE showed higher well-being and efficacy, and decreased stress and burnout, when compared to control group peers (Jennings, Frank, Snowberg, Coccia, & Greenberg, 2013). The Mindfulness Training program similarly randomized teachers from across grades and found that those who received training had greater attention, working memory, and self-compassion, along with lower stress and burnout, than their counterparts in the control group (Roeser et al., 2013). Although these programs did not directly aim to increase a sense of safety, it is consistent with the overall benefits that teachers reported. Further research is needed to see how these kinds of programs could improve teachers' sense of physical and emotional safety at school.

Leading Together takes a somewhat different approach than the previously described programs by improving the adult climate within the school as a whole. After principals and one other adult attend the initial training with their counterparts from other schools, they return to their school and focus on sharing and implementing new community building practices with others. The initial training involves mindfulness and other practices, and an initial evaluation with pre-post comparisons showed increases in teacher self-efficacy and trust (Rimm-Kaufman, Leis, & Paxton, 2014). Similar to research on authoritative school climate, it is possible that the adult climate could benefit from programs such as Leading Together, and cultivate a sense of safety that permeates the school.

These programs align with suggestions from the field that administrators should also attend to their own biases and social-emotional skills. As one administrator described, this role requires abilities to interact with adults who have a wide range of opinions and backgrounds. These adults, teachers in particular, are also often facing a high level of stress and burnout that decreases their sense of safety and leaves them less open to suggestions from administrators and mentors. When teachers say, "I've told them that but they don't get it," or, "I've done everything I can," their comments may initially sound like they are driven by high expectations, but can often be unintentionally filled with implicit biases. They have specific belief systems that they may or may not be aware of, that are shaping their interpretations of student behavior and choices about what is needed next. Facing those beliefs and biases requires self-work, and self-work requires vulnerability. As an administrator, it is necessary to create safe spaces for teachers so they can feel free to engage in this work. In many cases, teachers may have gone through trauma themselves and may be unaware of how student behaviors may trigger these memories. In one case, a teacher who was being abused at home, was in the hallway between classes, talking to a girl who was struggling with a situation with her boyfriend. Although the teacher's intention was to be supportive, the situation had similarities with the teacher's own relationship challenges, and that made it more difficult for her to respond empathetically. When the girl confided in the teacher that her boyfriend was being physically abusive, the teacher asked the girl, "What did you do to make that boy hit you?" Upon further conversation with her administrator, the teacher began to see that her accusatory response was partially driven by her ongoing experience in an abusive relationship. In this example, the administrator had to balance the need to be firm and fair with this teacher, with the need to support the teacher's own reflection and development. By modeling a certain level of vulnerability and self-reflection, administrators may be able to build trust with their teachers, so they can begin to understand the triggers, scripts, and experiences that drive their teachers' interactions with students.

There are also beginning efforts to build related approaches into preservice teacher education programs in higher education institutions. There are many programs that emphasize social-emotional skill development for future students and preservice teachers, and incorporate mindfulness and social justice or restorative practices. Evaluation efforts are in their early stages, but the theoretical underpinnings of these forward-thinking programs often mimic the emphasis on a trusting climate, individual social-emotional competence, and mindfulness practices.

Conclusion

Physical and emotional safety are necessary for both students and teachers to function effectively at school. Evidence-based efforts are emerging to support specific instructional and relationship strategies to cultivate safety. These may be particularly useful when specific students or teachers experience a particular type of threat or are responding fearfully based on their background or previous experiences. In addition, a more general and universal focus on school climate and the social-emotional skills of students and teachers may create an environment where safety may flourish throughout schools, facilitating academic engagement and promoting social development.

References

American Psychological Association Zero Tolerance Task Force. (2008). Are zero tolerance policies effective in the schools? An evidentiary review and recommendations. *American Psychologist, 63*, 852–862.

Anderson, E. (2000). *Code of the street: Decency, violence, and the moral life of the inner city*. New York: W. W. Norton.

Arsten, A. F. T. (2009). Stress signaling pathways that impair prefrontal cortex structure and function. *Nature Reviews Neuroscience, 10*(6), 410–422.

Bachman, R., Randolph, A., & Brown, B. L. (2011). Predicting perceptions of fear at school and going to and from school for African American and white students: The effects of school security measures. *Youth & Society, 43*(2), 705–726.

Baumrind, D. (1968). Authoritarian vs. authoritative parental control. *Adolescence, 3*, 255–272.

Belmi, P., Barragan, R. C., Neale, M. A., & Cohen, G. L. (2015). Threats to social identity can trigger social deviance. *Personality and social psychology bulletin, 41*, 467–484.

Berg, J. K., & Cornell, D. (2016). Authoritative school climate, aggression toward teachers, and teacher distress in middle school. *School Psychology Quarterly, 31*, 122–139. doi:10.1037/spq0000132

Borum, R., Cornell, D., Modzeleski, W., & Jimerson, S. R. (2010). What can be done about school shootings?: A review of the evidence. *Educational Researcher, 39*, 27–37. doi:10.3102/0013189X09357620

Bradshaw, C. P., Koth, C. W., Thornton, L. A., & Leaf, P. J. (2009). Altering school climate through school-wide positive behavioral interventions and supports: Findings from a group-randomized effectiveness trial. *Prevention Science, 10*, 100–115.

Brouwers, A., Evers, W. J. G., & Tomic, W. (2001). Self-efficacy in eliciting social support and burn-out among secondary-school teachers. *Journal of Applied Social Psychology, 31*, 1474–1491. doi:10.1111/j.1559-1816.2001.tb02683.x

Bryk, A., & Schneider, B. (2002). *Trust in schools: A core resource for improvement.* New York: Russell Sage Foundation.

Buhs, E., Ladd, G., & Herald, S. (2006). Peer exclusion and victimization: Processes that mediate the relation between peer group rejection and children's classroom engagement and achievement? *Journal of Educational Psychology, 98*, 1–13.

Cornell, D. (2006). *School violence: Fears versus facts.* Mahwah, NJ: Lawrence Erlbaum.

Cornell, D., Allen, K., & Fan, X. (2012). A randomized controlled study of the Virginia Student Threat Assessment Guidelines in grades K–12. *School Psychology Review, 41*, 100–115.

Cornell, D., Gregory, A., & Fan, X. (2011). Reductions in long-term suspensions following adoption of the Virginia Student Threat Assessment Guidelines. *Bulletin of the National Association of Secondary School Principals, 95*, 175–194.

Cornell, D., & Huang, F. (2016). Authoritative school climate and high school student risk behavior: A cross-sectional multi-level analysis of student self-reports. *Journal of Youth and Adolescence, 45*, 2246–2259.

Cornell, D., Huang, F., Konold, T., Shukla, K., Malone, M., Datta, P., . . . Meyer, J. P. (2016). *Development of a Standard Model for School Climate and Safety Assessment: Final report.* Charlottesville, VA: Curry School of Education, University of Virginia.

Cornell, D., Maeng, J., Burnette, A. G., Jia, Y., Huang, F., Konold, T., . . . Meyer, P. (2018). Student threat assessment as a standard schools safety practice: Results from a statewide implementation study. *School Psychology Quarterly, 33*, 213–222.

Cornell, D., Maeng, J., Huang, F., Shukla, K., & Konold, T. (2018). Racial/ethnic parity in disciplinary consequences using student threat assessment. *School Psychology Review, 47*, 183–195.

Cornell, D., & Mayer, M. (2010). Why do school order and safety matter? *Educational Researcher, 39*, 7–15. doi:10.3102/0013189X09357616

Cornell, D. G., & Sheras, P. L. (2006). *Guidelines for responding to student threats of violence*. Longmont, CO: Sopris West Educational Services.

Cornell, D., Shukla, K., & Konold, T. (2015). Peer victimization and authoritative school climate: A multilevel approach. *Journal of Educational Psychology*. Advance online publication. doi:10.1037/edu0000038

Cornell, D., Shukla, K., & Konold, T. R. (2016). Authoritative school climate and student academic engagement, grades, and aspirations in middle and high schools. *AERA Open, 2*(2), 1–18.

DeBono, A., & Muraven, M. (2014). Rejection perceptions: Feeling disrespected leads to greater aggression than feeling disliked. *Journal of Experimental Social Psychology, 55*, 43–52.

Domitrovich, C. E., Durlak, J. A., Staley, K. C., & Weissberg, R. P. (2017). Social-emotional competence: An essential factor for promoting positive adjustment and reducing risk in school children. *Child Development, 88*, 408–416.

Eccles, J. S., & Roeser, R. W. (2011). Schools as developmental contexts during adolescence. *Journal of Research on Adolescence, 21*(1), 225–241.

Edmondson, A. C., & Lei, Z. (2014). Psychological safety: The history, renaissance, and future of an interpersonal construct. *Annual Review of Organizational Psychology and Organizational Behavior, 1*(1), 23–43. doi:10.1146/annurev-orgpsych-031413-091305

Espelage, D., Anderman, E. M., Brown, V. E., Jones, A., Lane, K. L., McMahon, S. D., . . . Reynolds, C. R. (2013). Understanding and preventing violence directed against teachers: Recommendations for a national research, practice, and policy agenda. *American Psychologist, 68*(2), 75–87.

Every Student Succeeds Act of 2015, Pub. L. 114-95, 129 Stat. 1802, codified as amended at 20 U.S.C. § 6301.

Flannery, D., Wester, K., & Singer, M. (2004). Impact of violence exposure at school on child mental health and violent behavior. *Journal of Community Psychology, 32*, 559–574.

Fox, N. A., & Shonkoff, J. P. (2012, February). How persistent fear and anxiety can affect young children's learning, behaviour and health. In Institute of Medicine and National Research Council (Eds.), *Social and economic costs of violence: Workshop summary* (pp. 69–83). Washington, DC: National Academies Press.

Gage, N. A., Larson, A., Sugai, G., & Chafouleas, S. M. (2016). Student perceptions of school climate as predictors of office discipline referrals. *American Educational Research Journal*. Advance online publication. doi:10.3102/0002831216637349

Gill, M. G., Ashton, P., & Algina, J. (2004). Authoritative schools: A test of a model to resolve the school effectiveness debate. *Contemporary Educational Psychology, 29*, 389–409. doi:10.1016/j.cedpsych.2003.10.002

Gottfredson, G. D., Gottfredson, D. C., Payne, A. A., & Gottfredson, N. C. (2005). School climate predictors of school disorder: Results from the National Study of Delinquency Prevention in Schools. *Journal of Research in Crime and Delinquency, 42*, 412–444.

Gregory, A., Clawson, K., Davis, A., & Gerewitz, J. (2015). The promise of restorative practices to transform teacher-student relationships and achieve equity in school discipline. *Journal of Educational and Psychological Consultation, 25*, 1–29.

Gregory, A., Clawson, K., Davis, A., & Gerewitz, J. (2016). The promise of restorative practices to transform teacher-student relationships and achieve equity in school discipline. *Journal of Educational and Psychological Consultation, 26*(4), 325–353.

Gregory, A., & Cornell, D. (2009). "Tolerating" adolescent needs: Moving beyond zero tolerance policies in high school. *Theory into Practice, 48*(2), 106–113.

Gregory, A., Cornell, D., & Fan, X. (2012). Teacher safety and authoritative school climate in high schools. *American Journal of Education, 118*, 401–425. doi:10.1086/666362

Gregory, A., Cornell, D., Fan, X., Sheras, P., Shih, T., & Huang, F. (2010). Authoritative school discipline: High school practices associated with lower student bullying and victimization. *Journal of Educational Psychology, 102*, 483–496. doi:10.1037/a0018562

Hammond, Z. (2014). *Culturally responsive teaching and the brain: Promoting authentic engagement and rigor among culturally and linguistically diverse students*. Thousand Oaks, CA: Corwin Press.

Hatfield, B. E., & Williford, A. P. (2017). Cortisol patterns for young children displaying disruptive behavior: Links to a teacher-child, relationship-focused intervention. *Prevention Science, 18*(1), 40–49.

Huang, F. L., & Cornell, D. G. (2016). Multilevel factor structure, concurrent validity, and test-retest reliability of the high school teacher version of the Authoritative School Climate Survey. *Journal of Psychoeducational Assessment, 34*, 536–549. doi:10.1177/0734282915621439

Huang, F. L., Cornell, D. G. Konold, T., Meyer, P., Lacey, A., Nekvasil, E., . . . Shukla, K. (2015). Multilevel factor structure and concurrent validity of the teacher version of the Authoritative School Climate Survey. *Journal of School Health, 85*, 843–851. doi:10.1111/josh.12340

Huang, F. L., Eklund, K., & Cornell, D. (2016). Authoritative school climate, number of parents at home, and academic achievement. *School Psychology Review*. Advance online publication. doi:10.1037/spq0000182

Jennings, P. A., Frank, J. L., Snowberg, K. E., Coccia, M. A., & Greenberg, M. T. (2013). Improving classroom learning environments by Cultivating Awareness and Resilience in Education (CARE): Results of a randomized controlled trial. *School Psychology Quarterly, 28*(4), 374–390.

Jennings, P. A., & Greenberg, M. T. (2009). The prosocial classroom: Teacher social and emotional competence in relation to student and classroom outcomes. *Review of Educational Research, 79*(1), 491–525.

Jennings, P. A., Minnici, A., & Yoder, N. (2018). Creating the working conditions to enhance teacher social and emotional well-being. In D. Osher, M. Mayer, T. Osher, R. Jagers, & K. Kendziora (Eds.), *Keeping students safe and helping them thrive: A collaborative handbook for education, mental health, child welfare, safety, and justice professionals, families, and communities* (Vol. 1, chapter 8). Santa Barbara, CA: Praeger.

Jia, Y., Konold, T., Cornell, D., & Huang, F. (2016). The impact of validity screening on associations between self-reports of bullying victimization and student outcomes. *Educational and Psychological Measurement, 45*, 2246–2259. doi:10.1007/s10964-016-0424-3

Jia, Y., Konold, T. R., & Cornell, D. (2016). Authoritative school climate and high school dropout rates. *School Psychology Quarterly, 31*(2), 289–303.

Johnson, S. L. (2009). Improving the school environment to reduce school violence: A review of the literature. *Journal of School Health, 79*, 451–465. doi:10.1111/j.1746-1561.2009.00435.x

Johnson, S. M., Kraft, M. A., & Papay, J. P. (2012). How context matters in high-need schools: The effects of teachers' working conditions on their professional satisfaction and their students' achievement. *Teachers College Record, 114*, 1–39.

Konold, T., & Cornell, D. (2015a). Measurement and structural relations of an Authoritative School Climate model: A multi-level latent variable investigation. *Journal of School Psychology, 53*, 447–461. doi:10.1016/j.jsp.2015.09.001

Konold, T., & Cornell, D. (2015b). Multilevel multitrait–multimethod latent analysis of structurally different and interchangeable raters of school climate. *Psychological Assessment, 27*, 1097–1109. doi:10.1037/pas0000098

Konold, T., Cornell, D., Huang, F., Meyer, P., Lacey, A., Nekvasil, E., . . . Shukla, K. (2014). Multi-level multi-informant structure of the Authoritative School Climate Survey. *School Psychology Quarterly, 29*, 238–255. doi:10.1037/spq0000062

Konold, T., Cornell, D., Shukla, K., & Huang, F. (2016). Racial/ethnic differences in perceptions of school climate and its association with student engagement and peer aggression. *Journal of Youth and Adolescence, 46*, 1–15.

Lacoe, J. (2016). Too scared to learn? The academic consequences of feeling unsafe in the classroom. *Urban Education*, 1–34.

Larzelere, R. E., Morris, A. S., & Harrist, A. W. (2013). *Authoritative parenting: Synthesizing nurturance and discipline for optimal child development*. Washington, DC: American Psychological Association.

Morgan, E., Salomen, N., Plotkin, M., & Cohen, R. (2014). *The school discipline consensus report: Strategies from the field to keep students engaged in school and out of the juvenile justice system.* New York: Council of State Governments Justice Center. Retrieved from http://csgjusticecenter.org/wp-content/uploads/2014/06/The_School_Discipline_Consensus_Report.pdf

Nansel, T. R., Overpeck, M. O., Pilla, R. S., Ruan, W. J., Simons-Morton, B., & Scheidt, P. (2001). Bullying behavior among US youth: Prevalence and association with psychosocial adjustment. *Journal of the American Medical Association, 285*, 2094–2100.

National Center on Safe Supportive Learning Environments. (2016). *ED School Climate Surveys.* Retrieved from https://safesupportivelearning.ed.gov/edscls

Nekvasil, E., & Cornell, D. (2015). Student threat assessment associated with positive school climate in middle schools. *Journal of Threat Assessment and Management, 2*, 98–113. doi:10.1037/tam0000038

Nekvasil, E., Cornell, D., & Huang, F. (2015). Prevalence and offense characteristics of multiple casualty homicides: Are schools at higher risk than other locations? *Psychology of Violence, 5*, 236–245. doi:10.1037/a0038967

Nishina, A., Juvonen, J., & Witkow, M. R. (2005). Sticks and stones may break my bones, but names will make me feel sick: The psychosocial, somatic, and scholastic consequences of peer harassment. *Journal of Clinical Child and Adolescent Psychology, 34*, 37–48.

OSEP Technical Assistance Center on Positive Behavioral Interventions and Supports. (2017). *Positive Behavioral Interventions & Supports* [Website]. Retrieved from http://www.pbis.org

Osher, D., & Dwyer, K. (2006). Safe, supportive, and effective schools: Promoting school success to reduce school violence. In S. R. Jimerson & M. L. Furlong (Eds.), *Handbook of school violence and school safety: From research to practice* (pp. 51–71). Mahwah, NJ: Lawrence Erlbaum.

Pellerin, L. A. (2005). Applying Baumrind's parenting typology to high schools: Toward a middle-range theory of authoritative socialization. *Social Science Research, 34*, 283–303. doi:10.1016/j.ssresearch.2004.02.003

Rimm-Kaufman, S. E., Leis, M., & Paxton, C. (2014). Innovating together to improve the adult community in schools: Results from a two-year study of the initial implementation of Leading Together. Retrieved from https://www.couragerenewal.org/PDFs/UVA_LeadingTogether_July_11_2014_Final_Full_Report.pdf

Roeser, R. W., Schonert-Reichl, K. A., Jha, A., Cullen, M., Wallace, L., Wilensky, R., . . . Harrison, J. (2013). Mindfulness training and reductions in teacher stress and burnout: Results from two randomized, waitlist-control field trials. *Journal of Educational Psychology, 105*(3), 787–804.

Schonert-Reichl, K. A., Kitil, M. J., & Hanson-Peterson, J. (2017). *To reach the students, teach the teachers: A national scan of teacher preparation and social and emotional learning.* A report prepared for the Collaborative for

Academic, Social, and Emotional Learning (CASEL). Vancouver, BC: University of British Columbia.

Schwartz, D., Gorman, A., Nakamoto, J., & Toblin, R. (2005). Victimization in the peer group and children's academic functioning. *Journal of Educational Psychology, 97*, 425–435.

Spencer, S. J., Logel, C., & Davies, P. G. (2016). Stereotype threat. *Annual Review of Psychology, 67*, 415–437.

Tanner-Smith, E. E., & Fisher, B. W. (2016). Visible school security measures and student academic performance, attendance, and postsecondary aspirations. *Journal of Youth and Adolescence, 45*, 195–210.

Thapa, A., Cohen, J., Guffey, S., & Higgins-D'Alessandro, A. (2013). A review of school climate research. *Review of Educational Research, 83*, 357–385.

U.S. Department of Justice and U.S. Department of Education. (2014). Dear colleague letter on the nondiscriminatory administration of school discipline. Retrieved from https://www2.ed.gov/about/offices/list/ocr/letters/colleague-201401-title-vi.pdf

Wachtel, T., O'Connell, T., & Wachtel, J. (2009). *The restorative practices handbook for teachers, disciplinarians and administrators*. Bethlehem, PA: International Institute of Restorative Practices.

Wang, M. T., & Degol, J. L. (2016). School climate: A review of the construct, measurement, and impact on student outcomes. *Educational Psychology Review, 28*, 315–352. doi:10.1007/s10648-015-9319-1

Wanless, S. B. (2016). The role of psychological safety in human development. *Research in Human Development, 13*(1), 6–14.

Wanless, S. B., & Domitrovich, C. E. (2015). Readiness to implement school-based social-emotional learning interventions: Using research on factors related to implementation to maximize quality. *Prevention Science, 16*(8), 1037–1043.

Wanless, S. B., Rimm-Kaufman, S. E., Abry, T., Larsen, R. A., & Patton, C. L. (2015). Engagement in training as a mechanism to understanding fidelity of implementation of the Responsive Classroom Approach. *Prevention Science, 16*(8), 1107–1116.

Wismer Fries, A. B., Ziegler, T. E., Kurian, J. R., Jacoris, S., and Pollak, S. D. (2005). Early experience in humans is associated with changes in neuropeptides critical for regulating social behavior. *Proceedings of the National Academy of Sciences USA, 102*(47), 17237–17240.

CHAPTER EIGHT

What Is School Safety?

School Safety Trends, Data, and Key Issues

Matthew J. Mayer and Thomas W. Tramaglini

School safety issues periodically receive national attention, especially connecting to tragic events such as school shootings that are often followed by expressions of public outrage and demands by political leaders for rapid and dramatic responses. These suggestions for preventing future violence are typically simplistic and not necessarily well reasoned, including zero tolerance policies linked to harsh consequences, arming school staff members, and issuing bullet-proof backpacks to students. This chapter seeks to avoid such errors by presenting a more balanced, research-based discussion of a range of complex issues that help us understand causes and consequences and inform solutions, leveraging a transdisciplinary literature base.

Preventing school violence and fostering positive youth development has received attention from multiple disciplines and is not exclusively an educational issue. Education, clinical, counseling, and school psychology, school and community level social work, juvenile justice, public health, and related areas of professional practice and research share these concerns, utilizing related methodologies, and overlapping standards for what is often called "evidence-based research" (Mayer, 2012). These disciplines have consistently maintained an overarching interest in areas such as physical and psychological safety, engagement and collaboration among key stakeholders, pathways to academic and social-emotional progress for students, and school-wide management and change approaches. These broader areas relate to a wide range of research foci, including the achievement gap, disciplinary practices, needs of economically impoverished students and their families and culturally and linguistically diverse populations, school climate, and so forth (Cornell & Mayer, 2010). An empirical integrationist approach that draws upon transdisciplinary work can inform solution paths in school safety promotion and violence prevention.

This chapter will begin exploring key areas in promoting safe schools and preventing school violence with a historical overview and summary of trend data. We next consider measurement issues, ways of considering school safety, and harmful outcomes of school violence and harassment, intimidation, and bullying. We also devote a significant portion of the chapter to consider stakeholder perspectives and institutional structures and major challenges facing school leadership, all presented as a "voices from the field" callout section within the chapter. We close the chapter with a discussion of future challenges across research, policy, and practice.

Historical Trends in School Safety

School-related violence and bullying have come front and center in media accounts since the late 1990s, particularly as they relate to events such as the horrific Columbine and Sandy Hook school shootings. But such school-based violence is not limited to the past 20–25 years. Accounts from circa 2000 BCE in Mesopotamia offer details of student violence (Midlarsky & Klain, 2005), as do reports of many periods of violent student behaviors in Europe over hundreds of years up to the 1800s (Aries, 1962), as well as accounts of student disruptions in American schools in the 1700s and 1800s (Crew & Counts, 1997). More current post-Vietnam era attention to school violence was seen in the 1978 federal study, *Violence Schools—Safe Schools: The Safe School Study Report to Congress* and the 1984 national report, *Disorder in Our Public Schools*. These publications paralleled increased public attention to school violence.

While most research has maintained that schools are generally safe places (Nevasil, Cornell, & Huang, 2015), and the chances of a school shooting taking place at a particular school are exceedingly remote (Borum, Cornell, Modzeleski, & Jimerson, 2010), data from recent decades demonstrate that serious concerns have existed, despite recent improvements in some areas of concern. For the most part, there have been major declines in measures of school-related violent victimization from 1992 to 2004, less dramatic reductions from 2004 to 2010, with greater variability from 2010 to 2014 (see figure 8.1; Zhang, Musu-Gillette, & Oudekerk, 2016). Bullying has remained a serious problem, with recent survey data demonstrating fluctuations.

For example, 2013 Youth Risk Behavior Survey (YRBS) data from the Centers for Disease Control (CDC) indicated that 14.8% of students reported being cyberbullied during the previous year with 21% for females (25.2% white; 17.1% Hispanic, 10.5% black) compared to 8.5% for males (8.7% white; 8.3% Hispanic, 6.9% black). Ninth grade students were electronically bullied at higher rates compared to twelfth-graders (16.1% vs. 13.5%). However, a meta-analysis (Kowalski, Giumetti, Schroeder, & Lattanner, 2014) presented contrasting data, indicating that about 75% of students have experienced some form of cyberbullying.

YRBS data from 2013 also presented bullying data, where 19.6% of 9th to 12th grade students reported they had been bullied at school during the previous year (23.7% female; 15.6% male), with comparable gender differences for rates across racial and ethnic groups and overall rates of 21.8%, 12.7%, and 17.8% for white, black, and Hispanic students, respectively. National crime victimization (NCVS) data showed that among students ages 12–18, 22% indicated they had been bullied during the preceding school year, compared to 28% in 2005, 2009, and 2011, and 32% in 2007 (Zhang, Musu-Gillette, & Oudekerk, 2016). Alternatively, the Health Behaviors in School-Age Children Survey (HBSC), a World Health Organization (WHO) cross-national survey, reported that 12%–15% of 11- to 13-year-old students had experienced bullying during the 2009–2010 school year (Currie et al., 2012), with boys showing somewhat higher levels of victimization than girls and younger students reporting more bullying victimization than older students. U.S. data was not available as part of the more recent 2013–2014 administration HBSC survey.

The general picture is somewhat different for data on carrying a weapon to school and having been threatened or injured with a weapon at school, compared to general trends in violent victimization at and away from school. There was a reduction in student reports of having carried a weapon in school at least one day in the past month from 11.8% 1993 to 6.1% in 2003, but an increase to 6.5% in 2005, and a decline to 5.2% in 2013. In contrast, reports from high school students of having been in a fight in school or threatened or injured with a weapon at school fluctuated, but did not decline greatly during the period, 1993–2013.

The overall picture can change as a function of how data is collected. Time references in survey questions can produce varying data time depending on whether students are reporting bullying experiences at school from the past few months or the entire school year (Gladden, Vivolo-Kantor, Hamburger, & Lumpkin, 2014). Overall, the longer-term trend data suggest that there have been great declines in many measures of school violence and disruption, but that serious problems remain.

Measuring School Violence, Disruption, and Bullying

School safety data collection and analysis employs multiple sources and methods, such as national-level victimization, behavior, and attitude or belief surveys, crime data systems (national, state, and local level), and educational record systems. Data can reflect victimization experiences through self-reports as well as officially documented arrests and convictions. Crime data from state and local law enforcement agencies such as the FBI Uniform Crime Reporting Program (UCR) may be at odds with other data sources, especially as arrest data does not necessarily equate to conviction and many crimes may go undetected (Cook & Laub, 1998). Survey data can be unreliable and inaccurate as a function of problematic sample design, lack of valid survey instruments, and respondent errors, which can reflect inaccurate recall, confusion over question meaning, and so-called telescoping effects, where respondents may incorrectly refer to a point in time earlier or later than intended by the question (Biemer, Groves, Lyberg, Mathiowetz, & Sudman, 1991). Also, surveys may vary as to their design to estimate risk factors versus providing broad estimates of population-based characteristics of interest. And surveys have been used for purposes quite distinct from those for which they were designed (Sharkey, Dowdy, Twyford, & Furlong, 2012).

Consumers of survey data should always consider that data they review in terms of point and interval estimates, as applicable. For instance, when a major federal school safety survey report indicated that 4.7% of students aged 12–18 reported avoiding places at school out of fear of attack or harm, that figure of 4.7% is not a precise measurement of how many students nationally reported such behavior, but rather, it is a probability-based estimate that is affected by multiple sources of error. Data on changes in survey-based variables over several years include interval estimates that are a function of standard error. While many take such data at face value in terms of precise point estimates, such an approach can result in grave errors. For example, an increase of 25% in national data on serious violent crime from 201,800 in 1997 to 252,700 in 1998 seems substantively significant, but is statistically nonsignificant at the .05 level due to high standard error values (Mayer & Furlong, 2010).

State-level educational systems have demonstrated problems in school safety data collection and reporting. New York underreported school violence, where close to one-third of audited schools did not report approximately 80% of violent incidents (Office of the New York State Comptroller, 2006). California ended two separate school safety data efforts due to highly variable administrative interpretations of procedures and problems with data reporting, including systemic underreporting of school violence (California Legislative

Analyst Office, 2002). There exist no official national standards for school safety data collection and recording. Procedures may vary across states with regard to handling duplicated and unduplicated (e.g., counting multiple suspensions of a particular student as one suspension) counts and reporting as a function of people versus incidents. Office disciplinary referrals have often been used as a proxy for measuring behavior related to school-based interventions, yet research has demonstrated limitations with accuracy and reliability for this approach (Morrison, Peterson, O'Farrell, & Redding, 2004).

Other factors that can impact data analysis include differing definitions of observed behavior and victimization experiences, collecting information on perpetrators versus victims, different approaches to counting events, and time windows associated with specific data collection foci (Mayer & Leone, 2007; Reiss & Roth, 1993). Variation in reported data on bullying and cyberbullying can be linked in part to varying definitions and survey question construction. For instance, Swearer, Siebecker, Johnsen-Frerichs, and Wang (2010) found differences in reported bullying across several major surveys and other forms of data collection ranging from 13% to 75%. While the widely used definition of bullying has included three attributes—(a) unwanted, intentional aggressive behavior, (b) that involves a real or perceived power imbalance, and (c) that is often repeated over time (Olweus, 1993)—major portions of research on bullying-related processes as well as epidemiological investigations have employed a variety of respondent prompts and definitions (American Educational Research Association, 2013). Different dimensions of aggression and school-related victimization have been conflated with what has historically been labeled bullying across many investigations. The American Educational Research Association Task Force on Bullying (2013) recommended that research examine multiple forms of victimization and bullying simultaneously, as distinctions between the two remain unclear.

Considering School Safety and Related Harm

School violence and disruption can be considered based on reports of problem behaviors at school that are commonly reported, such as theft, bullying, and fighting, as well as school programs designed to address at-risk segments of the school population (e.g., Positive Behavioral Supports), but also through data on school climate. While periodic media coverage of extreme forms of violence at schools (e.g., shootings) may lead the public to believe schools are unsafe, national level data make it clear that schools are quite safe, as compared to other places in the local school environment. School violence and disruption can be understood by considering some of the most common forms of student behaviors of concern. As a group, bullying, low-level aggression and intimidation, incivility, and theft represent the clear majority of regular behavioral problems at school. Bullying has been the primary focus of concern in many locales, where theft and incivility in general have received less attention.

Negative Effects of School Violence and Bullying

Research across related disciplines has found multiple forms of shorter- and longer-term negative effects on young people as a result of school violence and bullying or cyberbullying victimization. These include, but are not limited to: reduced investment and engagement in school activities, attention problems, reduced motivation, cognitive processing problems, school avoidance, difficulties with having socially appropriate friendships, social exclusion and loneliness, reduced self-esteem, elevated anxiety, and increased risk of depression (Buhs, Ladd, & Herald, 2006; Delaney-Black et al., 2002; Flannery, Wester, & Singer, 2004; Glew, Fan, Katon, Rivara, & Kernic, 2005; Hanish & Guerra, 2002; Ladd, 2003; Margolin & Gordis, 2000; Nansel et al., 2001; Nishina, Juvonen, & Witkow, 2005; Schwartz, Gorman, Nakamoto, & Toblin, 2005; Thomas, Bierman, & Conduct Problems Prevention Research Group, 2006). These problem areas are not necessarily singular in causal linkages, and more research needs to be done to better explicate these areas, especially where multiple related harmful interactive trajectories are implicated.

Media has periodically devoted intensive coverage to school shootings, with much less attention to day-to-day incivility in schools. Yet recent research has demonstrated harmful effects of such "low-level aggression," which can also include bullying (Arseneault et al., 2006; Ladd, 2003; Nansel et al., 2001). Increases in aggression by victims, lower self-expectations for the future, and feelings of being unsafe at school are among the more common negative outcomes (Boxer, Edwards-Leeper, Goldstein, Musher-Eizenman, & Dubow, 2003; Thomas et al., 2006). A sense of connectedness, school climate, and incivility-related experiences all moderated students' perceptions of a safe environment at school (Skiba et al., 2004). A structural equation modeling analysis of national-level victimization report data determined that measurements of incivility accounted for about double the influence on students' anxiety, fear, and avoidant behaviors, when compared to an alternate model lacking the incivility data, but with measures of gang, drug, theft, and personal violence activity to represent school disorder (Mayer, 2010).

Multiple forms of psychological difficulties and social interaction problems have been associated with experiences as a bullying victim, bully, or both, including experiencing electronic forms of bullying, where there may also be increased risk of suicidal ideation or suicidal attempts (Hinduja & Patchin, 2010; Tokunaga, 2010). Victims of bullying have demonstrated elevated levels of anxiety, social adjustment problems, depression, compared to students more generally, where certain difficulties may persist into the adult years (Carlisle & Rofes, 2007; Espelage, Low, & De La Rue, 2012; Gini & Pozzoli, 2009; Ttofi, Farrington, Lösel, & Loeber, 2011). High schools with relatively high rates of bullying tend to have reduced engagement in school activities, reduced scores on standardized tests, and lower graduation rates, compared to high schools overall (Cornell, Gregory, Huang, & Fan, 2013; Juvonen, Wang, & Espinoza, 2011).

Violence Involving Adults in Schools

Teachers and other school-based professionals have regularly experienced violence for decades, yet this topic has received relatively little attention compared to student violence and bullying (Cornell & Mayer, 2010; Robers et al., 2015). Adults in schools may experience physical violence, threats, property damage, and theft. Violent victimization of adults may occur at the hands of students or other adults in the school. Violence against teachers has been associated with multiple areas of psychosocial problems, as well as poor job performance (Espelage et al., 2013; Wilson, Douglas, & Lyon, 2011).

A federal Schools and Staffing Survey (SASS) for the 2011–2012 school year found that 9% of teachers reported having been threatened with injury by a student and 5% reported having been physically attacked, figures higher than the two previous surveys, going back to 2003 (Musu-Gillette, Zhang, Wang, Zhang, & Oudekerk, 2017). The 5% report of physical attacks was the highest for SASS data since the 1980s (Robers, Zhang, Morgan, & Musu-Gillette, 2015). While there were no gender-based differences of rates of reported threats in that 2011–2012 SASS data, 6% of female teachers and 4% of male teachers reported physical attacks. Fourteen percent of black teachers reported having been threatened with injury compared to 9% of white teachers, with physical attack reported at double the rate for black teachers compared to Hispanic teachers, and elementary teachers reporting physical attacks at higher rates than secondary teachers (8% versus 3%) (Robers et al., 2015). Trend data from the early 1990s shows that threats of injury to teachers were highest around 1993, reaching a low around 2003, and climbing slightly since then. Rates of physical attacks on teachers declined somewhat from 1993 to 2003 and later surpassed 1993 levels by 2010 and beyond.

Some aspects of teacher victimization at schools have been linked to greater disorganization in a school, problems with supportive relationships among adults working in schools, overcrowding, and a generally negative school climate, resulting in increased reports of threats of harm and physical attacks on teachers (Espelage et al., 2013; Gregory, Cornell, & Fan, 2012). In contrast, well-organized, efficiently run schools with more positive climates and greater support from school administration and positive relationships among adults in the schools experienced fewer problems. Gregory, Cornell, and Fan (2012) analyzed survey data from 280 high schools in Virginia, finding that both school structure and supports for students and teachers were cumulative in their contributions to reducing teacher victimization, and support systems had a greater effect, compared to school structure in preventing such problem behaviors.

In sum, violence directed at teachers and other adults working in schools remains a serious problem, with some data showing deterioration in recent years. Further research is needed to help determine factors contributing to these increases, especially with physical attacks on teachers. Federal, state, and local education leaders can benefit from implementing preventative approaches as outlined by Espelage and colleagues (2013).

Stakeholder Perspectives
Voices from the Field
Dr. Thomas W. Tramaglini, Superintendent, Kenilworth Public Schools, New Jersey

Safety: The Reality of Being a School Leader in the 21st Century

Regardless of the grade levels, urbanicity, poverty level, or size, school leaders generally understand the influence that school safety can have on the overall success of students. From planning a coordinated morning bus arrival to employment of a master schedule, safety is an underpinning of schooling that directly or indirectly can affect how students live and learn in schools each day. Also, leaders who plan for safety also know that there is no perfect plan and that school environments are never simple and predictable. That said, leaders must use what is known from evidenced-based research as a tool for achieving positive student outcomes.

School Safety: An Important Priority for School Leaders

In 1999, the massacre at Columbine High School in Littleton, Colorado, demonstrated how vulnerable schools were to shootings and violence. Columbine began a movement that shifted how schools kept students safe. Subsequent responses from schools and communities after Columbine have included frequent lock-down and evacuation drills, high-tech camera systems, as well as common language/communication systems. Today these actions are commonplace in schools. Schools should be safe places for students to learn and teachers to teach (Elliot, Hamburg, & Williams, 1998; Tramaglini, 2010) and schools today go to enormous lengths to make this happen. However, since Columbine, events like the Sandy Hook massacre still demonstrate that regardless of extensive prevention efforts, schools are still vulnerable places where safety remains of utmost importance. When media all around the world covered Columbine, questions surrounding why and how the event occurred. While not new to school communities, topics such as student mental health and behavior became amplified in these conversations. Not only did schools seek to better understand why events such as Columbine occur, but similar events in places like Red Lake, Minnesota, Virginia Tech, and Sandy Hook, Connecticut, remind us that school safety is never perfect and that schools, policy makers, and school leaders must continually focus on school safety in its entirety.

Regardless of the school, it's an expectation of all parents and community members that when their children go to school each day, their schools are safe. School leaders must not only understand that they must lead proactive efforts to protect students from outside predators and dangers, they must lead a healthy and safe environment inside their schools. School leaders must harness the expertise of their mental health staff, teachers, paraprofessionals, and police so that internal systems can guarantee that their schools are safe. Of course, this is easier said than done. However, failure of school leaders to prioritize school safety could have detrimental effects both in the short term and the long term.

Safety Systems: A Learning Tool That Needs Learning

School safety is important to various aspects of student learning as demonstrated through empirical research (Cornell & Mayer, 2010; Elliot, Hamburg, & Williams, 1998; Skiba, Simmons, Peterson & Forde, 2006; Tramaglini, 2010). However, some research suggests that some school leaders do not focus on school safety as a vehicle for influencing student learning (Carr, 2006). Notwithstanding the reality that some school leaders would rather focus on the technical aspects of student learning (e.g., differentiated instruction, effective questioning), there is growing support for understanding and using school safety as an important contributor to student learning. For instance, Association for Supervision and Curriculum Development (ASCD), one of the largest and most impactful organizations on the professional development of educators has focused on safety and health as part of their Whole Child platform and the U.S. Department of Education (USDE) has consistently included school climate and safety as part of its recent school improvement frameworks. Such initiatives should serve as a calling to leaders that school safety is important and should be a priority.

One perspective from the field is that many school leaders, while dynamic in their pedagogical or curriculum skills, are not equipped with the tools to become effective ambassadors of school safety in their schools. A good example of this issue is highlighted in New Jersey. The state has focused on educator effectiveness and accountability through legislation (Teach NJ) and administration of the code (Achieve NJ). Both initiatives strongly embrace academic achievement without having accountability for safety in any way. Furthermore, most institutes of higher education (IHE) in the state of New Jersey lack courses that highlight or teach school safety or security. Importantly, IHEs have not led in this area because the state's certification requirements do not include such course requirements other than the typical required training in areas such as harassment, intimidation, and bullying. Such training can be helpful, but leaders are expected to be "shovel ready" on day one with their ability to foster safe learning environments.

Quarterbacking School Safety

Clearly, with the importance that school safety holds with regards to educational outcomes, leaders who do not have the faculties or ability to set organizational conditions that target student learning by understanding the importance of such variables as student behavior, bullying, and harassment will not be proactive thinkers or doers in shaping safe educational contexts. Safety is an important condition for learning (Cornell & Mayer, 2010; Elliot, Hamburg, & Williams, 1998), and school leaders need to understand that quarterbacking safety can have positive or negative results. For instance, some studies suggest that some techniques such as "zero tolerance" or fortifying the building's defenses (e.g., cameras, surveillance, metal detectors) can lead to negative impacts on students and learning environments (Hankin, Hertz, and Simon, 2011; Mayer & Leone, 1999; Peterson & Skiba, 2001). Regardless, school leaders should have a broad base of understanding of what positively and negatively influences school safety and how to use that knowledge effectively.

School leadership is not paint by number and neither is the design of a safe learning environment. Each school is a unique place with its own environment and needs. Leaders must develop efficacy in areas such as customizing interventions and strategies to make their schools safer and leveraging opportunities for learning through safe schools, while relying on evidence-based approaches and avoiding popular fad-type initiatives.

Harassment, Intimidation, and Bullying

Perhaps one of the more prevalent issues that schools handle is in the area of harassment, intimidation, and bullying (HIB). There have been several high-profile HIB cases but one of the most prevalent cases that had an enormous impact on schools was the suicide of Tyler Clementi in 2010, a student at Rutgers, The State University of New Jersey. Tyler committed suicide after being victimized by cyberbullying and humiliation. Following this horrible incident, states and schools around the nation examined their HIB policies and practices, leading to further work on state laws and reforms in schools throughout the nation. Furthermore, the literature also suggests that issues such as HIB can negatively influence student learning and achievement (Swearer, Peugh, Espelage, Siebecker, Kingsbury, & Bevins, 2006).

One of the more important issues relating to HIB was the mechanisms of reporting HIB incidents and whether or not school employees were doing what they could so HIB incidents were eradicated before they rose to the level where students were being negatively affected, even to the level of suicide. The literature suggests that schools and communities can be successful if they are proactive in their efforts to stop such issues from growing (Catalano, Arthur, Hawkins, Berglund, & Olson, 1998; Sameroff, 2000; Twemlow & Sacco, 2012). However, before the Clementi issue, the mechanisms for identifying HIB and collecting such data were not accurate, and in some cases, ineffective. For instance, Tramaglini (2010) found that data collected yearly for accountability by the New Jersey Department of Education using the Electronic Violence and Vandalism Reporting System (EVVRS) did not adequately satisfy minimum statistical parameters, which would suggest that these self-reported data were probably not sufficient to support administrative decision-making or determine whether or not schools actually had issues requiring attention. Specifically, the average HIB incidents reported on average in lower socioeconomic status high schools in New Jersey was less than one per year. Common sense would suggest that this is inaccurate, connecting to under-reporting by school officials. This was one of the major issues underscored by the Clementi death.

New Jersey today has one of the most aggressive and tough HIB laws in the nation. School employees are now required and held accountable for making sure that HIB code and procedures are followed. Schools have exhaustive HIB protocols as well as specialists trained in each school. School leaders must become resident experts in this area as they are accountable and even liable to criminal charges if they do not follow procedures to ensure that HIB protocols are followed. Students deserve to have a safe and supportive learning environment. School leaders are the trustees to safe schools and HIB is a most important topic which failure to address issues can lead to horrible outcomes for students. Harnessing what research and best practice suggests works can promote learning environments that are most positive for students.

Institutional Structures and Major Challenges Facing School Leadership

Safety in the 21st Century Is Different

Regardless of the context or situation, school leaders must ensure that their schools are safe. When a child comes to school, school personnel, parents, and communities must be responsible to implement policies and procedures that are grounded in sound methodological research. However, easier said than done, school safety is never simple because schools are complex and dynamic learning environments where change is always a constant. The world is much different in the 21st century, and we must be focused on being proactive so that schools are safe, the teachers can teach, and the students can learn.

Need to Keep Focus on Safety

Although school leaders and standards for leadership that schools aspire to Interstate School Leaders Licensure Consortium (ISLLC) underscore the importance of safety in schools, accountability in schools is primarily driven by student achievement on standardized assessments. While the recent reauthorization of the No Child Left Behind Act of 2001 named the Every Student Succeeds Act (ESSA) allows for the incorporation of actions such as the addition of safety into school accountability metrics, overwhelmingly there are few accountability measures that encourage schools to address school safety first outside of the required HIB laws. As accountability might be driven by student achievement, it's imperative that schools and school leaders should not only have an understanding on how safe and healthy their schools are, but they should have accountability measures that provide for keeping schools safe and including programs and stopgaps to ensure safety.

School Funding and Safety

Keeping schools safe can get very costly. However, if schools are going to remain safe and lever safety as an underpinning of a successful education, they must prioritize their needs as budgetary expenditures. This has become quite a challenge to school leaders and Boards of Education because of the economy, rising operational costs, and budget reductions. As it becomes more difficult to fund safety at the local level, states and the federal government need to ensure that funding is available to keep the schools safe. There is uncertainty in funding safety and in recent years, valuable funding streams for schools (e.g., Title IV), which have fostered safe schools, have been cut and few schools have been able to keep up with the growing needs that schools have to keep the children safe.

Although just one example, Title IV provided schools at the local level funding to support programs that targeted the eradication of unsafe schools through programs or staffing. These programs were able to implement programs that were not afforded through the general funds in a local school district or hire counselors that allowed schools to target needy populations that they had in areas such as bullying prevention, social services, or case management. Without funds from the federal government many schools are forced to place their limited funding in areas such as instruction or compliance on federal curriculum or assessment initiatives such as Common Core, Partnership for Assessment of Readiness for College and Careers (PARCC), or SmarterBalance. Notwithstanding the important function that instruction has on learning, the need for services such as wraparound and school violence prevention are in many cases just as or more important than those services that positively can impact student learning (Osher, Dwyer, & Jimerson, 2006).

Not only are the programs important to have in schools, the physical plant also requires funding to ensure that security features that schools need are realized and maintained. Facilities require different components which help keep students safe. Schools need all types of physical apparatus and measures to ensure that perpetrators cannot access areas aimed for teaching and learning. For instance, before Sandy Hook occurred, few school leaders thought that their entrances should be reinforced so perpetrators cannot enter the building and open fire with guns. However, the event demonstrated that people can shoot their way into schools and into instructional areas without much resistance from the physical building. Just the reinforcement of entrances to deter events such as this cost thousands of dollars which schools do not have in their general funds. Therefore, schools and school leaders must continually focus on the importance to attain funding from policy makers through every way they can so their physical plants can remain effective in stopping unsafe acts from occurring, while taking a balanced approach involving physical security and other methods.

Social Media and Technology

Another safety challenge that school leaders must solve is the frequently growing use of social media and technology in schools. A paradox exists between the helpful influence that social media and technology can have on student learning and at the same time, the danger that it presents. For instance, school leaders embrace the important of social media tools and computer technology as an essential part of schools (Interstate School Leaders Licensure Consortium Standards) and most states have standards that require student mastery of basic technology skills associated with living in the 21st century. However, significant concerns over everyday occurrences in schools span a range of issues from cyberbullying to inappropriate communications between students. Regardless of the technology or tool, technology and its place has been cemented and nearly every student has a SmartPhone or access to computers and the Internet. Schools have to learn how to keep kids safe in their schools given the rapidly changing nature of technology in schools.

School officials and school leaders must also understand how to handle technology and social media effectively while protecting the students. Social media, television, and government reporting of school safety have opened school districts up to more scrutiny from stakeholders. School leaders are faced with immediate information being shared with parents and through social media in schools causing the need to continually focus on process versus speed. For instance, when parents learn about something that is going on in schools from their children, sometimes parents know about what is going on before school leaders do. Procedures for investigating and understanding incidents of school violence and vandalism are most important. Such procedures validate due process and best practice in being able to ensure that schools are safe. School leaders will tell you that while technology and social media are effective tools for learning, they will also tell you that technology is a prevalent area where it jeopardizes investigations and in some cases, causes unsafe situations. Researchers, schools, and their communities need to better understand how communications need refereeing or framing so that schools can keep the students and their rights protected at all times.

Future Challenges across Research, Policy, and Practice

Schools are relatively safe places in our communities, despite some media coverage suggesting otherwise. Levels of violence and disruption are generally lower now compared to the early to mid-1990s, but some indicators remain at alarming levels. Much work remains to be done, improving academic outcomes and overall school operations, while promoting positive youth development and minimizing behavior problems and violence.

While there have been some improvements in reducing school violence and disruption, bullying and other forms of conflict persist in schools at unacceptable levels. Schools are faced with continuing challenges to improve academic performance while addressing problems with violence, disruption, and bullying. It remains a point of contention the degree to which problems in schools are a reflection of more widespread social ills, and clearly, schools have taken on additional roles and responsibilities in recent decades, above and beyond the core academic mission, while access to adequate resources remains problematic.

Well-conceived and coordinated evidence-based approaches are needed, where fragmentation is reduced and broader stakeholder collaboration is facilitated. Emerging lines of research suggest that a balance of approaches that leverage lessons learned from social-emotional learning (SEL) and Positive Behavioral Supports (PBS) programs is a likely next step for schools. Yet key stakeholders in educational change may not always agree as to the optimal ways to reduce school violence, disruption, and bullying. And pressures at the national level for academic accountability may force schools to choose between allocating scarce resources for academic initiatives versus social-emotional and behaviorally oriented programming.

It is well understood that no quick and easy fixes exist for problems of violence, disruption, and bullying in schools. The connected nature of stakeholders in the educational process points to an overriding need to better promote more holistic, well-coordinated, and collaborative programs, with a shared investment in defining and answering key questions that will drive future efforts to make schools safer. Working in this direction requires an approach for linking research, policy, and practice toward those ends. Mayer and Furlong (2010) suggested the need for developing a national agenda to move the field forward in these ways. By taking a balanced approach, leveraging stakeholder buy-in at all levels, promoting effective communication, developing linked school and community programming that improves connectedness in schools and communities, while addressing core academic and social-emotional goals in schools, involving families and community leaders, and engaging in continuous evaluation of these efforts, great improvements can be realized in making schools more productive and safe for all.

References

American Educational Research Association. (2013). *Prevention of bullying in schools, colleges, and universities: Research report and recommendations.* Washington, DC: American Educational Research Association.

Aries, P. (1962). *Centuries of childhood: A social history of family life* (R. Baldick, Trans.). New York: Alfred A. Knopf.

Arseneault, L., Walsh, E., Trzesniewski, K., Newcombe, R., Caspi, A., & Moffitt, T. (2006). Bullying victimization uniquely contributes to adjustment problems in young children: A nationally representative cohort study. *Pediatrics, 118*, 130–138.

Biemer, P. P., Groves, R. M., Lyberg, L. E., Mathiowetz, N. A., & Sudman, S. (1991). *Measurement errors in surveys.* New York: Wiley.

Borum, R., Cornell, D., Modzeleski, W., & Jimerson, S. (2010). What can be done about school shootings? A review of the evidence. *Educational Researcher, 39*(1), 27–37. doi:10.3102/0013189X09357620

Boxer, P., Edwards-Leeper, L., Goldstein, S. E., Musher-Eizenman, D. R., & Dubow, E. F. (2003). Exposure to "low level" aggression in school: Effects on aggressive behavior, future expectations, and perceived safety. *Violence and Victims, 18*, 691–704.

Buhs, E., Ladd, G., & Herald, S. (2006). Peer exclusion and victimization: Processes that mediate the relation between peer group rejection and children's classroom engagement and achievement? *Journal of Educational Psychology, 98*, 1–13.

California Legislative Analyst Office. (2002). *Review of school crime reporting.* Sacramento: Author.

Carlisle, N., & Rofes, E. (2007). School bullying: Do adult survivors perceive long-term effects? *Traumatology, 13*(1), 16–26.

Carr, M. (2006). *The determinants of student achievement in Ohio's public schools.* Columbus, OH: Buckeye Institute for Public Policy Solutions.

Catalano, R. F., Arthur, M. F., Hawkins, J. D., Berglund, L., & Olson, J. J. (1998). Comprehensive community-based interventions to prevent antisocial behavior. In R. Loeber & D. P. Farrington (Eds.), *Serious and violent juvenile offenders: Risk factors and successful interventions* (pp. 248–83). Thousand Oaks, CA: Sage Publications.

Cook, P. J., & Laub, J. H. (1998). The epidemic in youth violence. In M. Tonry & M. H. Moore (Eds.), *Youth violence* (pp. 27–64). Chicago: University of Chicago Press.

Cornell, D., Gregory, A., Huang, F., & Fan, X. (2013). Perceived prevalence of teasing and bullying predicts high school dropout rates. *Journal of Educational Psychology, 105*(1), 138–149. doi:10.1037/a0030416

Cornell, D. G., & Mayer, M. J. (2010). Why does school order and safety matter? *Educational Researcher, 39*, 7–15.

Crews, G. A., & Counts, M. R. (1997). *The evolution of school disturbance in America.* Westport, CT: Praeger.

Currie, C., Zanotti, C., Morgan, A., Currie, D., de Looze, M., Roberts, C., . . . & Barnekow, V. (Eds.). (2012). *Social determinants of health and well-being among young people. Health Behaviour in School-aged Children (HBSC) study: International report from the 2009/2010 survey* (Health Policy for Children and Adolescents, No. 6). Copenhagen: WHO Regional Office for Europe.

Delaney-Black, V., Covington, C., Ondersma, S. J., Nordstrom-Klee, B., Templin, T., Ager, J., . . . Soko, R. J. (2002). Violence exposure, trauma, and IQ and/or reading deficits among urban children. *Archives of Pediatrics and Adolescent Medicine, 156*, 280–285.

Elliott, D. S., Hamburg, B., & Williams, K. R. (1998). *Violence in American schools: A new perspective.* New York: Cambridge University Press.

Espelage, D., Anderman, E. M., Brown, V. E., Jones, A., Lane, K. L., McMahon, S. D., . . . Reynolds, C. R. (2013). Understanding and preventing violence directed against teachers. *American Psychologist, 68*(2), 75–87.

Espelage, D. L., Low, S., & De La Rue, L. (2012). Relations between peer victimization subtypes, family violence, and psychological outcomes during adolescence. *Psychology of Violence, 2*(4), 313–324. doi:10.1037/a0027386

Flannery, D., Wester, K., & Singer, M. (2004). Impact of violence exposure at school on child mental health and violent behavior. *Journal of Community Psychology, 32*, 559–574.

Furlong, M. J., Sharkey, J. D., Bates, M. P., & Smith, D. C. (2004). An examination of the reliability, data screening procedures, and extreme response patterns for the Youth Risk Behavior Surveillance Survey. *Journal of School Violence, 3*(2/3), 109–130.

Gini, G., & Pozzoli, T. (2009). Association between bullying and psychosomatic problems: A meta analysis. *Pediatrics, 123*, 1059–1065.

Gladden, R. M., Vivolo-Kantor, A. M., Hamburger, M. E., & Lumpkin, C. D. (2014). *Bullying Surveillance among Youths: Uniform Definitions for Public Health and Recommended Data Elements*, Version 1.0. Atlanta: National Center for Injury Prevention and Control, Centers for Disease Control and Prevention and U.S. Department of Education.

Glew, G. M., Fan, M. Y., Katon, W., Rivara, F. P., & Kernic, M. A. (2005). Bullying, psychosocial adjustment, and academic performance in elementary school. *Archives of Pediatrics and Adolescent Medicine, 159*, 1026–1032.

Gregory, A., Cornell, D. & Fan, X. (2012). Teacher safety and authoritative school climate in high schools. *American Journal of Education, 118*, 1–25

Hanish, L. D., & Guerra, N. G. (2002). A longitudinal analysis of patterns of adjustment following peer victimization. *Development and Psychopathology, 14*, 69–89.

Hankin, A., Hertz, M., & Simon, T. (2011). Impacts of metal detector use in schools: Insights from 15 years of research. *Journal of School Health, 81*, 100–106.

Hinduja, S., & Patchin, J. (2010). Bullying, cyberbullying and suicide. *Archives of Suicidal Research, 14*, 206–221.

Juvonen, J., Wang, Y., & Espinoza, G. (2011). Bullying experiences and compromised academic performance across middle school grades. *Journal of Early Adolescence, 31*, 152–173.

Kowalski, R. M., Giumetti, G., Schroeder, A., & Lattanner, M. (2014). Bullying in the digital age: A critical review and meta-analysis of cyberbullying research among youth. *Psychological Bulletin, 140*, 1073–1137.

Ladd, G. W. (2003). Probing the adaptive significance of children's behavior and relationships in the school context: A child-by-environment perspective. In R. Kail (Ed.), *Advances in child behavior and development* (Vol. 31, pp. 43–104). New York: John Wiley.

Margolin, G., & Gordis, E. (2000). The effects of family and community violence on children. *Annual Review of Psychology, 51*, 445–479.

Mayer, M. J. (2010). Structural analysis of 1995–2005 School Crime Supplement datasets: Factors influencing students' fear, anxiety, and avoidant behaviors. *Journal of School Violence, 9*, 37–55.

Mayer, M. J. (2012). Evidence-based standards and methodological issues in school violence and related prevention research across the allied disciplines. In S. R. Jimerson, A. Nickerson, M. J. Mayer, & M. J. Furlong (Eds.), *Handbook of school violence and school safety: International research and practice* (2nd ed., pp. 227–257). New York: Routledge.

Mayer, M. J., & Furlong, M. J. (2010). How safe are our schools? *Educational Researcher, 39*, 16–26.

Mayer, M. J., & Leone, P. E. (1999). A structural analysis of school violence and disruption: Implications for creating safer schools. *Education and Treatment of Children, 22*, 333–358.

Mayer, M. J., & Leone, P. E. (2007). School violence and disruption revisited: Establishing equity and safety in the school house. *Focus on Exceptional Children, 40*(1), 1–28.

Midlarsky, E., & Klain, H. M. (2005). A history of violence in schools. In F. L. Denmark, H. H. Kraus, R. W. Wesner, E. Midlarsky, & U. P. Gielen (Eds.), *Violence in schools: Cross-national and cross-cultural perspectives* (pp. 37–57). New York: Springer.

Morrison, G. M., Peterson, R., O'Farrell, S., & Redding, M. (2004). Using office referral records in school violence research: Possibilities and limitations. *Journal of School Violence, 3*(2/3), 39–61.

Musu-Gillette, L., Zhang, A., Wang, K., Zhang, J., & Oudekerk, B. A. (2017). *Indicators of school crime and safety: 2016* (NCES 2017-064/NCJ 250650). Washington, DC: National Center for Education Statistics, U.S. Department of Education, and Bureau of Justice Statistics, Office of Justice Programs, U.S. Department of Justice.

Nansel, T. R., Overpeck, M. O., Pilla, R. S., Ruan, W. J., Simons-Morton, B., & Scheidt, P. (2001). Bullying behavior among US youth: Prevalence and association with psychosocial adjustment. *Journal of the American Medical Association, 285*, 2094–2100.

Nevasil, E. K., Cornell, D. G., & Huang, F. L. (2015). Prevalence and offense characteristics of multiple casualty homicides: Are schools at higher risk than other locations? *Psychology of Violence, 5*(3), 236–245.

Nishina, A., Juvonen, J., & Witkow, M. R. (2005). Sticks and stones may break my bones, but names will make me feel sick: The psychosocial, somatic, and scholastic consequences of peer harassment. *Journal of Clinical Child and Adolescent Psychology, 34*, 37–48.

Office of the New York State Comptroller. (2006). *Reporting of violent and disruptive incidents by public schools* (Rep. No. 2005–S–38). Albany, NY: Author.

Olweus, D. (1993). *Bullying at school.* Oxford, UK: Blackwell.

Osher, D., Dwyer, K., & Jimerson, S. (2006). Safe, supportive, and effective schools: Promoting school success to reduce school violence. In S. Jimerson & M. Furlong (Eds.), *Handbook of school violence and school safety: From research to practice* (pp. 51–71). Mahwah, NJ: Erlbaum.

Peterson, R. L., & Skiba, R. J. (2001). Creating school climates that prevent violence. *Clearing House, 74*(3), 155–163.

Reiss, A. J., & Roth, J. A. (Eds.). (1993). *Understanding and preventing violence.* Washington, DC: National Academy Press.

Robers, S., Zhang, A., Morgan, R. E., & Musu-Gillette, L. (2015). *Indicators of school crime and safety: 2014* (NCES 2015-072/NCJ 248036). Washington, DC: National Center for Education Statistics, U.S. Department of Education, and Bureau of Justice Statistics, Office of Justice Programs, U.S. Department of Justice.

Sameroff, A. J. (2000). Developmental systems and psychopathology. *Development and Psychopathology, 12*, 297–312.

Schwartz, D., Gorman, A., Nakamoto, J., & Toblin, R. (2005). Victimization in the peer group and children's academic functioning. *Journal of Educational Psychology, 97*, 425–435.

Sharkey, J. D., Dowdy, E., Twyford, J., & Furlong, M. J. (2012). An overview of measurement issues in school violence and school safety research. In S. R. Jimerson, A. B. Nickerson, M. J. Mayer, & M. J. Furlong (Eds.), *The handbook of school violence and school safety: International research and practice* (pp. 259–272). New York: Routledge.

Skiba, R., Simmons, A. B., Peterson, R., & Forde, S. (2006). The SRS safe school survey: A broader perspective on school violence prevention. In S. R. Jimerson & M. J. Furlong (Eds.), *Handbook of school violence and school safety: From research to practice* (pp. 157–170). Mahwah, NJ: Lawrence Erlbaum.

Skiba, R. J., Simmons, A. B., Peterson, R., McKelvey, J., Forde, S., & Gallini, S. (2004). Beyond guns, drugs and gangs: The structure of student perceptions of school safety. *Journal of School Violence, 3*, 149–171.

Swearer, S. M., Peugh, J., Espelage, D. L., Siebecker, A. B., Kingsbury, W. L., & Bevins, K. S. (2006). A socioecological model for bullying prevention and intervention in early adolescence: An exploratory examination. In S. R. Jimerson & M. J. Furlong (Eds.), *Handbook of school violence and school safety: From research to practice* (pp. 257–273). Mahwah, NJ: Erlbaum.

Swearer, S. M., Siebecker, A., Johnsen-Frerichs, L., & Wang, C. (2010). Assessment of bullying/victimization: The problem of comparability across studies and across methods. In S. Jimerson, S. Swearer, & D. Espelage (Eds.), *Handbook of bullying in schools: An international perspective* (pp. 305–327). New York: Routledge.

Thomas, D. E., Bierman, K. L., & Conduct Problems Prevention Research Group. (2006). The impact of classroom aggression on the development of aggressive behavior problems in children. *Development and Psychopathology, 18*, 471–487.

Tokunaga, R. S. (2010). Following you home from school: A critical review and synthesis of research on cyberbullying victimization. *Computers in Human Behavior, 26*, 277–287.

Tramaglini, T. W. (2010). *Student achievement in lower SES high schools in New Jersey* (Doctoral Dissertation). Rutgers, The State University of New Jersey, New Brunswick, NJ.

Ttofi, M. M., Farrington, D. P., Lösel, F., & Loeber, R. (2011). Do the victims of school bullies tend to become depressed later in life? A systematic review and meta-analysis of longitudinal studies. *Journal of Aggression, Conflict and Peace Research, 3*, 63–73.

Twemlow, S.W., & Sacco, F. C. (2012). *Preventing bullying and school violence*. Arlington, VA: American Psychiatric.

Wilson, C. M., Douglas, K. S., & Lyon, D. R. (2011). Violence against teachers: Prevalence and consequences. *Journal of Interpersonal Violence, 26,* 2353–2371.

Zhang, A., Musu-Gillette, L., & Oudekerk, B. A. (2016). *Indicators of school crime and safety: 2015* (NCES 2016-079/NCJ 249758). Washington, DC: National Center for Education Statistics, U.S. Department of Education, and Bureau of Justice Statistics, Office of Justice Programs, U.S. Department of Justice.

CHAPTER NINE

Understanding the Critical Links between School Safety and Mental Health

Creating Pathways toward Wellness

Amy-Jane Griffiths, Elena Liles Diamond, Jennifer Greif Green, Eui Kyung Kim, James Alsip, Kevin P. Dwyer, Matthew J. Mayer, and Michael J. Furlong

School violence has been a source of national concern since the early 1970s (Morrison, Furlong, & Morrison, 1994). With researchers from multiple professions (public health, juvenile justice, and later education) working to grasp the dynamics behind school violence and victimization, the understanding of the contributing factors has come a long way. Violence, aggressive behaviors, and resulting victimization, contribute to a hostile school climate that can negatively impact the academic performance and the mental health of students. Students exposed to such problematic environments are more likely to disengage from school (Yang, Sharkey, Reed, Chen, & Dowdy, 2018) and experience higher levels of mental health concerns (Hurd, Hussain, & Bradshaw, 2015) than those students who are not exposed to such campus conditions. Given these outcomes, the school violence field has shifted focus from aggressive, disruptive, and violent behaviors, to an expanded consideration of the psychological and developmental aspects of safety. To achieve this sense of safety, students need to not only be resilient but thrive in the face of adversity (Morrison, Furlong, & Morrison, 2000). With the growing interest in psychological well-being and helping students thrive, it is recognized that a core goal of school safety and intervention practices is to reduce negative mental health outcomes and enhance the psychological well-being and development of all students. This focus on enhancing student well-being rather than the delivery of traditional deficit-focused mental health services can be seen in various programs and initiatives that have emerged over recent years.

This chapter examines the relation between disruptive and violent behaviors that impact school safety and student mental health and well-being, as well as the contributing role of ecological factors. We begin with a brief overview of what is known about the linkage between students' school safety experiences and their mental health. The discussion then addresses factors that influence student risk and resiliency and offers examples of school-based initiatives designed to decrease school violence by promoting student mental health and well-being. In the conclusion we offer suggestions for continued efforts that promote overall well-being as a strategy to enhance mental health and increase school safety.

What Is the Association between School Violence and Mental Health?

Public awareness and concern about the linkages between school violence and mental health spikes after school shootings. This pattern has repeated itself since the Columbine shooting in 1999, when the Safe School/Healthy Students (SS/HS) initiative was initially funded. After the Sandy Hook school shooting in 2012, there were calls to make "mental health part of the school safety solution" (Murray, 2013). As a result, President Obama proposed legislation to fund broad school safety efforts that included mental health services (Klein, 2013). With the school shooting at Parkland High School in March 2018, the public dialog again conjoined the act of school violence with the mental health status of the perpetrator.

With continued effort to reduce school violence, it is important to consider the association between a perpetrator's mental health and an act of mass violence. However, focusing primarily on these rare acts of violence does not lead to a complete understanding of the negative effects that more common forms of school violence and victimization have on student mental health. Rather, we consider violence at school to be a much broader term that encompasses physical acts, verbal insults, social rejection, and other forms of victimization.

Some researchers have suggested whether an act is experienced as "violent" does not depend solely on the nature of the act itself, but on the meaning it has for the victim (Morrison, Furlong, & Morrison, 1994). Drawing from this perspective, a student's judgment about how safe they feel at school has been used as an indicator of their level of overall perceived risk on the school campus. This risk perception can emerge out of direct physical victimization; vicariously, as in witnessing the victimization of others; and indirectly, as in being exposed to media and other reports of school violence (Williams, Schneider, Wornell, & Langhinrichsen-Rohling, 2018).

Although students' school safety beliefs are linked with mental health indicators (Nijs et al., 2014), there is surprisingly limited surveillance information about how students' school violence victimization experiences are associated with indicators of emotional distress and positive well-being. To provide a perspective on how students' perceptions of school safety are associated with their complete mental health, in this section of the chapter, we draw on an ongoing two-year survey of adolescent mental health being conducted in California.[1] This survey offers access to unique information about students' school safety and violence-related perceptions, emotional distress experiences, and self-reported psychosocial well-being.

Table 9.1 shows the co-occurrence of students' school violence and mental health experiences. We note some generalizations and cautions about these relations. An important pattern is that most students report feeling safe at school. These students report that they are less likely to experience emotional distress and have positive daily psychosocial experiences. They report feeling positive affiliation with their school and high subjective well-being in general. For the majority of these high school students, schools were locations where their positive psychosocial development was fostered, which is consistent with similar research (Lester & Cross, 2015). Although the patterns

Table 9.1 Associations between high school students' perceptions of school safety and school connectedness, psychosocial distress, and psychosocial well-being

	How safe do you feel when you are at school? (%)			
Item	Unsafe *n* = 484	Neutral *n* = 1,228	Safe *n* = 3,049	phi[e]
Direct school violence				
. . . been pushed, shoved, slapped, hit, or kicked by someone who wasn't just kidding around (% yes)[a]	36.2	21.2	11.3	.24
. . . been in a physical fight? (% yes)[a]	21.8	8.8	5.4	.19
. . . been threatened with harm or injury? (% yes)[a]	21.9	9.6	4.7	.22

(continued)

Table 9.1 (continued)

Item	How safe do you feel when you are at school? (%)			
	Unsafe n = 484	Neutral n = 1,228	Safe n = 3,049	phi[e]
School connectedness				
I feel like I am part of this school (% agree or strongly agree)	19.4	30.4	65.7	.51
I feel close to people at this school (% agree or strongly agree)	33.5	46.2	80.9	.38
Psychosocial distress				
. . . did you ever feel so sad or hopeless almost every day for two weeks or more that you stopped doing some usual activities?[b]	55.0	47.7	29.2	.19
. . . did you ever seriously consider attempting suicide?[b]	34.5	24.3	13.4	.19
. . . I had a hard time breathing because I was anxious.[c]	36.0	27.7	20.3	.18
. . . it was hard for me to cope and I thought I would panic[c]	39.5	30.8	20.8%	.18
Psychosocial wellness				
I would describe my satisfaction with my school experience as (% satisfied or very satisfied)	19.7	24.3	54.6%	.40
My life is going well (% moderately or strongly agree)	40.0	58.8	68.4%	.27
% with flourishing mental health[d]	27.3	31.1	54.6%	.28

[a] During the past 12 months, how many times on school property have you . . .
[b] During the past 12 months . . .
[c] In the past month . . .
[d] Based on responses to 14 items included in the Mental Health Continuum-Short Form (Keyes, 2006). Students were grouped as having flourishing mental health when they reported experiencing at least 1 of 3 affective well-being items almost every day or every day in the past month AND they reported experiences 6 or 11 social and psychological well-being items almost every day or every day in the past month.
[e] phi is presented as an effect size indicator: small effect = .10–.30; moderate effect = .30–.50; large effect >.50.

reported in the section of the chapter are based on a regional sample, they demonstrate a meaningful subgroup of students (up to one-third) report having direct school violence experiences (physical bullying, fighting, and threats of personal harm). These victimized students were substantially more likely to report that they feel unsafe at school, experience the school context as less supportive, and experience emotional distress more frequently. Only about one-third of these students reported having flourishing psychosocial well-being because they were less likely to feel positive affect, experienced positive self-perceptions less often, and infrequently had feelings that society in general was moving in a positive direction. When considering school safety, it is essential to consider both rare acts, as well as more common forms of violence, and the implications of student mental health.

Bullying, Mental Health, and School Safety

Bullying, the most common form of victimization students experience at school, has gained attention in the popular media and in schools in large part because of increased recognition that students who experience bullying are at heightened risk for a wide range of negative psychosocial outcomes, including mental health problems and suicidality. While in the past bullying was considered a harmless or "normal" childhood experience, high-profile cases where targets of bullying committed suicide or acts of violence have brought the mental health implications of bullying to the forefront of public discourse. Consistent with popular media, researchers have been clear that exposure to bullying is strongly and consistently associated with diminished mental health and increased risk of suicide. Early research on this topic focused on mental health outcomes of targets (i.e., victims) of bullying; however, recent research has found that bullying involvement is also linked to worsened outcomes for aggressors (i.e., bullies) and for bystanders who observe but are not directly involved in bullying.

Bullying is defined as aggression that is repeated, intentional, and involves an imbalance of power between the target and the aggressor, such that the target is unable to defend themselves or make the bullying stop (Gladden, Vivolo-Kantor, Hamburger, & Lumpkin, 2014; Olweus, 1993). Bullying can be physical (e.g., hitting, pushing), verbal (e.g., name-calling, teasing), or relational (e.g., gossiping, purposeful exclusion) in form and can also occur online or electronically (i.e., cyberbullying). These defining characteristics of bullying distinguish it from the broader class of peer victimization (i.e., aggression that includes one-time acts of aggression and fighting between equal friends) and, because of these characteristics, bullying is thought to be a particularly harmful form of peer victimization due to its inherent chronicity and tendency to target the most vulnerable students.

Studies estimate that approximately one-third of youth are involved in bullying as a target, an aggressor, or both (Due & Holstein, 2008; Modecki, Minchin, Harbaugh, Guerra, & Runions, 2014; Nansel et al., 2001). Other students who are neither targets nor aggressors are present up to 80% of the time that bullying occurs (O'Connell, Pepler, & Craig, 1999). Together, these results suggest that the most school-aged students will be involved in bullying at some point (and likely at several points) throughout their schooling. As such, from a school safety perspective understanding the association of bullying involvement with mental health has important implications for prevention and intervention efforts in schools.

Mental Health and Types of Bullying Involvement

The most robust research on the association of bullying involvement with mental health outcomes has focused on the mental health of students involved as targets of bullying. Studies have generally found that targets of bullying report greater rates of depression and anxiety in childhood than their uninvolved peers (Hawker & Boulton, 2000; Klomek, Marrocco, Kleinman, Schonfeld, & Gould, 2007). Further, cross-sectional and longitudinal studies indicate that adults who were bullied in childhood are at increased risk for adult depression and anxiety (Holt et al., 2015; Takizawa, Maughan, & Arseneault, 2014). Although studies have tended to focus on mental health among targets, researchers have similarly found that aggressors are also at heightened risk for mental health problems (Swearer, Song, Cary, Eagle, & Mickelson, 2001). Further, the group of students who are involved as bully/victims (i.e., are both targets and aggressors in bullying situations) are at greater risk for both internalizing and externalizing disorders than youth who are either targets or aggressors only (Kaltiala-Heino, Rimpelä, Rantanen, & Rimpelä, 2000; Swearer et al., 2001).

In addition to research on students directly involved in bullying—as targets, aggressors, and bully/victims—some studies have investigated the mental health of the larger population of youth who are involved in bullying as bystanders, or witnesses. For example, in a study of over 2,000 adolescents in England, Rivers and colleagues (2009) found that witnessing bullying was associated with increased risk for mental health problems and that this association persisted even after the researchers statistically accounted for whether youth were also directly involved in bullying as a target or aggressor. This finding mirrors broader research, which has documented that witnessing violence is associated with decreased youth mental health (Mohammad, Shapiro, Wainwright, & Carter, 2015) and suggests the importance of schools attending to the impact of serving in a bystander role on student well-being.

Cyberbullying has received attention as a particularly harmful form of bullying given its (a) large audience, (b) constant access that youth have to technology, and (c) possible anonymity of aggression (Sticca & Perren, 2013). Contrary to popular perception, studies generally find that cyberbullying is less common than other forms of bullying victimization. For example, Modecki and colleagues (2014) found that across 80 studies the mean prevalence rate for cyberbullying involvement as a target or aggressor was 15%, compared to 35% for traditional bullying involvement. Further, youth who were targets of cyberbullying are frequently also targets of traditional forms of bullying victimization (Modecki et al., 2014). However, results of a U.S. nationally representative study of adolescents found that targets of cyberbullying reported higher rates of depression than targets of other forms of bullying (Wang, Nansel, & Iannotti, 2011), suggesting that it might indeed be more harmful than other forms.

Suicide and Bullying

Research on bullying and its mental health implications has raised the question on whether bullying is specifically linked with increased risk for suicidal thoughts and behaviors. A number of studies, including a recent large-scale meta-analysis, have found that childhood bullying has a moderate-sized positive association with suicidal behaviors in childhood (Holt et al., 2015). Most notably, Holt and colleagues (2015) reported that targets of bullying had increased risk for suicidal thoughts and behaviors, as did aggressors. Several longitudinal studies have found associations of bullying involvement and suicide persist into adulthood (Lereya, Copeland, Costello, & Wolke, 2015; Takizawa, Maughan, & Arseneault, 2014). Although studies consistently find an association between bullying and suicide, there is no evidence of a causal link. Most youth involved in bullying do not report suicidality and a number of other factors, such as mental health problems (e.g., depression), are associated with both bullying and suicide, potentially explaining the linkage (Duong & Bradshaw, 2016).

Bullying and Other Forms of Victimization

Research on victimization has consistently found that victimization exposures tend to co-occur, such that some people are exposed to many forms of violence and victimization, while others are exposed to none or only a few (Finkelhor, Ormrod, & Turner, 2007). Youth who experience more victimization in childhood are at greater risk of poor mental health outcomes than those who experience only a few. Consequently, researchers have demonstrated the importance of simultaneously examining multiple forms of victimization, so that the impact of any one form is not overestimated (Green et al., 2010). Studies find that bullying, specifically, is highly co-occurring with other forms of child victimization (e.g., physical assault, family violence; Finkelhor, Turner, Hamby, & Ormrod, 2011). Given this high degree of overlap, a question has emerged regarding the relative importance of bullying as a risk factor for mental health problems as compared to other forms of victimization and maltreatment that bullied youth may have experienced.

Studies that have specifically examined bullying in relation to other forms of victimization have generally found that bullying is significantly and independently associated with key mental health outcomes. For example, using two longitudinal samples, Lereya and colleagues (2015) found that being bullied in childhood was more strongly associated with mental health in young adulthood than childhood maltreatment by adults. Takizawa and colleagues (2014) similarly found an association of bulling with suicidality, when controlled for childhood adversity.

Reciprocal Relationships between Bullying and Mental Health

Whereas the majority of studies have focused on mental health as an outcome of bullying involvement (e.g., depression, anxiety, suicidality), some studies have also explored the potential role of mental health problems as a precursor to bullying. For example, researchers have studied attention-deficit/hyperactivity disorder (ADHD) in relation to self-control and have found that ADHD is associated with both being a target and aggressor in bullying situations and also that early signs of ADHD are associated with later involvement in bullying aggression (Holmberg & Hjern, 2008; Unnever & Cornell, 2003). This research suggests that the association between mental health and bullying might be both complex and reciprocal (Turner, Finkelhor, & Ormrod, 2010). As such, consideration of ecological factors can help one better understand the intricate nature of mental health as it relates to school safety.

Ecological Factors

Despite this correlation between childhood bullying exposure and mental health problems, not all children involved in bullying experience negative outcomes. It is important to consider additional ecological risk and protective factors that may impact the experiences of perpetrators, victims, and witnesses of childhood bullying. In a systematic review of protective factors, researchers found that strong academic and social skills, a stable family environment, attachment to parents, and prosocial friends all helped disrupt the link between bullying perpetration/victimization and internalizing/

externalizing problems later in life (Ttofi, Bowes, Farrington, & Lösel, 2014). Similarly, Brendgen and Poulin (2018) found that friendship support decreased the link between school victimization and subsequent depression symptoms. Together, these studies indicate that strong relationships with others may protect from both incidence of victimization as well as mental health outcomes as a result of victimization.

Additional studies have looked specifically at the school environment and its role as both a risk or protective factor. Schools with inferior teacher support and poor classroom management, as well as those lacking antibullying norms, experience higher incidence of bullying (Machado Azeredo, Rinaldi, Leite de Moraes, Bertzzi Levy, & Rossi Menezes, 2015), whereas having a safe and supportive school environment can help foster the development of individual resilience. Rather than serving as a direct protective factor in itself, research indicates that schools provide the space for children to develop their own personal protective factors and resilience (Jackson, Chou, & Browne, 2017). High perceptions of the school environment are linked to engagement in learning, academic achievement, and hope, all of which may protect against victimization and subsequent negative mental health outcomes (Van Ryzin, Roseth, Fosco, Lee, & Chen, 2016). In fostering individual resilience, therefore, it is important for schools to promote prosocial relationships with peers and develop a safe and supportive learning environment.

School Safety and Mental Health

It is crucial that schools are safe places for children, families, and educators. While many school teams are successful in providing a safe environment, they also recognize that safety must successfully align with the primary purpose of schools: to provide developmentally appropriate instruction, experiences, and support in order to achieve academic and social-emotional learning competencies for all (Lane, Menzies, Parks Ennis, & Bezdek, 2013). With this in mind, many schools have turned to a multitiered system of supports (MTSS) framework that addresses academic, social-emotional, and behavioral concerns. MTSS pulls strongly from the three-tiered public health model, including early identification and prevention (universal intervention), targeted intervention (secondary), and intensive intervention (tertiary) to ensure all individuals are receiving an appropriate level of support. For most students, universal interventions (e.g., schoolwide positive behavioral interventions and supports; social-emotional learning) provide sufficient support to foster appropriate development. However, some students require more intensive supports (e.g., mental health counseling, check-in check-out, special education services; Lane et al., 2013).

In addressing school climate and student behavior specifically, positive behavioral interventions and supports (PBIS) has become one of the most prominent applications of the three-tiered MTSS framework. At the universal intervention level, PBIS helps foster a safe school environment by developing positively worded expectations, explicitly teaching the expectations to staff and students, rewarding students when they meet schoolwide expectations, and establishing a continuum of logical consequences for student misbehavior (Burke, Davis, Hagan-Burke, Lee, & Fogarty, 2014; Kincaid et al., 2016). Schools implementing PBIS use various sources to make data-based decisions regarding implementation fidelity, effectiveness of interventions, and level of support for individual students.

Similarly, social-emotional learning (SEL) has become a prominent prevention strategy in teaching students core competencies in: recognizing and managing emotions, setting and achieving positive goals, appreciating others and their perspectives, and establishing and maintaining healthy relationships (Durlak, Weissberg, Dymnicki, Taylor, & Schellinger, 2011). SEL can be employed to facilitate academic engagement, work ethic, commitment, and overall school success through explicitly teaching social-emotional skills. SEL programs aim to increase positive social behaviors and decrease conduct problems and emotional distress (Durlak et al., 2011).

While programs such as PBIS and SEL, which utilize the MTSS framework, foster a safe and supportive school environment, many of the more serious mental health and safety concerns require Tier 3 intensive supports. As a result, Tier 3 has become more well-established in terms of intervention and response, and Tiers 1 and 2 need to be established more clearly as they relate to promotion of safety and prevention of school violence. In an attempt to operationalize the MTSS framework approach, particularly at the Tier 1 level, various initiatives have been implemented in the school setting to promote safety and mental health.

Safe Schools/Healthy Students

Beginning in 1999 and for more than a decade, the Safe Schools/Healthy Students (SS/HS) initiative concentrated on decreasing violence and promoting a safe and secure school environment for all students. It emerged out of an awakening of consciousness after the violence that occurred at Columbine (see Appendix) and aimed to operationalize concerns and issues related to school violence at a national level. This cross-agency federal initiative provided more than $2 billion in funding to 365 communities. It is the longest running, most comprehensive approach that has examined the link between school violence and mental health to date. The design of the SS/HS initiative was based on the research identifying family-school-community partnerships as critical components of strategies to foster safe, respectful school environments, healthier development, and that ultimately improved academic success for students (Modzeleski et al., 2011). From this initiative, communities collaborated to implement comprehensive models of intervention to prevent violence and promote mental health among students. Projects covered many areas including prevention of violence, bullying, and suicide, as well as the promotion of student mental health and wellness. According to Modzeleski and colleagues (2011), in a national cross-site evaluation of the initiative, findings revealed encouraging results. Following implementation, investigators found that fewer students reported experiencing and witnessing violence. Most school staff (96%) indicated that school safety had improved due to the initiative. Related to mental health, data indicated a significant increase in access to mental health services, specifically there was a 263% increase in the number of students accessing mental health services in the schools, and a 519% increase in students receiving mental health services in the community.

Advancing Wellness and Resilience in Education

Building on the success of the SS/HS initiative, Project Advancing Wellness and Resilience Education (AWARE) was developed to focus on student wellness and resilience. Project AWARE is a Substance Abuse and Mental Health Services Administration (SAMHSA) grants program dedicated to the promotion of youth mental health awareness in schools and communities. The program intends to build capacity across systems to effectively implement science-based prevention and intervention practices and scale these practices up. Project AWARE has a direct link to previous school safety efforts; yet seeks to take it a step further by addressing wellness promotion. Specifically, Project AWARE aims to assist state and local agencies in improving mental health awareness, training educators and other providers in identifying and intervening with mental health issues, as well as connecting youth and their families with needed services. This project works to improve, expand, or implement a variety of systems level programs and services with an emphasis on: outreach, increased access, enhanced coordination and collaboration, improved screening and identification practices, and implementation of culturally specific and developmentally appropriate mental health practices (Project Advancing Wellness and Resilience Education, n.d.).

A program developed from Project AWARE is Project Cal-Well (Project Cal-Well, n.d.), established in California by a consortium of educators including the California Department of Education, select school districts, and a County Office of Education. The purpose is to promote mental health awareness and wellness among students in K–12 settings. Through cross-system collaboration this consortium is focused on promoting awareness, early identification, and intervention for students within their local education agencies. Cal-Well has implemented Youth Mental Health First Aid (YMHFA) training with a goal training at least 3,000 providers by the end of the grant period. Further, the project promotes positive school climate practices by using evidence-based prevention and intervention programs within their schools.

Nevada was another one of the 20 states awarded the Project AWARE grant and it has collected some encouraging implementation data. The Nevada State Department of Education partnered with a tri-county Frontier Community Coalition (FCC), three county school districts and the University of Nevada, Reno (one district eventually dropped out). Activities in the first year included: hiring mental health professionals, providing mental health awareness training, developing a triage and referral system for referrals, and implementing mental health services in the schools. Data indicated that within six months, 101 adults were trained in YMHFA and 181 students (out of approximately 4,200 students) were referred for mental health services. A survey of 231 teachers, school district administrators, mental health providers, and community members indicated referral patterns of these providers, and found that 50% of these providers felt that AWARE had improved access to services. Investigators reported ongoing challenges such as: (a) the high volume of referrals, (b) challenges in coordination across agencies, and (c) concerns with long-term sustainability of the program (Ryst, Rock, Albers, & Everheart, 2016).

As can be seen with both Project AWARE efforts, there has been some change in the communities regarding establishing systems and approaches for connecting students with mental health services; however, more work is needed to create sustainable models that address the broad community mental health needs and monitor the outcomes of such programs. Some institutions have focused on creating systems for schools to collect data and monitor such outcomes. A key institution, in support of collaborative comprehensive approaches and multitiered intervention to improve mental health programming in schools, is the National Center for School Mental Health (CSMH) at the University of Maryland School of Medicine. The CSMH has developed and hosts a School Health Assessment and Performance Evaluation (SHAPE) System. This free, private, web-based tool can be used by school mental health teams to collaboratively assess, plan, and document mental health services and supports offered. The system also offers access to targeted evidence-based resources and materials. In addition, data that entered the Shape System is used in the National School Mental Health Census, which supports the center's goal of mapping the status of school mental health at a national level (School Health Assessment and Performance Evaluation System, n.d.).

Many of the current school-based mental health initiatives are not only dedicated to improving school safety but include the promotion of student wellness as a primary emphasis. There are some common themes and identified needs that run across these emerging programs, with focus on mental health planning and integration, programs seek to: (a) enhance coordination and collaboration across providers, agencies, and policy makers; (b) improve awareness and access to needed services; and (c) effectively implement screening and identification practices within a multitiered system of evidence-based intervention. While these initiatives are reputable, there is a need to have an established framework and theory in place when determining how to approach mental health in schools that includes looking at distress alongside wellness.

Theoretical Frameworks for Research, Policy, and Practice

Although the importance of students' mental well-being to positive school experience is widely accepted, little consensus exists on what it means for youth to be mentally well in school. Traditional mental health approaches have primarily targeted and addressed mental health dysfunction among youth such as disruptive emotions and behaviors. Little emphasis is placed on positive indicators of mental health such as hope, happiness, and gratitude (Seligman & Csikszentmihalyi, 2000). These approaches are based on a unidimensional view of illness-health, which conceptualizes positive mental health and psychopathology as two extremes on a continuum and expects people with low psychopathology to have high positive mental health (Lyons, Huebner, Hills, & Shinkareva, 2012). However, current research provides evidence for a multidimensional view of mental health illness (i.e., a dual-factor model of mental health), indicating that a decrease in one is not necessarily related to an increase in the other (Greenspoon & Saklofske, 2001). According to Brunzell, Stokes, and Waters (2016), a dual-factor approach suggests that school-based mental health support can be conceived from both a deficit perspective (e.g., what deficiencies or struggles do students face?) and a strengths perspective (e.g., what psychological strengths and resources do students have to build upon for future success?). Furthermore, recent studies argue that positive indicators of mental health can act as protective factors against emotional and behavioral distress among youth, indicating the need for a more balanced approach in mental health support in school settings.

In order to build safe school environments for students to learn and thrive, every school should implement a process to monitor and screen for students' mental health and safety. However, well-being still remains a narrowly defined term in education, complicating efforts to monitor it effectively in schools (Ereaut & Whiting, 2008; Fraillon, 2004). Specifically, evaluations of youth well-being in schools frequently involve grades, attendance records, or number of discipline incidents (Soutter, O'Steen, & Gilmore, 2014). However, emerging policy and research has conceptualized student well-being in broader terms and placed increased attention on physical and mental wellness, risk prevention and resilience, as well as social-ecological contexts that facilitate safe schooling (Soutter et al., 2014). For example, with increased need for positively framed models that represent a more holistic view of student well-being, the Student Well-Being Model (SWBM) was developed and implemented in New Zealand schools, a framework for the development of well-being indicators among students (Soutter et al., 2014). Foundations of the SWBM were identified through an extensive review of the well-being literature (Soutter, Gilmore, & O'Steen, 2011). Its seven domains include having, being, relating, feeling, thinking, functioning, and striving (for more information, see Soutter et al., 2014); each domain is worthy of considered attention in schools to support effective promotion of student well-being. The SWBM also draws from Bronfenbrenner's (1979) ecological framework in that its seven domains are considered to be embedded in the ecological systems of students' lives, such as school, family, and community (Davis & Simmt, 2003). In such models, school can recognize themselves as an important part of each child's ecological system that plays a meaningful role in giving shape to the well-being of each student.

With this broader conceptualization of student well-being, an important question must be addressed. How is well-being addressed in educational contexts? Currently, only 12.6% of school/district-level administrators across the nation report conducting schoolwide mental health screening with their students (Bruhn, Woods-Groves, & Huddle, 2014). However, most of them still take a traditional, imbalanced approach to mental health by searching for evidence of mental distress concerns among students, but not their psychological strengths and resources. A recent literature by Kim, Furlong, Dowdy, and Felix (2014) found that when a strength-based instrument and a symptom-based instrument were used in combination, prediction of students' subjective well-being was significantly better than using only one of the instruments. This balanced mental health approach in schools can help educators improve students' well-being by building students' psychological strengths, while reducing their mental health concerns. Thus, frequently and widely used general surveillance tools such as the Youth Risk Behavior Surveillance Survey (YRBSS, Kaan et al., 2016) are limited; although they provide meaningful information regarding current risky behaviors students engage in, they do not provide the opportunity to identify and promote psychological strengths and resources that may reduce students' risky behaviors, and in turn, create a safer school environment for them.

The Social Emotional Health Survey-Secondary (SEHS-S; Furlong, You, Renshaw, Smith, & O'Malley, 2014) is an example of a strength-based tool that measures positive psychological traits such as self-awareness, gratitude, and optimism, but also measures social-ecological strengths and resources such as family, peer, and teacher support. In addition to using a deficit-based measure identifying psychological distress, schools could utilize a strength-based measure that examines students' socioemotional strengths and resources. School-based mental health practice based on these dual-factor and social-ecological models can support research focusing on the development of student well-being indicators, which can inform policy and practice development for positive youth mental health.

Summary and Conclusions

School violence is an ongoing concern and with this concern remains a need for the development and implementation of comprehensive programs that address school safety. As the link between violence and mental health becomes more clearly established, there is an urgent call to address the social-emotional needs of students. Although it is understandable to cite school shootings as a motivation for expanding school mental health services, it is an incomplete approach to addressing the needs of students in schools and understanding the effects that more common forms of violence and victimization have on mental health.

We know that student mental health is impacted by incidents of school violence. For example, in the ongoing study of California high school students in this chapter, the majority of students (55%) who believed their school was unsafe also experienced sad/unhappy feelings in the past year. This suggests substantial psychosocial vulnerability in regard to low perceptions of school safety. In contrast, just 29% of students who feel safe at a school experience similar internalizing distress. In addition to students who directly experience violence and victimization, students who witness victimization or are exposed to violent media may also feel that school is unsafe and subsequently develop vulnerabilities. When it comes to understanding adolescent mental health, it is important to note that a number of students at any given school experience emotional distress, which may or may not be precipitated or exacerbated by school violence and victimization experiences.

As this chapter highlights, it is not enough to address student mental health alone. Rather, there is a need to enhance student overall well-being as a means to positively impact school safety. Although schools are the primary place in which students access mental health services, school-based services are often underfunded and student needs remain unmet (Cummings, Wen, & Druss, 2013). As educators, our ultimate goal is to help students thrive. Therefore, students need access to high-quality services that will support their overall well-being and place them on a positive trajectory. Ultimately, healthy children and adolescents in safe schools will be less likely to engage in violent behaviors. When challenges arise, these students will have the ability to cope with difficulties in a healthy and adaptive way.

It is essential that efforts to fund increased and enhanced school mental health services recognize the importance of fostering a student body that is characterized by high levels of affective, psychological, and social well-being as one of the best antidotes to school violence. Students with flourishing mental health feel energized, engaged, and contribute to the school community. These students are better able to cope with their own life challenges and in turn reach out to and support other students in need.

In order to foster student well-being, we need to begin taking essential steps toward building a healthy school environment. First, we must utilize an MTSS framework in our design and implementation of interventions that focuses on the whole child and includes ecological components that impact the child beyond the individual and school levels. This framework should include mental health and/or wellness screening, the use of data to make decisions regarding levels of support, and funding to support a sufficient number of highly qualified personnel to carry out the plan.

In February 2018, the Interdisciplinary Group on Preventing School and Community Violence put forth a Call for Action to Prevent Gun Violence in the United States of America that stresses the need for a more comprehensive approach. Among the recommendations, this plan calls for strategies that include: (a) the assessment of school climate in all schools and that all schools maintain physically and emotionally safe conditions; (b) sufficient staffing including counselors, psychiatrists, psychologists, and so on to coordinate school- and community-based mental health services for individuals with identified risk factors; (c) reduce exclusionary practices of school discipline as another strategy to foster positive social, behavioral, emotional, and academic success; and (d) train and maintain threat assessment teams that include mental health and law enforcement partners (Call for Action to Prevent Gun Violence in the United States of America, 2018). As we move forward with the development of strategies to decrease school violence, it is imperative that mental health and mental wellness are at the forefront of the discussion. Programs that address the needs of those who are both directly and indirectly involved in violence and victimization can have a powerful impact on the safety of schools and the overall well-being of students.

Note

1. The data used in this section include the responses of 4,806 students attending five geographically dispersed California high schools (grades 9–12). The sample included characteristics as follows (largest subgroup shown): female (52.1%), white (40.8%), parent college graduate (38.8%), home language English (77.6%), and not eligible for subsidized school lunch program (51.9%). Items included in this study's comprehensive survey were drawn from the Youth Risk

Behavioral Surveillance Survey (Kaan et al., 2018), The School Connectedness Sale (Furlong, O'Brennan, & You, 2011), the Mental Health Continuum-Short form (Keyes, 2005), the Social Emotional Distress Scale-Secondary (Dowdy, Furlong, Nylund-Gibson, Moore, & Moffa, 2018), and the Brief Multidimensional Life Satisfaction Scale (Fun, Huebner, & Valois, 2006). See Project CoVitality for more information (http://www.project-covitality.info).

References

Altheide, D. L. (2009). The Columbine shootings and the discourse of fear. *American Behavioral Scientist, 52*, 1354–1370.

Brendgen, M., & Poulin, F. (2018). Continued bullying victimization from childhood to young adulthood: A longitudinal study of mediating and protective factors. *Journal of Abnormal Child Psychology, 46*, 27–39. doi:10.1007/s10802-017-0314-5

Bronfenbrenner, U. (1979). *The ecology of human development.* Cambridge, MA: Harvard University Press.

Bruhn, A. L., Woods-Groves, S., & Huddle, S. (2014). A preliminary investigation of emotional and behavioral screening practices in K–12 schools. *Education & Treatment of Children, 37*, 611–634. doi:10.1353/etc.2014.0039

Brunzell, T., Stokes, H., & Waters, L. (2016). Trauma-informed positive education: Using positive psychology to strengthen vulnerable students. *Contemporary School Psychology, 20*, 63–83. doi:10.1007/s40688-015-0070-x

Burke, M. D., Davis, J. L., Hagan-Burke, S., Lee, Y., & Fogarty, M. (2014). Using SWPBS expectations as a universal screening tool to predict behavioral risk in middle school. *Journal of Positive Behavioral Interventions, 16*, 3–15. doi:10.1177/1098300712461147

Call for Action to Prevent Gun Violence in the United States of America. (2018). *Interdisciplinary Group on Preventing School and Community Violence.* Retrieved from https://curry.virginia.edu/prevent-gun-violence

Cornell, D., & Sheras, P. (2006). *Guidelines for responding to student threats of violence.* Longmont, CO: Sopris West.

Cummings, J. R., Wen, H., & Druss, B. G. (2013). Improving access to mental health services for youth in the United States. *Journal of the American Medical Association, 309*, 553–554. doi:10.1001/jama.2013.437

Davis, B., & Simmt, E. (2003). Understanding learning systems: Mathematics education and complexity science. *Journal for Research in Mathematics Education, 34*, 137–167. doi:10.2307/30034903

Dowdy, E., Furlong, M. J., Nylund-Gibson, K., Moore, S., & Moffa, K. (2018). Initial validation of the Social Emotional Distress Scale to support complete mental health screening. *Assessment for Effective Intervention.* First online January 5, 2018. doi:10.1177/1534508417749871

Due, P., & Holstein, B. E. (2008). Bullying victimization among 13- to 15-year-old school children: Results from two comparative studies in 66 countries and regions. *International Journal of Adolescent Medicine and Health, 20*, 209–222. doi:10.1515/IJAMH.2008.20.2.209

Duong, J., & Bradshaw, C. P. (2016). Household income level as a moderator of associations between chronic health conditions and serious mental illness. *Journal of Community Psychology, 44*, 367–383. doi:10.1002/jcop.21774

Durlak, J. A., Weissberg, R. P., Dymnicki, A. B., Taylor, R. D., & Schellinger, K. B. (2011). The impact of enhancing students' social and emotional learning: A meta-analysis of school-based universal interventions. *Child Development, 82*, 405–432. doi:10.1111/j.1467-8624.2010.01564.x

Dwyer, K., & Osher, D. (2000). *Safeguarding our children: An action guide.* Washington, DC: U.S. Departments of Education and Justice, American Institutes for Research. https://www2.ed.gov/admins/lead/safety/actguide/action_guide.pdf

Dwyer, K., Osher, D., & Wagner, C. (1998). *Early warning, timely response: A guide to safe schools.* Washington, DC: U.S. Department of Education. Retrieved from https://files.eric.ed.gov/fulltext/ED418372.pdf

Ereaut, G., & Whiting, R. (2008). *What do we mean by 'Wellbeing'? And why might it matter?* (Research Report DCSF–RW073). London: Department for Business Innovation and Skills. Retrieved from http://dera.ioe.ac.uk/8572/1/dcsf-rw073%20v2.pdf

Finkelhor, D., Ormrod, R. K., & Turner, H. A. (2007). Poly-victimization: A neglected component in child victimization. *Child Abuse & Neglect, 31*, 7–26. doi:10.1016/j.chiabu.2006.06.008

Finkelhor, D., Turner, H., Hamby, S. L., & Ormrod, R. (2011). *Poly-victimization: Children's exposure to multiple types of violence, crime, and abuse.* OJJDP Juvenile Justice Bulletin (NCJ235504, 1-12). Washington, DC: US Government Printing Office.

Fraillon, J. (2004). *Measuring student wellbeing in the context of Australian schooling: Discussion paper.* Commissioned by the South Australian Department of Education and Children's Services as an agent of the Ministerial Council on Education, Employment, Training and Youth Affairs. Retrieved from https://research.acer.edu.au/cgi/viewcontent.cgi?article=1008&context=well_being

Frieden, T. R., Jaffe, H. W., Cono, J., Richards, C. L., & Iademarco, M. F. (2014). Youth Risk Behavior Surveillance—United States, 2013. Surveillance Summaries. *MMWR, 63*(No. SS-4).

Funk, B. A., Huebner, E. S., & Valois, R. F. (2006). Reliability and validity of a brief life satisfaction scale with a high school sample. *Journal of Happiness Studies, 7*, 41–54. doi:10.1007/s10902-005-0869-7

Furlong, M. J., O'Brennan, L. M., & You, S. (2011). Psychometric properties of he Add Health School Connectedness Scale for 18 sociocultural groups. *Psychology in the Schools, 48*, 986–997. doi:10.1002/pits.20609

Furlong, M. J., You, S., Renshaw, T. L., Smith, D. C., & O'Malley, M. D. (2014). Preliminary development and validation of the Social and Emotional Health Survey for secondary school students. *Social Indicators Research, 117*, 1011–1032. doi:10.1007/s11205-013-0373-0

Gladden, R. M., Vivolo-Kantor, A. M., Hamburger, M. E., & Lumpkin, C. D. (2014). *Bullying surveillance among youths: Uniform definitions for public health and recommended data elements, version 1.0.* Atlanta: National Center for Injury Prevention and Control, Centers for Disease Control and Prevention and U.S. Department of Education.

Green, J. G., McLaughlin, K. A., Berglund, P. A., Gruber, M. J., Sampson, N. A., Zaslavsky, A. M., & Kessler, R. C. (2010). Childhood adversities and adult psychiatric disorders in the national comorbidity survey replication I: Associations with first onset of DSM-IV disorders. *Archives of General Psychiatry, 67*, 113–123. doi:10.1001/archgenpsychiatry.2009.186

Greenspoon, P. J., & Saklofske, D. H. (2001). Toward an integration of subjective well-being and psychopathology. *Social Indicators Research, 54*, 81–108. doi:10.1023/A:1007219227883

Griffiths, A. J., Sharkey, J. D., & Furlong, M. J. (2008). Targeted threat assessment: Ethical considerations for school psychologists. *School Psychology Forum: Research in Practice, 2*, 1–13.

Hawker, D. S., & Boulton, M. J. (2000). Twenty years' research on peer victimization and psychosocial maladjustment: A meta-analytic review of cross-sectional studies. *Journal of Child Psychology and Psychiatry and Allied Disciplines, 41*, 441–455. doi:10.1111/1469-7610.00629

Holmberg, K., & Hjern, A. (2008). Bullying and attention-deficit-hyperactivity disorder in 10-year-olds in a Swedish community. *Developmental Medicine & Child Neurology, 50*, 134–138. doi:10.1111/j.1469-8749.2007.02019.x

Holt, M. K., Vivolo-Kantor, A. M., Polanin, J. R., Holland, K. M., DeGue, S., Matjasko, J. L., . . . Reid, G. (2015). Bullying and suicidal ideation and behaviors: A meta-analysis. *Pediatrics, 135*, 1–14.

Hurd, N. M., Hussain, S., & Bradshaw, C. P. (2015). School disorder, school connectedness, and psychosocial outcomes: Moderation by a supportive figure in the school. *Youth & Safety, 50*, 328–350.

Jackson, V., Chou, S., & Browne, K. (2017). Protective factors against child victimization in the school and community: An exploratory systematic review of longitudinal predictors and interacting variables. *Trauma, Violence, & Abuse, 18*, 303–321. doi:10.1177/1524838015611675

Kaan, L., McManus, T., Harris, W. A., Shankin, S. L., Flint, K. H., Hawkins, J., . . . Zaza, S. (2016). Youth risk behavior surveillance—United States, 2015. *MMWR Surveillance Summary, 65*(6), 1–174.

Kaltiala-Heino, R., Rimpelä, M., Rantanen, P., & Rimpelä, A. (2000). Bullying at school—An indicator of adolescents at risk for mental disorders. *Journal of Adolescence, 23*, 661–674. doi:10.1006/jado.2000.0351

Kann, L., McManus, T., Harris, W. A., Shanklin, S. L., Flint, K. H., Queen, B., . . . Ethier, K. A. (2018). Youth risk behavior surveillance—United States, 2017. *MMWR, 67*(8), 1–479.

Keyes, C. L. M. (2006). Mental health in adolescence: Is America's youth flourishing? *Journal of Orthopsychiatry, 76*, 395–402. doi:10.1037/0002-9432.76.3.395

Kim, E. K., Furlong, M. J., Dowdy, E., & Felix, E. D. (2014). Exploring the relative contributions of the strength and distress components of dual-factor complete mental health screening. *Canadian Journal of School Psychology, 29*, 127–140. doi:10.1177/0829573514529567

Kincaid, D., Dunlap, G., Kern, L., Lane, K. L., Bambara, L. M., Brown, . . . Knoster, T. P. (2016). Positive behavior support: A proposal for updating and refining the definition. *Journal of Positive Behavior Interventions, 18*, 69–73. doi:10.1177/1098300715604826

Klein, A. (2013, January 22). Obama presses school safety, mental health initiatives. *Education Week*. Retrieved from http://www.edweek.org/ew/articles/2013/01/23/18guns.h32.html?print=1

Klomek, A. B., Marrocco, F., Kleinman, M., Schonfeld, I. S., & Gould, M. S. (2007). Bullying, depression, and suicidality in adolescents. *Journal of the American Academy of Child & Adolescent Psychiatry, 46*, 40–49. doi:10.1097/01.chi.0000242237.84925.18

Lane, L. L., Menzies, H. M., Parks Ennis, R., & Bezdek, J. (2013). School-wide systems to promote positive behaviors and facilitate instruction. *Journal of Curriculum and Instruction, 7*, 6–31. doi:10.3776/joci.2013.v7n1pp6-31

Lereya, S. T., Copeland, W. E., Costello, E. J., & Wolke, D. (2015). Adult mental health consequences of peer bullying and maltreatment in childhood: Two cohorts in two countries. *The Lancet Psychiatry, 2*, 524–531. doi:10.1016/S2215-0366(15)00165-0

Lester, L., & Cross, D. (2015). The relationship between school climate and mental and emotional wellbeing over the transition from primary to secondary school. *Psychology of Well-Being, 5*(1), 9. doi:10.1186/s13612-015-0037-8

Lyons, M. D., Huebner, E. S., Hills, K. J., & Shinkareva, S. V. (2012). The dual-factor model of mental health: Further study of the determinants of group differences. *Canadian Journal of School Psychology, 27*, 183–196. doi:10.1177/0829573512443669

Machado Azeredo, C., Rinaldi, A. E. M., Leite de Moraes, C., Bertzzi Levy, R., & Rossi Menezes, P. (2015). School bullying: A systematic review of contextual-level risk factor observational studies. *Aggression and Violent Behavior, 22*, 65–76. doi:10.1016/j.avb.2015.04.006

Modecki, K. L., Minchin, J., Harbaugh, A. G., Guerra, N. G., & Runions, K. C. (2014). Bullying prevalence across contexts: A meta-analysis measuring cyber and traditional bullying. *Journal of Adolescent Health, 55*, 602–611. doi:10.1016/j.jadohealth.2014.06.007

Modzeleski, W., Mathews-Younes, A., Arroyo, C. G., Mannix, D., Wells, M. E., Hill, G., . . . Murray, S. (2012). An introduction to the Safe Schools/

Healthy Students Initiative. *Evaluation and Program Planning, 35*, 269–272. doi:10.1016/j.evalprogplan.2011.11.001

Mohammad, E. T., Shapiro, E. R., Wainwright, L. D., & Carter, A. S. (2015). Impacts of family and community violence exposure on child coping and mental health. *Journal of Abnormal Child Psychology, 43*, 203–215. doi: 10.1007/s10802-014-9889-2

Morrison, G., Furlong, M. J., & Morrison, R. (1994). School violence to school safety: Reframing the issue for school psychologists. *School Psychology Review, 23*, 236–256.

Morrison, G. M., Furlong, M. J., & Morrison, R. L. (2000). Beyond resilience: Building relationships to promote thriving. *Reaching Today's Youth: The Community of Circle Caring Journal, 5*, 72–76.

Murray, L. C. (2013, January 29). Making mental health part of the school safety solution. *Education Week*. Retrieved from https://www.edweek.org/ew/articles/2013/01/30/19murray.h32.html?print=1

Nansel, T. R., Overpeck, M., Pilla, R., Ruan, W. J., Simons-Morton, B., & Scheidt, P. (2001). Bullying behaviors among US youth: Prevalence and association with psychosocial adjustment. *Journal of American Medical Association, 285*, 2094–2100.

Nijs, M. M., Bun, C. J., Tempelaar, W. M., de Wit, N. J., Burger, H., Plevier, C. M., & Boks, M. P. (2014). Perceived school safety is strongly associated with adolescent mental health problems. *Community Mental Health, 50*, 127–134. doi:10.1007/s10597-013-9599-1

O'Connell, P., Pepler, D., & Craig, W. (1999). Peer involvement in bullying: Issues and challenges for intervention. *Journal of Adolescence, 22*, 437–452. doi:10.1006/jado.1999.0238

Olweus, D. (1993). *Bullying at school: What we know and what we can do.* Malden, MA: Blackwell.

O'Toole, M. E. (2000). *The school shooter: A threat assessment perspective.* Quantico, VA: Federal Bureau of Investigation.

Project Advancing Wellness and Resilience Education (AWARE). (n.d.). Retrieved from https://www.samhsa.gov/nitt-ta/project-aware-grant-information

Project Cal-Well. (n.d.). Retrieved from https://www.cde.ca.gov/ls/cg/mh/projectcalwell.asp

Rivers, I., Poteat, V. P., Noret, N., & Ashurst, N. (2009). Observing bullying at school: The mental health implications of witness status. *School Psychology Quarterly, 24*, 211–223. doi:10.1037/a0018164

Ryst, E., Rock, S. L., Albers, E. C., & Everheart, C. A. (2016). Implementation of Project AWARE (Advancing Wellness and Resilience Education) in three rural Nevada school districts to increase mental health awareness, early identification of mental health issues, and intervention with school-aged youth. *Journal of the American Academy of Child and Adolescent Psychiatry, 55*(10), S180. doi:10.1016/j.jaac.2016.09.249

School Health Assessment and Performance Evaluation System. (n.d.). Retrieved from https://theshapesystem.com/

Seligman, M. P., & Csikszentmihalyi, M. (2000). Positive psychology: An introduction. *American Psychologist, 55*, 5–14. doi:10.1037/0003-066X.55.1.5

Soutter, A. K., Gilmore, A., & O'Steen, B. (2011). How do high school youths' educational experiences relate to well-being? Towards a trans-disciplinary conceptualization. *Journal of Happiness Studies, 12*, 591–631. doi:10.1007/s10902-010-9219-5

Soutter, A. K., O'Steen, B., & Gilmore, A. (2014). The student well-being model: A conceptual framework for the development of student well-being indicators. *International Journal of Adolescence and Youth, 19*, 496–520. doi:10.1080/02673843.2012.754362

Sticca, F., & Perren, S. (2013). Is cyberbullying worse than traditional bullying? Examining the differential roles of medium, publicity, and anonymity for the perceived severity of bullying. *Journal of Youth and Adolescence, 42*, 739–750. doi:10.1007/s10964-012-9867-3

Swearer, S. M., Song, S. Y., Cary, P. T., Eagle, J. W., & Mickelson, W. T. (2001). Psychosocial correlates in bullying and victimization: The relationship between depression, anxiety, and bully/victim status. *Journal of Emotional Abuse*, 2(2–3), 95–121. doi:10.1300/J135v02n02_07

Takizawa, R., Maughan, B., & Arseneault, L. (2014). Adult health outcomes of childhood bullying victimization: Evidence from a five-decade longitudinal British birth cohort. *American Journal of Psychiatry, 171*, 777–784.

Ttofi, M. M., Bowes, L., Farrington, D. P., & Lösel, F. (2014). Protective factors interrupting the continuity from school bullying to later internalizing and externalizing problems: A systematic review of prospective longitudinal studies. *Journal of School Violence, 13*, 5–38. doi:10.1080/15388220.2013.857345

Turner, H. A., Finkelhor, D., & Ormrod, R. (2010). Child mental health problems as risk factors for victimization. *Child Maltreatment, 15*, 132–143. doi:10.1177/1077559509349150

Unnever, J. D., & Cornell, D. G. (2003). Bullying, self-control, and ADHD. *Journal of Interpersonal Violence, 18*, 129–147. doi:10.1177/0886260502238731

Van Ryzin, M. J., Roseth, C. J., Fosco, G. M., Lee, Y., & Chen, I.-C. (2016). A component-centered meta-analysis of family-based prevention programs for adolescent substance use. *Clinical Psychology Review, 45*, 72–80. doi:10.1016/j.cpr.2016.03.007

Wang, J., Nansel, T. R., & Iannotti, R. J. (2011). Cyber and traditional bullying: Differential association with depression. *Journal of Adolescent Health, 48*, 415–417. doi:10.1016/j.jadohealth.2010.07.012

Williams, S., Schneider, M., Wornell, C., & Langhinrichsen-Rohling, J. (2018). Student's perceptions of school safety: It is not just about being bullied.

Journal of School Nursing. First published online March 14, 2018. doi:10.1177/1059840518761792

Yang, C., Sharkey, J. D., Reed, L. A., Chen, C., & Dowdy, E. (2018). Bullying victimization and student engagement in elementary, middle, and high schools: Moderating role of school climate. *School Psychology Quarterly*, 33, 54–64. doi:10.1037/spq0000250

Appendix

Post-Columbine High School Safe Guarding our Children: An Action Guide Safe Schools/Healthy Students (Five main components, including mental health)

All schools desire to be the safest places for children, families, and educators. Most schools are successful in providing that safety, and most also recognize that safety must successfully align with the primary purpose of schools: to provide developmentally appropriate instruction, experiences, and support in order to achieve academic and social-emotional learning competencies for all. Balancing these priorities is critical.

During the 1990s, a series of mass school shootings occurred that captured headlines and the 24/7 television news media, leaving many among the public with the impression that in general, schools were not safe. A series of three school shootings in 1997–1998 (Health High School, Kentucky; Wayside Middle School, Arkansas, and Thurston High School, Oregon) where multiple deaths (11) and woundings (38) occurred confirmed this belief, despite the facts that schools were generally safer than a decade earlier. Communities responded to the heightened media with requests for more school policing, use of metal detectors, and secure entry and lock-down procedures (Altheide, 2009). These incidents also resulted in President Clinton requesting that his Secretary of Education, Richard Riley, and Attorney General, Janet Reno, assemble a group of experts and academics from the fields of education, mental health, and juvenile justice to create preventive solutions and interventions to guide schools in their development of safe school plans for the 1998–1999 school year and beyond. *Early Warning, Timely Response: A Guide to Safe Schools* (Dwyer, Osher, & Wager, 1998) was thus designed and distributed to provide the practical research-based guidance to help schools "keep every child in school out of harm's way." The *Guide* was produced and distributed to every public school in the nation and provided guidance for improving school climate, universally supporting social-emotional and coping skills, and intervening early for children needing support. It also helped with identifying and addressing warning signs and imminent signs of violence. Within two years, the follow-up "how to" guide *Safeguarding Our Children: An Action Guide* (Dwyer & Osher, 2000) was endorsed by Secretary Riley and Attorney General Reno. This action guide provided practical steps that had been vetted by school, community representatives, and applied research-to-practice experts to help schools design comprehensive safety action plans. These documents helped reframe the problem of safety and tragic violence into one of mental health promotion. Caring and connection in a positive school climate were the focus of resources, training, and strategic plans.

School Violence: A Public Health Issue

These documents enabled policy makers, researchers, practitioners, and advocates to convert school safety concerns into positive mental health promotion and prevention goals and practices. These documents, through their supporting organizations, now defined school violence as a public health issue subject to the public health prevention and intervention paradigm. Rather than a focus on hardware and criminalizing student behaviors, the focus turned to universal promotion of mentally healthy behaviors and prevention of negative behaviors through positive policies and practices, as well as early intervention. These guides encouraged schools to evaluate and, when necessary, improve their school climate and the conditions for learning for all students, including those receiving special education or English as a Second Language (ESL) services.

Although the *Warning Guide* was distributed in September 1998, its impact increased after another tragic school shooting. The horrific violence at Columbine High School that occurred during the 1998–1999 school year (April 20th) resulted in the death of 12 students and one teacher, and left 21 wounded. The two assailants, students in the school, committed suicide. This tragedy heightened the public's anxiety, leading to more cries for security and mental health services (Altheide, 2009). It also resulted in further federal reports, including reports by the Federal Bureau of Investigation (O'Toole, 2000) and the Secret Service that focused more on the behavioral characteristics and histories of assailants and their environments. Even in these reports, the school climate was seen as a part of the four-pronged assessment to gauge the level of the student's threat to use violence. These four prongs included the student behaviors, family dynamics, school climate and connectedness, and the community culture (O'Toole, 2000). The FBI report implied that a trusting school environment, where there is caring and connection, is a positive factor in preventing serious school violence. These reports also supported early interventions and the value of peer support (avoiding the *code of silence* among students) in helping identify youth who are troubled. The reports also cautioned schools to avoid seeking a "checklist" of symptoms that may stigmatize some and produce false positives, impacting trust and depleting school mental health resources. In relation to threat assessment and intervention, the FBI report recommended schools have procedures that are consistent and that students have access to qualified mental health assessment and treatment services. Assessing threats requires trained personnel who can utilize a decision-making tree to determine if the threats are transient or serious. The Virginia Student Threat Assessment Guidelines (Cornell & Sheras, 2006) provides such a process. In addition, to using these guidelines in practice, professionals must consider all relevant ethical implications when conducting such threat assessments (Griffiths, Sharkey, & Furlong, 2008). Since the initial increase of school safety concerns in the 1990s, several strategies have been developed and implemented nationwide to help create safe school environments that focus on prevention and early intervention. Through the identification of student risk behaviors and the implementation of prevention and intervention efforts, we can continue in the promotion of safe school environments that foster academic achievement and social-emotional learning for all students.

CHAPTER TEN

The Scientific Evidence Supporting an Eight-Point Public Health-Oriented Action Plan to Prevent Gun Violence

Daniel J. Flannery, George Bear, Rami Benbenishty, Ron Avi Astor, Catherine P. Bradshaw, George Sugai, Dewey G. Cornell, Denise C. Gottfredson, Maury Nation, Shane R. Jimerson, Amanda B. Nickerson, Matthew J. Mayer, Russell J. Skiba, Mark D. Weist, Dorothy L. Espelage, Michael J. Furlong, Nancy G. Guerra, Robert J. Jagers, Pedro A. Noguera, Daniel W. Webster, and David Osher

School shootings and community gun violence happen more frequently in the United States than other developed nations. The United States cannot be great and realize its promise of life, liberty, and the pursuit of happiness if our children are not safe from gun violence. Although security measures are important, a focus on simply preparing for shootings is insufficient. We need a change in mindset and policy from reaction to prevention. Prevention entails more than security measures and begins long before a gunman comes to school. We need a comprehensive public health approach to gun violence that is informed by scientific evidence and free from partisan politics.

Following a series of serious acts of violence in U.S. schools in the spring of 2018, including the shooting at Stoneman Douglas High School in Parkland, Florida, a group of youth violence prevention researchers and experts came together to outline an "Action Plan" to prevent gun violence, which included the following three levels of prevention: (1) universal approaches promoting safety and well-being for everyone; (2) practices for reducing risk and promoting protective factors for persons experiencing difficulties; and (3) interventions for individuals where violence is present or appears imminent. The purpose of this chapter is to provide an overview of a multilevel public health approach to protecting children, as well as adults, from gun violence. After summarizing these three levels, we provide a brief overview of the evidence base for these practices and policies most relevant in the plan for school and community safety as it relates to gun violence prevention. As of May 2018, the Action Plan has been endorsed by 84 national organizations, 163 additional organizations, and over 4,400 individuals. This group of endorsers included multiple professional organizations representing over 5 million professionals working in and with schools, such as the American Counseling Association, American Federation of Teachers, American Psychological Association, Committee for Children, the National Education Association, National Parent Teacher Association, National Association of Secondary School Principals, National Association of School Psychologists, the National Association of Social Workers, and the Society for Prevention Research (https://curry.virginia.edu/prevent-gun-violence).

Overview of the Three-Level Prevention Plan

Level 1: Universal Approaches Promoting Safety and Well-being for Everyone

1. A national requirement for all schools to assess school climate and maintain physically and emotionally safe conditions and positive school environments that protect all students and adults from bullying, discrimination, harassment, and assault;
2. A ban on assault-style weapons, high-capacity ammunition clips, and products that modify semi-automatic firearms to enable them to function like automatic firearms.

Level 2: Practices for Reducing Risk and Promoting Protective Factors for Persons Experiencing Difficulties

3. Adequate staffing (e.g., counselors, psychiatrists, psychologists, nurses, and social workers) of coordinated school- and community-based mental health

services for individuals with risk factors for violence, recognizing that violence is not intrinsically a product of mental illness;

4. Reform of school discipline to reduce exclusionary practices and foster positive social, behavioral, emotional, and academic success for students;
5. Universal background checks for firearm purchases to screen out violent offenders, persons who have been hospitalized for violence towards self or others, and persons on no-fly, terrorist watch lists.

Level 3: Interventions for Individuals Where Violence Is Present or Appears Imminent

6. A national program to train and maintain school- and community-based threat assessment teams that include mental health and law enforcement partners. Threat assessment programs should include practical channels of communication for persons to report potential threats as well as interventions to resolve conflicts and assist troubled individuals;
7. Removal of legal barriers to sharing safety-related information among educational, mental health, and law enforcement agencies in cases where a person has threatened violence;
8. Laws establishing Gun Violence Protection Orders that allow courts to issue time-limited restraining orders requiring that firearms be recovered by law enforcement when there is evidence that an individual is planning to carry out acts against others or against themselves.

The Evidence-Base to Support the Plan

In the sections that follow, we provide a brief review of the relevant literature to support and implement this plan. Although not an exhaustive or complete review, we aim to stimulate additional attention, policy, and action by multiple stakeholders to enact elements of this plan to improve the safety of youth, adults, schools, and communities.

Social and Emotional Learning

One of the most effective means of improving child emotional well-being and competence is to expose them early on to universal preventive intervention efforts. The social and emotional learning (SEL) approach is consistent with multiple aspects of the Action Plan, but especially its emphasis on (a) preventive practices that foster positive social, behavioral, emotional, and academic success; (b) promoting protective factors and reducing risk factors; (c) creating and maintaining a positive school climate, which includes physical and emotional safety; and (d) reducing the use of exclusionary practices in school discipline. Related to each of those aspects of the Action Plan, the SEL focuses on the development of five areas of social and emotional learning (Durlak, Domitrovich, Weissberg, & Gullotta, 2015):

- *Self-awareness*—recognizing and understanding one's own thoughts, emotions, values, strengths, and weaknesses, and how they influence behavior. This incorporates self-concept, self-confidence, and self-efficacy.
- *Responsible decision-making at school, home, and in the community*—possessing and applying ethically guided problem-solving strategies and skills, including goal-setting, understanding of consequences for oneself and others, and persistence in the face of obstacles.
- *Self-management*—managing, or regulating, one's emotions, thoughts, and behavior across settings. This includes impulse control, stress management, organizational skills, setting goals and motivating oneself to achieve them, and persevering when faced with setbacks and obstacles.
- *Relationship skills*—establishing and maintaining positive and cooperative relationships with others; resisting peer pressure, resolving interpersonal conflicts peacefully, and respecting diversity and individual and group differences.
- *Social awareness*—accurately recognizing the feelings of others, assuming the perspective of others, experiencing empathy, recognizing and respecting individual and group differences, and seeking and using family, school, and community resources and supports, when needed.

Although SEL programs vary widely in their components and emphases, they share a focus on targeting not only behaviors but also cognitions and emotions related to each of the above areas of SEL—particularly those shown by research to underlie the targeted behavior. A large number of studies and several comprehensive reviews of the literature have demonstrated the effectiveness of SEL programs in preventing conduct problems and aggression, fostering academic engagement and achievement, and promoting mental health (for reviews, see Durlak, Weissberg, Dymnicki, Taylor, & Schellinger, 2011; Korpershoeck, Harms, de Boer, van Kuijk, & Doolaard, 2016; Taylor, Oberle, Durlak, & Weissberg, 2017). Durlak and colleagues' (2011) comprehensive meta-analysis concluded that a core feature of many SEL programs with demonstrated effectiveness used the format: Sequenced, Active, Focused, and Explicit (i.e., SAFE). That is, engaging lessons are taught in a *sequential* manner within and across school years; students play an *active*, rather than passive role in learning and applying SEL skills; professional development and sufficient time in the school day *focus* on developing SEL skills; and the skills and program goals are *explicit* (e.g., integrated into the school mission statement and linked to standards). The teaching of SEL lessons, presented either through a packaged program or integrated throughout the existing academic curriculum (e.g., into literacy, social studies, health), is a core feature of many evidence-based SEL programs (for extensive reviews of SEL programs, see https:// CASEL.org). Additional important features of SEL programs include the following areas (CASEL, 2017; Osher, Bear, Sprague, & Doyle, 2010):

Planned opportunities for students to observe, apply, practice, and further develop SEL competencies. It is not sufficient that students simply learn what to say (e.g., citing knowledge of SEL skills) and are able to demonstrate an SEL skill to an adult when asked to do so. A key aim of the SEL approach is that students demonstrate SEL skills under their own volition, across settings, and in the absence of adult monitoring and supervision. To help achieve this long-term aim, students are provided multiple opportunities throughout the school, as well as at home and in the community, to observe models of others demonstrating SEL skills (leveraging a range of models most students can identify with and demonstrating ways of overcoming challenges), to practice the skills themselves, and to come to value their importance. Opportunities are provided in such contexts as cooperative learning, conflict resolution and restorative justice learning opportunities, student government, sports and extracurricular activities, service learning, and cross-age mentoring.

Supportive and respectful relationships in school. Supportive teacher-student and student-student relationships not only promote the development of social and emotional competencies but also prevent behavior problems and promote safety (Danielsen, Wiium, Wilhelmsen, & Wold, 2010). Although research and many SEL programs highlight the importance of supportive teacher-student relationships, this component is seldom targeted in SEL and other prevention programs (Korpershoeck et al., 2016).

Support and coordination across classrooms, schools, home, and communities. Research in preventive science and school improvement has consistently emphasized the importance of support and coordination across important stakeholders. This includes the provision of multitiered supports and resources, as well as ongoing professional development (Weissberg, Durlak, Domitrovich, & Gullotta, 2015). Of particular importance in the maintenance and generalization of SEL skills is working closely with the families of students.

Classroom management and school discipline practices that emphasize prevention and development of self-discipline rather than *use* of discipline as a consequence. Consistent with the Action Plan, the SEL approach emphasizes disciplinary practices shown to greatly limit the need for punishment and especially exclusionary practices like removing students from the classroom or suspension. Drawing largely from decades of research on effective classroom management for preventing behavior problems (Bear, 2015) but also integrating practices more central to the aims of the SEL approach, emphases are placed on the following evidence-based strategies: (a) clear procedures and routines, high behavioral expectation, and fair rules and consequences; (b) frequent monitoring and supervision of behavior, and immediate response to early signs of misbehavior; (c) developmentally appropriate instruction and lessons that are motivating; (d) the wise and strategic use of praise and rewards, which includes using them in a manner that does not harm intrinsic motivation and moral development; (e) building and maintaining supportive teacher-student, student-student, and home-school relationships, which includes students, teachers, and parents sharing responsibility for student behavior; and (f) a physical environment that is conducive to teaching and safety, and to the development of social, emotional, and academic skills. In applying each of those strategies, a focus is on teaching, learning, and applying the core SEL skills of self-management, responsible decision-making, relationship skills, social awareness, and self-awareness. This can occur, for example, during class meetings and supportive disciplinary encounters that emphasize perspective taking, empathy, peer support, responsible decision-making, and social problem-solving.

School Climate and School Connectedness

Another critical aspect of the Action Plan's emphasis on universal preventive interventions to address gun violence is to focus on improving school climate, as well as student connectedness to school, and building positive relationships with peers and adults. Positive school climate and school connectedness have both been documented as important factors associated with promoting safe, supportive, and effective schools.

There is a substantial and growing literature indicating that school climate is an important influence on students' behavior (for a review, see Thapa, Cohen, Guffey, & Higgins-D'Alessandro, 2013). Generally, school climate is used to describe the social and cultural milieu within a school. The specific elements of school climate vary across studies, but most include perceptions of relationships among students and teachers, safety, and rules and norms for student behavior. More expansive conceptualizations of school climate include additional constructs such as school connectedness or belonging, and student engagement (Bradshaw, Waasdorp, Debnam, & Lindstrom Johnson, 2014). Positive school climate has been linked to myriad youth developmental and educational outcomes including improved academic achievement and graduation rates, and decreases in emotional and behavioral problems (Thapa et al., 2013). For example, several studies have shown that secondary schools characterized by authoritative characteristics of high expectations for students and supportive teacher-student relationships have higher student engagement, academic performance, and graduation rates (Cornell, Shukla, & Konold, 2016), but lower rates of bullying and peer aggression (Cornell, Shukla, & Konold, 2015), less aggression toward teachers (Berg & Cornell, 2016), and less involvement in risk behaviors such as substance use and weapon carrying (Cornell & Huang, 2016).

As it relates to school violence and safety, there are some clear and direct associations between school climate and physical safety at school. Negative school climate, for example, has been associated with higher rates of bullying/peer victimization and behavior problems (Cornell et al., 2015). In turn, positive school climate has been associated with lower risk behaviors among students, including decreases in bullying behavior and aggressive attitudes (Klein, Cornell, & Konold, 2012).

Numerous studies indicate a connection between school climate and emotional safety. Students are more likely to seek help from adults in schools where there is a positive climate (Williams & Cornell, 2006). This finding is consistent with other studies that indicate that students in schools with a positive climate report better mental health, higher self-esteem, and a stronger sense of connectedness to school. School climate research also highlights a paradox in which observable security measures such as school resource officers (SROs) and metal detectors (measures designed to improve safety) do not consistently improve students' sense of safety and may have iatrogenic effects on overall school climate (Lindstrom Johnson, Bottiani, Debnam, & Bradshaw, 2018).

Research has repeatedly demonstrated the importance of student engagement at school (i.e., school connectedness) as an indicator associated with student achievement and positive behavior in schools. Student engagement represents a student's sense of belonging and connectedness with his or her school. Typically, school engagement is measured by obtaining a student's perception of affective, behavioral, and cognitive indicators of his or her connections with teachers, peers, and activities at school. There is a consistent positive association between teacher and student reports of behavioral engagement and achievement. Moreover, a higher level of cognitive engagement is found to be positively related to students' in-depth understanding and synthesis of academic material. That can be a pivotal issue in more toxic school environments where teachers are challenged to provide vibrant, engaging lessons, and students may have difficulty focusing on learning. This can set the stage for a somewhat debilitating cycle relative to achieving the understanding and synthesis of academic material, and related to that, improved cognitive engagement.

Student engagement also relates to a wide range of developmental and adjustment outcomes, such as substance use, delinquency, antisocial behavior, and self-esteem. Positive student engagement has been linked to student perception of safety of their school, increased hope, life satisfaction, and decreased bully victimization. Research examining the impact of student engagement at school on academic and behavioral outcomes highlights the importance of this construct in promoting safe, supportive, and effective schools (Bradshaw et al., 2014; Thapa et al., 2013).

Bystander Intervention

Research across a number of fields has highlighted the important role of youth intervention or "bystander intervention" in a range of violence- and aggression-related situations, including bullying, fighting, and school violence (Nickerson, Aloe, Livingston, & Feely, 2014; Waasdorp & Bradshaw, 2018). Two converging phenomena implicate the important contributions of bystanders in the prevention of school shootings: (a) in a large majority of school shootings, the perpetrators leaked their intentions to one or more individuals prior to the attacks; and (b) when school shootings have been averted, it was most often due to reports made by concerned individuals who became aware of the attackers' plans (Daniels et al., 2007; Madfis, 2014). Although the obvious solution appears to be to just get students, staff, parents, and community members to step forward and make a report, it is not that simple. As Stueve and colleagues (2006) have noted, "under what circumstances should youth and adult bystanders come forward with information about potential violence? When should bystanders try to defuse violent situations themselves, when should they involve authorities, and when should they 'mind their own business'" (p. 117)? Strategies that address contextual factors that foster school-community bystander expectations and behavior are informed by core social psychology research.

For example, it is well documented in social psychology and related fields that although individuals often see and hear high-risk or emergency situations (e.g., violent crimes), they are unlikely to intervene due to the diffusion of responsibility that occurs when other people are present (Latané & Nida, 1981). This phenomenon also occurs in relation to threats of violence, bullying, and sexual assault. Although students and other community members see and hear potential or actual indicators of violence, many barriers prevent them from intervening, including the presence of others, fear of retaliation, costs (e.g., time, effort, personal distress), relationships with the person(s) involved, and perceptions about peer norms (see Meter & Card, 2015). Mobilizing bystanders to intervene by reporting incidents, getting the person out of the threatening situation, seeking help, or supporting the victim is a key focus of many prevention and intervention efforts.

The classic bystander intervention model (Latané & Darley, 1970) includes a five-step process. The first step is for someone to notice the event, as something has to be observed in order for one to intervene. Next, one must interpret the situation as an emergency, or a serious enough issue that help is required. Third, one must accept personal responsibility for intervening, as opposed to believing that someone else will help. Next, the person must have the knowledge of how to help, whether that is who to report to or how to intervene directly to deescalate a situation. The final step of the model is to act on the decision to help. This bystander intervention model has been found to be applicable to sexual harassment, bullying (Nickerson et al., 2014), and other high-risk or violent situations. Indeed, mobilizing bystanders to intervene directly or indirectly has been found to be effective in decreasing bullying victimization (Garandeau, Poskiparta, & Salmivalli, 2014) and other threats of violence (Daniels et al., 2007).

A safe climate in schools and communities is characterized by relationships in which people are willing to support others and seek help for concerns. Students whose peers intervene to defend them when they are being bullied are more likely to perceive their schools as safe (Gini, Pozzoli, Borghi, & Franzoni, 2008). If the environment makes students and other members of a community fear that bystander intervention will result in retaliation, ineffectual responses, or being perceived negatively by peers, they will be less likely to take the risk to help others. In schools where the peer culture endorses and supports aggressive behavior, students are less likely to stand up against bullying (Millspaugh, Cornell, Huang, & Datta, 2015) and less likely to report a threat of violence such as a student bringing a gun to school (Datta, Cornell, & Huang, 2016). Therefore, in addition to explicit teaching and training students, school personnel, and community members about how to take appropriate action as a bystander, it is important that this be done while also creating an environment that will be most likely to encourage and support bystander intervention.

School Threat Assessment

The sixth point of the Action Plan calls for a national program to train and maintain school- and community-based threat assessment teams that include mental health and law enforcement partners. Threat assessment programs should include practical channels of communication for persons to report potential threats as well as interventions to resolve conflicts and assist troubled individuals. Threat assessment is a systematic process of evaluation and intervention for persons who have communicated threats to harm others.

After the 1999 Columbine school shooting, law enforcement authorities recommended that threat assessment be adapted for schools (e.g., O'Toole,

2000). In response, a group at the University of Virginia developed a threat assessment model for schools, recognizing that educators face unique threat assessment challenges in working with children and adolescents, and must uphold the goal of helping every student succeed (Cornell & Sheras, 2006). The resulting Virginia Student Threat Assessment Guidelines (VSTAG) uses school-based multidisciplinary teams consisting of school administration, mental health professionals, and law enforcement officers.

Threat assessment teams strive to avoid two errors: (1) overreacting to student misbehavior that does not pose a serious threat of violence, and (2) underreacting to troubled students on a pathway to violence. Threats vary from figures of speech and jokes to expressions of frustration or anger, and their purpose can vary from merely seeking attention to communicating an intent to attack. Unlike a zero tolerance approach to discipline that applies the same severe consequences to all cases regardless of the circumstances, a threat assessment process must be flexible and responses must be calibrated to the seriousness of the situation. The VSTAG model takes a problem-solving approach to violence prevention, recognizing that serious threats of violence arise when someone has become distressed and frustrated over a problem they cannot solve, and the most effective strategy is to assist the individual in resolving that problem. Controlled studies have found that schools using the VSTAG model have decreased use of school suspension and increased use of school counseling, and that students and teachers report a safer and more supportive school climate (Cornell, Allen, & Fan, 2012; Nekvasil & Cornell, 2015).

In 2013, Virginia legislation mandated that all K–12 public schools establish threat assessment teams. A statewide analysis of 1,865 cases found that fewer than 1% of student threats were carried out and no cases resulted in a serious physical injury (Cornell & Maeng, 2017). Less than half (43%) of the students received an out-of-school suspension and approximately 1% were expelled. A follow-up study (Cornell, Maeng, Huang, Shukla, & Konold, 2018) found no statistically significant racial disparities between black, Hispanic, and white students in out-of-school suspensions, expulsions, school transfer, or legal actions (arrest, incarceration, or criminal charges).

In 2018, Congress passed legislation that would fund national training in threat assessment for schools. Threat assessment teams can operate in both school and community settings, permitting coordination of services and coverage of threats made by persons who are not students. Threat assessment is valuable so that students (and others) are not stigmatized or punished for minor misbehavior. At the same time, threat assessment can identify individuals in need of mental health services and other support. In the small number of very serious threats, teams can recognize the danger and take appropriate protective action in collaboration with law enforcement.

School Resource Officers

School shootings are almost always followed by calls to increase the physical safety of students by using technology and security devices—including metal detectors, locks, monitoring systems, improved lighting—and by increasing the presence of law enforcement officers and other security personnel on campuses. For example, the school shooting at Stoneman Douglas High School in Parkland, Florida, was followed by calls to arm teachers and other school staff with concealed handguns. Although these responses are understandable, they do not reflect what is known about how to create safe schools. We know very little about the effectiveness of security practices such as those mentioned earlier. Studies have found that schools using more security measures both increase and decrease student victimization levels. In a recent study that looked at this relationship longitudinally, Fisher, Mowen, and Boman (2018) found that adolescents in schools with more security measures later report *higher* odds of being threatened with harm, a finding consistent with the possibility that overreliance on security measures may erode the school climate and promote victimizing behaviors. No effects of increased security were found on other forms of victimization. A decision to increase use of these security measures in order to improve school safety is inconsistent with the existing research on this topic.

Arming teachers as a means to increase school safety is an ill-advised policy option. In a recent essay responding to calls to arm North Carolina teachers, Cook (2018) points out that if a policy to arm teachers resulted in 10 teachers in every school carrying a concealed handgun, 1.3 million additional guns would be added to U.S. schools. These guns might be fired accidentally, the teachers who carry them might deliberately use them for unintended purposes, and, even more likely, the guns might end up in the hands of students. A recent study of hospital-based shootings, for example, found that 23% of all shootings that happen in hospital emergency departments were with guns taken from armed guards who were posted there for protection (Kelen, Catlett, Kubit, & Hsieh, 2012). In general, the available research suggests that more guns are likely to lead to more gun violence.

A more common response to school shootings has been to increase law enforcement presence in schools. Indeed, the practice of placing police officers in schools has sky-rocketed over the past 30 years. In the 1970s, virtually no schools had law enforcement officers stationed in them.[1] By 2013, 70% of schools had security or police officers assigned to the school (Musu-Gillette et al., 2017). How has this major shift in the use of security or law enforcement personnel in schools affected school safety? Recent reviews of the effect of increasing police presence in schools agree that, all else equal, schools with police report more crimes to law enforcement than schools without police (Devlin & Gottfredson, 2018). This might suggest that schools are safer with than without police, especially if the referrals to law enforcement typically result in removing potentially dangerous students from the schools. However, the research suggests instead that police presence is associated only with increases in the reporting of *non-serious* crimes reported to law enforcement. The practice does not increase the reporting of serious crime to law enforcement, most likely because these crimes are reported to law enforcement regardless of whether or not police are present (Na & Gottfredson, 2011). The most rigorous study of police presence in schools to date also found that increased police presence is related to increased arrest rates, particularly for youth under the age of 15 (Owens, 2017).

Unfortunately, estimates of the effect of police presence on less ambiguous indicators of school safety are difficult to come by. Although several relevant studies have been conducted, most have methodological shortcomings that prevent confident conclusions about the effect of police on school safety from being drawn.[2] Reviews of this research (Devlin & Gottfredson, 2018; Hirschfield, 2018) conclude that we simply do not know whether adding law enforcement officers to school settings increases safety, decreases safety, or makes no difference. The recent school shooting incident in Parkland, Florida, however, demonstrated clearly that the presence of police officers in schools does not fully protect schools from experiencing school shootings, as the law enforcement officer stationed at the school failed to intervene to stop the shooter (http://www.sun-sentinel.com/local/broward/parkland/florida-school-shooting/fl-florida-shooting-sro-20180222-story.html).

Any policy adopted in an attempt to increase school safety should have a reasonable expectation of actually increasing safety. "School hardening" policies involving increased security measures and law enforcement presence do not pass this test. Further, because these strategies carry substantial risk for negative outcomes, they should be avoided. Many of the proposed strategies discussed in this chapter aim to protect students and youth by promoting a more cohesive school environment in which expectations for behavior are clear and "normal" sanctions are consistently applied in response to rule-breaking. In sharp contrast to school hardening efforts, strategies to promote these protective environments have been demonstrated through rigorous scientific research to increase school safety. These strategies should clearly be preferred over school hardening strategies.

Positive Behavioral Interventions and Supports

A number of programs and strategies have been developed and demonstrated significant impacts on youth violence, including acts of aggression, violence, and bullying at school (for reviews, see Matjasko et al., 2012; National Academies of Science, Engineering, and Medicine, 2016). Equally important as selecting and implementing evidence-based violence prevention interventions is making the right decision about which practice or program to select and then implementing it in an accurate, culturally responsive, and sustainable manner. One system or framework for maximizing the impact and outcomes of evidence-based practices is Positive Behavioral Interventions and Supports (PBIS; Sugai & Horner, 2006).

PBIS is a prevention-based framework modeled after the public health approach to disease prevention. The framework is used to select and organize evidence-based practices into a three-tiered continuum (i.e., universal, targeted, indicated) that supports the academic and behavioral success of all students. Tier 1 is the foundation for positive schoolwide and classroom climate or culture and is particularly important for (a) preventing the development of antisocial behavior, (b) screening for and supporting students with high risk for mental health needs, (c) enhancing the climate and organizational health of the school, (d) reducing the rates of reactive management (e.g., office discipline referrals for major offenses, in and out of school suspensions), (e) reducing bullying, and (f) increasing student prosocial behavior and emotional regulation (see Bradshaw, Waasdorp, & Leaf, 2012; Bradshaw, Mitchell, & Leaf, 2010).

From a violence prevention perspective, PBIS Tier 1 has two main purposes. The first purpose is to establish a positive social culture in which all students and staff and family members have a common vision about important social and emotional behaviors, a common language for personal and interpersonal communications, and common procedures for typical places and routines (e.g., making transitions, handling disagreements, asking for assistance). Research indicates that when achieved, these school and classroom environments are rated by students and staff members as positive school climates and to have less problem behavior, such as bullying (see Bradshaw, Waasdorp, & Leaf, 2012; Horner et al., 2009). In addition, these supportive environments enable schools to be better prepared for crisis and emergency situations by (a) early screening for and acting on risk factors, (b) having formal response routines in place, and (c) supporting students and faculty and family members after a traumatic incident.

The second Tier 1 purpose is to explicitly and continuously teach, practice, and reinforce setting-specific (e.g., hallways, cafeteria, playground, assemblies, bus) behavior expectations (e.g., "walk to the right in the hallways is being responsible," "when in a disagreement, stop and think before you act respectfully," "use helping safe words when a friend is being teased," "being safe on the playground is reporting to teacher if a stranger is on playground"). Equally important, teaching of social skills is linked to three to five character traits or values (e.g., "respect self, others, and environment," "be safe, be respectful, be responsible, be a learner"), and frequent informative acknowledgments (e.g., "Well done, thank you for letting us know about that suspicious note. You were responsible for keeping our school safe").

Students who are fluent with important social skills are better prepared to (a) reduce the likelihood of problem situations occurring, (b) respond to antisocial behaviors when they are occurring, and (c) navigate confusion and stress after a traumatic incident.

Utilizing local data to facilitate decision-making, school leadership teams provide guidance and coaching regarding the development, adaptation, and sustained implementation of a continuum of evidence-based practices that are linked to multiple academic, social, emotional, and behavioral student outcomes. As a team-based, whole school approach, implementation efforts are shaped by local cultural and contextual norms. As such, student voice and participation, family communications, and formal collaborations with community agents are important to shaping a more culturally responsive and contextually relevant implementation of evidence-based practices.

As schools seek to promote safety and reduce the risk of violence, partnerships with the local mental health system have the potential to add strength to a multitiered system of support (MTSS) involving Tier 1 promotion-prevention, Tier 2 early identification and intervention, and more intensive Tier 3 intervention (Barrett, Eber, & Weist, 2013). However, there are a number of considerations to ensure these partnerships are successful, including: (1) establishing memoranda of agreement between the school district and local mental health system, (2) integrating the clinician into the MTSS and assuring effective team functioning, and (3) optimizing the roles of all staff on the MTSS in implementing evidence-based practices.

Integrating elements of SWPBS and SEL. An emerging literature suggests that schools should jointly leverage aspects of SEL and School Wide Positive Behavior Supports (SWPBS). Osher, Bear, Sprague, and Doyle (2010) argued that neither SEL nor SWPBS, which are each necessary to meet a range of student needs, can be sufficient for many school communities with more complex needs. The issue of moving from standalone prevention, promotion, and intervention approaches to more complex integrated models was addressed by Domitrovich et al. (2010), where the authors predicted "additive and synergistic effects" that would lead to improved student outcomes. The authors discussed combining the PAX-Good Behavior Game and the Promoting Alternative THinking Strategies (PATHS) curriculum into the PATHS to PAX model. Bradshaw and colleagues (2014) further discussed the idea of blending approaches, with particular focus on leveraging elements of PBIS and SEL, building a strong case for the approach, and providing a roadmap for change to the field. Cook and colleagues (2015) reported on outcome research, demonstrating reductions in externalizing behaviors and overall improved mental health from an approach that blended elements of SEL and PBIS, where the results were superior to interventions using either SEL or

PBIS alone. Extending on this literature, a loose analogy can be drawn between the ideas behind blending elements of SEL and PBIS, and providing an authoritative schooling model, where recent research has demonstrated beneficial outcomes from such models. Well over 15,000 schools across the nation have committed to a SWPBS model and likewise, a similar number to a SEL model. Emerging research and practice suggests that an exploration of key research questions and demonstration model research are timely next steps for the field over the next 5 to 10 years, as we take what has been learned and further develop approaches that combine elements of PBIS and SEL.

Establishing memoranda of agreement (MOAs) to effectively coordinate services between schools and mental health providers. As the movement toward mental health systems in schools has grown in recent decades (Weist, Lever, Bradshaw, & Owens, 2014), an emerging concern is to avoid *co-located* services, or clinicians operating in isolation or in parallel to the school's MTSS efforts. In this regard, a foundational strategy is to establish clear MOAs between the school and collaborating mental health centers. These MOAs should indicate the expectation that the clinician is an active participant on the MTSS team, helping to guide and implement programs and services at all tiers. They should also specify hours and days worked by the clinician (ideally with daily start and end times that at least match hours worked by education employees), services provided (e.g., focused assessment; individual, group and family therapies), particular evidence-based practices (EBPs) to be implemented, and quality improvement and evaluation strategies. For example, in Baltimore, in order for community clinicians to deliver services in the schools, they are required to undergo common training in EBPs, conduct common evaluation activities, engage in quality assurance, and report on progress along key dimensions, such as student emotional, behavioral, and academic functioning (Weist, Paternite, Wheatley-Rowe, & Gall, 2009).

Integrating clinician into the MTSS and assuring effective team functioning. Mental health clinicians often play a primary role in delivering Tier 3, or treatment services. However, when MOAs as above specify active roles on teams, and involvement in Tier 1 and 2 services, clinicians are better able to assist in schoolwide efforts (e.g., bullying prevention, assuring safe and supportive schools) and early intervention (e.g., providing support to teachers in classrooms). MTSS teams should be inclusive (e.g., school- and community-employed mental health staff, teachers, school health staff, administrators, family members) and should follow systematic strategies to assure effective decision-making, implementation, and refinement of EBPs, such as the Team Implemented Problem Solving (TIPS) system developed by researchers connected to the national Center for Positive Behavioral Interventions and Supports (see https://www.pbis.org/training/tips).

Optimizing roles of all staff on the MTSS in implementing evidence-based practices. In addition to assuring that clinicians are able to be active in programs at Tiers 1 and 2, efforts focusing on improving school safety should also assure that school-employed staff such as psychologists and counselors are able to be fully engaged in prevention and intervention. This requires school leadership to analyze roles of these staff, moving away from primary emphases on traditional roles (e.g., school psychologists conducting evaluations, counselors providing academic advisement), and involving them in EBPs at all tiers of the MTSS. Ideally, school- and community-employed staff collaborate in delivering these EBPs. An example would be clinicians and counselors working together to assist teachers in delivering the Support for Students Exposed to Trauma (SSET) program (Jaycox et al., 2009). SSET is a structured 10 session program delivered in classrooms to provide education about trauma and key skills associated with recovery from exposure, and also emphasizes this critical approach for improving school safety (i.e., providing early intervention and assistance to students exposed to trauma).

Addressing Theoretical, Empirical, and Policy Gaps on Weapons in the School Context

Mass shootings in school are having a major impact on practice, policy, and legislation. But most research and policy formulations related to guns in school focus mainly on shootings and ignore other weapon-related behaviors in schools. Weapons at school affect far more students in the United States than those involved in a fatal shooting, either as victim or bystander, but that is an issue that is rarely addressed. We endorse a theoretical conceptualization of school violence in which the school context is at the center (Astor & Benbenishty, 2019; Benbenishty & Astor, 2005). The school is embedded in multiple interrelated and nested contexts that impact the school. School climate, policies, and organization mediate and moderate the influence of the outside context and are responsible for final outcomes, such as bullying, weapon victimization, academic achievement, suicide, and student and staff well-being.

This model highlights the relationships between multiple types of victimization and perpetration (i.e., physical, social, sexual, cyber, and weapon-related) that occur at school. It also acknowledges the differences in epistemology, predictors, and consequences of the specific types of school violence behaviors and weapon behaviors on school grounds. This conceptualization provides a nuanced approach to researching weapons in school. It also highlights new ways to incorporate weapon behaviors into the school safety literature with stronger links to school climate, social and emotional learning, and bullying prevention interventions. Consistent with this conceptual framework, we outline five steps that are intended to help advance school-based, weapon-related research and policy.

1. **Focus broadly on weapon-related victimization and focus less on firearms, shootings, and mass murder.** In the aftermath of a mass school shooting, researchers and policy makers tend to focus on the prevention of future mass shootings. To a large extent, the school safety research literature has overlooked the larger impact of weapons on students and on the school as a community. This is problematic since research suggests that most gun-related incidents and injuries at school are not the result of mass shootings (Shultz, Cohen, Muschert & Flores de Apodaca, 2013) and that many more students are affected by the presence of weapons on school grounds than are victims of shootings. According to the Centers for Disease Control and Prevention, in 2015, 4.1% of students nationwide reported carrying a weapon on school grounds (5.9% among males) and 6% had been threatened or injured with a weapon on school property one or more times during the 12 months before the survey (Kann et al., 2016). In California, self-report data suggest that over the past decade 20% to 30% of secondary school students have seen a weapon at their school within the most recent 12-month period (Astor & Benbenishty, 2019). Moreover, 3% to 5% of students reported bringing a firearm to school, while 7% to 9% reported being threatened on school grounds with a weapon (California Healthy Kids Survey). Together, in California alone, this accounts for hundreds of thousands of middle and high students affected by weapons each year at school (Astor & Benbenishty, 2019).

   Each of these weapon-related behaviors can affect student well-being and school connectedness. Seeing or knowing about weapons on school grounds can dramatically affect perceptions of safety. Even rumors about a student bringing a weapon to school with the intention of harming someone has negative implications for school safety. Urban schools and especially students of color disproportionally experience such ongoing, daily exposure to weapon violence and threats. In general, research and policy efforts do not address these more widespread and persistent weapon-related behaviors in schools, even though nationwide, these issues affect millions of students annually. A broad research agenda that focuses on the full range of weapon-related violence in schools is needed to benefit all students, as well as the adults who work in schools. Even more concerning is the fact that many schools have a chronic weapon problem, with a large proportion of students affected by weapons on school grounds. Table 10.1, for example, shows the distribution of weapon-related behaviors in over 1,800 California high schools.

Table 10.1 Distribution (percentage) of weapon-related behaviors in schools (N = 1,849)

Percentage of Students in the School	Carried a Gun	Carried Knife or Club	Threatened or Injured with a Weapon	Saw Someone Carrying a Weapon
0.00	10.2	4.3	4.8	0.5
0.01–1.99	11.2	0.9	1.5	0.0
2.00–3.99	32.7	7.4	10.0	0.1
4.00–5.99	22.5	14.0	21.4	0.2
6.00–7.99	21.3	19.8	22.0	0.8
8.00–14.99	9.0	39.5	33.3	9.8
15.00+	3.3	12.1	7.0	88.6

In 88.6% of secondary schools in California, at least 15% of the students reported seeing a gun in school. In about 90% of schools, at least one student reported carrying a gun to school in the previous year, and in 12.1% of the schools, at least 15% of the students admitted bringing a knife to school. The high prevalence and the skewed distribution of weapon-related behaviors in schools suggests that a comprehensive public health approach should be attempted with a focus on identifying schools with especially high rates of weapon-related behaviors reported by students. Taken together these data, along with the findings reported in table 10.1, suggest that additional research is needed to better understand a range of issues related to weapon carrying, such as why students bring weapons to school, what other types of weapons in addition to guns students carry, students' experiences of being threatened at school with a weapon, and the impact of seeing or hearing about weapons on school grounds.

2. **Address the role of gangs in understanding and preventing weapons in schools.**

With weapon-related victimization in schools, the impact of gangs on school climate needs to be recognized and addressed. Traditionally, gang research has been focused on the sociology of the community. Some studies have explored schools situated in communities with high gang activity. Few studies have explored the convergence of school safety and gang affiliation of students, or the possibility that school social dynamics and organizations may be contributing to gang activity. However, there are strong empirical indications that with regard to weapons on school grounds gangs are associated with weapon carrying, threats by weapons, and seeing a weapon on school grounds (Estrada, Huerta, Hernandez, Hernandez, & Kim, 2018).

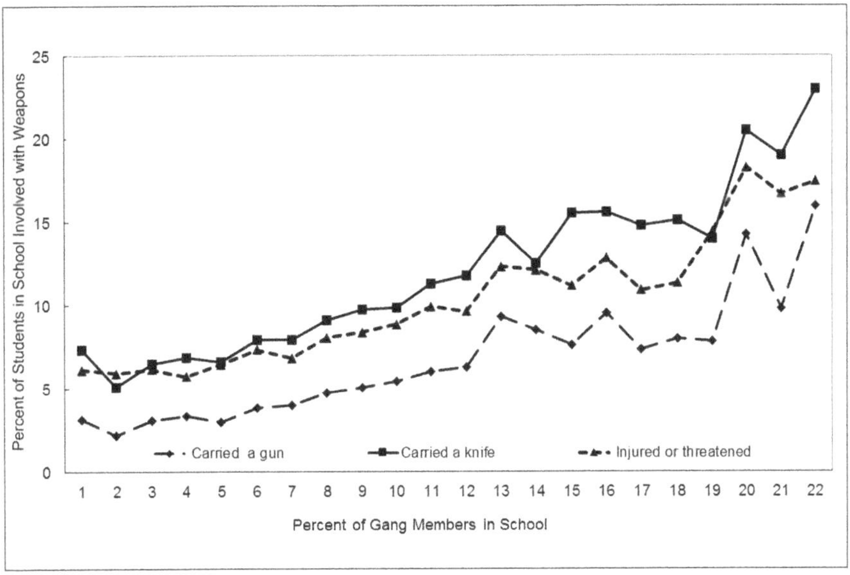

Figure 10.1 School-level percentage of students involved with weapons by percentage of gang members in school

School safety researchers should explore multiple means of creating a supportive context that reduce students' need for gang affiliation (Astor & Benbenishty, 2019; Estrada, Gilreath, Astor, & Benbenishty, 2016). Figure 10.1 shows the association between the percent of gang members in a school and the corresponding percent of students who bring a knife or a gun and that are threatened by weapons in that school. This figure suggests a strong association between the presence of gang members in school and the prevalence of weapon-related problems in school.

3. **Combine an empowerment strategy with a school-centric public health monitoring approach.** Based on Astor and colleagues' monitoring framework (e.g. Astor & Benbenishty, 2018; Astor, Jacobson, Wrabel, Benbenishty & Pineda, 2017), local empowerment solutions that encourage and learn from the voices of students and educators increase the chances of effective and sustainable interventions because they better fit the circumstances of a local school and district. Local responses are built and designed around the input of students and staff members who can provide reliable and valid views of the needs of a district and school. Furthermore, by empowering and engaging students and staff members in the process of responding to local challenges, a climate of trust is created that is necessary for reducing weapon-related victimization. For example, with the mapping procedure (Astor & Benbenishty, 2018), students and teachers map hot spot locations, times and areas in the school where violent behaviors occur. This data is

then aggregated and presented back to focus groups of students and teachers where they discuss why these locations and times are riskier. They also generate local solutions that involve students, teachers, and administrators. To illustrate this, in one school they identified routes to and from school that were dangerous and suggested alternative routes and supervision, peer support strategies, and bus stop changes that significantly reduced risk in that school. This monitoring and empowerment strategy fits well with a public health approach to weapon-related victimization on school grounds. Through local voice it is possible to: (a) identify vulnerable schools through surveys and incident data from multiple school participants, including staff members, students, and administrators; (b) employ preventive measures, before tragic events occur; and (c) focus on providing resources (including pupil personnel, such as social workers, counselors, and psychologists) to vulnerable schools and communities. School-related interventions need to link to comprehensive efforts to address the challenges of the local community as a whole.

4. **Employ professional discretion and a range of alternatives to weapon-related discipline.** Instead of predetermined zero-tolerance discipline responses (e.g., suspension and exclusion), staff members need to weigh the specific characteristics of the student, the gravity of the offense, student recidivism, and any mitigating circumstances. There needs to be a better empirical understanding on how to do this in the best way. There is very little research on which disciplinary processes work best in specific situations where weapon use is involved. There should be a range of responses to weapon-related violations that are gradual and sequential in nature and which reflect the seriousness of the weapon involvement. These responses may range from ongoing educational interventions (such as class discussions of the perils of weapons on school grounds), counseling, threat assessment (Cornell, Allen, & Fan, 2012), and restorative justice measures implemented as part of school policies, suspensions, expulsions, and referrals to the justice system. There is a clear need to integrate professional development regarding fair and effective disciplinary responses around weapon behaviors into the implementation of disciplinary practices.

   In situations where all other measures have failed, it is essential to strengthen the effectiveness of alternative schools. There is too little systematic empirical research on expelled and referred students sent to alternative schools. More studies are needed about programs or practices that reintegrate these students back into regular schools. Research can provide an empirical picture of best practices or pathways to reintegration.

5. **Expand accountability for weapon-related challenges beyond individual schools.** Addressing the challenges of weapons in school is a burden that educators and school leaders cannot bear alone. Districts, counties, and states should take responsibility for implementing policies and providing resources to schools to help prevent weapon-related victimization. These

higher-level organizational units have the knowledge and resources to monitor the prevalence of weapon-related incidents and to help identify and target school sites that need support (Astor & Benbenishty, 2019).

Finally, weapon-related victimization has some unique aspects that clearly distinguish it from other forms of school victimization, such as socially isolating and humiliating students based on characteristics such as gender, sexual orientation, ethnic affiliation, and physical and mental characteristics. Nevertheless, within schools, many of these different types of victimization and perpetration behaviors intersect and exacerbate each other. Hence, efforts to prevent weapon-related victimization should not be isolated. Dealing with weapon-related victimization needs to be an integral part of school policies and practices that aim to create a supportive and safe school climate that promotes students' social, emotional, and academic development.

Avoid the Harmful. Besides its greater likelihood of preventing violence, a national plan should avoid or mitigate the iatrogenic consequences of more police presence and more exclusionary discipline. This is important because in the interest of one type of safety—physical safety—schools may undermine other aspects of safety. Safety is more than physical safety; it includes emotional safety, psychological safety, and identity safety (Osher, Moroney, & Williamson, 2018), and involves effects over a child's life course. The presence of additional security personal and the use of exclusionary discipline can undermine student learning, wellness, and development (American Academy of Pediatrics, 2013; Osher, Cantor, Berg, Strayer, & Rose, 2018) and these harmful effects, which are particularly pronounced for many students of color, particularly African American Students, as well as for first- and second-generation immigrant students, GLBTQ students, and students with high incidence disabilities (Anyon, Zhang, & Hazel, 2016, Okonofua, Walton, & Eberhardt, 2016).

Two harmful effects are particularly notable. The first is the amplification of the school to prison pipeline, which has harmful life course effects on children, youth, families, and communities (Kirk & Sampson, 2011, 2013; Osher, Woodruff, & Sims, 2002; Theriot, 2009; Western, 2006). The second is undermining student connectedness (Anyon et al., 2016; Bachman, Randolph, & Brown, 2011; Gastic, 2011; Hankin, Hertz, & Simon, 2011; Morgan, Salomon, Plotkin, & Cohen, 2014; Theriot, 2009). School connectedness, which was defined by Resnick and colleagues (1997) as the perception of safety, belonging, respect, and being cared for, can contribute to the prevention of risky behaviors and mental health problems including emotional distress, suicidal ideation and attempts (Blum, McNeely, & Rinehart, 2002; Cairns & Cairns, 1994; Goodenow, 1993; Resnick et al., 1997; Yang & Anyon, 2016).

Conclusion

This chapter provides the evidence base for the core components of a national Action Plan to prevent gun violence, with specific attention to gun violence in schools. Congress and the executive branch must remove barriers to gun violence research and institute a program of scientific research on gun violence that encompasses all levels of prevention. We contend that well-executed laws can reduce gun violence while protecting all constitutional rights. It is time for federal and state authorities to take immediate action to enact these proposals and provide adequate resources for effective implementation. We call on law enforcement, mental health, and educational agencies to begin actions supporting these prevention efforts. We ask all parents and youth to join efforts advocating for these changes, and we urge voters to elect representatives who will take effective action to prevent gun violence in our nation.

Notes

1. Data from the Safe School Study, a national study of school violence conducted in 1976 by Research Triangle Institute for the National Institute of Education (NIE), showed that only 1% of the nation's schools had police stationed in them (NIE, 1978).

2. For example, some studies find that when police are placed in schools, crimes increase. This finding is ambiguous, however, because the studies measure school safety outcomes using official records of school crime, which may be influenced by the placement of police in schools. Clearly, more rigorous research using outcomes measures that are not reactive to the intervention being tested is needed.

References

American Academy of Pediatrics. (2013). Out of school suspension and expulsion. *Pediatrics, 131*, 1000–1007. Retrieved from http://pediatrics.aappublications.org/content/131/3/e1000.full.pdf+html

Anyon, Y., Zhang, D., & Hazel, C. (2016). Race, exclusionary discipline, and connectedness to adults in secondary schools. *American Journal of Community Psychology, 57*, 342–352.

Appleton, J. J., Christenson, S. L., & Furlong, M. J. (2008). Student engagement with school: Critical conceptual and methodological issues of the construct. *Psychology in the Schools, 45*, 369–386. doi:10.1002/pits.20303

Astor, R. A., & Benbenishty, R. (2018). *Mapping and monitoring bullying and violence: Building a safe school climate.* New York: Oxford University Press.

Astor, R. A., & Benbenishty, R. (2019). *Bullying, school violence, and climate in evolving contexts: Culture, organization, and time.* New York: Oxford University Press.

Astor, R. A., Jacobson, L., Wrabel, S., Benbenishty, R., & Pineda, D. (2017). *Welcoming practices: Creating schools that support students and families in transition.* New York: Oxford University Press.

Bachman, R., Randolph, A., & Brown, B. (2011). Predicting perceptions of fear at school and going to and from school for African American and white students: The effects of school security measures. *Youth and Society, 43,* 705–726. doi:10.1177/0044118X1036667

Barrett, S., Eber, L., & Weist, M. D. (2013). *Advancing education effectiveness: An interconnected systems framework for Positive Behavioral Interventions and Supports (PBIS) and school mental health.* Center for Positive Behavioral Interventions and Supports (funded by the Office of Special Education Programs, U.S. Department of Education). Eugene: University of Oregon Press.

Bear, G. G. (2015). Preventive classroom management. In E. T. Emmer & E. J. Sabornie (Eds.), *Handbook of classroom management* (2nd ed., pp. 15–39). New York: Routledge.

Benbenishty, R., & Astor, R. A. (2005). *School violence in context: Culture, neighborhood, family, school, and gender.* New York: Oxford University Press.

Berg, J., & Cornell, D. (2016). Authoritative school climate, aggression toward teachers, and teacher distress in middle school. *School Psychology Quarterly, 31,* 122–139. doi:10.1037/spq0000132

Blum, R. W., McNeely, C. A., &Rinehart, P. M. (2002). *Improving the odds: The untapped power of schools to improve the health of teens.* Minneapolis: University of Minnesota Center for Adolescent Health and Development.

Bradshaw, C. P., Bottiani, J., Osher, D., & Sugai, G. (2014). Integrating Positive Behavioral Interventions and Supports (PBIS) and social emotional learning. In M. D. Weist, N. A. Lever, C. P. Bradshaw, & J. Owens (Eds.), *Handbook of school mental health: Advancing practice and research* (2nd ed., pp. 101–118). New York: Springer.

Bradshaw, C. P., Mitchell, M. M., & Leaf, P. J. (2010). Examining the effects of School-Wide Positive Behavioral Interventions and Supports on student outcomes: Results from a randomized controlled effectiveness trial in elementary schools. *Journal of Positive Behavior Interventions, 12,* 133–148. doi:10.1177/1098300709334798

Bradshaw, C. P., Waasdorp, T. E., Debnam, K. J., & Lindstrom Johnson, S. (2014). Measuring school climate: A focus on safety, engagement, and the environment. *Journal of School Health, 84,* 593–604. doi:10.1111/josh.12186

Bradshaw, C. P., Waasdorp, T. E., & Leaf, P. J. (2012). Effects of School-Wide Positive Behavioral Interventions and Supports on child behavior problems. *Pediatrics, 130*(5), e1136–e1145. doi:10.1542/peds.2012-0243

Cairns, R. B., & Cairns, B. D. (1994). *Lifelines and risks: Pathways of youth in our time.* Cambridge: Cambridge University Press.

Cook, C. R., Frye, M., Slemrod, T., Lyon, A., & Renshaw, T. (2015). An integrated approach to universal prevention: Independent and combined effects of PBIS and SEL on youths' mental health. *School Psychology Quarterly, 30*, 165–180.

Cook, P. J. (2018, March 8). "How to reduce school shootings (arming teachers won't help)." *The News & Observer.*

Cornell, D., Allen, K., & Fan, X. (2012). A randomized controlled study of the Virginia Student Threat Assessment Guidelines in grades K–12. *School Psychology Review, 41*, 100–115.

Cornell, D., & Huang, F. (2016). Authoritative school climate and high school student risk behavior: A cross-sectional multi-level analysis of student self-reports. *Journal of Youth and Adolescence, 45*, 2246–2259. doi:10.1007/s10964-016-0424-3

Cornell, D., & Maeng, J. (2017). Statewide implementation of threat assessment in Virginia K–12 schools. *Contemporary School Psychology.* doi:10.1007/s40688-017-0146-x

Cornell, D., Maeng, J., Huang, F., Shukla, K., & Konold, T. (2018). Racial/ethnic parity in disciplinary consequences using student threat assessment. *School Psychology Review, 47*, 183–195. doi: 10.17105/SPR-2017-0030.V47-2

Cornell, D., & Sheras, P. (2006). *Guidelines for responding to student threats of violence.* Longmont, CO: Sopris West.

Cornell, D., Shukla, K., & Konold, T. (2015). Peer victimization and authoritative school climate: A multilevel multivariate approach. *Journal of Educational Psychology, 107*, 1186–1201. doi:10.1037/edu0000038

Cornell, D., Shukla, K., & Konold, T. (2016). Authoritative school climate and student academic engagement, grades, and aspirations in middle and high schools. *AERA Open, 2*, 1–18. doi:10.1177/2332858416633184

Daniels, J. A., Buck, I., Croxall, S., Gruber, J., Kime, P., & Govert, H. (2007). A content analysis of news reports of averted school rampages. *Journal of School Violence, 6*, 83–99. doi:10.1300/J202v06n01_06

Danielsen, A. G., Wiium, N., Wilhelmsen, B. U., & Wold, B. (2010). Perceived support provided by teachers and classmates and students' self-reported academic initiative. *Journal of School Psychology, 48*, 247–267. doi:10.1016/j.jsp.2010.02.002

Datta, P., Cornell, D., & Huang, F. (2016). Aggressive attitudes and prevalence of bullying bystander behaviors in middle schools. *Psychology in the Schools, 53*, 804–816.

Devlin, D. N., & Gottfredson, D. C. (2018). Policing and the school-to-prison pipeline. In J. Deakin, E. Taylor, & A. Kupchik (Eds.), *The Palgrave international handbook of school discipline, surveillance, and social control* (pp. 291–308). Cham: Palgrave MacMillan.

Domitrovich, C. E., Bradshaw, C. P., Greenberg, M. T., Embry, D., Poduska, J., & Ialongo, N. S. (2010). Integrated preventive interventions: The theory and logic. *Psychology in the Schools, 47*, 71–88.

Durlak, J. A., Domitrovich, C. E., Weissberg, R., & Gullotta, T.P. (2015). *Handbook of social and emotional learning: Research and practice*. New York: Guilford.

Durlak, J. A., Weissberg, R. P., Dymnicki, A. B., Taylor, R. D., & Schellinger, K. B. (2011). The impact of enhancing students' social and emotional learning: A meta-analysis of school-based universal interventions. *Child Development, 82*, 405–432. doi:10.1111/j.1467-8624.2010.01564.x

Estrada, J. N., Gilreath, T. D., Astor, R. A., & Benbenishty, R. (2014). Gang membership, school violence, and the mediating effects of risk and protective behaviors in California high schools. *Journal of School Violence, 13*, 228–251. doi:10.1080/15388220.2013.846860

Estrada, J. N., Gilreath, T. D., Astor, R. A., & Benbenishty, R. (2016). A statewide study of gang membership in California secondary schools. *Youth & Society, 48*, 720–736. doi:10.1177/0044118X14528957

Estrada, J. N., Huerta, A. H., Hernandez, E.A., Hernandez, R. , & Kim, S. W. (2018). Socio-ecological risk and protective factors for youth gang involvement. In H. Shapiro (Ed.), *The handbook of violence in education: Forms, factors, and preventions* (pp. 185–202). Wiley Online.

Fisher, B. W., Mowen, T. J., & Boman, J. H., IV. (2018). School security measures and longitudinal trends in adolescents' experiences of victimization. *Journal of Youth and Adolescence, 47*(6), 1221–1237. doi:10.1007/s10964-018-0818-5

Gage, N. A., Prykanowski, D. A., & Larson, A. (2014). School climate and bullying victimization: A latent class growth model analysis. *School Psychology Quarterly, 29*(3), 256.

Garandeau, C. F., Poskiparta, E., & Salmivalli, C. (2014). Tackling acute cases of school bullying in the KiVa anti-bullying program: A comparison of two approaches. *Journal of Abnormal Child Psychology, 42*, 981–991. doi:10.1007/s10802-014-9861-1

Gastic, B. (2011). Metal detectors and feeling safe at school. *Education and Urban Society, 43*(4), 486–498.

Gini, G., Pozzoli, T., Borghi, F., & Franzoni, L. (2008). The role of bystanders in students' perception of bullying and sense of safety. *Journal of School Psychology, 46*, 617–638. doi:10.1016/j.jsp.2008.02.001

Goodenow, C. (1993). Classroom belonging among early adolescent students: Relationships to motivation and achievement. *Journal of Early Adolescence, 13*(1), 21–43.

Hankin, A., Hertz, M., & Simon, T. (2011). Impacts of metal detector use in schools: Insights from 15 years of research. *Journal of School Health, 81*(2), 100–106. doi:10.1111/j.1746-1561.2010.00566.x

Hirschfield, P. (2018). Schools and crime. *Annual Review of Criminology, 1*, 149–169. doi:10.1146/annurev-criminol-032317-092358

Horner, R. H., Sugai, G., Smolkowski, K., Eber, L., Nakasato, J., Todd, A. W., & Esperanza, J. (2009). A randomized, wait-list controlled effectiveness trial assessing school-wide Positive Behavior Support in elementary schools. *Journal of Positive Behavior Interventions, 11*, 133–144.

Jaycox, L. H., Langley, A. H., Stein, B. D., Wong, M., Sharma, P., Scott, M., & Schonlau, M. (2009). Support for students exposed to trauma: A pilot study. *School Mental Health, 1*(2), 49–60.

Kann, L., MacManus, T., Harris, W. A., Shanklin, S. L., Flint, K. H., Hawkins, J., & Zaza, S. (2016). Youth Risk Behavior Surveillance—United States, 2015. Retrieved from https://www.cdc.gov/healthyyouth/data/yrbs/pdf/2015/ss6506_updated.pdf

Kelen, G. D., Catlett, C. L., Kubit, J. G., & Hsieh, Y. H. (2012). Hospital-based shootings in the United States: 2000 to 2011. *Annals of Emergency Medicine: An International Journal, 60*(6), 790–798.e1. doi:10.1016/j.annemergmed.2012.08.012

Kirk, D. S., & Sampson, R. J. (2011). Crime and the production of safe schools. In G. J. Duncan & R. J. Murnane (Eds.), *Whither opportunity? Rising inequality, schools, and children's life chances* New York: Russell Sage.

Kirk, D. S., & Sampson, R. J. (2013). Juvenile arrest and collateral educational damage in the transition to adulthood. *Sociology of Education, 86*, 36–62.

Klein, J., Cornell, D., & Konold, T. (2012). Relationships between bullying, school climate, and student risk behaviors. *School Psychology Quarterly, 27*(3), 154–169.

Korpershoeck, H., Harms, T., de Boer, H., van Kuijk, M., & Doolaard, S. (2016). A meta-analysis of the effects of classroom management strategies and classroom management program on students' academic, behavioral, emotional, and motivational outcomes. *Educational Researcher, 86*, 643–680. doi:10.3102/0034654315626799

Latané, B., & Darley, J. M. (1970). *The unresponsive bystander: Why doesn't he help?* Englewood Cliffs, NJ: Prentice Hall.

Latané, B., & Nida, S. (1981). Ten years of research on group size and helping. *Psychological Bulletin, 89*, 308–324. doi:10.1037/0033-2909.89.2.308

Lindstrom Johnson, S., Bottiani, J., Debnam, K., & Bradshaw, C. P (2018). Surveillance or safekeeping? How school security officer and camera presence influence students' perceptions of safety, equity, and support. Manuscript submitted for publication.

Madfis, E. (2014). Averting school rampage: Student intervention amid a persistent code of silence. *Youth Violence & Juvenile Justice, 12*, 229–249. doi:10.1177/1541204013497768

Matjasko, J. L., Vivolo-Kantor, A. M., Massetti, G. M., Holland, K. M., Holt, M. K., & Dela Cruz, J. (2012). A systematic meta-review of evaluations of youth violence prevention programs: Common and divergent findings from 25 years of meta-analyses and systematic reviews. *Aggression and Violent Behavior, 17*(6), 540–552. doi:10.1016/j.avb.2012.06.006

Meter, D. J., & Card, N. A. (2015). Defenders of victims of peer aggression: Interdependence theory and an exploration of individual, interpersonal, and contextual effects on the defender participant role. *Developmental Review, 38*, 222–240. doi:10.1016/j.dr.2015.08.001

Millspaugh, S., Cornell, D., Huang, F., & Datta, P. (2015). Prevalence of aggressive attitudes and student willingness to report threats of violence in middle schools. *Journal of Threat Assessment and Management, 2*, 11–22. doi:10.1037/tam0000031

Morgan, E., Salomon, N., Plotkin, M., & Cohen, R. (2014). *The school discipline consensus report: Strategies from the field to keep students engaged in school and out of the juvenile justice system.* New York: Council of State Governments Justice Center.

Musu-Gillette, L., Zhang, A., Wang, K., Zhang, J., & Oudekerk, B. A. (2017). *Indicators of School Crime and Safety: 2016* (NCES 2017-064/NCJ 250650). Washington, DC: National Center for Education Statistics, U.S. Department of Education, and Bureau of Justice Statistics, Office of Justice Programs, U.S. Department of Justice.

Na, C., & Gottfredson, D. C. (2011). Police officers in schools: Effects on school crime and the processing of offending behaviors. *Justice Quarterly, 30*(4), 619–650. doi:10.1080/07418825.2011.615754

National Academies of Science, Engineering, and Medicine. (2016). *Preventing bullying through science, policy, and practice.* Washington, DC: National Academies Press. doi:10.17226/23482

National Institute of Education. (1978). *Violent schools—safe school: The Safe School Study Report to the Congress.* Washington, DC: U.S. Government Printing Office.

Nekvasil, E., & Cornell, D. (2015). Student threat assessment associated with positive school climate in middle schools. *Journal of Threat Assessment and Management, 2*, 98–113. doi:10.1037/tam0000038

Nickerson, A. B., Aloe, A. M., Livingston, J. A., & Feeley, T. H. (2014). Measurement of the bystander intervention model for bullying and sexual harassment. *Journal of Adolescence, 37*(4), 391–400. doi:10.1016/j.adolescence.2014.03.003

Okonofua, J. A., Walton, G. M., & Eberhardt, J. A. (2016). A vicious cycle: Racial bias and perceptions of bias interactively perpetuating disproportionate discipline. *Perspectives on Psychological Science.* doi:10.1177/1745691616635592

Osher, D., Bear, G. G., Sprague, J. R., & Doyle, W. (2010). How can we improve school discipline? *Educational Researcher, 39*(1), 48–58. doi:10.3102/0013189x09357618

Osher, D., Cantor, P., Berg, J., Strayer, L., & Rose, T. (2018). Drivers of human development: How relationships and context shape learning and development. *Applied Developmental Science,* 1–31. doi:10.1080/10888691.2017.1398650

Osher, D., Moroney, D., & Williamson, S. (2018). *Creating safe, equitable, engaging schools: A comprehensive, evidence-based approach to supporting students.* Cambridge, MA: Harvard Education Press.

Osher, D., Woodruff, D., & Sims, A. (2002). Schools make a difference: The relationship between education services for African American children and youth and their overrepresentation in the juvenile justice system. In D. Losen (Ed.), *Minority issues in special education* (pp. 93–116). Cambridge, MA: The Civil Rights Project, Harvard Education Publishing Group, Harvard University.

O'Toole, M. E. (2000). *The school shooter: A threat assessment perspective.* Quantico, VA: National Center for the Analysis of Violent Crime, Federal Bureau of Investigation.

Owens, E. (2017). Testing the school-to-prison pipeline. *Journal of Policy Analysis and Management, 36*(1), 11–37. doi:10.1002/pam.21954

Reschly, A. L., Huebner, E. S., Appleton, J. J., & Antaramian, S. (2008). Engagement as flourishing: The contribution of positive emotions and coping to adolescents' engagement at school and with learning. *Psychology in the Schools, 45*(5), 419–431. doi:10.1002/pits.20306

Resnick, M. D., Bearman, P. S., Blum, R. W., Bauman, K. E., Harris, K. M., Jones, J., . . . Udry, J. R. (1997). Protecting adolescents from harm: Findings from the National Longitudinal Study on Adolescent Health. *Journal of the American Medical Association, 278*, 823–832.

Seeley, K., Tombari, L., Bennett, J., & Dunkle, B. (2009). *Peer victimization in schools: A set of quantitative and qualitative studies of the connections among peer victimization, school engagement, truancy, school achievement, and other outcomes.* Denver: National Center of School Engagement.

Shultz, J. M., Cohen, A. M., Muschert, G. W., & Flores de Apodaca, R. (2013). Fatal school shootings and the epidemiological context of firearm mortality in the United States. *Disaster Health, 1*(2), 84–101.

Stueve, A., Dash, K., O'Donnell, L., Tehranifar, P., Wilson-Simmons, R., Slaby, R. G., & Link, B. G. (2006). Rethinking the bystander role in school violence prevention. *Health Promotion Practice, 7*, 117–124. doi:10.1177/1524839905278454

Sugai, G., & Horner, R. (2006). A promising approach for expanding and sustaining school-wide positive behavior support. *School Psychology Review, 35*, 245–259.

Tanner-Smith, E. E., Fisher, B. W., Addington, L. A., & Gardella, J. H. (2018). Adding security, but subtracting safety? Exploring schools' use of multiple visible security measures. *American Journal of Criminal Justice, 43*(1), 102–119.

Taylor, R. D., Oberle, E., Durlak, J. A., & Weissberg, R. P. (2017). Promoting positive youth development through school-based social and emotional learning interventions: A meta-analysis of follow-up effects. *Child Development, 88*(4), 1156–1171. doi:10.1111/cdev.12864

Thapa, A., Cohen, J., Guffey, S., & Higgins-D'Alessandro, A. (2013). A review of school climate research. *Review of Educational Research, 83*(3), 357–385. doi:10.3102/0034654313483907

Theriot, M. T. (2009). School resource officers and the criminalization of student behavior. *Journal of Criminal Justice, 37*(3), 280–287.

Waasdorp, T. E., & Bradshaw, C. P. (2018). Examining variation in adolescent bystanders' responses to bullying. *School Psychology Review, 47*, 18–33. doi:10.17105/SPR-2017-0081.V47-1

Wang, M. T., & Dishion, T. J. (2012). The trajectories of adolescents' perceptions of school climate, deviant peer affiliation, and behavioral problems during the middle school years. *Journal of Research on Adolescence, 22*(1), 40–53.

Weissberg, R. P., Durlak, J. A., Domitrovich, C. E., & Gullotta, T. P. (2015). Social and emotional learning: Past, present, and future. In J. Durlak, T. Gullotta, C. Domitrovich, P. Goren, & R. Weissberg (Eds.), *Handbook of social and emotional learning* (pp. 3–19). New York: Guilford Press.

Weist, M. D., Lever, N., Bradshaw, C., & Owens, J. S. (2014). Further advancing the field of school mental health. In M. Weist, N. Lever, C. Bradshaw, & J. Owens (Eds.), *Handbook of school mental health: Research, training, practice, and policy* (2nd ed., pp. 1–16). New York: Springer.

Weist, M. D., Paternite, C. E., Wheatley-Rowe, D., & Gall, G. (2009). From thought to action in school mental health promotion. *International Journal of Mental Health Promotion, 11*(3), 32–41.

Western, B. (2006). *Punishment and inequality in America*. New York: Russell Sage.

Williams, F., & Cornell, D. (2006). Student willingness to seek help for threats of violence. *Journal of School Violence, 5*, 35–49. doi:10.1300/J202v05n04_04

Yang, J., & Anyon, J. (2016). Race and risk taking behavior. *Children & Youth Services Review, 69*, 39–48.

You, S., Furlong, M. J., Felix, E., Sharkey, J. D., Tanigawa, D., & Green, J. G. (2008). Relations among school connectedness, hope, life satisfaction, and bully victimization. *Psychology in the Schools, 45*(5), 446–460. doi:10.1002/pits.20308

CHAPTER ELEVEN

Major Systems for Facilitating Safety and Pro-Social Behavior

Positive Schoolwide Behavior Supports and Interventions

Rhonda N. T. Nese, Sara C. McDaniel, Shanna E. Hirsch, Ambra L. Green, Jeffrey R. Sprague, Kent McIntosh, and Barbara McClung

The Need for Coordinated Interventions

School-aged children and youth in the United States may face a number of environmental risk factors, such as high rates of crime, drug use, and poverty (Jenson, 2010). These risk factors have led to a significant public health issue due to high prevalence rates, early onset, and impact of mental health disorders among children and youth (Perou et al., 2013). As many as one in five children and youth have reported significant mental health concerns (e.g., anxiety, depression) in a given year (Perou et al., 2013). In 2011, mental health disorders were included among the five most costly conditions to address in children (Soni, 2011).

Despite recent increases in the availability of community mental health services, most children and youth do not receive them (Merikangas et al.,

2011). In addition, there are significant racial, ethnic, and socioeconomic disparities in access to mental health services. For example, racially and ethnically diverse students are less likely to receive services than white children (Pires, Grimes, Allen, Gilmer, & Mahadevan, 2013). Around 13% of racially and ethnically diverse children receive mental health services, compared to 31% of white children (Pires et al., 2013). Black children in the child welfare system have less access to counseling than their white peers also in the welfare system (Wells, Hillemeier, Bai, & Belue, 2009). Despite the costliness of the conditions and increased services, the current mental health service delivery model has been insufficient in meeting the needs of children and youth (Pires et al., 2013). Consequently, the lack of an effective service delivery model presents barriers to identifying children and youth with and at-risk for mental health disorders (Green, McKenzie, & Stormont, 2018) and providing needed supports.

Research has demonstrated that many students and educators report feeling unsafe at school (e.g., Gregory, Cornell, & Fan, 2012). These feelings of physical and emotional vulnerability are due in part to school climate (Thapa, Cohen, Guffey, & Higgins-D'Alessandro, 2013). In response to school violence, gang violence, and bullying in schools, educators, policy makers, and researchers alike have increasingly advocated for improving school safety. However, efforts to improve school safety have largely focused on reactionary and punitive approaches, such as installing metal detectors, hiring school resource officers in place of counselors, and adopting zero tolerance policies. Many of these approaches have mixed reports of effectiveness, whereas others (e.g., zero tolerance policies) have proven to be ineffective in reducing school violence and tend to increase discipline disparities among racially and ethnically diverse students and their white peers (Skiba et al., 2014). Research has established that positive and preventative practices are effective models to reduce safety issues and produce more supportive environments for students and teachers (Osher, Dwyer, Jimerson, & Brown, 2012; Thapa et al., 2013).

In accordance with Bronfenbrenner's (1979) social ecological model, effective school discipline practices should target individual, relational (e.g., peers, teachers, administrators), community, and societal factors to address overall school climate and increase safety in schools (Thapa et al., 2013). Likewise, the National School Climate Council (NSCC; 2007) identifies four essential characteristics of positive school climate: (1) safety, (2) relationships, (3) teaching and learning, and (4) institutional environment. The NSCC (2007) defines positive school climate as follows:

> A sustainable, positive school climate fosters youth development and learning necessary for a productive, contributing and satisfying life in a democratic society. This climate includes norms, values and expectations

> that support people feeling socially, emotionally and physically safe. People are engaged and respected. Students, families and educators work together to develop, live and contribute to a shared school vision. Educators model and nurture attitudes that emphasize the benefits and satisfaction gained from learning. Each person contributes to the operations of the school and the care of the physical environment. (p. 4)

Mental health is critical to student success. An abundance of research has demonstrated that school climate has great impact on a student's mental health (e.g., self-esteem, self-criticism, self-concept) and physical health while affecting a wide range of educational outcomes (Payton, 2008; Way, Reddy, & Rhodes, 2007). When educators work together to improve school climate, students feel safer and experience healthy development, translating into healthy adult relationships and the ability to function in and contribute to society (Cohen, 2006; Devine & Cohen, 2007; NSCC, 2007).

The causes of maladaptive behavior in children and youth are complex and multifaceted. Further, reducing the crime, violence, drug abuse, and dropout associated with challenging behaviors of individuals with or at-risk for mental health concerns can be difficult in schools. However, key protective factors (e.g., positive school climate, supportive adults, cognitive skills) can help improve well-being for students, especially those with higher risk factors, while steering them away from crime, drug use, and other negative behaviors (Jenson, 2010). As such, given that students spend most their time in schools, school personnel are increasingly being called upon to address student mental health concerns. Currently, mental services for students with mental health concerns are often limited, and what exists is often siloed and fragmented (Swain-Bradway, Johnson, Eber, Barrett, & Weist, 2015). As a result, educators can magnify the positive effects of their efforts by implementing mental health interventions not as stand-alone efforts, but rather within empirically sound frameworks that are positive, preventative, and grounded in protective factors. By using coordinated and integrated frameworks, educators can more effectively address the broader contexts (e.g., effects of mental health concerns, teacher practices) associated with developing or maintaining a positive school culture (McIntosh & Goodman, 2016).

The purpose of this chapter is twofold: first, to examine major schoolwide models that can contribute to safety, wellness, and mental health; and second, to provide suggestions as to ways these models can be aligned or integrated, as well as the challenges to doing so. The models and approaches discussed in this chapter include a focus on changing the ecology of the school through using the schoolwide positive behavioral interventions and supports (SWPBIS) framework to facilitate the process of social-emotional learning (SEL).

Challenges and Solutions to Implementing Practices in Schools

Schools are challenging environments for full and sustained school-wide prevention implementation, for a range of reasons (McIntosh et al., 2018). In the following section, we describe potential barriers to schoolwide prevention implementation: teacher turnover, intervention fatigue, low fidelity of implementation, limited training and support, and uncoordinated interventions. In addition, we include potential solutions related to these challenges.

Teacher Turnover

Currently, educators are leaving the profession at a high rate. Specifically, 10% of all teachers leave before the end of their first year, and between 40% and 50% of educators leave the classroom within their first five years of teaching (Ingersoll, 2012). High rates of teacher stress (Herman, Hickmon-Rosa, & Reinke, 2018) contribute to increased staff turnover, creating a revolving door that would appear to make schoolwide program implementation an uphill climb.

Teacher turnover can be addressed through team-based implementation. Effective teaming is a critical variable that predicts whether a schoolwide prevention model is sustainable (Coffey & Horner, 2012; McIntosh et al., 2018). Teaming involves attending trainings, creating materials to support implementation, providing professional development, evaluating implementation, and meeting on a regular basis to evaluate schoolwide data (Lewis & Sugai, 1999; Mathews, McIntosh, Frank, & May, 2014; Newton, Horner, Algozzine, Todd, & Algozzine, 2012). Implementing schoolwide prevention, namely SWPBIS, may also lessen teacher burnout and increase levels of efficacy, due to the visible effects on valued outcomes for teachers (Kelm & McIntosh, 2012; Ross, Romer, & Horner, 2012). This is a promising finding, given the link between high teacher burnout and greater intentions to leave the field (Goddard & Goddard, 2006).

Intervention Fatigue

In addition, schools experience an ongoing cycle of the introduction of new interventions every few years, which can be time-consuming and costly (Greenberg, Weissberg, & O'Brien, 2003). According to Greenberg and colleagues (2003), the frequent introduction of new initiatives is a common problem, in which educators are inundated and overwhelmed by multiple, poorly coordinated innovations, causing intervention fatigue, or resistance to novel initiatives (Hume & McIntosh, 2013; Kendziora & Osher, 2016). The prospect of new initiatives can lead teachers to be pessimistic about feasibility of change (McIntosh & Goodman, 2016).

Implementing any new framework or practice requires an investment in time. Therefore, it is not surprising, that teachers report the lack of time as an obstacle to implementation (Klingner, Ahwee, Pilonieta, & Menendez, 2003). It is important for administrators to consider how to allocate (and protect) time for teams to meet and work schoolwide prevention models. With that, a systems-based approach (as recommended by Sugai & Horner, 2002) can help integrate current school practices to maximize academic and social outcomes, working smarter, not harder. Furthermore, the model is built around a school's goals, climate, and culture, rather than investing in a packaged curriculum or product, leading to the allocation of time and resources for school teams to build a comprehensive model while receiving faculty input (Lane, Menzies, Ennis, & Bezdek, 2013). This input allows multiple stakeholders to improve the development, evaluation, and modification of schoolwide prevention models.

Low Fidelity of Implementation

Complex interventions such as schoolwide prevention models contain multiple components that make implementation more difficult compared to simple interventions (Dusenbury, Brannigan, Falco, & Hansen, 2003). That is, schoolwide prevention models incorporate multiple levels of interventions (e.g., Tiers 1–3), across multiple domains (e.g., academic, social-behavioral, mental health), grade levels, providers (e.g., general educators, special educators, interventionists), and settings (e.g., classrooms, hallways, cafeterias). As a result, it can be difficult to implement interventions with fidelity, or as intended by developers. Fidelity is vital to understanding student responsiveness and nonresponsiveness across all tiers of a schoolwide prevention model. For example, if a student engages in challenging behavior, it is important for educators to consider whether they have received a quality Tier 1 intervention prior to determining whether the student's behavior warrants a targeted intervention. In contrast, if an intervention was implemented with fidelity and the student's behavior does not respond, then the student may need (a) a more intense intervention or (b) further evaluation (Bruhn & Hirsch, 2017).

Professional development is one avenue to promote fidelity. Historically, schools have provided professional development as stand-alone workshops. However, isolated professional development sessions tend to have a minimal effect on teacher knowledge or implementation of skills (Darling-Hammond, Wei, Andree, Richardson, & Orphanos, 2009; Wei, Darling-Hammond, & Adamson, 2010). Many education researchers emphasize a well-designed professional development model must incorporate the following practices: (a) collaborative effort to coordinate training, (b) explicit skills instruction, (c) provision of learning opportunities to practice skills, and (d) feedback delivered through an established infrastructure (Ball & Cohen, 1999; Borko, Koellner, Jacobs, & Seago, 2011; Wei et al., 2010). Ongoing technical assistance and professional development requires thoughtful triangulation of data to determine areas to strengthen. Together this helps teams coordinate trainings. It also helps teams allocate the limited resources to critical areas and support effective coaching.

In addition, as one looks closer at increasing fidelity, administrator support should be considered (Mathews et al., 2014). Within tiered systems, administrator support is perceived as one of the strongest factors related to sustainability of schoolwide practices (Coffey & Horner, 2012; McIntosh et al., 2014). That is, administrators help facilitate the adoption of new practices, allocation of resources, communication of expectations, as well as navigating changes that may occur over time (Fixsen, Naoom, Blase, Friedman, & Wallace, 2005; Mathews et al., 2014; Strickland-Cohen, McIntosh, & Horner, 2014).

Multitiered Systems of Support

Recent research demonstrates the effectiveness of implementing multiple evidence-based interventions, specifically prevention programs, as part of a unified system (Domitrovich et al., 2010; Ferrer-Wreder, Saint-Eloi, Domitrovich, Small, Caldwell, & Cleveland, 2010; Lonigan et al., 2015). Providing multiple universal interventions can improve outcomes across multiple areas, including social, emotional, and behavioral wellness (Domitrovich et al., 2010). Additive, synergistic effects have been measured on integrated Head Start instruction compared to traditional Head Start programming (Bierman et al., 2008; Bierman et al., 2014; Nix, Bierman, Domitrovich, & Gill, 2013). Although aligning and integrating several interventions introduces challenges in implementation fidelity, efforts to identify common underlying mechanisms of change, creating flexible intervention approaches, and determining the appropriate dosage can both ease implementation of integrated prevention models and increase effectiveness of the intervention (Domitrovich et al., 2010).

The use of multitiered systems of support (MTSS) has grown widely in the last decade. These approaches most often deliver services through three tiers of support: universal, targeted, and intensive (Sugai, Horner, & Lewis, 2009; Tilly, 2008; Walker et al., 1996), in which the universal prevention level targets all students to optimize academic and social functioning and prevent challenges. The targeted level focuses on use of additional evidence-based practices for students who struggle but for whom highly individualized support is not necessary. The intensive level supports students with the most significant needs, often through individualization. The driving principle behind MTSS is that providing preventive support to all students occurs as a first step because it is most efficient and effective, and it allows students with additional needs to be provided supports without the cost of screening systems, danger of misidentification, and stigma of labeling (Fuchs, Mock, Morgan, & Young, 2003; Walker et al., 1996). Over the years, multiple forms of MTSS have been developed for implementation of academic and behavior supports, with the most well-known MTSS frameworks being academic Response to Intervention (RTI) and schoolwide positive behavioral interventions and supports (SWPBIS). Because of its evidence base and widespread adoption (over 25,000 schools; Center on PBIS), this chapter will focus on SWPBIS as the MTSS framework for implementing other service delivery models in an integrated approach.

SWPBIS is a framework for making schools more effective learning environments by establishing the social culture and behavior supports needed to improve social and academic outcomes for all students (Sugai et al., 2000). In addition to employing evidence-based practices that are organized and delivered within each tier of the model, SWPBIS includes careful integration of data collection, practices, and teaming systems (Sugai, Fallon, & O'Keefe, 2012). A wealth of empirical research conducted over the last 20 years documents the positive effects of adequate implementation of SWPBIS on student academic and behavior outcomes and on organizational health. Specifically, SWPBIS has been associated with decreases in problem behavior referrals (Bradshaw, Mitchell, & Leaf, 2010) and increases in academic achievement (McIntosh, Bennett, & Price, 2011), student social and emotional competencies (Bradshaw, Waasdorp, & Leaf, 2012), and perceived school safety (Horner et al., 2009).

Using Schoolwide Positive Behavioral Interventions and Supports to Implement Coordinated Interventions

As a three-tiered framework for prevention of challenging behavior, improving school climate, and making data-based decisions for students with unwanted behavior, SWPBIS is an opportune vehicle to include coordinated interventions, such as SEL programs, restorative practices, trauma-informed care, and equity-focused interventions (Barrett, Eber, McIntosh, Perales, & Romer, 2018). Two primary approaches to including coordinated interventions within the SWPBIS framework are alignment and integration (McIntosh & Goodman, 2016). These approaches can be implemented at the universal level for schools that may require additional universal intervention, or at the targeted level for schools that require additional layers of intervention at the secondary tier.

Alignment

In the first approach, SWPBIS components are implemented (e.g., three to five positively stated schoolwide expectations, teaching of schoolwide expectations, and reinforcement system) and a separate, but linked, intervention is implemented alongside SWPBIS to address similar but distinct needs. Aligned interventions that are well suited to complement SWPBIS are positive, preventative, proactive, and contribute to improved school climate. Some examples of complementary interventions that can be aligned with SWPBIS include SEL programs (to improve specific competencies), restorative practices (to address peer conflicts), and equity-focused interventions (to neutralize bias in teacher decision-making). These interventions should serve a specific need of the school and can be implemented with educators (e.g., bias-reduction interventions) or students (e.g., SEL curricula). These interventions can be modified to fit the three-tiered logic of the foundational SWPBIS framework. For example, interventions could be implemented universally with all students in a limited scope (e.g., weekly SEL lessons) and modified to be implemented in a more targeted manner at the secondary tier (e.g., additional small group SEL lessons), and coordinated with intensive, individualized interventions at the tertiary level (e.g., teaching social-emotional competencies as replacement behaviors within a behavior intervention plan). Implementing several SWPBIS-aligned interventions requires careful coordination, evaluation of implementation fidelity across SWPBIS and all interventions, and additional resources. Given the need for more resources, interventions should be added only when necessary, and educators should be provided additional resources to implement SWPBIS and aligned interventions with fidelity.

Integration

The second approach to coordinating implementation of interventions with SWPBIS requires integrated models of prevention, which can address varied and multiple areas of need. Two types of integration can be used to improve efficiency and encourage a synergistic effect: (a) conceptual integration and (b) component integration. Conceptual integration requires a specific evaluation of common concepts across multiple strategies and interventions. For example, if trauma-informed care calls for classrooms to be made more safe, positive, and predictable, teams can achieve these objectives by implementing SWPBIS and providing brief professional development on identifying students showing signs of traumatization. This approach reduces the need for implementing separate interventions that may divide teacher time. Similarly, SWPBIS does not dictate what consequences should be assigned, so restorative practices, such as the use of a restorative chat could be integrated into the SWPBIS framework as a response within the graduated discipline system. In another example, SWPBIS requires explicit teaching of specifically defined expectations across school settings. This concept could be integrated with a universal SEL approach to improving student problem-solving and emotional regulation, tying together concepts across domains.

Specific component integration involves carefully inspecting additional interventions for core components that overlap with SWPBIS strategies or other intervention components. For example, trauma-informed care or equity-focused strategies could be added as a teacher component to SWPBIS by providing teachers with strategies for understanding student contexts and backgrounds in an effort to improve equitable and consistent teaching and reinforcement of schoolwide expectations. Similarly, components from restorative practices, such as daily proactive circles, could be used by teachers to revisit or practice schoolwide expectations identified as necessary by discipline data. For example, schoolwide expectations could be reviewed daily on the morning announcements, followed by brief, 15-minute homeroom circles that integrate discussions of schoolwide expectations and help students solve problems and communicate effectively. In another example, SWPBIS components could be integrated with a parent/caregiver training program offered to all parents to improve consistency in proactive, positive disciplinary practices and teaching at home.

A Process for Coordinating Interventions

Presented here are five steps for coordinating interventions such as restorative practices, SEL, and equity-focused interventions within an existing SWPBIS framework: (1) determine the need for additional interventions, (2) identify appropriately matched evidence-based interventions, (3) develop a plan for either aligning additional interventions or integrating intervention components with SWPBIS, (4) provide educators with coordinated training and coaching, and (5) implement using a team-based approach.

Step 1: Determine the need for additional interventions based on ecology or student data. Research regarding the effectiveness of SWPBIS in improving school climate and reducing challenging behavior is well-established (Lewis, McIntosh, Simonsen, Mitchell, & Hatton, 2017; Lewis, Jones, Horner, & Sugai, 2010). However, some schools or school districts may identify a need for additional universal or targeted interventions that may be needed to enhance the existing SWPBIS framework. To determine whether coordinated interventions are necessary, schools should first assess implementation of SWPBIS to determine whether it has been implemented with fidelity. Tools such as the Tiered Fidelity Inventory (TFI; Algozzine et al., 2014) and the Schoolwide Evaluation Tool (SET; Horner, Todd, Lewis-Palmer, Irvin, Sugai, & Boland, 2004) provide a valid marker for implementation. If scores are below the fidelity criterion, improving implementation may improve outcomes without additional modifications. If school teams are implementing SWPBIS with fidelity, teams may examine school data to find specific (e.g., peer conflict) or general (e.g., student populations exposed to community violence) needs. Data to be considered in the decision-making process include schoolwide disciplinary data (e.g., office discipline referrals, suspensions, alternative program placement), attendance data (e.g., tardies, unexcused absences), schoolwide behavioral and/or mental health screeners (e.g., Systematic Screening for Behavior Disorders; Walker & Severson, 1992; Strengths and Difficulties Questionnaire, Goodman, 1997), and school climate and safety surveys (e.g., Georgia School Climate Survey; Georgia Department of Education, La Salle, & Meyers, 2014]). Inspection of these data will help educators to determine the specific need for additional, coordinated interventions. These data will also provide baseline data from which ongoing progress monitoring data can be compared to determine whether interventions have improved student outcomes.

Step 2: Identify appropriately matched evidence-based interventions. After identifying the specific need for coordinated interventions within the existing SWPBIS framework, educators should carefully assess options for evidence-based interventions that address the identified need. Resources such as the What Works Clearinghouse (https://ies.ed.gov/ncee/wwc/) can be used to determine intervention effectiveness for specific programs and interventions within categories that can be matched to the identified need. Once several options for evidence-based interventions have been identified, educators should determine the most useful intervention based on cost, feasibility of implementation, ease of use and required training, and age or grade levels for which the intervention was determined effective.

Step 3: Develop a plan for either aligning additional interventions or integrating intervention components with SWPBIS. Next, careful planning is required to first determine whether the new intervention should be aligned as a layered intervention with the existing SWPBIS framework or whether concepts and components from the new intervention could be integrated within the existing SWPBIS framework. After determining the appropriate approach for coordinating the new intervention, educators should inspect the intervention training and implementation materials (e.g., lesson plans, scripts) to identify commonalities and entry points for coordination between SWPBIS and the new intervention. In many cases, a matrix of interventions, SWPBIS strategies, and the specific components of each may be developed to explicitly determine the most efficient approach for coordinating interventions within the SWPBIS framework.

Step 4: Provide educators with coordinated training and coaching. As previously mentioned, implementation fidelity of any adopted strategies and interventions (a) promotes the effectiveness of the intervention, (b) optimizes the investment in the intervention, and (c) establishes a true lack of response to intervention for students whose targeted behaviors do not improve. To ensure that educators implement interventions with fidelity, it is necessary to provide explicit, coordinated professional development with ongoing coaching. Most newly adopted interventions require an initial training with materials and procedures followed by scaffolded coaching from a trained specialist, with targeted ongoing booster sessions to remind teachers of the core components, implementation procedures, and any new modifications or adaptations since the initial training.

Step 5: Implement using a team-based approach. The final step to effectively coordinating interventions within the existing SWPBIS framework is to implement the new intervention through a data-driven school leadership team. Teachers are required to provide differentiated instruction using multiple practices. Often, their instructional day also includes data collection, committee meetings, and communication with school leadership and caregivers. Specifically, teachers need to understand where the new intervention fits within the existing framework, whether the new intervention is replacing an existing intervention, the expectations for implementation, and a data-based rationale for adopting the new intervention. Similarly, caregivers and community members may also benefit from a description of new interventions. The efforts can be coordinated and communicated by a single school leadership team, such as an existing SWPBIS leadership team serving a new, integrated role. Importantly, this team should include school leaders, those who have been trained to implement, and those in varying and affected roles. For example, if the school counselor will be coaching teachers to implement the new SEL lessons across grade levels, the implementation team should include the counselor and a representative from each grade. Other beneficial team members include parent liaisons, social workers, behavior specialists, SWPBIS coaches, school psychologists, and instructional specialists. The team should meet regularly to evaluate implementation fidelity across teachers and data-based decision-making to determine intervention effectiveness.

Integrating SWPBIS and SEL

Integrating SWPBIS and SEL approaches can address the limitations of each while capitalizing on their strengths (Bradshaw, Bottiani, Osher, & Sugai, 2014). A major contribution of the SWPBIS approach is providing system-based strategies for managing student behavior, and the major contribution of the SEL approach is providing support and direct teaching of social-emotional competencies for self-discipline. Implementing both together can maximize student outcomes (Barrett et al., 2018; Osher, Bear, Sprague, & Doyle, 2010; Osher et al., 2008).

There are a few examples of effective integration of SWPBIS and SEL, with nearly all focusing on Tier 1 in the MTSS framework. One of the earliest SWPBIS studies evaluated the integration of SWPBIS and Second Step, a widely used SEL program (Sprague et al., 2001), in elementary and middle schools. A quasi-experimental and qualitative research design was used to compare the one-year effects of the intervention. The treatment schools implemented a schoolwide discipline plan based on the SWPBIS approach in addition to the Second Step violence prevention curriculum (Grossman et al., 1997) for one year. Treatment schools showed greater reductions in office discipline referrals.

Other studies have focused on classroom rather than schoolwide integration. Cook and colleagues (2015) conducted a quasi-experimental study in which they assessed the effects of an SEL Curriculum called Strong Kids (Merrell, Carrizales, Feuerborn, Gueldner, & Tran, 2007), Class-Wide PBIS (CWPBIS), and SEL. This study suggested that the combination of SEL and CWPBIS was effective for decreasing both externalizing (i.e. disruptive behaviors) and internalizing (i.e. depression, anxiety) behavior patterns of students. This is in comparison to CWPBIS alone, which was effective for reducing externalizing behaviors and only slightly effective for reducing internalizing behaviors, and SEL, which was effective for reducing externalizing behaviors and moderately effective for reducing internalizing behaviors.

A Case Study of Integrated Multitiered Systems of Support

The following case study provides a real-world example of integrated systems. East Oakland Pride Elementary (EOP) is a school of 355 students located in one of the most impoverished neighborhoods in Oakland, California. Seventy percent of its students are Latino/a/x, and 23% are African American. Academically, roughly 85% of EOP students were performing below grade level in math and English language arts (ELA) in 2016–2017. It has had four principals in the past seven years and a teacher turnover rate of 65%, with only one-third of its teachers returning after three years. Regarding the school's surrounding community, 42% of residents were born outside of the United States. Property values are lower than 71% of California neighborhoods, and median household income is $38,871, with 96% of students at EOP eligible for free and reduced lunch. Neighborhood crime rates reflected intensive risk, with almost a 1 in 70 chance of becoming a victim of violent crime, as compared to 1 in 255 in California as a whole.

Leadership and Teaming

In 2016, things began changing at EOP when Michelle Grant was hired as the principal. To her credit, Principal Grant has developed a core team that is both loyal and skilled. Her Tier 2 Team (called Coordination of Services Team or COST) meets regularly and is staffed by a diverse team, including a community school manager, mental health clinician, after-school program manager, special education teacher, restorative justice (RJ) facilitator, family advocate, and grade-level lead teachers. EOP was one of only a few of Oakland Unified School District's (OUSD) 87 schools to achieve 100% completion of the Student Risk Screening Scale (SRSS; Drummond, 1994), a universal screener for behavior, due to principal leadership and follow up. Principal Grant, a former teacher and teacher leader at this school, brings social capital and has built relational trust through a successful transition from classroom teaching to site leadership. Respected by her former colleagues, her team works well together, addressing significant challenges without losing hope. This team has buoyancy and often laughs together, prompted by its leader.

Practices

Using the Tiered Fidelity Inventory to measure PBIS implementation, EOP scored 77% fidelity at Tier 1 PBIS after two years. In addition to continued teaching of its schoolwide expectations, this year their PBIS team focused on strengthening its student acknowledgement systems. Their plan included morning assemblies with the principal, as well as family and special awards assemblies and events for improved attendance, academics, and behavior.

Professional development is grounded in RJ practices, universal screening, understanding the functions of student behavior, and implementing pre-referral interventions for minor unwanted behaviors. Staffwide RJ training has been ongoing and has focused on restorative conversations and building staff community. Site supports include a full-time RJ facilitator who, in addition to addressing and facilitating harm circles, provides RJ classes during teacher prep periods in efforts to provide each student weekly opportunities for SEL in restorative circle format. RJ circle practices at Tier 1 teach SEL as well as build community among students and staff with the goal of embedding OUSD's adopted CASEL's SEL standards within academic instruction. EOP also implements Responsive Classroom, an evidence-based classroom SEL program. The school uses RJ as its approach in response to office discipline referrals and when students experience interpersonal conflict.

Data

EOP's Coordination of Services Team reviews academic data as well as attendance and discipline referrals for referred students. It also employs the SRSS to identify students for early behavior intervention supports. The team meets twice per month and invites teachers to attend to get consult on at risk students. The team organizes interventions using an MTSS framework, with examples that include a girls group, ELL pull-out groups for newcomer students, and mental health counseling for students in need of individualized intervention. Community partners are contracted to provide additional behavior support using a push-in approach to classrooms (i.e., supporting teachers in their implementation). Committed to ensuring equity, Principal Grant is willing to try multiple interventions before referring students for exclusionary discipline or special education eligibility determinations.

Outcomes

Student outcomes show considerable improvement over two years of integrated MTSS systems. Effects over this time include a reduction in out-of-school suspensions from 53 to 1 and a reduction in office discipline referrals from over 1,000 to just 16. Chronic absences have decreased by almost five percentage points. In addition, no students from EOP were referred for special education determination for Emotional Disturbance in the past two years. EOP represents an early adopter of Oakland's efforts to align PBIS, RJ, and SEL within an integrated MTSS framework, and these results provide an indication of its promise.

Conclusion

This chapter examined the strengths and challenges of implementing schoolwide models that can contribute to safety, wellness, and mental health, and suggested ways that they can be aligned or integrated. The two major approaches included SWPBIS and SEL, both of which are widely implemented, and likely many schools are already integrating the two approaches in some manner. SWPBIS provides an evidence-supported framework for building a common vision, common language, and a set of explicit procedures and systems for ensuring consistency in practice based on team-oriented implementation and data-based decision-making. SEL curricula can contribute evidence-based, developmentally appropriate teaching and support strategies for developing self-discipline and additional social and emotional competencies. It is when these two approaches are well integrated that schools are most likely to achieve the aims of improving academic achievement, reducing problem behavior, and promoting positive mental health development for children and youth.

References

Algozzine, B., Barrett, S., Eber, L., George, H., Lewis, T., Putnam, B., . . . Sugai, G. (2014). *School-wide PBIS tiered fidelity inventory.* OSEP Technical Assistance Center on Positive Behavioral Interventions and Supports. Retrieved from https://www.pbis.org/Common/Cms/files/pbisresources/SWPBIS%20Tiered%20Fidelity%20Inventory%20%28TFI%29.pdf

Ball, D., & Cohen, D. (1999). Developing practice, developing practitioners: Toward a practice-based theory of professional education. In L. Darling-Hammond & G. Sykes (Eds.), *Teaching as the learning profession* (pp. 3–32). San Francisco, CA: Jossey-Bass.

Barrett, S., Eber, L., McIntosh, K., Perales, K., & Romer, N. (2018). *Teaching social-emotional competencies within a PBIS framework.* OSEP Technical Assistance Center on Positive Behavioral Interventions and Supports. Retrieved from https://www.pbis.org/Common/Cms/files/pbisresources/TeachingSocialEmotionalCompetenciesWithinAPBISFramework.pdf

Bierman, K. L., Domitrovich, C. E., Nix, R., Gest, S., Welsh, J. A., Greenberg, M. T., . . . Gill, S. (2008). Promoting academic and social-emotional school readiness: The Head Start REDI program. *Child Development, 79,* 1802–1817.

Bierman, K. L., Nix, R. L., Heinrichs, B. S., Domitrovich, C. E., Gest, S. D., Welsh, J. A., & Gill, S. (2014). Effects of Head Start REDI on children's outcomes one year later in different kindergarten contexts. *Child Development, 85,* 140–159.

Borko, H., Koellner, K., Jacobs, J., & Seago, N. (2011). Using video representations of teaching in practice based professional development programs. *Zentralblatt für Didaktik der Mathematik/International Reviews on Mathematical Education, 43*(1), 175–187.

Bradshaw, C. P., Bottiani, J. H., Osher, D., & Sugai, G. (2014). The integration of positive behavioral interventions and supports and social and emotional learning. In M. D. Weist (Ed.), *Handbook of school mental health: Research, training, practice, and policy* (pp. 101–118). New York, NY: Springer Publishing Company.

Bradshaw, C. P., Mitchell, M. M., & Leaf, P. J. (2010). Examining the effects of schoolwide positive behavioral interventions and supports on student outcomes: Results from a randomized controlled effectiveness trial in elementary schools. *Journal of Positive Behavior Interventions, 12,* 133–148. doi:10.1177/1098300709334798

Bradshaw, C. P., Waasdorp, T. E., & Leaf, P. J. (2012). Effects of school-wide positive behavioral interventions and supports on child behavior problems and adjustment. *Pediatrics, 130*(5), e1136–e1145. doi:10.1542/peds.2012-0243

Bronfenbrenner, U. (1979). *The ecology of human development.* Cambridge, MA.: Harvard University Press.

Bruhn, A. L., & Hirsch, S. E. (2017). From good intentions to great implementation. *Emotional and Behavioral Disorders in Youth, 17* (3), 64–70.

Coffey, J. H., & Horner, R. H. (2012). The sustainability of schoolwide positive behavior interventions and supports. *Exceptional Children, 78*(4), 407–422.

Cohen, J. (2006). Social, emotional, ethical, and academic education: Creating a climate for learning, participation in democracy, and well-being. *Harvard Educational Review, 76*, 201–237, 285.

Cook, C. R., Frye, M., Slemrod, T., Lyon, A. R., Renshaw, T. L., & Zhang, Y. (2015). An integrated approach to universal prevention: Independent and combined effects of PBIS and SEL on youths' mental health. *School Psychology Quarterly, 30*, 166–183. doi:10.1037/spq0000102

Devine, J., & Cohen, J. (2007). *Making your school safe: strategies to protect children and promote learning.* New York: Teachers College Press.

Domitrovich, C. E., Bradshaw, C. P., Greenberg, M. T., Embry, D., Poduska, J. M., & Ialongo, N. S. (2010). Integrated models of school-based prevention: Logic and theory. *Psychology in the Schools, 47*(1), 71–88.

Domitrovich, C. E., Cortes, R. C., & Greenberg, M. T. (2007). Improving young children's social and emotional competence: A randomized trial of the Preschool PATHS curriculum. *Journal of Primary Prevention, 28*, 67–91.

Drummond, T. (1994). *The Student Risk Screening Scale (SRSS).* Grants Pass, OR: Josephine County Mental Health Program.

Dusenbury, L., Brannigan, R., Falco, M., & Hansen, W. B. (2003). A review of research on fidelity of implementation: Implications for drug abuse prevention in school settings. *Health Education Research, 18*(2), 237–256.

Fallon, L. M., O'keeffe, B. V., Gage, N. A., & Sugai, G. (2015). Brief report: Assessing attitudes toward culturally and contextually relevant schoolwide positive behavior support strategies. *Behavioral Disorders, 40*(4), 251–260.

Ferrer-Wreder, L., Saint-Eloi, H., Domitrovich, C. E., Small, M. L., Caldwell, L. L., & Cleveland, M. J. (2010). Is more better? Outcome and dose of a universal drug prevention effectiveness trial. *Journal of Primary Prevention, 31*, 349–363.

Fixsen, D. L., Naoom, S. F., Blase, K. A., Friedman, R. M., & Wallace, F. (2005). *Implementation research: A synthesis of the literature* (FMHI Publication #231). Tampa: University of South Florida, The National Implementation Research Network.

Fuchs, D., Mock, D., Morgan, P., & Young, C. (2003. Responsiveness-to-intervention: Definitions, evidence, and implications for the learning disabilities construct. *Learning Disabilities Research & Practice, 18*, 157–171.

Georgia Department of Education, La Salle, T. P., & Meyers, J. P. (2014). *The Georgia Student Health Survey 2.0.* Atlanta: Georgia Department of Education.

Goddard, R., & Goddard, M. (2006). Beginning teacher burnout in Queensland schools: Associations with serious intentions to leave. *Australian Educational Researcher, 33*, 61–75. doi:10.1007/bf03216834

Goodman, R. (1997). The strengths and difficulties questionnaire: A research note. *Journal of Child Psychology and Psychiatry, 38*, 581–586.

Green, A. L., McKenzie, J. M., & Stormont, M. (2018). Prevention of behavior problems through increasing culturally responsive pedagogy in early childhood settings. *Perspectives on Early Childhood Psychology and Education, 3*(1), 61–88.

Greenberg, M. T., Weissberg, R. P., & O'Brien, M. E. (2003). Enhancing school-based prevention and youth development through coordinated social, emotional, and academic learning. *American Psychologist, 58*, 466–474.

Gregory, A., Cornell, D., & Fan, X. (2012). Teacher safety and authoritative school climate in high schools. *American Journal of Education, 118*, 401–425. doi:10.1086/666362

Grossman, D. C., Neckerman, H. J., Koepsell, T. D., Liu, P.-Y., Asher, K. N., Beland, K., . . . Rivara, F. P. (1997). Effectiveness of a violence prevention curriculum among children in elementary school: A randomized controlled trial. *Journal of the American Medical Association, 277*, 1605–1611. doi:10.1001/jama.277.20.1605

Herman, K. C., Hickmon-Rosa, J. E., & Reinke, W. M. (2018). Empirically derived profiles of teacher stress, burnout, self-efficacy, and coping and associated student outcomes. *Journal of Positive Behavior Interventions, 20*, 90–100. doi:10.1177/1098300717732066

Horner, R. H., Sugai, G., Smolkowski, K., Eber, L., Nakasato, J., Todd, A. W., & Esparanza, J. (2009). A randomized, wait-list controlled effectiveness trial assessing school-wide positive behavior support in elementary schools. *Journal of Positive Behavior Interventions, 11*, 133–144.

Horner, R. H., Todd, A., Lewis-Palmer, T., Irvin, L., Sugai, G., & Boland, J. (2004). The school-wide evaluation tool (SET): A research instrument for assessing school-wide positive behavior support. *Journal of Positive Behavior Interventions, 6*, 3–12. doi:10.1177/10983007040060010201

Hume, A. E., & McIntosh, K. (2013). Construct validation of a measure to assess sustainability of school-wide behavior interventions. *Psychology in the Schools, 50*, 1003–1014. doi:10.1002/pits.21722

Ingersoll, R. (2012). Beginning teacher induction: What the data tell us. *Phi Delta Kappan, 93*(8), 47–51.

Jenson, J. M. (2010). Advances in preventing childhood and adolescent problem behavior. *Research on Social Work Practice, 20*, 701–713. doi:10.1177/1049731509349105

Kelm, J. L., & McIntosh, K. (2012). Effects of school-wide positive behavior support on teacher self-efficacy. *Psychology in the Schools, 49*, 137–147. doi:10.1002/pits.20624

Kendziora, K., & Osher, D. (2016). Promoting children's and adolescents' social and emotional development: District adaptations of a theory of action. *Journal of Clinical Child & Adolescent Psycholog, 45* (6), 797–811.

Klingner, J. K., Ahwee, S., Pilonieta, P., & Menendez, R. (2003). Barriers and facilitators in scaling up research-based practices. *Exceptional Children, 69*(4), 411–429.

Lane, K. L., Menzies, H. M., Ennis, R. P., & Bezdek, J. (2013). School-wide systems to promote positive behaviors and facilitate instruction. *Journal of Curriculum and Instruction, 7*, 6–31. doi:10.3776/joci.2013.v7n1p6-31

Lewis, T. J., Jones, S. E. L., Horner, R. H., & Sugai, G. (2010). School-wide positive behavior support and students with emotional/behavioral disorders: Implications for prevention, identification and intervention. *Exceptionality, 18*(2), 82–93.

Lewis, T. J., McIntosh, K., Simonsen, B., Mitchell, B. S., & Hatton, H. L. (2017). School-wide systems of positive behavior support: Implications for students at-risk and with emotional/behavioral disorders. *AERA Open, 3*(2), 1–11.

Lewis, T. J. & Sugai, G. (1999, Feb). Effective behavior support: A systems approach to proactive schoolwide management. *Focus on Exceptional Children, 31*(6), 1–24.

Lonigan, C. J. (2006). Development, assessment, and promotion of preliteracy skills. *Early Education and Development, 1*, 91–114.

Lonigan, C. J., Phillips, B. M., Clancy, J. L., Landry, S. H., Swank, P. R., Assel, M., . . . Barnes, M. (2015). Impacts of a comprehensive school readiness curriculum for preschool children at risk for educational difficulties. *Child Development, 86*, 1773–1793.

Mathews, S., McIntosh, K., Frank, J. L., & May, S. (2014). Critical features predicting sustained implementation of school-wide PBIS. *Journal of Positive Behavior Interventions, 16*, 168–178. doi:10.1177/1098300713484065

McIntosh, K., Bennett, J. L., & Price, K. (2011). Evaluation of social and academic effects of school-wide positive behaviour support in a Canadian school district. *Exceptionality Education International, 21*, 46–60.

McIntosh, K., & Goodman, S. (2016). *Integrated multi-tiered systems of support: Blending RTI and PBIS*. New York: Guilford Press.

McIntosh, K., Mercer, S. H., Hume, A. E., Frank, J. L., Turri, M. G., & Mathews, S. (2013). Factors associated with sustained implementation of school-wide positive behavior support. *Exceptional Children, 79*, 293–311.

McIntosh, K., Mercer, S. H., Nese, R. N. T., Strickland-Cohen, M. K., Kittelman, A., Hoselton, R., & Horner, R. H. (2018). Factors predicting sustained implementation of a universal behavior support framework. *Educational Researcher, 47* (5), 307–316.

McIntosh, K., Predy, L. K., Upreti, G., Hume, A. E., Turri, M. G., & Mathews, S. (2014). Perceptions of contextual features related to implementation and sustainability of school-wide positive behavior support. *Journal of Positive Behavior Interventions, 16*, 29–41. doi:10.1177/1098300712470723

Merikangas, K. R., Jin, R., He, J.-P., Kessler, R. C., Lee, S., Sampson, N. A., . . . Zarkov, Z. (2011). Prevalence and correlates of bipolar spectrum disorder in the World Mental Health Survey Initiative. *Archives of General Psychiatry, 68*, 241–251. doi:10.1001/archgenpsychiatry.2011.12

Merrell, K. W., Carrizales, D., Feuerborn, L., Gueldner, B. A., & Tran, O. K. (2007). *Strong kids: A social and emotional learning curriculum for students in grades 3–5*. Baltimore: Brookes Publishing.

National School Climate Council (NSCC). (2007). The School Climate Challenge: Narrowing the gap between school climate research and school climate policy, practice guidelines and teacher education policy. Retrieved November 21, 2018, from https://www.schoolclimate.org/themes/schoolclimate/assets/pdf/policy/school-climate-challenge-web.pdf

Newton, J. S., Horner, R. H., Algozzine, B., Todd, A. W., & Algozzine, K. (2012). A randomized wait-list controlled analysis of the implementation integrity of team-initiated problem solving processes. *Journal of School Psychology, 50*, 421–441.

Nix, R. L., Bierman, K. L., Domitrovich, C. E., & Gill, G. (2013). Promoting children's social-emotional skills in preschool can enhance academic and behavioral functioning in kindergarten: Findings from Head Start REDI. *Early Education & Development, 24*, 1000–1019.

Osher, D., Bear, G. G., Sprague, J. R., & Doyle, W. (2010). How can we improve school discipline? *Educational Researcher, 39*, 48–58. doi:10.3102/0013189X09357618

Osher, D., Dwyer, K. P., Jimerson, S. R., & Brown, J. A. (2012). Developing safe, supportive, and effective schools: Facilitating student success to reduce school violence. In S. R. Jimerson, A. B. Nickerson, M. J. Mayer, & M. J. Furlong (Eds.), *Handbook of school violence and school safety: International research and practice* (2nd ed., pp. 27–44). New York: Routledge.

Osher, D., Sprague, J. R., Weissberg, R. P., Axelrod, J., Keenan, S., Kendziora, K., & Zins, J. E. (2008). A comprehensive approach to promoting social, emotional, and academic growth in contemporary schools. In A. Thomas & J. P. Grimes (Eds.), *Best practices in school psychology V*. Bethesda, MD: National Association of School Psychologists.

Payton, J., Weissberg, R. P., Durlak, J. A., Dymnicki, A. B., Taylor, R. D., Schellinger, K. B., & Pachan, M. (2008). *The positive impact of social and emotional learning for kindergarten to eighth-grade students: Findings from three scientific reviews*. Chicago, IL: Collaborative for Academic, Social, and Emotional Learning.

Perou, R., Bitsko, R. H., Blumberg, S. J., Pastor, P., Ghandour, R. M., Gfroerer, J. C., . . . Parks, S. E. (2013). Mental health surveillance among children—United States, 2005–2011. *MMWR Surveillance Summaries, 62*(Suppl 2), 1–35.

Pires, S. A., Grimes, K. E., Allen, K. D., Gilmer, T., & Mahadevan, R. M. (2013). *Faces of Medicaid: Examining children's behavioral health service utilization and expenditures*. Hamilton, NJ: Center for Health Care Strategies.

Podolsky, A., Kini, T., Bishop, J., & Darling-Hammond, L. (2016). *Solving the teacher shortage: How to attract and retain excellent educators.* Palo Alto, CA: Learning Policy Institute.

Ross, S. W., Romer, N., & Horner, R. H. (2012). Teacher well-being and the implementation of school-wide positive behavior interventions and supports. *Journal of Positive Behavior Interventions, 14* (2), 118–128.

Skiba, R. J. (2014). The failure of zero tolerance. *Reclaiming Children and Youth, 22,* 27–33.

Skiba, R. J., Chung, C.-G., Trachok, M., Baker, T. L., Sheya, A., & Hughes, R. L. (2014). Parsing disciplinary disproportionality: Contributions of infraction, student, and school characteristics to out-of-school suspension and expulsion. *American Educational Research Journal, 51,* 640–670. doi:10.3102/0002831214541670

Soni, A. (2014). *The five most costly children's conditions, 2011: Estimates for U.S. civilian noninstitutionalized children, ages 0-17.* Statistical Brief #434. April 2014. Agency for Healthcare Research and Quality, Rockville, MD. Retrieved from http://www.meps.ahrq.gov/mepsweb/data_files/publications/st434/stat434.pdf

Sprague, J. R., Walker, H., Golly, A., White, K., Myers, D. R., & Shannon, T. (2001). Translating research into effective practice: The effects of a universal staff and student intervention on key indicators of school safety and discipline. *Education and Treatment of Children, 24,* 495–511.

Strickland-Cohen, M. K., McIntosh, K., & Horner, R. H. (2014). Sustaining effective practices in the face of principal turnover. *Teaching Exceptional Children, 46*(3), 18–24.

Sugai, G., & Horner, R. H. (2002). The evolution of discipline practices: School-wide positive behavior supports. *Child and Family Behavior Therapy, 24,* 23–50.

Sugai, G., Horner, R. H., Dunlap, G., Hieneman, M., Lewis, T. J., Nelson, C. M., . . . Ruef, M. (2000). Applying positive behavioral support and functional behavioral assessment in schools. *Journal of Positive Behavior Interventions, 2,* 131–143.

Sugai, G., Horner, R. H., & Lewis, T. (2009). *School-wide positive behavior support implementers' blueprint and self-assessment.* Eugene, OR: OSEP TA-Center on Positive Behavioral Interventions and Supports.

Swain-Bradway, J., Johnson, J., Eber, L., Barrett, S., & Weist, M. D. (2015). Interconnecting school mental health and school-wide positive behavior support. In S. Kutcher, Y. Wei, & M. D. Weist (Eds.), *School mental health* (pp. 282–298). Cambridge, UK: Cambridge University Press. doi:10.1017/CBO9781107284241.023

Thapa, A., Cohen, J., Guffey, S., & Higgins-D'Alessandro, A. (2013). A review of school climate research. *Review of Educational Research, 83,* 357–385.

Tilly, W. D., III. (2008). The evolution of school psychology to science-based practice: Problem solving and the three-tiered model. In A. Thomas &

J. Grimes (Eds.), *Best practices in school psychology V* (pp. 17–36). Bethesda, MD: National Association of School Psychologists.

Walker, H. M., Horner, R. H., Sugai, G., Bullis, M., Sprague, J. R., Bricker, D., . . . Kaufman, M. J. (1996). Integrated approaches to preventing antisocial behavior patterns among school-age children and youth. *Journal of Emotional and Behavioral Disorders, 4*, 194–209.

Walker, H. M., & Severson, H. H. (1992). *Systematic screening for behavior disorders* (2nd ed.). Longmont, CO: Sopris West.

Way, N., Reddy, R., & Rhodes, J. (2007). Students' perceptions of school climate during the middle school years: Associations with trajectories of psychological and behavioral adjustment. *American Journal of Community Psychology, 40*, 194–213. doi:10.1007/s10464-007-9143-y

Wei, R. C., Darling-Hammond, L., & Adamson, F. (2010). *Professional development in the United States: Trends and challenges.* Dallas: National Staff Development Council.

Wei, R. C., Darling-Hammond, L., Andree, A., Richardson, N., & Orphanos, S. (2009). *Professional learning in the learning profession: A status report on teacher development in the United States and abroad.* Dallas, TX. National Staff Development Council.

Wells, R., Hillemeier, M. M., Bai, Y., & Belue, R. (2009). Health service access across racial/ethnic groups of children in the child welfare system. *Child Abuse & Neglect, 33*(5), 282–292.

CHAPTER TWELVE

Supporting Students Involved in Bullying Behaviors

Moving Beyond a Disciplinary Framework

Deborah A. Temkin

Since the late 1990s, concern about bullying and its associated negative outcomes has led policy makers and school officials to enact and implement a wide array of anti-bullying policies and programs aimed at curbing the behavior. Despite nearly two decades of work, current approaches have only limited efficacy at reducing the behavior (Ttofi & Farrington, 2011). In 2015, around 21% of youth ages 12–18 in the United States reported being bullied at school (Lessne & Yanez, 2016). Although this figure has declined since its peak in 2007 of 32% (Musu-Gillette, Hansen, & Spiegelman, 2016), it still represents over five million students experiencing bullying every year. Current approaches to preventing and intervening in bullying typically focus on a punitive model: implementing policies that define and then restrict bullying behavior resulting in disciplinary consequences should the policy be violated (Stuart-Cassel, Bell, & Springer, 2011). Although many bullying prevention programs certainly include elements that go beyond this frame (e.g., educating students about bullying and its impacts [Olweus, Limber, & Mihalic, 1999], building students' social-emotional skills [Espelage, Low, Polanin, & Brown, 2013]), the underlying assumption that bullying is a behavior that must be punished if it occurs, persists. Indeed, in recent years, many states have introduced legislation focused on criminalizing bullying, threatening to fine or even jail children for bullying others (Temkin, 2018).

Yet, there is often a fundamental disconnect between students' experiences of bullying victimization and the parallel intentions of students to engage in bullying perpetration; a student may still feel bullied even if the accused peer did not intentionally or objectively engage in behavior that warrants discipline. This disconnect means that, under current policies and procedures, many students who feel they have been bullied are not recognized as such by their schools; even though 21 percent of students self-reported being bullied in 2015 (Lessne & Yanez, 2016), school reported allegations of bullying based on race, sex, sexual orientation, religion, and disability correspond to a bullying rate of less than one-half of 1% (U.S. Department of Education, 2018). The current disciplinary approach to bullying fails to recognize the trauma many students experience, even if that experience does not meet the definition of bullying contained in policy.

This chapter outlines our current understanding of bullying, including the varied definitions contained in research, policy, and practice, as well as how bullying is currently addressed in the school setting. It then presents an alternative framework, based on the trauma-informed care model, that moves beyond using discipline as a mechanism to prevent bullying behavior to providing support for all students to prevent bullying and to help students recover should bullying occur.

What Is Bullying?

Although bullying is a commonly used term, definitions of what constitutes bullying behavior vary considerably across contexts and stakeholders (Arora, 1996; Gladden, Vivolo-Kantor, Hamburger, & Lumpkin, 2014; Hellström, Persson, & Hagquist, 2015; Vaillancourt et al., 2008). The lack of a common definition affects our understanding of the risk and protective factors and consequences associated with bullying as well as our ability to identify and intervene when it occurs. Even where definitions align, nearly all definitions of bullying require some form of subjectivity—determining whether a behavior is "reasonably" harmful or whether a perpetrator intended to cause harm—which furthers the disconnect between how bullying is perceived by different stakeholders.

Research Definitions

The Centers for Disease Control and Prevention (CDC), in an effort to create a uniform definition of bullying for use in research and surveillance, convened a panel of researchers and practitioners to discuss the challenges around defining bullying and produce a consensus statement (Gladden et al., 2014). The resulting definition largely aligns with a definition first used by researcher Dan Olweus in his pioneering work on bullying (Olweus, 1993). Broadly, this research definition has three components. First, the behavior must be *aggressive*, or intended to cause harm. Such aggression can take several forms, including verbal (e.g., teasing, name-calling), physical (e.g., pushing, hitting), and social (e.g., rumor spreading, social exclusion). It can also occur in several contexts including in-person and through electronic technology (i.e., cyberbullying). Second, the behavior must be *repeated*, or have the potential to be repeated over time. Finally, the behavior occurs in the context of a *power imbalance*, in which the party perpetrating the behavior has more real—or perceived—power over the targeted child. Such power can be earned in a host of ways, from physical strength and prowess, to social popularity, to access to information. The CDC definition explicitly values the perception of the targeted youth, relying on their perception of whether a power imbalance exists, whether the behavior is likely to repeat, and whether the behavior has caused harm.

Student Definitions

Yet, if a student is asked if they have been bullied, they are unlikely to consider these definitional components in their response (Arora, 1996; Hellström, Persson, & Hagquist, 2015; Vaillancourt et al., 2008). In research by Vaillancourt and colleagues (2008), only 6% of surveyed 8- to 18-year-old students included repetition as a key element and only around a quarter (26%) included a power imbalance. Similarly, research by Hellström, Persson, and Hagquist (2015) suggests that such elements are irrelevant for students, and, instead, students focus in on the hurt or harm of the behavior. Hellström and colleagues (2015) additionally found that, for many students, bullying was self-defined; many students suggested that only the target of bullying can define the behavior as bullying because only they can know how the behavior made them feel. The same behavior could be perceived as bullying by one student but interpreted as playful banter or joking around to an outside observer (Temkin, 2014).

Students' own perceptions of whether they have been bullied or not is of critical importance when considering the potential outcomes associated with experiencing the behavior. The recent push to reduce bullying in schools comes amidst increasing media attention to bullying's associations with school shootings and youth suicide (Leary, Kowalski, Smith, & Phillips, 2003; Hertz, Donato, & Wright, 2013). Although these are among the most extreme potential outcomes, bullying is also more commonly linked to several other negative outcomes including reduced academic achievement, increased risk of drug and alcohol use, and increased risk of depression and anxiety (Cook, Williams, Guerra, Kim, & Sadek, 2010; Nansel, Overpeck, Pilla, Ruann, Simons-Morton, & Scheidt, 2001). Our knowledge of these associations is largely derived from research that relies on students' self-reported involvement in bullying behaviors. That is, the vast majority of studies exploring the potential effects of bullying victimization rely on survey instruments that ask students directly whether they have been bullied (Furlong, Sharkey, Felix, Tanigawa, & Green, 2010). The form and content of survey bullying items do vary study to study, which can affect students' interpretation of the question (Swearer, Siebecker, Johnsen-Frerichs, & Wang, 2010). However, across studies, the associations between self-reported bullying and these outcomes persist (Cook et al., 2010). In sum, it is a student's own subjective experience of being bullied that is linked to negative outcomes and not necessarily an outside observer's assessment.

Policy Definitions

Policy definitions, however, which primarily function to direct required actions on the part of schools, and, in some communities, law enforcement, do not focus on the experience of the targeted child. Most policies focus instead on the intent of the perpetrating child and whether their actions would be "reasonably" assumed to cause harm to their target. Consider the definition of bullying contained in Kansas statute:

> "Bullying" means: (A) Any intentional gesture or any intentional written, verbal, electronic or physical act . . . that is sufficiently severe, persistent or pervasive that . . . a reasonable person, under the circumstances, knows or should know will have the effect of . . . harming a student. (Kan. Stat. Ann. § 72-6417)

Here, even if a child feels harmed by bullying, the state definition deems their experience to not be bullying if the intent of the child who engaged in the behavior cannot be established and if the behavior is deemed "harmless" to a reasonable person. Kansas's definition is consistent with those in several states (Stuart-Cassel, Bell, & Springer, 2011).

The focus in anti-bullying policies on whether a behavior is intentional and whether a reasonable person would know it would lead to harm is consistent with the basic tenants of criminal law; punishment should only be applied to someone whose behavior can be determined with relative certainty (Mendes, 2004). There is an inherent disconnect, then, between the experience of the child who is targeted and whether the behavior of the perpetrating child is deemed bullying. A child can feel bullied—and experience negative outcomes as a result—even if the perpetrating child cannot be deemed to have bullied. Similarly, a child could potentially be found to have bullied another child—because their behavior was intentional and could reasonably be assumed to cause harm—even if the targeted child does not feel bullied.

Discrepancies between Definitions

Perhaps it is for this reason we see such large differences between student-reported and school-reported rates of bullying. The School Crime Supplement (SCS) is a federal, nationally representative data collection in the United States that asks youth ages 12–18 to self-report whether they have been bullied in school. As noted in the introduction to this chapter, approximately 21%, or just over 5 million, adolescents reported being bullied in 2015 (Lessne & Yanez, 2016). The Civil Rights Data Collection asks all schools in the United States to report their total number of incidents of bullying and harassment based on race, sex, sexual orientation, religion, and disability. For school-year 2015–2016, 72% of schools that serve at least one grade 6–12 in the United States reported having zero incidents of bullying and harassment on these bases (U.S. Department of Education, 2018). Assuming each reported incident represents a unique student, the 114,478 reported incidents amount to a bullying rate of less than one-half of 1% (0.35%). Even if we discount the nearly 57% of students who report being bullied on the SCS that also indicated they never told an adult and instead assume a known bullying rate of 9%, still over 96% of students who feel like they have been bullied are not being recognized by their schools.

The disconnect between how schools understand and respond to bullying incidents and how students perceive their experience likely underscores much of the tension that results in students feeling as though schools do not adequately address bullying (Evans, Cotter, & Smokowski, 2017). This sentiment is often reflected in media reports of suicides that were in some way linked to bullying victimization; often parents are quoted that schools "did nothing" or "should have done more." It is not necessarily clear, however, what more schools can do when they are limited to a disciplinary model for bullying, requiring a stringent and rigorous definition to prevent undue punishment. Many schools have embraced evidence-based bullying programs in an effort to stem bullying before intervention is needed, however, as described in the next section such programs have limited efficacy and their content often relies on the research definition of bullying, leading to conflicts with the definitions and procedures outlined under discipline-focused policies.

Existing Approaches to Bullying Prevention and Intervention

As attention toward and concerns about bullying in schools increased over the past decade, so too did the number of available "solutions." Bullying prevention became an easy marketing tool for speakers, software systems, and curriculum developers building upon increasing concerns about bullying's apparent link to youth suicide and school administrators' anxieties about potential liability for not doing enough to prevent bullying on their campuses. Despite the abundance of available bullying prevention programs, few have been evaluated (National Academies of Sciences, Engineering, and Medicine [NASEM], 2016). Among those that have been evaluated, reductions in reported bullying perpetration and victimization have generally been small (Ttofi & Farrington, 2011), and the effectiveness of programs diminishes as students get older (Yeager, Fong, Lee, & Espelage, 2015). Overall, evaluations of programs based in the United States show limited efficacy, even for those programs that are effective elsewhere (Ttofi & Farrington, 2011).

Traditional Bullying Prevention Programs

Many of the available, evaluated, bullying prevention program are based largely on a framework established by the Olweus Bullying Prevention Program (OBPP) (NASEM, 2016; Ttofi & Farrington, 2011). That program largely focuses on three main components: (1) training of students, as well as school officials and other key stakeholders, on the definition of bullying and its potential negative outcomes; (2) establishing bullying policies in an effort to change norms around tolerance for bullying, and; (3) creating spaces (e.g., through classroom meetings) that allow students to talk about their experiences with bullying (Olweus, Limber, & Mihalic, 1999). Although OBPP has demonstrated efficacy in evaluations conducted outside of the United States, to date, evaluations conducted in the United States have either lacked rigor or found null results (Espelage, 2013; Ttofi & Farrington, 2011).

Although other bullying prevention programs have adapted and expanded the OBPP framework, they, too, have either not shown efficacy in the United States. For example, the KiVa anti-bullying program, developed in Finland, focuses on engaging peers to take more active roles in stopping bullying behavior as well as providing instruction to parents and school staff on how to intervene if bullying is identified (Kärnä, Voeten, Little, Poskiparta, Alanen, & Salmivalli, 2011). Evaluations conducted in Finland show that KiVa had a modest but significant effect at reducing bullying victimization and perpetration among students in grades 1–9 (Kärnä et al., 2011), but a similar evaluation has not yet been conducted in the United States.

Both OBPP and KiVa use the research definition of bullying rather than the definitions of bullying contained in schools' existing policies. As noted previously in this chapter, the research definition of bullying largely depends on the perception of the targeted child. Schools implementing this program set up a natural conflict between encouraging students to report bullying behavior using one definition while only considering, and responding to, a more finite set of behaviors under their policy definitions. Most students who report experiencing bullying behaviors on anonymous surveys also report that they have never informed adults about their experience (Lessne & Yanez, 2016). Students cite both concern about either lack of or inappropriate adult response and differing definitions as key reasons they do not disclose their experience (DeLara, 2012). Such perceptions are likely reinforced when students receive mixed messages between program implementation and policy enforcement.

Moreover, OBPP, KiVa, and other similar programs, rely on the notion that informing students about the potential negative consequences of bullying behavior will lead to students refraining from engaging in such behavior or stepping in to discourage the behavior in their peers. Evaluations of efforts to prevent alcohol and drug use, however, demonstrate, that such "inform and scare" tactics do little to change behavior without either addressing the root causes of behavior or providing alternatives for any perceived benefits of engaging in the behavior (Botvin & Griffin, 2003). This may be especially true of bullying where most of the focus on negative consequences is for students who are victimized by bullying rather than the students engaging in the behavior.

Discipline and Criminalization

Discipline provides a direct consequence for children engaging in the behavior. As concerns about bullying have grown, so too has the push for increasingly punitive punishments to serve as deterrents. In several states, for instance, legislatures are pushing to not only subject children who bully to school-based discipline, but institute criminal penalties including steep fines and potential jail time (Temkin, 2018). Other jurisdictions are considering instituting fines and penalties not only for children engaging in such behaviors, but their parents (Temkin, 2013).

Discipline in and of itself is largely ineffective at preventing bullying (NASEM, 2016). Removing students from school or placing them into the juvenile justice system does not and cannot address the underlying reasons students are engaging in bullying behavior (Orr & Abramson, 2014; Temkin, 2018). There is no single reason students bully; some may be responding to trauma or victimization in their own lives while still others may be using bullying in order to fit in with the norms of their social networks (Cook et al., 2010; Faris & Felmlee, 2011). Punishing students does not provide them with the skills or support they need to change their behavior. Rather, discipline assumes that students are able to simply stop their behavior instead of face such consequences.

Further, reliance on discipline may actually undermine efforts to impact perceived bullying victimization. Under a disciplinary framework, students are implicitly taught that behavior can only cause harm if they *intended* to cause harm (Mendes, 2004). That is, disciplinary-focused strategies fail to help students recognize that others can be hurt by their actions even if they did not intend those behaviors to be purposefully hurtful. Developing empathy, perspective-taking skills, and overall emotional intelligence may be key to fostering such recognition, reducing aggressive behavior, and ameliorating the effects of perceived bullying victimization (Brackett & Rivers, 2014).

Social-Emotional Learning and Bullying Prevention

Social-emotional learning (SEL) programs are beginning to emerge as an alternative to more traditional bullying prevention programs such as OBPP through their focus on helping children regulate their own emotions as well as identify and respond to the emotions of others (Zins, Bloodworth, Weissberg, & Walberg, 2004). Although evidence is emerging that such programs are at least somewhat effective at reducing aggressive behaviors and other forms of conduct problems (Durlak, Weissberg, Dymnicki, Taylor, & Schellinger, 2011; Taylor, Oberle, Durlak, & Weissberg, 2017), there is currently limited evidence regarding the efficacy of such programs at reducing self-reported bullying victimization as only a handful of studies have included such measures (Bradshaw, 2015).

A recent evaluation of the middle school version of *Second Step*, a targeted SEL program for reducing aggression and violence, found significant effects only for physical aggression perpetration and no significant effects on self-reported victimization (Espelage et al., 2013). Similarly, an evaluation of the *RULER* ("Recognizing, Understanding, Labeling, Expressing, and Regulating emotion") approach found that while the program significantly improves objective observations of classrooms' emotional support and positive climate, there are no significant effects on student-rated classroom supportiveness (Rivers, Brackett, Reyes, Elbertson, & Salovey, 2013).

Further research is critically needed to better understand SEL programs' potential to impact self-reported victimization. It may be that though current SEL programs better equip overtly aggressive youth with the skills they need to manage their emotions, such programs may need more explicit focus on how even unintentional behaviors may lead peers to feel hurt or harmed. Many SEL programs do focus on building empathy, which could lead to better support for students who have been victimized, however this pathway has not been directly tested. As with more traditional bullying prevention programs, SEL programs are implemented under the shadow of punitive anti-bullying policies.

Restorative Justice and Alternative Disciplinary Approaches

While concern about bullying has grown, so too has concern around the "school to prison pipeline," or the finding that students who face exclusionary discipline at school (e.g., suspensions and expulsions) are significantly more likely to become involved in the juvenile or adult justice system (Skiba & Losen, 2016). This finding is juxtaposed with the fact that, overall, black youth and youth with disabilities face disproportionate amounts of discipline compared with white students and youth without disabilities (Skiba & Losen, 2016). Even in states and jurisdictions that call for more progressive or adaptive forms of discipline, anti-bullying policies often include suspensions or expulsions as consequences for bullying (Temkin, Horton, & Kim, 2014).

In an effort to curb the school to prison pipeline and racial disparities in school discipline, many states and school systems are embracing programs that provide alternatives to exclusionary discipline including restorative justice approaches. Restorative justice in schools focuses on building and repairing the school's community by identifying harm, providing support for those who have been harmed, identifying reasons why the harm occurred, and helping those who have offended to make amends (Morrison, 2002). Like SEL, restorative justice has been operationalized and implemented differently across a number of different programs, but generally operates by bringing together students who have been harmed with those who have perpetrated the harm as well as other members of the community who provide leadership and support through the process. Although evidence about the impact of restorative justice practices is still preliminary, the available, largely observational evaluations suggest associations between restorative justice and reductions in disciplinary referrals and improvements in attendance, school connectedness, and overall school climate (Fronius, Persson, Guckenburg, Hurley, & Petrosino, 2016).

The use of restorative justice for bullying is hotly contested (Molnar-Main et al., 2014). Because bullying, by research definition, involves a perceived power imbalance between the target and the perpetrator, mediation of any sort may further exacerbate the target's sense of powerlessness (Fronius et al., 2016; Molnar-Main et al., 2014). If not facilitated fairly, and not conducted with the full buy-in of the harmed child, restorative justice approaches may further victimize the child (NASEM, 2016). Still, some argue that if carefully facilitated in a fully voluntary manner, restorative justice could be an appropriate intervention for bullying (Molnar-Main et al., 2014).

There is little available evidence about the potential impact of such approaches on bullying—neither whether restorative justice approaches can prevent bullying or whether they exacerbate it (Fronius et al., 2016). One emerging exception is the *No Bully* system that implements a modified version of restorative justice practices. Under the program, a team of students including the accused aggressors, but not including the student who has been bullied, meets to discuss ways to support the student who has been bullied. The student who has been bullied then joins the structured meeting to respond to the team's plans. Initial pilot data of the *No Bully* system suggest that targeted students feel safer following engagement in the system and report fewer and less intensive bullying incidents over time (DeNike, 2017). Further research is needed to fully understand the potential for such approaches.

Even though restorative justice frameworks provide improved focus on repairing harm, rather than punishment, they still rely on the determination that one child indeed bullied another. Only after a determination of bullying has occurred are children referred to restorative sessions. Thus, although restorative justice provides a more positive approach to addressing bullying, it may still not be able to overcome the disconnect between students' and schools' definitions of bullying.

Programs That Discourage Reporting of Bullying

Minimizing the gap between students' perceptions of bullying and schools' available responses is critical. There are two logical approaches to doing so: (1) building systems that provide support for students, regardless of the definition of bullying (as will be described later in this chapter), or (2) encouraging students to not consider—or report—behaviors as bullying, even if they are hurtful. This latter idea underscores the *Bullies to Buddies* program, which explicitly discourages students from expressing negative reactions to bullying behavior (e.g., anger, hurt, resistance) and instead encourages them to play along with the bullying. The program further discourages students from reporting their behavior to adults. The *Bullies to Buddies* program and other similar approaches are rarely mentioned in summaries of bullying prevention approaches (e.g., NASEM, 2016), but are being adopted by increasing numbers of schools and districts (as reported on the program's website).

In a small pilot evaluation of *Bullies to Buddies*, students were significantly less likely to believe telling an adult was an appropriate response to bullying after participating in the program (McNamara, McKelvey, & Winders, 2009). Although the pilot found a small statistically significant reduction in the frequency students reported having rumors spread about them, there were no other significant changes in experiencing bullying. In sum, instead of actually changing the experience of bullying for these students, and their associated risk for other negative outcomes, this program simply discourages students from seeking help.

The program recently received widespread condemnation after a flyer reflecting the program's "golden rules" (including about not telling an adult about bullying experiences) was posted on the *Jezebel* website (Rose, 2014). Still, the appetite of schools to embrace such a misguided approach suggests that we must do more to bridge the divide between students' perceptions of bullying and the ability for schools to respond. As addressed in the next section, doing so requires a fundamental shift in our thinking about addressing bullying, separating the experience of a child who is bullied from the actions and intentions of a child who engages in bullying behavior.

Toward a More Supportive Framework for Addressing Bullying

As outlined in the previous two sections, bullying is a concept that is both hard to define and hard to address. The drive to prevent and intervene in bullying primarily stems from concerns about the potential negative outcomes—including suicidality and extreme retaliation—for those who have been bullied. Even though our concern lies with those who have been bullied, our systems are driven by a disciplinary framework that focuses not on the harm someone experiences, but rather on demonstrating that the person that harmed them did so intentionally. This framework thus leaves students whose bullying cannot be proven with little support or recourse.

Consider, for instance, a recent case from New Jersey, which has one of the most comprehensive, and restrictive, anti-bullying laws in the United States (Stuart-Cassel, Bell, & Springer, 2011). In that case, an 8th-grade boy ("C.H.") shoved crumpled paper down the shirt of a classmate. That classmate felt bullied, reported the bullying, and the school system deemed the behavior as bullying and punished C.H. C.H. then appealed the ruling to state education commissioner who called the behavior a "prank" and overturned the discipline (Mooney, 2013). Over the course of the year that it took for the administrative system to determine whether bullying occurred or not, it is unclear whether anything was done to support the child who felt bullied. The bureaucratic system established by anti-bullying legislation to ensure bullying is adequately handled often means that students' needs are not addressed until or unless bullying is deemed to have occurred.

The current systems neglect the reality that for every case of bullying, there are at least two perspectives that are equally valid and equally in need of support: that of the child who is engaging in negative behavior and that of the child who feels as though they have been bullied. Addressing the needs of each student separately requires moving beyond considering discipline as the ultimate response for bullying to tailoring support to ensure the sense of safety and security is restored for all students.

Addressing the Needs of Students Who Feel Bullied

Supporting students who feel bullied starts with understanding that experiencing bullying is traumatic. In recent years, researchers exploring the impact of "adverse childhood experiences" (ACEs) have begun to include whether a child has been bullied among other experiences, which include witnessing violence, emotional and physical abuse, emotional and physical neglect, having an incarcerated family member, and other similarly traumatizing experiences (Finkelhor, Shattuck, Turner, & Hamby, 2015). Although the degree of trauma experienced by bullying can vary, acknowledging that those who feel they have been bullied are likely experiencing related harm helps frame their need for additional support.

Increasingly, schools are embracing *Trauma Informed Care* (TIC) or "trauma-informed schools" to address the needs of students who have ACEs (Oral et al., 2015). As an ACE, bullying can and should be addressed under the same framework. The Substance Abuse and Mental Health Administration outlines six key principles that underscore trauma-informed approaches (Box 12.1). Extending these principles to address bullying requires three key considerations:

(1) *Validation of experience.* Approaching bullying through a trauma-informed lens requires acknowledging that a child has been traumatized even if their experience does not match others' definitions of bullying. Helping children understand their experience, without being dismissive is essential to ensuring students feel empowered. All students who feel bullied should be provided with at least some level of validation and support.

(2) *Restoring a sense of safety.* Because most incidents of bullying happen at school, schools must actively work not only to promote a sense of safety but also to restore that safety if and when a child feels bullied. Safety may look and feel different for each child and they must have a voice in designing plans that do not further stigmatize, isolate, or traumatize them. For example, redesigning seating charts for an entire classroom is preferable to only moving the targeted student.

(3) *Transparency about action against offending students.* It is critical for students who feel bullied to understand the actions the school is taking to address

Box 12.1 Key Principles of Trauma-Informed Care

1. Safety
2. Trustworthiness and Transparency
3. Peer support
4. Collaboration and mutuality
5. Empowerment, voice, and choice
6. Cultural, Historical, and Gender Issues

Source: Substance Abuse and Mental Health Services Administration, n.d.

bullying behavior. This includes action—or inaction—taken against the students who they perceive as having bullied them. Although schools are often restricted from sharing full details of disciplinary actions taken against other students, they can and should be transparent about whether action is taken against the offending students. Even if action is not taken against another student, students who feel bullied should be offered support and reassured that their experience is being taken seriously.

Addressing the Needs of Students Who Bully

Although this chapter largely focuses on the fact that students can feel bullied, even if no one intended to bully them, many children do purposefully and intentionally hurt others. As noted previously in this chapter, disciplinary approaches do not and cannot address the underlying reasons students bully nor equip students with the skills to prevent bullying in the future. SEL programs hold great promise for helping build these skills, but recent evaluations suggest they may not be sufficient to truly deter bullying behavior (Espelage et al., 2013). Especially for children whose bullying is a manifestation of their own ACEs, a tailored, trauma-informed approach may be critical to change behavior (Oral et al., 2015).

Bullying perpetration, therefore, should be considered a symptom of trauma first, leading to more in-depth assessment of the potential stressors and needs in a child's life that could be addressed. Emerging evidence, for example, suggests that children who have food insecurity (Jackson & Vaughn, 2017), children who lack sufficient sleep (Kubiszewski, Fontaine, Potard, & Gimenes, 2014), and children who are maltreated at home (Hong, Espelage, Grogan-Kaylor, & Allen-Meares, 2012) are all at greater risk for engaging in bullying behaviors. Addressing these underlying issues may lead to greater efficacy at reducing overall bullying perpetration.

Addressing the Needs of the Broader School Community

Not only is bullying a manifestation of individual ACEs, it can also be a symptom of the norms and values held by the school's social climate (Bradshaw, Sawyer, & O'Brennan, 2009; Salmivalli & Voeten, 2004). Bullying is much more likely to occur in schools that implicitly or explicitly condone bullying and in schools that have overall negative school climates (Bradshaw, Sawyer, & O'Brennan, 2009). As with students who bully, understanding bullying as a symptom of a negative school climate can expand how schools approach prevention.

Rather than implementing programs only targeted at bullying, schools can instead leverage the opportunity to identify underlying needs within their own climates (Osher et al., 2016). Although school climate improvement is neither easy nor a one-size-fits-all approach, developing a positive school climate has the potential to not only prevent and reduce bullying but also improve academic achievement and other student outcomes (Thapa, Cohen, Guffey, & Higgins-D'Alessandro, 2013).

Conclusion

This chapter focused on how our current discipline-centered approach to bullying conflicts with and is disconnected from the broader understanding of students' experiences with bullying. Whereas policies define bullying largely using the tenants of criminal law—that the behavior must be intentional and reasonably assumed to cause harm—most students suggest that bullying is instead a subjective and personal experience (Hellström, Persson, & Hagquist, 2015). The disconnect between how prevention programming frames bullying and how disciplinary codes determine whether bullying occurs may underscore the relative lack of efficacy of bullying prevention programs in the United States (Ttofi & Farrington, 2011).

Although there are many promising approaches to preventing and intervening in bullying, including SEL programs and restorative justice practices, much more research is needed to truly understand their potential impact (Bradshaw, 2015). Further, until and unless we separate the experience of being bullied from the intent to bully others, our understanding of the true impact of such programs will be limited.

Using a trauma-informed framework to address the needs and validate the experiences of those who feel bullied, as well as those who engage in bullying behaviors, has the potential to bridge the gap between student and schools' definitions of bullying. Further research is needed, however, to understand how such approaches not only impact bullying but also its associated outcomes.

References

Arora, C. M. J. (1996). Defining bullying: Towards a clearer general understanding and more effective intervention strategies. *School Psychology International, 17*(4), 317–329.

Botvin, G. J., & Griffin, K. W. (2003). Drug abuse prevention curricula in schools. In Z. Sloboda & W. J. Bukoski (Eds.), *Handbook of drug abuse prevention: Theory, science, and practice* (pp. 45–74). New York: Kluwer Academic/Plenum.

Brackett, M.A. & Rivers, S.E. (2014). Transforming students' lives with social emotional learning. In R. Pekrung & L. Linnebrink-Garcia (Eds.),

International handbook of emotions in education (pp. 368–388). New York, NY: Taylor and Francis. http://dx.doi.org/10.4324/9780203148211.ch19

Bradshaw, C. P. (2015). Translating research to practice in bullying prevention. *American Psychologist, 70*(4), 322–332.

Bradshaw, C. P., Sawyer, A. L., & O'Brennan, L. M. (2009). A social disorganization perspective on bullying-related attitudes and behaviors: The influence of school context. *American Journal of Community Psychology, 43*(3–4), 204–220.

Cook, C. R., Williams, K. R., Guerra, N. G., Kim, T. E., & Sadek, S. (2010). Predictors of bullying and victimization in childhood and adolescence: A meta-analytic investigation. *School Psychology Quarterly, 25*(2), 65–83.

DeLara, E. W. (2012). Why adolescents don't disclose incidents of bullying and harassment. *Journal of School Violence, 11*(4), 288–305.

DeNike, M. (2017). No Bullying Solution Team: Outcomes evaluation 2012–17. Retrieved from https://www.nobully.org/sites/default/files/page/files/No%20Bully%20Solution%20Team%20Cumulative%20Report%202017_0.pdf

Durlak, J. A., Weissberg, R. P., Dymnicki, A. B., Taylor, R. D., & Schellinger, K. B. (2011). The impact of enhancing students' social and emotional learning: A meta-analysis of school-based universal interventions. *Child Development, 82*(1), 405–432.

Espelage, D. L. (2013). Why are bully prevention programs failing in US schools? *Journal of Curriculum and Pedagogy, 10*(2), 121–124.

Espelage, D. L., Low, S., Polanin, J. R., & Brown, E. C. (2013). The impact of a middle school program to reduce aggression, victimization, and sexual violence. *Journal of Adolescent Health, 53*(2), 180–186.

Evans, C. B., Cotter, K. L., & Smokowski, P. R. (2017). Giving victims of bullying a voice: A qualitative study of post bullying reactions and coping strategies. *Child and Adolescent Social Work Journal, 34*(6), 543–555.

Faris, R., & Felmlee, D. (2011). Status struggles: Network centrality and gender segregation in same- and cross-gender aggression. *American Sociological Review, 76*(1), 48–73.

Finkelhor, D., Shattuck, A., Turner, H., & Hamby, S. (2015). A revised inventory of adverse childhood experiences. *Child Abuse & Neglect, 48*, 13–21.

Fronius, T., Persson, H., Guckenburg, S., Hurley, N., & Petrosino, A. (2016). *Restorative justice in US schools: A research review.* San Francisco: WestEd Justice and Prevention Training Center.

Furlong, M. J., Sharkey, J. D., Felix, E. D., Tanigawa, D., & Green, J. G. (2010). Bullying assessment: A call for increased precision of self-reporting procedures. In S. R. Jimerson, S. M. Swearer, & D. L. Espelage (Eds.). *Handbook of bullying in schools: An international perspective* (pp. 329–346). New York: Routledge.

Gladden, R. M., Vivolo-Kantor, A. M., Hamburger, M. E., & Lumpkin, C. D. (2014). *Bullying surveillance among youths: Uniform definitions for public health and recommended data elements, Version 1.0.* Atlanta: National

Center for Injury Prevention and Control, Centers for Disease Control and Prevention and US Department of Education.

Hellström, L., Persson, L., & Hagquist, C. (2015). Understanding and defining bullying–adolescents' own views. *Archives of Public Health, 73*(4), 1–9.

Hertz, M. F., Donato, I., & Wright, J. (2013). Bullying and suicide: A public health approach. *Journal of Adolescent Health, 53*(1), S1–S3.

Hong, J. S., Espelage, D. L., Grogan-Kaylor, A., & Allen-Meares, P. (2012). Identifying potential mediators and moderators of the association between child maltreatment and bullying perpetration and victimization in school. *Educational Psychology Review, 24*(2), 167–186.

Jackson, D. B., & Vaughn, M. G. (2017). Household food insecurity during childhood and adolescent misconduct. *Preventive Medicine, 96*, 113–117.

Kärnä, A., Voeten, M., Little, T. D., Poskiparta, E., Alanen, E., & Salmivalli, C. (2011). Going to scale: A nonrandomized nationwide trial of the KiVa antibullying program for grades 1–9. *Journal of Consulting and Clinical Psychology, 79*(6), 796–805.

Kubiszewski, V., Fontaine, R., Potard, C., & Gimenes, G. (2014). Bullying, sleep/wake patterns and subjective sleep disorders: Findings from a cross-sectional survey. *Chronobiology International, 31*(4), 542–553.

Leary, M. R., Kowalski, R. M., Smith, L., & Phillips, S. (2003). Teasing, rejection, and violence: Case studies of the school shootings. *Aggressive Behavior, 29*(3), 202–214.

Lessne, D., & Yanez, C. (2016). Student reports of bullying: Results from the 2015 School Crime Supplement to the National Crime Victimization Survey. Web Tables. NCES 2017–015. National Center for Education Statistics. Retrieved From: https://nces.ed.gov/pubs2017/2017015.pdf

McNamara, K., McKelvey, K., & Winders, E. (2009, February). *Bullies to buddies: A victim empowerment intervention.* Paper presented at the Annual Meeting of the National Association of School Psychologists, Boston, MA.

Mendes, S. M. (2004). Certainty, severity, and their relative deterrent effects: Questioning the implications of the role of risk in criminal deterrence policy. *Policy Studies Journal, 32*(1), 59–74.

Molnar-Main, S., Bisbing, K., Blackburn, S., Galkowski, L., Garrity, R., Morris, C., . . . Singer, J. (2014). Integrating bullying prevention and restorative practices in schools: Considerations for practitioners and policy-makers. Center for Safe Schools, Clemson Institute on Family and Neighborhood Life, Highmark Foundation. Retrieved from http://www. safeschools .info/content/BPRPWhitePaper2014.pdf

Mooney, J. (2013, May 16). Reversal of bullying ruling upheld by State Education Chief. *NJ Spotlight*. Retrieved from http://www.njspotlight.com/stories /13/05/15/judge-s-reversal-of-bullying-ruling-upheld-by-state-education -chief/

Morrison, B. (2002). *Bullying and victimisation in schools: A restorative justice approach* (Vol. 219). Canberra: Australian Institute of Criminology.

Musu-Gillette, L., Hansen, R., & Spiegelman, M. (2016). Bullying down from a decade ago, but unchanged since 2013. NCES Blog. National Center for Educational Statistics. Retrieved from https://nces.ed.gov/blogs/nces/post/bullying-down-from-a-decade-ago-but-unchanged-since-2013

Nansel, T. R., Overpeck, M., Pilla, R. S., Ruann, W. J., Simons-Morton, B., & Scheidt, P. (2001). Bullying behaviors among US youth: Prevalence and association with psychosocial adjustment. *JAMA*, 285(16), 2094–2100.

National Academies of Sciences, Engineering, and Medicine (NASEM). (2016). *Preventing bullying through science, policy, and practice.* Washington, DC: National Academies Press.

Olweus, D. (1993). *Bullying at Schools: What we know and what we can do.* Cambridge, MA: Blackwell.

Olweus, D., Limber, S., & Mihalic, S. F. (1999). *Blueprints for violence prevention, book nine: Bullying prevention program.* Boulder, CO: Center for the Study and Prevention of Violence.

Oral, R., Ramirez, M., Coohey, C., Nakada, S., Walz, A., Kuntz, A., . . . Peek-Asa, C. (2015). Adverse childhood experiences and trauma informed care: The future of health care. *Pediatric Research, 79*(1–2), 227–233.

Orr, D. P., & Abramson, C. P. (2014). *The People of the State of New York v Marquan W. Macky-Meggs: Brief of Amici Curiae.* Retrieved from http://www.advocatesforchildren.org/sites/default/files/on_page/nyvmarquan_amicus_brief.pdf?pt=1

Osher, D., Kidron, Y., DeCandia, C. J., Kendziora, K., Weissberg, R. P., Wentzel, K. R., & Ramani, G. (2016). Interventions to promote safe and supportive school climate. In *Handbook of social influences in school contexts, emotional, motivation, and cognitive outcomes* (pp. 384–404). New York: Routledge.

Rivers, S. E., Brackett, M. A., Reyes, M. R., Elbertson, N. A., & Salovey, P. (2013). Improving the social and emotional climate of classrooms: A clustered randomized controlled trial testing the RULER approach. *Prevention Science, 14*(1), 77–87.

Rose, R. (2014). Nebraska school gives most idiotic advice ever to deal with bullies. *Jezebel.* Retrieved from https://jezebel.com/nebraska-school-gives-most-idiotic-advice-ever-to-deal-1564016234

Salmivalli, C., & Voeten, M. (2004). Connections between attitudes, group norms, and behaviour in bullying situations. *International Journal of Behavioral Development, 28*(3), 246–258.

Skiba, R. J., & Losen, D. J. (2016). From reaction to prevention: Turning the page on school discipline. *American Educator, 39*(4), 4–11.

Stuart-Cassel, V., Bell, A., & Springer, J. F. (2011). *Analysis of state bullying laws and policies.* Washington, DC: Office of Planning, Evaluation and Policy Development, US Department of Education.

Swearer, S. M., Siebecker, A. B., Johnsen-Frerichs, L. A., & Wang, C. (2010). Assessment of bullying/victimization: The problem of comparability across studies across methodologies. In S. R. Jimerson, S. M. Swearer, &

D. L. Espelage (Eds.), *Handbook of bullying in schools: An international perspective* (pp. 305–328). New York: Routledge.

Taylor, R. D., Oberle, E., Durlak, J. A., & Weissberg, R. P. (2017). Promoting positive youth development through school-based social and emotional learning interventions: A meta-analysis of follow-up effects. *Child Development, 88*(4), 1156–1171.

Temkin, D. (2013). Ticketing parents for children's bullying? Exploring a new anti-bullying trend. *Huffington Post.* Retrieved from http://www.huffingtonpost.com/deborah-temkin/ticketing-parents-for-chi_b_3423246.html

Temkin, D. (2014). Playful banter or bullying—Whose perception matters? *Huffington Post.* Retrieved from https://www.huffingtonpost.com/deborah-temkin/playful-banter-or-bullyin_b_5845348.html

Temkin, D. (2018). Criminalizing bullying will hurt kids [Blog]. *Child Trends.* Retrieved from https://www.childtrends.org/criminalizing-bullying-will-hurt-more-kids/

Temkin, D., Horton, S., & Kim, A. (2014). Bullying prevention in District of Columbia educational institutions: School Year 2013–14 Compliance Report. Publication# 2014-49. *Child Trends.*

Thapa, A., Cohen, J., Guffey, S., & Higgins-D'Alessandro, A. (2013). A review of school climate research. *Review of Educational Research, 83*(3), 357–385.

Ttofi, M. M., & Farrington, D. P. (2011). Effectiveness of school-based programs to reduce bullying: A systematic and meta-analytic review. *Journal of Experimental Criminology,* 7(1), 27–56.

U.S. Department of Education. (2018). Civil Rights Data Collection 2015–2016. Retrieved from https://ocrdata.ed.gov/

Vaillancourt, T., McDougall, P., Hymel, S., Krygsman, A., Miller, J., Stiver, K., & Davis, C. (2008). Bullying: Are researchers and children/youth talking about the same thing? *International Journal of Behavioral Development, 32*(6), 486–495.

Yeager, D. S., Fong, C. J., Lee, H. Y., & Espelage, D. L. (2015). Declines in efficacy of anti-bullying programs among older adolescents: Theory and a three-level meta-analysis. *Journal of Applied Developmental Psychology, 37,* 36–51.

Zins, J. E., Bloodworth, M. R., Weissberg, R. P, & Walberg, H. J. (2004). The scientific base linking social and emotional learning to school success. In J. E. Zins, R. P. Weissberg, M. C. Wang, & H. J. Walberg (Eds.), *Building Academic Success on Social and Emotional Learning* (pp. 3–22). New York: Teachers College Press.

CHAPTER THIRTEEN

Reflections on Twenty Years of Restorative Justice in Schools

Brenda E. Morrison and Nancy Riestenberg

Restorative justice in education (RJE) can be characterized as a paradigm shift from social control to social engagement, through developing the relational ecology of the school community—administrators, staff, teachers, students, and parents—as they implement schoolwide restorative justice practices (SWRJP). The culture change required to embrace these practices can be understood through a shift in motivational levers that offer a distinct praxis for the regulation of safety and justice within school communities. First, rather than focusing on external sanctioning systems (rewards and punishment) as motivational levers, restorative justice focuses on the motivational levers of relational ecologies that nurture and develop value-based internal sanctioning systems. Second, the process of responding to safety concerns includes those members of the school community most affected and closest to the harm. This enables a more socially responsive relational intervention, as compared to prescriptive disciplinary measures, wherein third parties (e.g., principals) respond to rule violations. Third, RJE develops relational literacy through developing the social and emotional intelligence of the school community. As such, reason does not trump emotion; instead, community safety is nurtured through finding reason for emotion. This practice is distinct from most institutional responses, which focus on establishing the facts, with little focus on the social, emotional, and spiritual dimensions that make up the rich motivational ecologies within the lives of individuals and communities.

This chapter reflects on (1) the history of the rise of zero tolerance policies, as a mechanism of social control; (2) theory and rational for the RJE paradigm shift; (3) three-tiered framework for SWRJP; (4) evidence base for SWRJP; and (5) moving beyond the promise of restorative justice in education.

Social Control: The Rise of Zero Tolerance

Since the 1980s, neoliberal economic policies, socio-political conservatism (e.g., child-saving movement), the rise of moral panic and fear mongering, the rhetoric of the school accountability narrative (e.g., No Child Left Behind Act, 2001), and tough-on-crime criminal justice policies have given rise to highly punitive school disciplinary strategies, supported by zero tolerance policies (Hirschfield, 2008; Payne & Welch, 2018; Reyes, 2006; Sellers & Arrigo, 2018; Simon, 2007). Zero tolerance policies have led to hundreds of thousands of students, the majority of whom are young people of color, to be drawn into the prison-industrial complex. This discriminatory trajectory, known as the school-to-prison pipeline, cripples democratic institutions and systems of justice (Braithwaite, 2017). Not only do these policies adversely affect young people of color, they adversely affect all members of the school community—students, teachers, parents, and school administrators (Dohrn, 2001; Robbins, 2005; Simon, 2007; Skiba, Arredondo, & Rausch, 2014; Skiba et al., 2011).

Zero tolerance exacerbates socio-structural challenges faced by students who are pushed out of school, as these students often live in poor under-resourced neighborhoods characterized by persistent and pervasive conditions of personal, cultural, and structural trauma (Alexander, 2012; Dutro & Bien, 2014; Fabelo et al., 2011; Oudshoorn, 2016). Students living with these forms of trauma often experience maladaptive self-regulation and mental health challenges; yet, we expect them to perform well at school. Further, school personnel often lack trauma-informed professional development (Oudshoorn, 2016). Given limited professional development, school staff often attribute disruptive behavior to the student's poor self-regulation or mental health, rather than developing understanding of the root cause, or context, that leads to the disruptive behavior. This attribution, known as the fundamental attribution error, sets young people up in a negative cycle, wherein responsibility for behavior change rests solely with the individual, side-stepping responsibility at a socio-cultural systemic level (Gil, 2006; González, 2015; Morrison, 2013; Zamudio, Russell, Rios, & Bridgeman, 2011; Zimbardo, 2007).

This individualistic view of human nature, stripped of relational context—social and emotional—is challenged by the theory and practice of restorative justice (Brown, 2018; Evans and Vaandering, 2016; Llewellyn & Downie,

2011, Morrison, 2007; Riestenberg, 2012). The theory and practice of restorative justice in education (RJE) challenges that of zero tolerance, confronting the lack of evidence for zero tolerance, with the growing evidence for RJE's effectiveness in increasing school safety and academic success. Further, RJE confronts the inability of zero tolerance to disrupt the disproportional representation of young people of color being pushed out of school; instead, RJE recognizes the psychological reality of social groups in individuals lives. As such RJE can be responsive to social justice issues through interventions that are inclusive and holistic.

Zero Tolerance: History, Impacts, and Evidence

In the United States, zero tolerance policies are handed down from the federal government to the state and school districts, mandating automatic suspension and expulsion for a range of infractions (Gregory & Cornell, 2009). While zero tolerance expanded in the wake of school rampage shootings in predominantly white, suburban schools (Giroux, 2009), it is students of color that are expelled at disproportional rates (Skiba, Arredondo, & Rausch, 2014). The evidence of disproportional representation is clear, predominantly being students of color (Advancement Project, 2009; Carter, Skiba, Arredondo & Pollock, 2017; Ferguson, 2000; Gordon, Della Piana, & Keleher, 2001; Losen, Hewitt, & Toldson, 2014; Welch & Payne, 2010) and working-class students (Jordan & Bulent, 2009; Skiba, Nardo, & Peterson, 2002). Further, the racial disparities in the school system are reflected in the criminal justice system, where black males are incarcerated at a rate six times that of white males (Human Rights Watch, 2009).

At the same time, school suspensions have increased for all students, not just minority students. In the United States, since 1973, the number of students suspended annually has more than doubled to 3.3 million students (Dignity in Schools, 2009). Suspension increases the likelihood of a student being expelled, dropping out, and being incarcerated (Ladson-Billings, 2001; Sandler, Wong, Morales, & Patel, 2000), a phenomenon dubbed the "school to prison pipeline" (Wald & Losen, 2003). Through zero tolerance and an increasing reliance on police presence in schools, many school officials are in effect helping to create an "institutional link" of formal social control between schools and prisons (Casella, 2003; Noguera, 2008; Wallace, Goodkind, Wallace, & Bachman, 2008). Prisoner statistics reveal further links between schools and prisons: in 1997, nearly 70% of prisoners never graduated high school and approximately 70% of juvenile offenders had learning disabilities (Wald & Losen, 2003, p. 11). Through the strengthening of these formal institutional mechanisms of social control, families and communities have become less involved in enabling justice, education, and dignity for young people: 18 million instructional days were lost to exclusionary discipline in the 2011–2012 school year (Losen, Hodson, Keith, Morrison, & Belway, 2015).

School safety and academic achievement are not realized through harsh discipline policies; indeed, the evidence shows that zero tolerance puts students at greater risk for disconnection from school, participation in risky or illegal behavior, dropout of school and into the prison pipeline (Boccanfuso & Kuhfeld, 2011; Skiba, Arredondo, & Rausch, 2014. Further, exclusionary disciplinary results in lost instructional time, poor academic achievement, not advancing in grade levels, not graduating, and eroding the relationship between families and schools (Fabelo et al., 2011; Osher, Bear, Sprague, & Doyle, 2010; Skiba & Rausch, 2006).

Zero tolerance school discipline policies have been recognized as discriminatory by grassroots organizations (e.g., Dignity in Schools) as well as the U.S. Department of Education Office of Civil Rights (USDOE OCR) and the U.S. Department of Justice (USDOJ) (Blad, 2014; Shah & McNeil, 2013). Following the Obama administration's "Supportive School Discipline Initiative" in January 2013, the federal government acknowledged that the disproportionate disciplining of primarily African American males caused by zero tolerance policies has become one of the most pressing civil rights issues of this decade (Shah & McNeil, 2013). Federal guidelines were developed jointly by the USDOE and the USDOJ to support schools in developing policies that do not discriminate against racial or ethnic groups (USDOE, 2014). These guidelines were backed up by sanctions if schools were found to be in violation of Title IV or VI of the Civil Rights Act of 1964. Of particular significance within the guidelines is that power is returned to teachers, counselors, and administrators to solve problems, and school resources officers and other law enforcement officers are used as a back-up measure. The focus of the guidelines was to create a positive environment, prevent behavioral incidents, and prioritize non-punitive interventions, including restorative justice.

Paradigm Shift: From Social Control to Social Engagement

The practice of RJE enables schools and communities to tap into the rich ecology of relationships in an individual's life. School communities, together with families and nongovernmental organizations, can respond in ways that broaden the scope for achieving school safety, nurturing relationships, and fostering academic achievement. Restorative justice draws on three broad leverage points that offer a distinct perspective to typical institutional responses of social control. First, rather than focusing on punishment as a primary motivational lever, restorative justice focuses on relationships as a primary motivational lever. This shift is characterized by a shift in questions that relate to the harm caused by the behavior. Instead of asking questions that focus on the institutional rules and the offender ("What rule has been broken?", "Who did it?", and "What punishment is deserved?"), the questions shift to a focus on the community and victims ("What happened?", "Who has been affected?", and "How do we repair the harm done?") (Zehr, 1990/2015). Second, the process of answering these questions includes those closest to the harm and those closest to the community affected. This is distinct to current school-based practice, wherein the decision-making is often left to third parties, removed from the direct incident, particularly in the context of serious threat or harm. Schools, like courts, have been characterized as stealing conflict from those most affected (Christie, 1977). Third, restorative justice finds reason for emotion (Sherman, 2003). Emotions become the vehicle of engagement in the process through asking how people were affected by the harmful behavior.

The practice of restorative justice is theoretically eclectic, cutting across disciplinary silos, with a range of normative and explanatory theories making a case for restorative justice (Braithwaite, 2002). Normative theories draw on a range of worldviews from indigenous and faith-based to sociological, such as Durkheim's and Foucault's (see Braithwaite, 2002). Explanatory theories, in different ways drawing on normative theory, include reintegrative shaming theory, which builds understanding of the role of the moral emotion of shame, and the process of shaming (see Ahmed, Harris, Braithwaite, & Braithwaite, 2001; Morrison, 2007); defiance theory (Sherman, 1993), which builds understanding of when punishment increases crime, decreases crime, and has no effect; social identity theory (Tajfel & Turner, 1979) and self-categorization theory (Turner, Hogg, Oakes, Reicher, & Wetherell, 1987), which builds understanding of the social psychological mechanism that bridges the self and society. Building on the latter theoretical analysis, Tyler's (2006) argument on rule-breaking, procedural justice, and restorative justice concludes that a shift from regulation by external sanctions to self-regulation is important:

> Sanctioning-based models, which dominate current thinking about managing criminals, have negative consequences for the individual wrongdoer and for society. It is argued that greater focus needs to be placed on psychological approaches whose goal is to connect with and activate internal values within wrongdoers with the goal of encouraging self-regulatory law-related behavior in the future.

This analysis resonates with that of Braithwaite (2009a,b), who brings together her work on social values and motivational postures within a responsive regulation framework. In particular, her work identifies institutional practices that generate defiance, undermining individual's capacity and willingness to cooperate in core facets of social life from family and school to work and governance. Responsive regulation is contrasted with formalized regulatory responses (Braithwaite, 2002), which Braithwaite argues are institutionally siloed. Within a formalized regulatory system, the implicit belief is that clear rules and laws within the architecture of the system, backed up by clear and consistent sanctions, will elicit the desired behavior. The basic assumption is that at some level all actors are rational, assuming individuals and groups are uniformly programmed in the way they respond to rules and laws. In contrast, Braithwaite (2009a) has identified five motivational postures: commitment, capitulation, resistance, disengagement, and game-playing that characterize the social and emotional relationship individuals have with institutions. Braithwaite's (2009b) analysis develops the understanding of relational dynamics of individuals within institutions (vertical relationships), bridging with the relational analysis of restorative justice processes that develop interpersonal (horizontal) relationships. Through this lens, the focus shifts from the individual to the socio-cultural context of behavior.

Social identity and self-categorization theory offer further insights beyond standard rational choice theory of individuals. The conceptual shift can be framed through an understanding of the nature of power. Turner (2005) proposes a new theory of power emphasizing group identity, social organization, and ideology, rather than dependence as the basis of power.

The theory proposes that processes of power, underlying basic mechanisms of social control—persuasion, authority and coercion—can account for more explanatory variance by reversing the causal sequence of the standard theory, which is based on individual rational actors. The latter argues that control of resources produces power, power is the basis of influence and that mutual influence leads to the formation of the psychological group. The three-process theory argues that psychological group formation produces influence, that influence is the basis of power, and that power leads to control of resources (Turner, 2005, p. 1). The basic premise of the theory is that all behavior needs to be understood in the context of the power dynamics between individuals and social groups; as such, shifting the analysis from the fundamental attribution error of scapegoating a "bad apple."

This conceptual shift has implications for theories of social change, emphasizing that power is leveraged as a function of social relationships, in the context of "definite social, ideological and historical content rather than reifying it as an abstract external force producing generic psychological effects" (Turner, 2005, p. 1). As such, differential social engagement across ideology and context, is the basis for social identification that leads to enhancing the power base for access to resources; in other words, school safety not only rests on access to resources (e.g., mental health support) but understanding the social and emotional context underpinning mental health and well-being. Safety and justice go hand in hand. Individuals care about justice because our experience of justice, and injustice, communicates a message of our social status, as a member of a social group, and our status within the social group (Morrison, 2006a, 2007).

Restorative Justice in Education

Educators started using restorative justice principles in schools in the 1990s, by and large being influenced by developments in Australia and New Zealand, where the theory and practice of restorative justice was demonstrating the efficacy of restorative justice in juvenile justice and in schools (Ahmed, Harris, Braithwaite and Braithwaite, 2001; Braithwaite, 2002; Morrison, 2006b). In the United States, schools in Colorado, Pennsylvania, and Minnesota were early adopters of restorative justice principles and practices in the classroom and offices of regular schools, as well as alternative learning centers, with promising effect (for a fuller history, see Morrison, 2006b).

Minnesota was the first state in the United States whose state education agency actively promoted the use of restorative principles in schools as a response to student discipline problems and as primary prevention of violence. In the early 1990s, Minnesota's Department of Education (MDE) began experimenting with restorative justice in schools when the Minnesota Department of Corrections brought restorative justice trainers from Australia and Canada. In 1995, the MDE published a state plan, *Unlearning Violence*, that included the description of "restorative interventions" followed by *Restorative Measures: Respecting Everyone's Ability to Resolve Problems* (MDE, 1996). These publications lay the conceptual framework for a three-year (1998–2001) demonstration project in four school districts. In Minnesota, the Circle process has become the primary prevention practice as it allows all students to get to know each other and the teacher, gives a forum for practicing social skills, and provides a framework for the repair of harm process. The evaluation of these demonstration projects showed promise: through using Circle processes in classrooms to build community and using restorative community conferencing or Circle processes to repair harm, schools reduced suspensions and office referrals. These early studies received support from the state, with results being reported back: *The In-School Behavior Intervention Grants: Report to the Legislature* (MDE, 2001).

For many, restorative practices became an alternative to suspension and expulsion, a way of interrupting the school-to-prison pipeline, largely as a process for repairing harm following a school fight or conflict. However, MDE soon realized that, when responding to harm, there also needed to be a healthy school community to reintegrate the student back into and restore a healthy sense of belonging. A healthy school community and classroom climate was built through teaching children how to get along in an organic way, by sharing likes and dislikes, stories and anecdotes, thoughts, impressions, and feelings. These practices improved the classroom climate and reduced the need to repair harm, as reported in *The In School Behavior Intervention Grants: Report to the Legislature* (MDE, 2002).

Restorative justice principles and practices applied in schools are alternately referred to as restorative measures, restorative discipline, restorative approaches, restorative practices, and RJE (for review, see Morrison, 2006b, 2007). The *Little Book of Restorative Discipline in Schools* (Stutzman Amstutz & Mullet, 2005) captures the essence of RJE in reference to inclusivity and giving voice to those marginalized.

> Restorative justice promotes values and principles that use inclusive, collaborative approaches for being in community. These approaches validate the experiences and needs of everyone within the community, particularly those who have been marginalized, oppressed, or harmed. These approaches allow us to act and respond in ways that are healing rather than alienating or coercive.

More recently, Evans and Vaandering (2016), in *The Little Book of Restorative Justice in Education*, highlight the interconnectedness of community building and repairing harm and define the practice of RJE as creating just and equitable learning environments, nurturing healthy relationships, and repairing harm and transforming conflict. Underpinning these concepts are the values of respect, dignity, and mutual concern. Evans and Vaandering (2016) explain the difference between equality—treating everyone the same—and equity:

> Equity means fairness or impartiality . . . (with) focus on equal outcomes and requires that everyone gets what they need in order to experience well-being. We often assume that in order to be fair, everyone has to be treated the same. That would be fine if we all started from the same place—but we don't.

A restorative process seeks to be equitable by addressing three questions: Who has been hurt? What are their needs? Who has obligations to meet those needs? (Zehr, 1990/2015). A restorative school is not concerned with what punishment people deserve, but rather what needs they have, and who can best meet those needs. When one is hurt or when one hurts someone else, the needs seem to be universal: to be listened to, to be believed, to be cared for, to be allowed to fix the problem, to be able to show remorse, to know that you are not a bad person even if your behavior was bad, to be safe, to be protected, to be loved, to be forgiven.

Equity, like dignity, is a function of one's experience of justice; as such, justice is a function of one's social status as a member of a social groups and status within those social groups (Morrison, 2006a; Tyler and Blader, 2000). As the praxis of RJE developed in Minnesota, the practice of restorative justice became more nuanced. For example, the most common behaviors that get students sent to the office are not fighting or assault, but more likely some action, look, or word that is perceived by an adult as "willful defiance" or "insubordination." Indeed, 38% of students who are suspended in Minnesota are suspended for these kinds of subjective behaviors: "disruptive, disorderly conduct or insubordination" [Minnesota Department of Education (MDE), 2016].

The goal of a restorative justice process is to meet the needs of the people affected by the harm, as identified for themselves. Each restorative process is different, as each situation, and the people affected by it are different. In some instances, the person who has been harmed has also hurt others; sometimes, the adults in the school have some obligations to meet. Sometimes the school itself has responsibility in part, to repair the harm. But perhaps the most significant elements of the restorative process is that everyone gets a chance to tell their story, everyone participates in problem-solving and suggesting how harm can be repaired, and everyone decides. In a restorative process, decisions are made by consensus; in other words, decisions are not made by one administrator, or a group of adults, guided by the student code of conduct. Whether they are a first grader, a friend of the student who started the fight, the educational aide who discovered the graffiti, a mom and her child who wrote the cyber bullying message, the bus driver or a member of the debate team: the people most affected by the harm make the decision (Zehr, 1990/2015). A restorative process has the possibility of being equitable because all people affected by the harm participate, tell their story, and help to make the plan to repair the harm. A restorative school carries this focus of all voices heard and listened to—into the classroom through community-building processes. The insights gain in such processes can be startling. Sitting in Circle, one assistant principal, in a large urban school district, shared with middle school students that the anniversary of his father's death was coming soon. He was surprised to learn that several of the boys were grieving their fathers' deaths as well. He had no idea. Through the Circle, he developed first-hand experience of how grief can impact a student's ability to learn and on a student's behavior.

Zehr's (1990/2015) *Changing Lenses* set the stage for a paradigm shift 25 years ago. This iconic text is a testimonial to the power of metaphor to capture our imagination and change the landscape of justice. The metaphor, changing lenses, is drawn from Howard Zehr's experience as a photographer.

> One of the lessons I have learned is how profoundly the lens I look through affects the outcome. My choice of lens determines in what circumstances I can work and how I see. . . . The choice of lens, then, affects what is in the picture. . . . Indeed, the lens we look through determines how we frame both the problem and the "solution." (Zehr, 1990/2015, pp. 19–20)

In the context of education, Zehr's 3 R's of restorative justice—Respect, Responsibility, and Relationship—found their place beside education's traditional 3 R's—Reading, 'Riting, and 'Rithmatic. The relevance to education was clearly seen early in the development of restorative justice; in that, Zehr's 3 R's grounded citizenship education hand in hand with the traditional 3 R's of education that ground the labor market (see Morrison, 2015). "In schools we have society in miniature and persons in the process of learning to become citizens. . . . How well we manage our schools will determine how well our society works a generation later" (Marshall, 1997; see also Morrison, 2001, 2007; Walgrave, 2008).

Schoolwide Restorative Practices

Schools now practice a wide range of responses—proactive and reactive—that develop a culture of well-being and safety, under the rubric of "restorative"—that is, schools that put relationships first and have practices to reaffirm, repair, and rebuild relationships. Restorative practices build community and develop relationships between students and adults, students and students, adults and family members, staff and staff, in the context of the lived experience of individuals, communities, and schools (Morrison, 2007; Riestenberg, 2012). The practices can be organized through a multitiered system of support:

Tier One (Primary/Universal Practices): Reaffirming relationships. Affective statements, Circle to build community, Circle to teach, youth-led Circles.

Tier Two (Secondary/Targeted Practices): Repairing Relationships. Restorative questions are used with one or a few students for issues identified early, conflict Circles, classroom Circles to address class issues or to repair harm. Circles are also used to address community issues such as grief after a student or staff death, or to address community or national events that may affect the learning environment.

Tier Three (Tertiary/Intensive Practices): Rebuilding Relationships. Repairing harm and rebuilding relationships using either Circle or conferencing, or family group conferencing, for attendance issues, re-entry, in lieu of suspension, expulsion or administrative transfer, or as a means of developing a re-entry plan for a student who has left the school for any reason and is returning.

Restorative Ethos

Underpinning all three levels is a restorative ethos: addressing concerns *with* people (rather than *to* them or *for* them), being mindful of one's thoughts and intentions, and acting with compassion (rather than retribution). Taken together, a restorative ethos is characterized by working *with* each other, and *with* students and families, wherein all members of the community work mindfully and have compassion for all members of the school. Accountability includes helping students and adults repair harm as they rebuild community. Adults in a restorative school are trained to be mindful of the words they speak and also the way they speak them: their tone, facial expression, body language, and proximity to the person they are talking to, as well as eye contact. Any group of words, as a question or comment, can help or hurt, depending upon how the words are delivered. Adults in a restorative school are curious. Restorative practices apply to everyone—we all need to be in good relationship with each other and we all need processes that help us repair harm—student to student, staff to staff, staff to student, and family members to staff or student.

Adult Practices

Relationships among staff are fostered intentionally. Staff meetings start with a mindful moment, so that people can set aside the stressors of the day for a bit, and with a check-in—with the entire staff, speaking one at a time, or in small groups. Each meeting ends with a final go-round asking each person to give one word, "How was the meeting for you?" Any meeting starts with names and ends with feedback, to ensure that every voice is included, each person is seen. Staff have agreed how they will be with each other and how they will greet the students. Because all school staff receive professional development in the adverse effects of trauma and maltreatment on the brain and trauma-sensitive practices, they all understand that in order to learn, students need to feel a sense of safety. They smile at students, call them by name, and show interest in their lives. They are as aware of their nonverbal communication as they are aware of providing encouragement, focusing on more positive than negative behaviors. They use affective statements to teach, model, and reinforce empathy. They use "I" statements to role model how to speak respectfully by owning one's own thoughts, beliefs, and feelings. These behaviors—providing kind affect though smiling and conscious use of body language so as not to intimidate or threaten—is carried into the use of Circle process.

Reaffirming Relationships (Tier 1)

A restorative school uses practices that ensure that all students are seen and all students get the chance to share who they are as a person. The Circle process is a common practice to help foreground relationships and help students and adults practice social-emotional skills. Based in Indigenous knowledge and informed by the values of the community, Circle is used in a variety of ways in a restorative school. Sitting in Circle, students and adults practice speaking and listening, sharing values and experiences with each other—that is getting to know each other. The more we know of each other, the less likely we are to hurt each other, the easier it is to work together.

Circle is also used to teach academic subjects; it is a practice to use any time the teacher wants to ensure that everyone participates, in either an all-class discussion, small group work, or any time the teacher wants to ensure that everyone has a chance to contribute and be seen by all.

Circle can also be used as a problem-solving process, a way for the class to make decisions, a process for conflict resolution and to repair harm. Its use extends beyond the classroom or the office to use in individual educational program planning meetings, staff meetings, meetings with parents and other family members, and community meetings. The Circle ensures that all voices are heard in an equitable manner because the talking piece goes around in order, no one voice dominates discussion, and decisions are made by consensus.

Repairing and Rebuilding Relationships (Tiers 2 and 3)

All faculty and staff are versed in the problem-solving process of using restorative questions to repair harm. Questions frame the restorative response for all involved: (1) What has happened? (2) What was the impact on those involved; that is, who has been affected and in what way they have been affected? (3) What needs to happen to put things right or to make things better in the future? These questions carry through all repair-of-harm processes, from the most basic, where two people may have had difficulty with each other, to the most complex, where the person harmed and their family or supporters meet with the person who did the harm and their family and supporters, along with other people affected by the harm in a facilitated Circle or conference.

Through a whole school approach, everyone in the school has had experience with the basic restorative questions. Staff have been taught how to use them and when to get further help when the problems are more complex. Students have had their own class to practice using the questions. That way, everyone in the school knows basically what happens in a repairing harm conference or Circle, whether they are in the conference or Circle or not. By knowing the basics of the process, it is easier for both adults and students to choose whether or not they will participate, for no one is forced to meet with the person they harmed, or who harmed them. Everyone gets to choose an RJ process as a first response to harm. Other discipline responses are used for accountability if the person who did the harm does not agree to participate.

A restorative school also offers a restorative process to the adults, both to build community (e.g., using Circle for Individual Education Program meetings), and when there is conflict or harm. A restorative school staff knows that they will be better able to teach the students if they are able to resolve their own problems with each other.

Community Connections

Community members, especially Elders from throughout the school's reach, are invited to provide their wisdom and support for restorative justice practices. Some Elders have experience in restorative justice from their culture and can share that with staff and students. Restorative justice community-based organizations also are connected to the school, providing consultancy, training, or restorative facilitation when needed. A restorative school has a relationship with local law enforcement or engages a school resource officer (SRO). In either case, the administration and law enforcement have agreed to respond to harm and rule violations with restorative conferencing or Circle to repair harm. The SROs are trained in the restorative questions and in facilitating conferences; they are willing to participate in Circles or conferences; they encourage students to participate; and they help set up restorative meetings.

The school administration and law enforcement work together, engaging the county or district attorney in diversion to restorative conferences, as a means of holding students accountable while getting them back to school as quickly as possible. However, there are fewer times when tier three responses are used, as students' needs are being met with the relationship building. The use of the restorative questions and conflict circles also helps address problems early.

Youth Engagement

Youth are engaged in RJE leadership roles at all levels of the school. Students take turns keeping Circle for their peers in the classroom. They participate in repair of harm as supporters of their friends or as people who have been affected by an incident of harm, or a community member. They, like the adults, know that their voice is helpful in supporting the person who was hurt, and in supporting the person who did the harm make amends, and repair the harm. Peer meditators conduct mediations for peers when there are conflicts and refer bullying situations to an adult Circle keeper for a restorative response. All students and staff have been taught the basic steps for conflict resolution.

Students also meet with peers to identify and address school climate and equity issues, to work with the administration in supporting restorative processes, and in sharing their perspectives and needs with the staff. Students are engaged in decision-making; they have representatives who are part of the RJE implementation team, to ensure that students are also engaged in the roll-out and continual use of restorative practices. Age appropriate courses in restorative justice, social justice, racial justice, and community justice theory and related topics are offered in the school for credit. Teachers in different subject areas look for ways to help students apply the ideas of repairing harm, reparations, and restitution within existing curricula.

Sustaining Practices

The process of culture change can only be sustained through ongoing professional development on restorative justice theory and principals as well as practice. Staff also study trauma and the effects of maltreatment on the brain, equity, and the school-to-prison pipeline. They support each other, taking time to acknowledge the bullfrogs and butterflies of their good work. There is a plan that is followed to ensure that all new staff are welcomed to this school, that they are trained in Circle, affective statements, and the restorative questions, and that they know and agree to the basic mindful practices that are expected of every member of the school community.

Policy has been reviewed and as needed rewritten, based on the data from emerging evidence-based practice, to ensure that zero tolerance language is changed, a vision based in relationships has been articulated, learning is used as a first response to difficulties and repairing relationships grounds all actions.

Culture Change: An Illustrative Example of One School's Story

Students do not come to school with all the same set of early childhood experiences, nor do they proceed through schooling with all the same supports and resources. Some early childhood experiences are noted on official transcripts while many others are hidden. But even without the school records of students, school staff and teachers can anticipate that several things may be true for any group of students. Some of them may have experienced alcoholism in the family, domestic violence, parents or care-givers who also have a mental illness, physical or emotional neglect, or other adverse childhood experiences. One in four or five students will have experienced some form of sexual abuse by the time they reach the age of 18. Parents and care-givers may die while students are in school. Other students may have had large gaps in learning due to migration, natural or civil disruption, famine, and war.

Students of color, American Indian students, and students living in poverty may also have in their families a legacy of problematic experiences with school. The dis-ease with formal education systems may stretch back to slave times for African American people or to the mid-1800s when the U.S. government set up boarding schools for American Indian children, taking them from family and tribe.

One charter school recognized that these are reality for many of their students. Serving high school aged students, most of their student body have transferred to the school after suspensions or expulsions from other schools and districts, or after engagement with the criminal justice system. The school set about teaching staff about trauma and the effects of maltreatment on the developing brain. As a means of making a trauma-informed environment for their students, the school implemented restorative justice practices, recognizing that their students needed safe supportive relationships with staff and with each other in order to learn.

The knowledge of trauma and how it can manifest itself in students encourages staff to get to know their students. Circle to build relationships and community is used in the classrooms on a regular basis. But in spite of those efforts, harm still happens in the school. This is a story of what it takes to apply restorative practices all the way, as a true alternative to suspension. One has to convince the staff, certainly, but the students and the parents as well. And one has to use a restorative response like one used suspension and expulsion: over and over and over again.

It takes time to rebuild relationships. This was the experience of one group of girls. It was the second week of school when the fight happened. In response to a perceived slight, one girl, Kisa, hit another in math class; her friend Jade stepped in to support her. The girl who was hit and her friend also squared off. Soon the four girls were on the floor, and just as soon, were separated by staff. All four were sent to the Dean who met with them, one at a time.

Upon entering the Dean's office, Kisa said, "Just give me my transcript now. I know you are going to suspend me or expel me, so I am not coming back." The Dean offered to her what he offered the others: a restorative process. "Come back in a day after I have talked to you and your mom, and all the other girls and their parents, and we will sit down to try to repair the harm. Then you will go back to class;" he said.

The idea was ridiculous. Kisa said no and left. Then the Dean talked to Jade. She said she'd think about it and left. Jade later called the Dean when she got home and said, "Let me get this straight—we will talk and fix things?" As he explained more, and though she was skeptical of the idea, she agreed to participate. Jade convinced Kisa to do the same. The other girls also agreed to participate. After several phone calls, some of them lively, some of them painful with the use of very colorful language, the Dean and the girls convinced at least one parent each to participate. Three staff members agreed to join the Circle: two teachers to support for each pair of girls, and the social worker. This gathering of the affected parties took about two days to arrange. Staff that were not invited to the Circle thought the Dean was overstepping his bounds. A punch, out of nowhere, was indeed grounds for suspension. This was not going to work. He should not do it.

At the beginning of the Circle, it seemed as if perhaps the rest of the staff were right. After saying her name and admitting she hit the girl, Kisa was adamantly quiet. She took the talking piece and passed it for several rounds. In each pass, though, her friend encouraged her to speak. The social worker, who had helped Kisa get registered at school, did the same. The social worker was at first frustrated with Kisa and said so when she got the talking piece.

But as the Circle proceeded, she saw Kisa start to look at each person as they spoke. She choked up as she apologized to Kisa for being mad at her for not speaking. She said she saw Kisa was trying. "I saw you looked at the girl you hit. You said you did it. You took responsibility. You are brave." Kisa had never had an adult apologize to her or say that she had done the right thing, much less cry in front of her. She never had people think that she was worth working with; by her estimation, people in school only waited for her to compile enough infractions to kick her out. Finally, Kisa started to talk.

Kisa had been suspended and expelled from or administratively transferred to most of the middle schools and all of the high schools in the large urban district in which she lived. The charter school was not the last educational option for her, but the options to "give me my transcripts" and go to another school were diminishing. As an African American and Native American girl, Kisa certainly felt that she was a target in the classroom. Something would happen while the teacher had her back turned, and she would be blamed. Kisa was aware that other kids—white kids—doing the same thing she had done would be treated differently, more leniently, by some teachers and administrators. Once she was suspended for smoking on the school lawn, and asked to leave the school, even though the white student who was caught smoking the day before was talked to and sent back to class. "They were done with me," she said. Kisa *was* a challenge. She got her sense of worth from being suspended, and she got suspended a lot. It was a badge of strength for her. The Dean noted that Kisa was hyper-vigilant. Her childhood had been unpredictable, a continuous stress experience. She learned to watch and strike before someone stuck her. Striking first was a way to be safe.

Finally, in Circle, Kisa opened up. She talked about that pattern, once her friend encouraged her and the social worker cried. She was new to school. It was early in the year. She thought she heard the girl call her a name. She thought other people could hear that she was called that derogatory name. She hit the girl in math class to give the message to everyone: don't mess with me. So it was indeed a surprise, a confusing surprise, that she was not suspended, that people expected her to explain herself, and that they waited until she could do that. People believed that she could repair the harm, and supported her in doing so. She returned to class, not with a badge of suspension, but with support and belief. That had never happened to her before.

Implementing restorative practices are not for the faint of heart. The Dean was nervous about his plan of action and as noted, there were many staff who shared their reasons for why he should be nervous. It would have been so much easier for him, personally, to suspended Kisa and the other students. After all, even they expected that, and would not have thought much about it. School as usual.

Is a new chapter in school life possible? Kisa did not get into another physical fight that year, but she did sit in Circle a number of times to work to repair the harm that came from derogatory language. And then there was the time she threatened to shoot another student. The morning the school staff learned of that threat, Kisa walked into school with a bag. She never has a bag. As the security staff huddled with the Dean to determine a course of action regarding the bag, the social worker went to Kisa, engaged her in a conversation and asked "What's in the bag? People are worried about your bag." Kisa showed her the contents. No gun.

Relationship made it possible for the social worker to talk to Kisa and determine safety for the school. Not a school resource officer or a confrontation with the Dean. Relationship is the key.

So Kisa was again in Circle with the student she threatened and his mother and her mother, the social worker, her friend, and another student leader. And again she worked in Circle to repair that harm, attended school without being suspended, and returned to class feeling supported.

Kisa was in Circle a sixth time, but this time she requested it. She came to the Dean's office with a talking piece saying she was feeling that three other girls wanted to fight *her.* They were glad to Circle with her, because they thought she wanted to fight *them.* The perceptions of danger and the need to be hyper-vigilant were talked about, and trouble was averted.

By this time, the staff were more supportive of the Dean's efforts to not suspend but to repair. Less anxiety accompanied any Circle to repair harm, regardless of who was invited, and for what reason. People saw the usefulness of the approach, and the usefulness of doing it over and over and over again. As a result, in part because Kisa is smart, and in part because she was able to stay in class through the school year, without interruption, she is caught up in her credits and looks to be able to graduate on time. At each step in Kisa's year, with each issue that came to the fore, no one would have argued with an administrator's decision to suspend, or even expel. Her behavior was very harmful in two instances. With "priors" there would be every reason to believe that she was incorrigible. Change is not easy when it comes to restorative justice practices. But it seems to hold out hope that it is better than the alternative: dropping out, getting arrested, getting pregnant, taking up unhealthy substances, "learning" in jail. All those are unintended outcomes of suspension and expulsion.

Implementation: Time & Tenacity

Since the 1990s, individual educators around the world have been learning restorative justice practices, trying it, then moving to another school and doing the same. Sustaining the practices of reaffirming, repairing, and rebuilding relationships has proven to be a critical challenge in assessing the usefulness of restorative justice practices over the long term. More attention is now being placed on the *how* as well as the *what*. Getting *everyone* in a school building to see their part and have the skills to play their part in making a restorative school is a multi-year effort; implementation is a process, not an event. Because a restorative school may need anyone from the school community or the wider community to help in repairing harm, everyone needs to become familiar with the principles, and have some idea what will happen should they be invited to a repair-of-harm practice. Indeed, it would be best if those inside and those outside of the school all engaged in community-building efforts. Scaling up an entire district with anywhere from 2 to 200 buildings will take time.

Implementation science provides a framework for districts wishing to implement and sustain restorative practices in all systems within a school (Active Implementation Hub, 2018). Just setting up the practices throughout the school requires a multi-year commitment of time and resources. Sustaining those practices is an ongoing enterprise. Implementation science provides a framework for organizing such a multifaceted, multi-year effort. The stages of this active implementation framework are:

Exploration: Decision to adopt and enact the process and procedures required to support implementation of restorative practices with fidelity. Establishment of a coordinator and team to oversee the processes. Learning enough about restorative practices so that all stakeholders-staff, students, families, and community partners can agree to move forward.

Installation (Training and Preparation): Training staff and setting up infrastructure required to implement restorative practices successfully. Involvement of students, staff, and families. Development of a core group or team to plan, implement, and collect data.

Initial Implementation: Adoption of restorative practices into all systems within the school. Staff are actively engaged in the practices. Students and families have knowledge of practices and are active participants. Clear evidence of restorative practices are visible. Data collection is ongoing.

Full Implementation: Data has been collected and reviewed with all stakeholders. Ongoing professional development for all staff. Benefits are present. Adjustments are made as needed.

Each stage has unique features, actions and events. The four stages of implementation are not always done in order, but each needs to be done fully. The starting points for restorative justice practices (RJP) in schools vary. In some instances, schools are implementing RJP after they have established the positive behavior interventions and supports (PBIS) framework. Others are implementing RJP with social-emotional learning (SEL) or are integrating PBIS and RJP together as they scale them up. School climate improvement efforts may involve RJP. Or a school staff may just start with RJP.

There is no one direct path to creating a restorative school (Brown, 2018). Some schools started using RJP because an individual was using Circle in the classroom, and others became curious. Some schools started because a student support staff member or administrator invited a teacher to a repairing harm process in the office, and the outcome peaked interest. Other schools have started with the kindergarteners, training systematically each grade's faculty and staff as the students moved on up through the school. Schools have started down a path of RJP, and then something might have upended the installation process—a change of administration, a budget crunch, a requirement to focus solely on academics. Following the stages of implementation gives everyone in the school a path—exploration and getting buy-in, training and installation, initial implementation and full implementation, evolving into a continuous cycle of improvement. It is often the case that staff and families are at different stages of knowledge of RJE principles and practices. Educators may have been exploring or using RJP for a decade or more. It is possible that within a school building or district, there are individuals who are practitioners and trainers, or who have attended a training, or use Circle in their classroom as well as in their faith community, or who have studied RJ in college. Part of the challenge of implementing anything is trying to move everyone through all the stages, more or less, so implementation can be solid.

Implementation: An Example from a Middle School

One middle school started with the 6th grade teachers. The teachers were trained in using Circle in the classroom. They were to use Circle to build community. The training also provided some ideas on how to use Circle to teach. The teachers, however, had not been given background on what a SWRJP entailed, what the basic principles they were applying were, and how the Circle in the classroom fit into the overall scheme of improving climate and behavior. Two teachers had attended several Circle trainings and were already using that practice in their classrooms. Other teachers had no experience with Circle and felt frustrated that their Circles were unsteady and unruly. Many did not understand what it meant to "repair harm" so when they were asked to join in a Circle with a student who had just called them many mean names, they were at best confused, and at the most, resistant.

That was just the challenge with the teachers. No one had a plan for explaining any of this to the parents, or the educational assistants. Realizing this, the implementation team made some adjustments. Basic questions were answered. All trainings and meetings started to be held in Circle, so people could become comfortable with the process. An overview session was given, and slowly more knowledge was added to the practices. Plans were developed to provide basic information to the family members and to the rest of the school staff, before sending people to new trainings. Through all of this the sixth grade staff asked questions and were skeptical and were curious, even as they continued to develop their practice of RJE.

The stages of implementation are not time-bound, or linear; they can be fluid and simultaneous. For instance, if a school recognized that they have people with training and experience for conducting Circles to repair harm or family group conferencing, the school may proceed with using their skills with students, even as exploration overview workshops are offered to the staff, students, and families. Some schools want to start right away with repairing harm. But if everyone does not know what that is, and why one would do it, frustrations may arise that can slow down the process of implementation. On the other hand, some schools have found that involving adults in repair of harm processes is the best introductory "workshop" devised, and desire for more knowledge rises out of those experiences.

Because the first element of a restorative school is relationships, it is hoped that any amount of time spent exploring restorative practices will be useful, as it will help staff get to know each other a bit more. Knowing each other helps to improve the climate of the school, regardless of the addition of further practice. Restorative justice is about each of us *taking responsibility*, in doing so, members of the school community internalized that *justice* is more than punishing rule breakers; rather, it is recognizing that to be our best self we need to be in good relationships with others. Accountability shifts from *passive punishment* to *active responsibility*, through understanding the impact of behavior(s) and relational empowerment to make amends, wherein dignity, empathy, restitution are actively learnt and earnt. By way of summary:

> A restorative philosophy emphasizes problem-solving approaches to discipline, attends to the social/emotional as well as the physical/intellectual needs of students, recognizes the importance of the group to establish and practice agreed-upon norms and rules, and emphasizes prevention and early restorative intervention to create safe learning environments. (Riestenberg, 2007, p. 10)

Research and Development: Evidence

As the practice of RJE increases in the United States, and around the world, it is being promoted as a legitimate disciplinary strategy in education, juvenile and criminal justice (e.g., U.S. Department of Education's *Rethinking Discipline in Schools*; *School-Justice Partnership Project*; Robert Wood Johnson Foundation's *Forward Promise*). At the same time, without comprehensive systematic reviews, it is challenging to fully comprehend the institutional and community capacity of RJE to create safe and inclusive school communities. Rigorous studies are emerging; at the same time, the gap in evidence, after 20 years of RJE training and development suggests that the promise of RJE is suffering from a case of the *cart before the horse* (Song & Swearer, 2016). Impact results, while limited, can be summarized in terms of a range of outcomes.

Impact: School Safety and Discipline

In a Texas school, out-of-school suspensions dropped by 84% for sixth graders and 19% overall in the first year RJ was implemented (Armour, 2013). In Denver schools, the reduction in out-of-school suspensions was 44% (Baker, 2009), and in Oakland schools implementing RJP reduced suspensions by 74% and office referrals for violence reduced by 77% (Davis, 2014; Sumner, Silverman, & Frampton, 2010). The Minnesota Department of Education significantly reduced behavioral referrals and suspensions in two schools by 45% to 63% and increased academic achievement using SWRJP across three levels (MDE, 2003). A more recent pilot study of a restorative conferencing program found, in a six-week follow-up, a decrease in self-reported incidents of physical fighting and skipping school among conference participants (McMorris, Beckman, Shea, Baumgartner, & Eggert, 2013). Further, conference participants progressed more steadily toward credit accrual and graduation. A study in Hong Kong found a whole school restorative justice approach resulted in significantly lower bullying, higher empathetic attitudes, and higher self-esteem in comparison to a partial intervention and a control group (Wong, Ma, Cheng, & Ngan, 2011).

Impact: Attendance

A study in Denver found that students who participated in the first year of an RJ program experienced a 50% reduction in absenteeism and a 64% reduction in tardiness (Baker, 2009). In an RJ program for expelled students, attendance rates increased in a pre/post study (McMorris et al., 2013). In Oakland, a middle school implementing RJ decreased absenteeism by 24%

while the control groups experienced an increase of 62.3% (Jain, Bassey, Brown, & Kalra, 2014). Yet, the implementation of RJ does not necessarily decrease absenteeism: one school in Minnesota reported a 2% increase in absenteeism (Riestenberg, 2003).

Impact: School Climate and Social and Emotional Learning

Theoretically, the promise of RJE goes deeper than disciplinary responses and attendance. At the core of the practice of RJE is healthy social relationships that reflect the culture and climate of the school. While the evidence is limited, there are findings to suggest that RJ improves the climate of the school. A study in Oakland found that the use of restorative justice Circles enhanced students' understanding of their peers, ability to manage emotions, develop empathy, resolve conflict with parents, improve home environment, and maintain positive relationships with peers (Jain et al., 2014). Another study in Minnesota, found increases in school connectedness and improved problem-solving for students (McMorris et al., 2013). In Oakland, 65% of staff perceived improvement in the social-emotional development of students in the RJ program, and 70% reported an overall improvement in school climate in the first year of implementation (Jain et al., 2014).

Impact: Academic Achievement

One Oakland study found Scholastic Reading Inventory (SRI) levels for grade 9 students increased from an average of 14% to 33% (Jain et al., 2014). A Texas school study found that the number of students who passed the standardized reading and math tests increased substantially (Armour, 2014). In Oakland, high schools implementing SWRJP increased graduation rates by 59.9%, reducing Black Suspension Percentage Disparity by 4.6 % in RJE schools, compared to non-RJE schools (Simson, 2012). In other studies, the results are mixed; for example, Norris (2009) reports no significant change in grade point average between RJ participants and nonparticipants.

Impact: Social Justice and Racial Disparity

Recent research is showing RJEs capacity to address racial disparity in school discipline. While racial composition and background are often risk factors for suspension, participation in a restorative justice intervention has been found to be a protective factor (Anyon, Zhang, & Hazel, 2014). Another study found that schools with high levels of RJE implementation have more positive relationships with a diversity of students, are perceived as being more respectful, and issuing fewer discipline referrals to Latino and African

American students than low-level RJE schools (Gregory, Clawson, David, and Gerewitz, 2016). A five-year study of RJP in Denver Public Schools reduced the average risk for suspension by 5%, with the drop for African American's being 7%, Latinos 6%, and whites 3%. The racial disparity gap was reduced from 12 to 8 points through implementation of RJE (González, 2015).

Restorative Justice: A Process of Culture Change

While outcome research is important, the zeitgeist of restorative justice has long held that process is product (Pranis, Stuart, & Wedge, 2003), wherein it is important to measure relational change at an institutional and individual level. As such, the focus is on the relational ecology of school life (Morrison & Vaandering, 2012). Song and Swearer (2016) in their review of RJE have followed this emerging framework: "We define RJ within an ecological framework encompassing the principles that schools and communities use to guide the development of their policies, programs, and practices. This framework focuses on relationships and their harms, empowerment of all persons, and collaboration, which is consistent with other seminal RJ work (p. 316)."

Brown (2018) used a relational ecology framework—school, classroom, individual—in her evaluation of two schools within Oakland Unified School District. In describing the shift of the relational ecology of the school, one teacher explained:

> We were starting to really shift how we do things towards restorative justice, and I think it's always helpful when [our principal] says it's not a program. Because lots of people try to do it as a program. Like "Oooo, reduce suspensions—throw restorative justice at it." You know, that's not what it's about. Right? And so we started shifting how we do things, how we resolve problems, in a more relational way. (Brown, 2018, p. 147)

Brown's (2018) study identified a number of key factors that shifted the school culture: revising the disciplinary policy, to include RJP; focus on conflict transformation; leadership needs to hold the vision and open institutional spaces for critical and reflective collaboration and professional development; democratic forms of governance, expressed in shared decision-making and teacher leadership; and implementation with relational fidelity, through developing social and emotional capacity of the school community that builds confidence over time.

Developing a classroom culture of restorative and relational pedagogy is also an important shift in teaching strategy, as one teacher explains:

> We have that commitment to holding Circle with them and using that as a tool in advisory and using that as a tool in our classrooms, to help them

> build relationships, both in getting to know each other, but also to use the Circle as a place to reflect on what's been going on in the class, on things that they would like to see improved. . . . things have to be both relational and academic. (Brown, 2018, p. 201)

Brown (2018) identified a number of factors important to this pedagogical shift, including development of a range of relational practices that develop social and emotional competency and incorporation of core RJE tenants into academic teaching pedagogy. In this study, these included the self-reported use of strategies wherein all students share their perspective (93%), activities wherein students get to know one another (89%), Circles in classroom to discuss issues (57%), and curriculum that promotes awareness of others (81%).

These shifts begin with individuals working within the school community, in particular, their attitude and how they frame their responsibility in creating a positive school culture. "I think about the school, colleagues, and students more as people with social and emotional influences rather than one big system" (Brown, 2018, p. 184). The key findings that were important to this shift: principals' leadership in affirming and transforming relational ecology of the school culture; teachers' witnessing decrease in conflicts between teachers (73%), teachers and students (71%), racial and ethnic groups (69%), school personal and parents (60%), and administrators and teachers (59%); teachers' witnessing the change for students building community (59%), asking restorative questions (49%), de-escalating conflict (31%), using Circles for instruction (29%), Circles after a harm (22%), and facilitation conferences (14%). As one teacher summarized, "restorative approaches make students honest, accountable, community-minded, thoughtful, and resilient" (Brown, 2018, p. 187).

Beyond Promise: Building Evidence

While it has long been held that there is nothing as practical as a good theory (Lewin, 1951), theory, practice, and evidence must support each other in developing the culture change necessary to building safe school communities and disrupting the school-to-prison pipeline. The clearest example of using RJP, in particular Circles, to drive culture change within institutions, using evidence-based practice is ROCA. Molly Baldwin, the founder, quickly recognized the power of Circles to drive culture change. She first implemented Circles for her staff to build connections and hone their organizational capacity. Only when she had developed this organizational capacity did she feel ready to use Circle with the young people they serve.

ROCA's mission is to *disrupt the cycle of incarceration and poverty by helping young people transform their lives.* Their intervention model is

> a cognitive-restructuring, behavioral change and skill development intervention, which focuses on high-risk young men in a non-mandated program. Roca's Model focuses on 17-to-24-year-old men who are either: 1) aging out of the juvenile justice or juvenile probation systems with a strong propensity for re-incarceration as an adult; 2) connected with the adult justice system; or 3) are high-risk members of the community being served who have a strong propensity for incarceration as an adult. (ROCA, 2017)

ROCA (2017) has infused a relational evidence-based culture in all aspects of organizational life. Through relentless outreach and follow-up, the core of their work builds on developing transformational relationships, followed by programing that builds life skills, educational and employment opportunities, and engaging institutions in formal and informal systems change. In 2017, Roca served 854 young men at the highest risk for long-term reincarceration and disconnection from employment and who cannot succeed in other educational and employment programs because they are neither ready nor willing. This is the type of rigorous evidence-based practice that we need in schools.

Because change takes time, ROCA evaluation framework is staged across four levels of intervention: developing transformational relational capacity (0–6 months); sustaining relational capacity, engaging in initial social and emotional skill-based development and education and/or employment programming (6–18 months); demonstration of positive behavior changes and gains in education and/or employment (18–24 months). The results indicate that by 24 months participants are at a lower risk of criminal recidivating (84%) and being unemployed (80%).

Roca's innovative theory of change has two levers that work hand in hand: programmatic and organizational. These two levels of change mirror the framework developed by Braithwaite (2002) in coupling the practice of restorative justice within a responsive regulatory framework at an institutional or organizational level:

> Restorative justice is not just about strengthening justice systems or strengthening democracy. It is also about strengthening communities, families and schools, which have profound value in themselves independent of the contribution they make to democracy or justice. We have a long way to go in learning how to evaluate how restorative justice can be improved so as to be more effective in strengthening individual people as human beings, as well as the families, schools and communities that nourish their humanness. (Braithwaite, 2016, p. 8)

The key fundamental premise is the recognition that individual change is best leveraged through responsive regulation within the institution. The programmatic lever "theorized that Roca participants would experience positive outcomes through the implementation of relentless outreach, relationships for the purpose of change, peacemaking circles and skill-building opportunities" (Pierce, 2009, p. 2; see also Boyes-Watson, 2008). The organizational theoretical lever "recognized that single programs were not sufficient to impact the trajectories of high risk people. Instead it is the combination of strategies and programs that would bring about change. The theory also documented that in order to reach the desired outcomes, leadership had to be strong and program performance tracked over time" (Pierce, 2009, p. 4). These theoretical shifts required Roca to move from programs to programming, wherein the key strategy was the management and tracking of transformational relationships (Pierce, 2009, p. 4). At the heart of all programming are two core premises: (1) change is possible for all young people and (2) people change in relationships. Relationships are built on a foundation of trust, truth, and transformation:

> Trust: Youth workers build trusting, long-term relationships with young people and others in their lives, including family, other adults and institutions.
>
> Truth: Youth workers are truthful with young people. They are truthful about what is going on in the lives of young people, the challenges, the realities of their families and communities, and that change is possible.
>
> Transformation: The trusting and truthful relationships support and encourage personal transformation through participation in life skills, education and employment.
>
> Outcomes are tracked and measured within the programmatic and organizational theory of change. (Pierce, 2009, p. 9)

The key theoretical shift resonates with that specified in Turner's (2005) analysis of power; in that, transformational power, in reference to economic, social, and emotional well-being, emerges as a function of social relationships.

The Way Forward: Restorative Justice and Responsive Regulation

Restorative justice, in theory and practice, working within the context of responsive regulation, reverses the causal chain of traditional behaviorist models. Together, they offer much more fertile ground for addressing the school-to-prison pipeline, particularly for youth who are disconnected and disengaged. The social psychological analysis of motivational postures (Braithwaite, 2009a,b), coupled with Turner's (2005) analysis of power, within a responsive regulatory framework offers further fertile explanatory variance in understanding and responding to youth who are disconnected and disengaged. This is particularly relevant to minority students of color, wherein power dynamics are particularly salient. Restorative justice practices, coupled with responsive regulation, shifts institutional culture beyond the limits of zero tolerance. The promise of restorative justice will only be realized when institutions engage in the full spectrum of rich ecologies of individuals and communities in developing culture change for a new way forward.

References

Active Implementation Hub. (2018). National implementation research network & state implementation and scaling-up of evidenced-based practices center. Retrieved from https://implementation.fpg.unc.edu/sites/implementation.fpg.unc.edu/files/resources/Caryn%20Ward%20Transcript.pdf

Advancement Project. (2009). Key components of a model discipline policy. Retrieved from http://www.njjn.org/uploads/digital-library/AdvProject_Code-of-Conduct-Tips-Examples.pdf

Ahmed, E., Harris, N., Braithwaite, J., & Braithwaite, V. (2001). *Shame management through reintegration*. Melbourne: Cambridge University Press.

Alexander, M. (2012). *The new Jim Crow: Mass incarceration in the age of colorblindness*. New York: New Press.

Anyon, Y., Zhang, D., & Hazel, C. (2016). Race, exclusionary discipline, and connectedness to adults in secondary schools. *American Journal of Community Psychology, 57*, 342–352.

Armour, M. (2013). *Ed White Middle School restorative discipline evaluation: Implementation and impact, 2012/2013 sixth grade*. Austin: University of Texas, Austin.

Armour, M. (2014). Ed White Middle School restorative discipline evaluation: Implementation and impact, 2013/2014. The Institute for Restorative Justice and Restorative Dialogue, The University of Texas at Austin.

Baker, M. (2009). *DPS Restorative Justice Project: Year three*. Denver: Denver Public Schools.

Baker, M. L., Sigmon, J. N., & Nugent, M. E. (2001). Truancy reduction: Keeping students in school (electronic version). Juvenile Justice Bulletin. Retrieved from https://www.ncjrs.gov/pdffiles1/ojjdp/188947.pdf

Blad, E. (2014). New federal school discipline guidance addresses discrimination, suspensions. Educ. Retrieved from http://blogs.edweek.org/edweek/rulesforengagement/2014/01/new_federal_school_ discipline_guidance_addresses_discrimination_suspensions.html

Boccanfuso, C., & Kuhfeld, M. (2011). Multiple responses, promising results: Evidence-based, nonpunitive alternatives to zero tolerance. Child Trends. Retrieved from https://www.childtrends.org/wp-content/uploads/2011/03/Child_Trends-2011_03_01_RB_AltToZeroTolerance.pdf

Boyes-Watson, C. (2008). *Peacemaking circles and urban youth: Bringing justice home*. St. Paul, MN: Living Justice Press.

Braithwaite, J. (2002). *Restorative justice and responsive regulation*. New York: Oxford University Press.

Braithwaite, J. (2016). Restorative justice and responsive regulation: The question of evidence (RegNet Working Paper No. 51). School of Regulation and Global Governance (RegNet).

Braithwaite, J. (2017). Criminal justice that revives republican democracy. *Northwestern University Law Review, 111*(6), 1507–1524.

Braithwaite, V. (2009a, June 25–26). *Dismissive and resistant defiance*. Paper presented at Legitimacy and Compliance in Criminal Justice: An International Symposium, University of Leeds, Leeds.

Braithwaite, V. (2009b, November 5–6). *Introducing responsive regulation*. Paper presented at the Child Protection as Regulation: Clarifying Principles Conference, Australian National University, Canberra.

Brown, M. (2018). *Creating restorative schools: Setting schools up to succeed*. St. Paul, MN: Living Justice Press.

Carter, P., Skiba, R., Arredondo, M., & Pollock, M. (2017). You can't fix what you don't look at: Acknowledging race in addressing racial discipline disparities. *Urban Education, 52*(2), 207–235.

Casella, R. (2003). Zero tolerance policy in schools: Rationale, consequences, and alternatives. *Teachers College Record, 105*, 872–892.

Christie, N. (1977). Conflicts as property. *British Journal of Criminology, 17*, 1–15.

Davis, F. (2014). Discipline with dignity: Oakland classrooms try healing instead of punishment. *Reclaiming Children and Youth, 23*(1), 38–41.

Dignity in Schools. (2009). Fact sheet: School discipline and the push out problem discipline. (2009). Merriam-Webster online dictionary. Retrieved from https://dignityinschools.org/resources/dsc-created-fact-sheets/

Dohrn, B. (2001). Look Out Kid/It's Something You Did?: Zero tolerance for children. In W. Ayers, B. Dohrn, & R. Ayers (Eds.), *Zero tolerance: Resisting the drive for punishment in our schools* (pp. xi–xvi). New York: New Press.

Dutro, E., & Bien, A. C. (2014). Listening to the speaking wound: A trauma studies perspective on student positioning in schools. *American Educational Research Journal, 51*(1), 7–35.

Evans, K., & Vaandering, D. (2016). *The little book of restorative justice in education: Fostering responsibility, healing and hope in schools*. New York: Good Books.

Fabelo, T., Thompson, M. D., Plotkin, M., Carmichael, D., Marchbanks, M. P., III, & Booth, E. A. (2011). *Breaking schools' rules: A statewide study of how school discipline relates to students' success and juvenile justice involvement*. New York: Council of State Governments Justice Center.

Ferguson, A. A. (2000). *Bad boys: Public schools in the making of black masculinity*. Ann Arbor: University of Michigan Press.

Gil, D. (2006). Perspectives on social justice. *Reflections, 10*(4), 32–39.

Gillborn, D. (2010). The colour of numbers: Surveys, statistics and deficit-thinking about race and class, *Journal of Education Policy, 25*(2), 253–276.

Giroux, H. (2009). Ten years after Columbine: The tragedy deepens. *Policy Futures in Education, 7*(3), 356–361.

González, T. (2015). Reorienting restorative justice: Initiating a new dialogue of rights consciousness, community empowerment and politicization. *Cardozo Journal of Conflict Resolution, 16*, 457–477.

Gordon, R., Della Piana, L., & Keleher, T. (2001). Zero tolerance: A basic racial report card. In W. Ayers, B. Dohrn, & R. Ayers (Eds.), *Zero tolerance: Resisting the drive for punishment in our schools* (pp. 77–88). New York: New Press.

Gregory, A., Clawson, K., Davis, A., & Gerewitz, J. (2016). The promise of restorative practices to transform teacher-student relationships and achieve equity in school discipline. *Journal of Educational and Psychological Consultation, 26*(4), 325–353.

Gregory, A., & Cornell, D. (2009). "Tolerating" adolescent needs: Moving away from zero tolerance policies in high school. *Theory into Practice, 48*, 106–113.

Hirschfield, P. J. (2008). Preparing for prison? The criminalization of school discipline in the USA. *Theoretical Criminology, 12*(1), 79–101.

Human Rights Watch. (2009, April). US: Prison numbers hit new high. Retrieved from https://www.hrw.org/news/2008/06/05/us-prison-numbers-hit-new-high

Jain, S., Bassey, H., Brown, M., & Kalra, P. (2014). *Restorative justice implementation and impacts in Oakland schools* (prepared for the Office of Civil Rights, U.S. Department of Education). Oakland, CA: Oakland Unified School District, Data In Action.

Jordan, J., & Bulent, A. (2009). Race, gender, school discipline, and human capital effects. *Journal of Agricultural and Applied Economics, 41*(2), 419–429.

Ladson-Billings, G. (2001). America still eats her young. In W. Ayers, B. Dohrn, & R. Ayers (Eds.), *Zero tolerance: Resisting the drive for punishment in our schools* (pp. 77–88). New York: New Press.

Lewin, K. (1951). *Field theory in social science: Selected theoretical papers* (D. Cartwright, Ed.). New York: Harper & Row.

Llewellyn, J., & Downie, J. (Eds.). (2011). *Being relational: Reflections on relational theory & health law.* Vancouver, BC: UBC Press.

Losen, D., Hewitt, D., & Toldson, I. (2014). Eliminating excessive and unfair exclusionary discipline in schools: Policy recommendations for reducing disparities. Bloomington: Equity Project at Indiana University. Retrieved from http://www.indiana.edu/~atlantic/wp-content/uploads/2014/04/Disparity_Policy_031214.pdf

Losen, D. J., Hodson, C. L., Keith, M. A., II, Morrison, K., & Belway, S. (2015). Are we closing the school discipline gap? UCLA: Civil Rights Project/Proyecto Derechos Civiles. Retrieved from https://escholarship.org/uc/item/2t36g571

Marshall, T. (1997). Seeking the whole justice. In S. Hayma (Ed.), *Repairing the damage: Restorative justice in action.* London: ISTD.

McMorris, B. J., Beckman, K. J., Shea, G., Baumgartner, J., & Eggert, R. C. (2013). *Applying restorative justice practices to Minneapolis Public Schools students recommended for possible expulsion*. Minneapolis: University of Minnesota.

Minnesota Department of Education. (1995). *Violence prevention plan: Unlearning violence*. Saint Paul, MB: State of Minnesota, Department of Education.

Minnesota Department of Education. (1996). *Restorative measures: Respecting everyone's ability to resolve problems*. Saint Paul, MB: State of Minnesota, Department of Children, Families and Learning.

Minnesota Department of Education. (2001). *In-school behavior intervention grant: Report to the legislature*. Saint Paul, MB: State of Minnesota, Department of Children, Families and Learning.

Minnesota Department of Education. (2003). *Restorative schools grants final report*. Saint Paul, MB: State of Minnesota, Department of Education.

Minnesota Department of Education. (2016). *Dangerous weapons and disciplinary incident report to the legislature*. Saint Paul, MB: State of Minnesota, Department of Education.

Morrison, B. E. (2006a). School bullying and restorative justice: Towards a theoretical understanding of the role of respect, pride and shame. *Journal of Social Issues*, Special Issue: *Restorative Justice and Civil Society*.

Morrison, B. E. (2006b). Schools and restorative justice. In G. Johnstone & D. Van Ness (Eds.), *Restorative justice handbook*. Devon: Willan Publishing.

Morrison, B. E. (2007). *Restoring safe school communities: A whole school response to bullying, violence and alienation*. Sydney: Federation Press.

Morrison, B. E. (2013). Beyond the bad apple: Analytical and theoretical perspectives on the development of restorative approaches in schools. In E. Sellman, H. Cremin, & G. McCluskey (Eds.), *Restorative approaches to conflict in schools: Interdisciplinary perspectives on whole school approaches to managing relationships*. London: Routledge.

Morrison, B. E. (2015). Restorative justice in education: Changing lenses on education's three Rs. *International Journal of Restorative Justice, 3*(3), 445–452.

Morrison, B. E., & Vaandering, D. (2012). Restorative justice: Pedagogy, praxis and discipline. *Journal of School Violence*. Special Issue: *Designing School Contexts in Support of Proactive Discipline: Applications to School Violence*.

Noguera, P. (2008). *The trouble with black boys . . . and other reflections on race, equity, and the future of public education*. San Francisco: Jossey-Bass.

Norris, A. (2009). Gender and race effects of a restorative justice intervention on school success (Conference papers). *Paper presented at the annual meeting of the ASC annual meeting, Philadelphia Marriott Downtown*. Philadelphia, PA. Retrieved from http://citation.allacademic.com/meta/p373243_index.html

Osher, D., Bear, G. G., Sprague, J. R., & Doyle, W. (2010). How can we improve school discipline? *Educational Researcher, 39*(1), 48–58.

Oudshoorn, J. (2016). *Trauma-informed juvenile justice in the United States*. Oudtshoorn: Canadian Scholars' Press.

Payne, A., & Welch, K. (2018). The effect of school conditions on the use of restorative justice in schools. *Youth Violence and Juvenile Justice, 16*(2), 224–240.

Pierce, B. (2009). *Roca's high risk youth intervention model: Initial implementation evaluation report*. San Francisco: Jossey-Bass.

Pranis, K., Stuart, B., & Wedge, M. (2003). *Peacemaking circles: From conflict to community*. St. Paul, MN: Living Justice Press.

Reyes, A. (2006). *Discipline, achievement, and race: Is zero tolerance the answer?* Lanham, MD: Rowman & Littlefield Pub. Group.

Riestenberg, N. (2003). *Restorative schools grants final report, January 2002–June 2003: A summary of the grantees' evaluation*. Roseville, MN: Minnesota Department of Education.

Riestenberg, N. (2007). The restorative recovery school: Countering chemical dependency. *Reclaiming Children and Youth, 16*(2), 21.

Riestenberg, N. (2012). *Circle in the square: Building community and repairing harm in school*. St. Paul, MN: Living Justice Press.

Robbins, C. (2005). Zero tolerance and the politics of racial injustice. *Journal of Negro Education, 74*(1), 2–17.

ROCA. (2017). Annual report: Less jail more future. Retrieved from http://roca-inc.org/wp-content/uploads/2017/11/Roca-2017_AR.pdf

Sandler, S., Wong, F., Morales, E., & Patel, V. (2000). *Turning "to" each other not "on" each other: How school communities prevent racial bias in school discipline. A preliminary report*. San Francisco: Justice Matters Institute.

Sellers, B., & Arrigo, B. (2017). Zero tolerance, social control, and marginalized youth in U.S. schools: A critical reappraisal of neoliberalism's theoretical foundations and epistemological assumptions. *Contemporary Justice Review, 21*(1), 60–79. doi:10.1080/10282580.2018.1415044

Shah, N., & McNeil, M. (2013). Suspension, expulsion data cast some in harsh light. *Education Week Quality Counts, 32*(16), 12.

Sherman, L. (1993). Defiance, deterrence and irrelevance: A theory of the criminal sanction. *Journal of Research in Crime and Delinquency, 30*, 445–473.

Sherman, L. (2003). Reason for emotion: Reinventing justice with theories, innovation, and research. *Criminology, 41*, 1–38.

Simon, J. (2007). *Governing through crime: How the war on crime transformed American democracy and created a culture of fear*. London: Oxford University Press.

Simson, D. (2012, May 12). Restorative justice and its effects on (racially disparate) punitive school discipline. *7th Annual Conference on Empirical Legal Studies Paper*. doi:10.2139/ssrn.2107240. Retrieved from SSRN http://ssrn.com/abstract=2107240

Skiba, R., Michael, R., Nardo, A., & Peterson, R. (2002). The color of discipline: Sources of racial and gender disproportionality in school punishment. *Urban Review, 34*(4), 317–342.

Skiba, R., & Rausch, M. K. (2006). Zero tolerance, suspension, and expulsion: Questions of equity and effectiveness. In C. M. Evertson & C. S.

Weinstein (Eds.), *Handbook of classroom management: Research, practice, and contemporary issues* (pp. 1063–1089). Mahwah, NJ: Lawrence Erlbaum.

Skiba, R. J., Arredondo, M. I., & Rausch, M. K. (2014). *New and developing research on disparities in discipline. Discipline disparities: A research-to-practice collaborative* (Report). Bloomington, IN: The Equity Project at Indiana University, Center for Evaluation and Education Policy.

Skiba, R. J., Horner, R. H., Chung, C. G., Rausch, M. K., May, S. L., & Tobin, T. (2011). Race is not neutral: A national investigation of African American and Latino disproportionality in school discipline. *School Psychology Review, 40*(1), 85–107.

Song, S., & Swearer, S. (2016). The cart before the horse: The challenge and promise of restorative justice consultation in schools. *Journal of Educational and Psychological Consultation, 26*(4), 313–324.

Stutzman Amstutz, L., & Mullet, J. (2005). *The little book of school discipline*. Intercourse, PA: Good Books.

Sumner, D., Silverman, C., & Frampton, M. (2010). *School-based restorative justice as an alternative to zero-tolerance policies: Lessons from West Oakland*. Berkeley: University of California, Berkeley, School of Law.

Tajfel, H., & Turner, J. C. (1979). An integrative theory of intergroup conflict. *The Social Psychology of Intergroup Relations? 33*, 47.

Taylor, R., Oberle, E., Durlak, J., & Weissberg, R. (2017, July/August). Promoting positive youth development through school-based social and emotional learning interventions: A meta-analysis of follow-up effects. *Child Development, 88*(4), 1156–1171.

Turner, J. (2005). Explaining the nature of power: A three-process theory. *European Journal of Social Psychology, 35*, 1–22.

Turner, J. C., Hogg, M. A., Oakes, P. J., Reicher, S. D., & Wetherell, M. S. (1987). *Rediscovering the social group: A self-categorization theory*. New York: Blackwell.

Tyler, T. (2006). Restorative justice and procedural justice: Dealing with rule breaking. *Journal of Social Issues, 62*(2), 307–326.

Tyler, T. R., & Blader, S. (2000). *Cooperation in groups: Procedural justice, social identity, and behavioral engagement*. Philadelphia: Psychology Press.

United States Department of Education (USDOE). (2014). *Guiding principles: A resource guide for improving school climate and discipline*. Retrieved from https://www2.ed.gov/policy/gen/guid/school-discipline/guiding-principles.pdf

Wald, J., & Losen, D. J. (Eds.). (2003). *New directions for youth development: Deconstructing the school to prison pipeline*, No. 99, Fall.

Walgrave, L. (2008). *Restorative justice, self-interest and responsible citizenship*. Devon, UK: Willan Publishing.

Wallace, J., Goodkind, S., Wallace, C., & Bachman, J. (2008). Racial, ethnic, and gender differences in school discipline among U.S. high school students: 1991–2005. *Negro Educational Review, 59*, 47–62.

Welch, K., & Payne, A. A. (2010). Racial threat and punitive school discipline. *Social Problems, 57*, 25–48.

Wong, D., Ma, S., Cheng, C., & Ngan, R. (2011). Program effectiveness of a restorative whole-school approach for tackling school bullying in Hong Kong. *International Journal of Offender Therapy and Comparative Criminology, 55*(6), 846–862.

Zamudio, M. M., Russell, C., Rios, F. A., & Bridgeman, J. L. (2011). *Critical race theory matters: Education and ideology*. New York: Routledge.

Zehr, H. (1990/2015). *Changing lenses: A new focus on crime and justice*. Scottsdale, PA: Herald Press. Page numbers are from the 2015 edition.

Zimbardo, P. (2007). *The Lucifer effect: How good people turn evil*. London: Random House.

CHAPTER FOURTEEN

Threat Assessment and School Crisis Preparedness

Amanda B. Nickerson and Dewey G. Cornell

Schools can promote the health and safety of children with mental health systems and supports that are responsive to threats of violence and unanticipated crises. Although school crises are relatively rare, their devastating consequences require that every school be prepared (Nickerson & Cornell, 2019). The U.S. Department of Education (2013) includes five mission areas of preparedness, including prevention (avoiding, preventing, or stopping a threat), protection (securing against threats), mitigation (reducing the impact of threats), response (saving lives, protecting property, meeting health and safety needs), and recovery (restoring physical, natural, health, social, and cultural resources and services).

This chapter focuses on two comprehensive, collaborative models grounded in federal guidance and prevention science literature to help schools and their communities prevent, respond, and recover from threats of violence and other crises. We organize this by prevention, response, and recovery, with protection and mitigation activities embedded. Other chapters in this volume focus on several critical aspects of crisis prevention, such as emotional and physical safety, positive behavioral interventions and supports, other multitiered approaches to school-based mental health and wellness, and social-emotional skills. The crisis prevention section of this chapter focuses primarily on the Virginia Threat Assessment Guidelines (Cornell & Sheras, 2006). The PREPaRE School Crisis Prevention and Intervention

Model (Brock et al., 2009, 2016) encompasses all aspects of a crisis, from prevention through recovery, but this chapter focuses on crisis response and recovery.

Overview of School Violence and Crises

It is critical to emphasize that, in terms of physical safety, schools are one of the safest places for youth. Contrary to public perception, national surveillance data indicate decreases in serious violent incidents and crime in schools since the early 1990s (e.g., CDC, 2010; Zhang, Musu-Gillette, & Oudekerk, 2016). There has been an understandable outcry about public safety due to high-profile and tragic shootings in schools, but to place this concern in perspective, shootings are less likely to occur in schools than in homes or public places such as stores and restaurants (Nekvasil, Cornell, & Huang, 2015). Many authorities responded by increasing school security measures (e.g., metal detectors or security personnel; Borum, Cornell, Modzeleski, & Jimerson, 2010) and using punitive, zero-tolerance discipline. Several studies indicate that security measures do not increase school safety and can make many students feel less safe at school (Bachman, Randolph, & Brown, 2011; Gastic, 2011; Hankin, Hertz, & Simon, 2011). There is insufficient research on the impact of security personnel on student behavior and school safety (Petrosino, Guckenburg, & Fronius, 2012), but there is concern that law enforcement presence in schools can lead to criminalization of ordinary student misbehavior and contribute to what has been termed the school-to-prison pipeline (James & McCallion, 2013). Furthermore, suspension and other forms of punitive or exclusionary discipline are linked to loss of instructional time, academic difficulties, disengagement from school, dropout, and incarceration (Gregory, Skiba, & Noguera, 2010; Morgan, Salomen, Plotkin, & Cohen, 2014). From a social justice perspective, both building security measures and punitive discipline are used disproportionately in schools with students from economically disadvantaged and racial and ethnic minority backgrounds (Bracy, 2011; Nickerson & Spears, 2007; Servoss & Finn, 2014), and for students with disabilities (Achilles, McLaughlin, & Croninger, 2007).

Although traumatic events, including physical or sexual violence, natural disasters, severe accident or injury, and death of a family member or friend (American Psychiatric Association, 2013; Brock et al., 2016) are rare, they adversely impact social-emotional, behavioral, and academic functioning (De Bellis, Woolley & Hooper, 2013; Nickerson, Reeves, Brock, & Jimerson, 2009). They can threaten mental health and compromise a person's ability to cope with stress, work and learn productively, and contribute to the community (World Health Organization, 2014). Schools are critical settings for promoting mental health. Schools are usually the first and often the only source of mental health services for children and youth (National Association of School Psychologists, 2016).

In order to promote school safety and engage crisis preparedness, school teams must plan for different kinds of crisis events, engage in interagency collaboration (school, police, fire, EMS, mental health), and use multitiered approaches that deliver evidence-based interventions to meet the needs of students who require various levels of support (Reeves, Kanan, & Plog, 2010). To facilitate efficiency and interagency collaboration, the U.S. Department of Homeland Security (2008) developed the National Incident Management System (NIMS) and Incident Command System (ICS) so that schools and any agency responding to a crisis use a common set of concepts, principles, terminology, and organizational processes. Oftentimes, school personnel do not have the training or expertise to engage in comprehensive crisis prevention and intervention efforts (Adamson & Gimple Peacock, 2007; U.S. Government Accountability Office [U.S. GAO], 2007). The Virginia Threat Assessment Guidelines and the PREPaRE Model were developed specifically for school-based multidisciplinary teams to engage in best practices in preventing, responding to, and recovering from violence and other crisis events.

Crisis Prevention

One common objection to violence prevention is that it is not possible to accurately predict who is going to commit a violent act (Nickerson & Cornell, 2019). Decades of research have found that there is only moderate accuracy in identifying individuals who subsequently commit serious acts of violence (Fazel, Singh, Doll, & Grann, 2012). It may seem plausible that if authorities cannot predict whether a person is going to commit a shooting rampage, there would be no way to prevent it from occurring. However, the unpredictability of violence in individual cases does not mean violence cannot be prevented on a larger scale. Prevention does not require prediction. There are many public health prevention programs that have saved lives from seemingly unpredictable dangers (Mozaffarian, Hemenway, & Ludwig, 2013). For example, motor-vehicle accidents seem unpredictable, but traffic safety laws, driver education, and well-designed vehicles reduce the rate of accidents. The American Psychological Association (2013) report on gun violence recommended a similar application of prevention principles to reduce violence.

Several meta-analyses have found that multiple forms of school-based prevention programs are effective in reducing levels of student aggression and violence (Barnes, Leite, & Smith, 2015; Durlak, Weissberg, & Pachan, 2010; Wilson & Lipsey, 2007). For example, Wilson and Lipsey (2007) examined 249 experimental and quasi-experimental studies of a wide range of school-based programs for aggressive behavior. The programs included individual, group, classroom, and schoolwide programs with interventions variously targeting anger management, social problem-solving, social skills, and reinforcement of desired behaviors. They estimated that the average effect sizes of these programs would decrease aggressive behavior by about 25% to 33%, with greater reductions among the most effective programs.

Prevention can be characterized on three levels or tiers (O'Connell, Boat, & Warner, 2009). The first level or tier is universal or primary prevention, which includes efforts aimed at the general population and targets general factors and environmental conditions that lead to a negative outcome such as violence. For example, the schoolwide Positive Behavioral Interventions and Supports (PBIS) model includes universal support strategies such as systematic training and reinforcement of expected behaviors for which 80% to 90% of students are projected to respond successfully (Bradshaw, Reinke, Brown, Bevans, & Leaf, 2008).

The second tier or level of prevention (also called targeted or selective prevention) is aimed at the 5% to 10% of individuals who are deemed to be at risk for a negative outcome. In the public health domain, a good example is the campaign to reduce risk factors for cancer such as tobacco use. In school settings, cognitively oriented individual and small group counseling services, social skills training, and behavioral strategies for at-risk students are examples of secondary prevention (Wilson & Lipsey, 2007).

The tertiary or indicated level is for the 1% to 5% of students with more chronic problems who already demonstrate the negative outcome and are in need of treatment to prevent recurrence or worsening. In the educational domain, these programs often involve special schools or special education classes that serve students outside of mainstream classrooms. These students typically have demonstrated substantial aggressive and disruptive behavior along with academic difficulties (Wilson & Lipsey, 2007).

Threat Assessment as a Violence Prevention Strategy

School shootings in the 1990s propelled schools to adopt zero tolerance discipline policies that suspended or expelled students who seemed dangerous or threatening (Skiba & Knesting, 2001). Critics charged that zero tolerance polices stimulated a massive increase in the use of school suspensions, which has a negative impact on student achievement (Morgan et al., 2014; Noltemeyer, Ward, & Mcloughlin, 2015). Multiple authorities concluded that zero tolerance had no discernible effect on school safety and did not prevent violence (American Psychological Association Zero Tolerance Task Force, 2008; Morgan et al., 2014).

Studies of school shootings by both the FBI (O'Toole, 2000) and the Secret Service (Vossekuil et al., 2002) recommended that schools move away from a zero tolerance approach and instead use a behavioral threat assessment approach. Threat assessment was unfamiliar to the education field, but was developed in law enforcement as a strategy to prevent violence by distinguishing serious threats from those that pose no real danger. Threat assessment is used by the U.S. Secret Service, the U.S. State Department, and the U.S. Marshals Service to protect federal officials and is a recommended practice for the prevention of workplace violence (American Psychological Association, 2013; ASIS International, 2011).

Threat assessment is a process of evaluating individuals who verbally threaten to harm others, or engage in threatening behavior, to determine whether their behavior demonstrates a serious intent to carry out a violent act. In practice, threat assessment involves both assessment and intervention to prevent violence. Some individuals threaten violence as an expression of frustration or anger, but lack genuine intent to harm someone. Others may contemplate violence, but the threat can be ameliorated through an intervention such as counseling or conflict mediation. In the most extreme cases involving a very serious threat, law enforcement intervention may be needed to prevent an imminent attack. Overall, threat assessment is a more flexible and less punitive alternative to zero tolerance that generates different responses to students depending on the circumstances and seriousness of their misbehavior. From a multitiered prevention perspective, threat assessment is a means of identifying the appropriate level of prevention needed for a specific individual. There is evidence that schools using threat assessment make less use of school suspension and do not generate racial or ethnic disparities in disciplinary outcomes (Cornell, Maeng, Huang, Shukla, & Konold, in press).

Virginia Model of Threat Assessment

The Virginia Student Threat Assessment Guidelines (Virginia Guidelines[1]) was developed at the University of Virginia in 2002 as a violence prevention strategy for school-based multidisciplinary teams (Cornell & Sheras, 2006). Conventional law enforcement approaches to threat assessment were adapted and supplemented for use in schools, recognizing the overarching educational mission of schools to serve all students, regardless of aptitude, disability status, and social, racial, or ethnic background. The Virginia Guidelines were designed to recognize the developmental differences and needs of children and youth, including their high base rates of playful behavior, verbal threats, and aggression in comparison to adults.

A school-based threat assessment team typically includes a school administrator, one or more mental health professional (such as counselors, school psychologists, and social workers) and a law enforcement representative such as a school resource officer. The threat assessment process was designed to be flexible so that relatively simple cases can be handled by one or two team members and only the most serious cases entail a comprehensive assessment involving all team members.

A case example illustrates how threat assessments are conducted. A 15-year-old female student named Emily sought out the school psychologist and reported that she was troubled by an online chat she had with a 16-year-old male student named Jacob the previous night. She related that Jacob was upset that his girlfriend Hannah had broken up with him and started dating his best friend, Michael. Jacob was especially angry with Michael and felt betrayed by him. In the course of the conversation, Jacob made a vague threat that "Michael is gonna regret what he did when I see him at school." Emily asked what he meant and he replied, "Beat the crap out of him." At this point Emily felt unsettled and broke off the chat.

A threat assessment team is trained to investigate threats promptly by gathering all relevant information to determine whether a student poses a serious threat to harm someone. The Virginia Guidelines use a decision tree (see figure 14.1) that begins with a triage phase during which the team determines whether the case can be quickly and easily resolved as a transient threat or will require more extensive evaluation and intervention as a substantive threat.

A team member usually begins by interviewing the student who made the threat, as well as others who may have knowledge of it. The interviewer uses a standard set of questions that are adapted to the specific situation. The interviewer is concerned with the context as well as the content of the threat. What were the circumstances and what did the student mean in making the threat? The student's account is compared to other witness reports.

In the case example, the school psychologist consulted with several other team members and they agreed on a triage plan. One team member interviewed Jacob to gain his perspective on what he said and what he meant. Other team members interviewed Michael and Hannah to ascertain whether Jacob had said and or done anything that would be cause for concern.

Most student threats can be resolved as transient threats, meaning that the student does not pose a threat. Transient threats can be figures of speech or expressions of anger (e.g., "I could kill you for that!") that do not reflect a sustained intent to harm someone. Transient threats are resolved when the student is offers an apology and explanation that satisfies the team that the student does not intend to carry out the threat. In situations where there is an argument or conflict that stimulated the threat, the student might be referred for counseling services or conflict mediation. The student also may be reprimanded and disciplined in some way if his or her behavior violated school rules.

A threat that cannot be easily resolved as a transient threat is classified as a substantive threat, which means that there is a sustained intent to harm

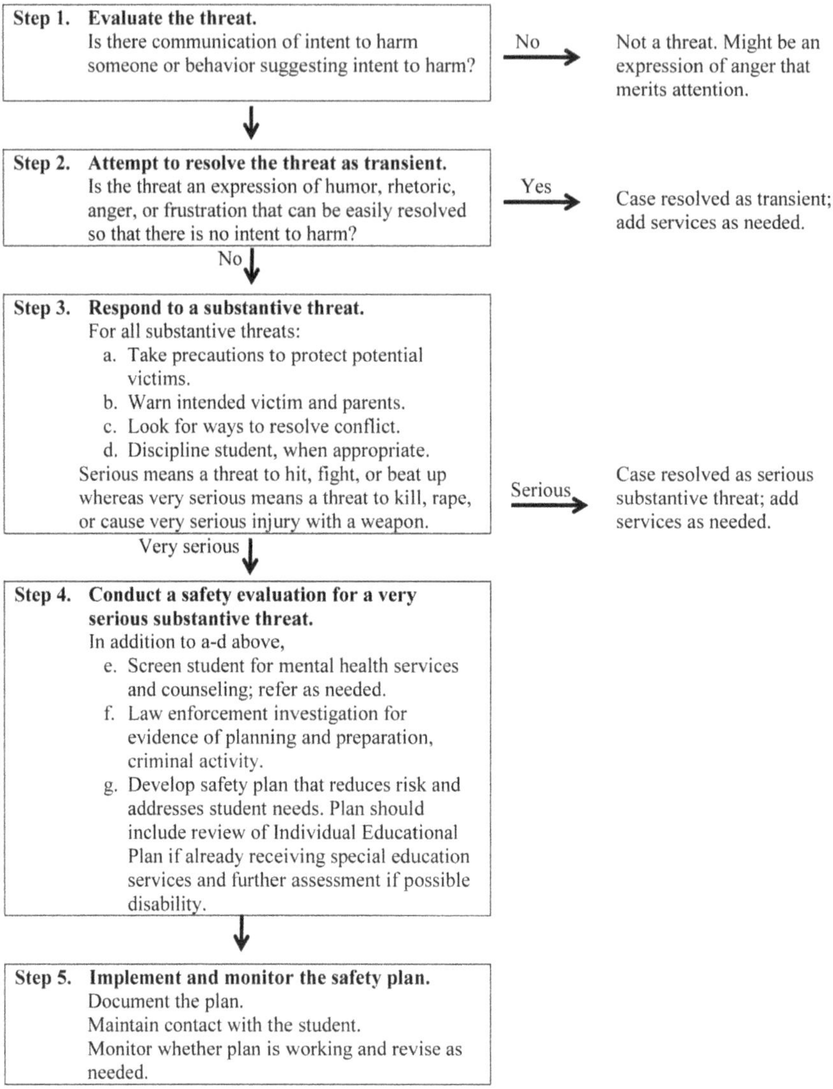

Figure 14.1 Threat Assessment Decision Tree. (© Dewey Cornell. All rights reserved. Used by permission)

someone beyond the immediate incident. Threats are considered more serious when they are more specific in details such as the time and place of an attack and /or if the student has engaged in planning or preparation to carry out the threat. In each case, the team must consider the totality of circumstances surrounding the threat and make reasoned judgments based on all available information.

In the case example, Jacob was initially uncooperative with the threat assessment team and refused to discuss his feelings about his best friend dating his former girlfriend. He denied any intention to harm them, but stated, "My personal life is none of your business." Jacob had no history of serious discipline problems at school, but both Michael and Hannah expressed concern that Jacob was very angry at them. Although he had made no direct threats, Michael thought it was possible that Jacob would want to fight him.

If Jacob had acknowledged his threatening statement and offered a convincing explanation that he was expressing his anger but did not intend to fight anyone, the threat might have been considered transient. However, Jacob's uncooperativeness made it impossible to easily resolve the threat and as a result, it had to be classified as substantive.

A substantive threat is classified as serious or very serious, a distinction based on the intended severity of injury. A threat to assault, strike, or beat up someone is classified as serious, whereas a threat to kill, sexually assault, or severely injure someone is very serious. In Jacob's case, the threat seemed serious, but did not involve a weapon or an expressed intent to kill or severely injure Michael.

The team responds to substantive threats by taking protective actions to prevent the threat from being carried out. In these cases, most often involving student threats to fight someone, the threat assessment team would notify the intended victim and victim's parents, contact the threatening student's parents, and strongly caution the student against attempting to carry out the threat. The threat assessment team may also recommend conflict resolution or counseling. In Jacob's case, a counselor spent time helping him come to terms with his disappointment and anger. A principal of threat assessment is to address the problem that underlies the threat. Threats are regarded as signs of frustration over a problem the student has been unable to resolve. The threat assessment team assumes a problem-solving role in helping the student to cope with the problem. Resolution of the problem is perhaps the most effective way to prevent violence because the reason for the threat is removed. Interventions by a threat assessment team can prevent a relatively minor conflict or problem from escalating into a more serious threat of violence. Many students cope with break-ups in their dating relationships, but in Jacob's case his threat indicated that he was not coping very well and the assessment indicated that there was a potential for him to carry out his threat.

In the case of very serious substantive threats (such as threats to kill, rape, or seriously harm someone), the team again takes protective actions but also initiates a more comprehensive safety evaluation, which can involve both a law enforcement investigation and a mental health assessment of the student. In cases involving a criminal act (such as possession of a firearm on school property), the law enforcement investigation could result in an arrest and legal charges.

In very serious substantive cases, students are usually referred for a mental health assessment, typically conducted by a mental health professional such as the school psychologist on the threat assessment team. These assessments are not intended to make predictions of violence, but are guided by two goals: (a) assess the student's mental state and need for mental health services; and (b) determine the reasons for the student's threat. In evaluating the student, it will be important to assess how angry, frustrated, or depressed the student may be. Is the student so discouraged or frustrated that he or she might take desperate action without concern for the consequences? Are there cognitive impairments, such as delusional ideas that could motivate aggressive action? A careful mental health assessment focused on understanding the student's mental state can be helpful in identifying potential interventions and preventive measures.

A second goal of the mental health assessment is to recommend strategies for resolving the problem or conflict underlying the threat. For example, in one case a student who is being bullied might plot revenge or in another case a student might have an escalating conflict with a teacher. The threat assessment team looks for the most effective way to resolve the conflict appropriate to the circumstances. In some cases, the student is struggling with depression and suicidal feelings. Although the use of long-term suspension is explicitly discouraged in the Virginia Guidelines, a short-term suspension (typically a few days) is recognized as an appropriate safety precaution until the team can complete its evaluation. Parents are contacted so that they can provide appropriate supervision outside of school and also collaborate with the school on resolving the problem so that the student can safely return to school.

After gathering information from all available sources, the team integrates findings into a written safety plan. The aim of the safety plan is twofold: (a) to take steps on behalf of the safety of potential victims and the larger school community; and (b) to determine the most appropriate educational provisions for the student. When the student is allowed to return to school, the safety plan includes specific instructions for the student's behavior and procedures to monitor and support him or her upon return (Cornell & Allen, 2011).

Safety plans include provisions for monitoring the student over a reasonable period of time. For example, a team member might be in regular contact with Jacob for several weeks to assess how things are going and whether he has overcome his disappointment in his relationships with Michael and Hannah. If Jacob is referred for counseling or mental health services, he and his parent should be asked for permission to share information with the threat assessment team on his progress. In the event that Jacob does not make progress and expresses a new intent to harm someone, the counselor should understand that she or he has a duty to take reasonable protective action such as notifying the team that further intervention is needed.[2] For students receiving special education services, there are often changes in the student's Individualized Education Program, such as developing a behavior support plan to help the student with angry feelings or interpersonal conflict.

Supporting Research

Research on violence prevention is a challenging endeavor. Like all prevention efforts, success may be largely invisible. When a counselor persuades a student not to fight someone, there is no evidence of this success. On the other hand, a single violent incident will cast doubt on the value of prevention efforts. Only controlled studies can provide rigorous evidence that prevention is successful, but studies of school violence are difficult to design and carry out.

Research on threat assessment began with a series studies designed to test the effects of training staff and implementing the model in school settings. Two studies (Allen, Cornell, Lorek, & Sheras, 2008; Cornell, Allen, & Fan, 2012) demonstrated that school staff training in the Virginia Guidelines produced a decrease in fears of school violence, increased willingness to use a threat assessment approach, and reduced support for a zero tolerance approach. These changes were observed across school administrators, counselors, psychologists, school-based police officers, and social workers. More important, however, is what happens when teams apply what they have learned to real cases. Two initial field-tests demonstrated that school-based teams could carry out threat assessments using the Virginia Guidelines in a practical, efficient manner without violent outcomes (Cornell et al., 2004; Strong & Cornell, 2008). Notably, almost all of the evaluated students were permitted to return to school and few of the students received long-term suspensions or transfers to another school.

Over the next 10 years as more schools adopted threat assessment, it was possible to carry out a series of retrospective and prospective studies that provided further evidence of positive outcomes. Three studies found that schools using the Virginia Guidelines experienced lower suspension rates and less peer aggression/bullying compared to schools not using threat assessment or using some other approach to threat assessment (Cornell, Gregory, & Fan, 2011; Cornell, Sheras, Gregory, & Fan, 2009; Nekvasil & Cornell, 2015). Two of these studies also found that their students reported greater willingness to seek help for threats of violence (Cornell et al., 2009, 2011).

A randomized control study of 40 schools compared 20 schools using the Virginia Guidelines with 20 schools using their regular practices (while waiting for threat assessment training the following year). Teams in each of the 20 intervention schools completed a one-day workshop in threat assessment and began using the threat assessment manual, Guidelines for Responding to Student Threats of Violence (Cornell & Sheras, 2006), which has detailed instructions and a decision-tree to guide team actions. Over the course of a school year approximately 100 students in each group were identified by school authorities as making a threat of violence. The study found that students who made threats of violence in schools using the Virginia Guidelines were approximately four times more likely to receive counseling services and two-and-a-half times more likely to receive a parent conference than students in wait-list control schools (Cornell, Allen, & Fan, 2012). In contrast, students in the control group were three times more likely to receive a long-term suspension and eight times more likely to be transferred to a different school. These results illustrated the benefit of using threat assessment to take a less punitive and exclusionary approach to school safety and discipline. Based on a series of controlled studies, in 2013, the Virginia Student Threat Assessment Guidelines became the first form of threat assessment recognized as an evidence-based practice in the National Registry of Evidence-based Programs and Practices (NREPP; 2013).

As schools across Virginia have adopted a threat assessment approach, suspension rates have declined (JustChildren and Cornell, 2013). Among Virginia's secondary schools, schools using the Virginia Guidelines recorded 15% fewer short-term suspensions and 25% fewer long-term suspensions per year than other schools, controlling for school size, the percentage of low-income students, and the percentage of minority students. A promising finding was that suspension rates were lower for both white and black students in schools using the Virginia Guidelines, and the lower rate for black students substantially reduced the racial disparity in long-term suspensions.

In 2013, Virginia legislation (Virginia Code § 22.1-79.4) mandated that all public schools establish threat assessment teams and use any model of threat assessment that conformed to general state guidelines. A state report of 3,172 student threat assessments conducted in Virginia public schools during the 2014–2015 school year found that fewer than 1% of the threats were carried out and no cases resulted in a serious physical injury (Cornell et al., 2016). Fewer than half (43%) of the students received an out-of-school suspension and approximately 1% were expelled.

A follow-up study (Cornell et al., in press) found no statistically significant racial disparities among black, Hispanic, and white students in out-of-school suspensions, expulsions, school transfer, and legal actions (arrest, incarceration, or criminal charges). The most consistent predictors of disciplinary consequences were the student's possession of a weapon and the team classification of the threat as serious. In summary, there is substantial evidence that threat assessment is a safe and effective violence prevention strategy that provides schools with an alternative to more punitive, zero tolerance practices. Threat assessment should be used as part of a school or district's comprehensive approach to school safety and crisis prevention, preparedness, and recovery.

Crisis Response and Recovery: The PREPaRE Model

The National Association of School Psychologists' (NASP) PREPaRE Model (Brock et al., 2009, 2016) focuses on all areas of school safety and crisis preparedness from prevention through recovery. The model balances physical and psychological safety, and focuses on building skills of interdisciplinary collaboration using the NIMS/ICS (U.S. Department of Homeland Security, 2008). The acronym stands for **P**revent/Prepare for psychological trauma; **R**eaffirm physical health, security, and safety; **E**valuate psychological trauma; **P**rovide interventions (**a**nd) **R**espond to psychological needs; and **E**xamine the effectiveness of prevention and intervention efforts. A multitiered system of approach to crisis preparedness is utilized with an explicit emphasis on the need to assess the differential impact of the crisis event on individuals-based risk and protective factors for psychological trauma (Nooner et al., 2012), and to provide group and individual crisis interventions to those who may benefit from them.

Prevent/Prepare for Psychological Trauma

Prevention and preparedness strategies are essential activities for schools to engage in, in partnership with local law enforcement and community mental health agencies, to promote physical and psychological safety (SAMHSA Now Is the Time Technical Assistance Center, 2016). *Crime Prevention Through Environmental Design* (Schneider, Walker, & Sprague, 2000) details ways the physical environment of the school can be designed to increase (a) natural surveillance (b) natural access control, and (c) territoriality (e.g., sense of shared ownership of the school by students and staff). As discussed in greater detail earlier in this chapter, effective school-based prevention programs are among the methods used to promote psychological safety.

A multidisciplinary school crisis response team consistent with the Incident Command System (ICS) framework (U.S. Department of Homeland Security, 2008) is an essential component of preparedness efforts. The expertise from administrators, mental health professionals, safety and security personnel, emergency responders, transportation agencies, nursing staff, and facilities and grounds personnel is used to plan comprehensively for crises. Teams should conduct needs assessments and hazard analyses to plan for a variety of potential crises most likely to impact a school (Brock et al., 2009, 2016). Preparedness activities include but are not limited to: (a) obtaining supplies and equipment; (b) establishing and exercising response protocols (e.g., evacuation, lockdown, shelter in place); (c) establishing student accounting procedures; (d) developing protocols for reunification (of students to parents); (e) establishing procedure to control crowds and manage traffic; (f) developing the capacity to meet emergency medical needs; and (g) developing the capacity to provide crisis intervention to psychological trauma victims. These procedures should be detailed in a comprehensive school crisis plan with frequent (at least annually) revisions, as well as routine practice and evaluation through drills (Reeves et al., 2010).

When a crisis event occurs, the PREPaRE model can be implemented, using the previously presented case example. For illustration purposes, we will assume that Emily did not report her concerns about Jacob and a threat assessment was not conducted. After several days of escalating conflict between Jacob and Michael, Jacob entered school at the beginning of the day and proceeded directly to Hannah's locker. As Hannah was talking with Michael, Jacob took a knife from his back pocket and stabbed Michael repeatedly, killing him and injuring two students who attempted to intervene.

Reaffirm Physical Health, Security, and Safety

The most immediate response to a crisis situation is to focus on physical safety and security by executing the emergency response plan (e.g., lockdown, evacuation) and providing necessary medical care. Adult reactions are critical to how children perceive threat in crisis situations (DeVoe, Klein, Bannon, & Miranda-Julian, 2011). In the case example, a teacher in a nearby classroom calls for an immediate lockdown over the intercom. School staff members quickly direct students and staff members in the hall into nearby rooms, lock the doors, and direct students to sit against the wall as practiced in lockdown drills. Simultaneously, the incident commander calls 911 and emergency responders arrest Jacob and take Michael and the two injured students to the hospital.

The school crisis team uses their ICS roles and divides responsibilities. Law enforcement coordinates with the school safety officer to ensure that the immediate threat to safety is removed and arranges to secure the crime scene and interview witnesses. Planning and logistics establish and verify information to be communicated to school staff, parents, and students. Planning and Logistics also identify space for (a) relocation of students who were in the classrooms surrounding the crime scene, (b) crisis interventions, (c) media staging area, and (d) reunification with parents (if deemed appropriate). The public information officer serves as the spokesperson for the media. The liaison officer communicates and coordinates with other agencies, such as the hospital, crisis interveners from the district, and community mental health agencies as needed. Operations conduct primary psychological triage to determine crisis intervention needed and deliver a continuum of crisis interventions, as described below.

Evaluate Psychological Trauma

The impact of a crisis on a school or community differs depending on the event's predictability, duration, impact, and intensity. More predictable events (e.g., death following a long-term terminal illness) tend to generate less traumatic stress than those that are sudden and unpredictable (e.g., accidental death, random shootings), likely due to the opportunity to prepare by making cognitive and emotional adjustments (Saylor, Belter, & Stokes, 1997). Traumatic reactions are experienced more following assaultive violence than natural disasters (Charuvastra & Cloitre, 2008; McLaughlin et al., 2013). An important task for school crisis response teams is to identify the level of risk the crisis is likely to generate in order to decide on the resources needed to respond effectively. Some events can be resolved with a routine response within one's typical role in the school (e.g., nurse providing first aid for a playground accident resulting in a minor injury to a couple of student), whereas others require a system-wide response involving district and community resources (e.g., emergency responders and school-based and community mental health providers intervening following a bus accident resulting in multiple deaths of students). Between these two extremes are events that can be responded to by a school-based crisis response team and/or a school district-level team (Brock et al., 2009, 2016), such as the death of a student from a prolonged illness. In the case example, a community level response was needed where emergency responders and additional community mental health services provided resources to the multiple students, school staff members, and community members impacted.

Recognizing that people who experience the same crisis may respond very differently, it is critical to evaluate individuals' risk for experiencing psychological trauma through psychological triage. Triage can be performed immediately after a crisis event to make initial decisions about who to prioritize for intervention, but it is an ongoing process in the days and weeks following an event as there are some individuals that may be missed at first and/or who develop reactions that may not have been predicted or identified earlier. An individual's risk for post-traumatic stress symptoms increases depending on exposure to a crisis event in terms of physical proximity (i.e., direct exposure), including sustaining injuries (Kolaitis et al., 2003) or witnessing death (Ma et al., 2011). Emotional proximity (e.g., relationship with the victim) is associated with negative mental health outcomes for children (Kolaitis et al., 2003), including complicated grief, depression, and post-traumatic stress disorder (PTSD; Cohen & Mannarino, 2004). The way the person perceives the event in terms of the threat it presents to oneself is also a key indicator of potential traumatic stress (Rubin, Bernsten, & Bohni, 2008).

School crisis teams must also consider individual vulnerabilities and protective factors when determining the need for crisis intervention. Children who grasp the gravity of a crisis yet lack experience using coping and decision-making skills in crisis situations are particularly vulnerable to problems (e.g., PTSD, affective disorders, disrupted learning) after a crisis (Lonigan, Phillips, & Richey, 2003). Prior traumatization is also a well-documented risk factor for more severe traumatic reactions to a crisis (Olff, Langeland, & Gersons, 2005; Trickey, Siddaway, Meiser-Stedman, Serpell, & Field, 2012). Social support buffers children from traumatic stress, whereas lack of family support due to parental distress, mental illness, or poor coping strategies is associated with more negative mental health outcomes for children following a crisis (Möhlen, Parzer, Resch, & Brunner, 2005; Trickey et al., 2012).

In the case example, Hannah was at moderate risk for psychological trauma given her physical and emotional proximity to both Michael and Jacob, as were the two injured students. Other students and staff members who witnessed the incident and those that had close relationships with any of the victim(s) were also at moderate risk for psychological trauma. Students with preexisting vulnerabilities, such as victims of child abuse or other forms of violence or other risk factors were also prioritized for crisis intervention.

Provide Interventions (and) Respond to Psychological Needs

As mentioned previously, an increasingly important role in the prevention and provision of mental health services is the use of a multitiered public health model. The PREPaRE model applies this approach to crisis response and intervention (Brock et al., 2009, 2016; see figure 14.2). Tier 1 (universal) crisis interventions are provided to all students to decrease the risk of developing psychological trauma and other adverse reactions after a crisis occurs, as well as to identify people who may need services that were not identified in primary psychological triage. These include ensuring physical safety and perceptions of safety. Another universal intervention is to reestablish connections to natural social supports by reunifying them with their parents or primary caregivers, providing opportunities for peer support, and returning to daily routines (Brock et al., 2009, 2016) as this is associated with reduced risk for traumatic stress and other negative mental health outcomes (Banks & Weems, 2014; Marsac, Donlon, Hildenbrand, Winston, & Kassam-Adams, 2014).

Other universal or Tier 1 approaches in crisis situations include psychoeducation, or providing information about the facts of the event, typical

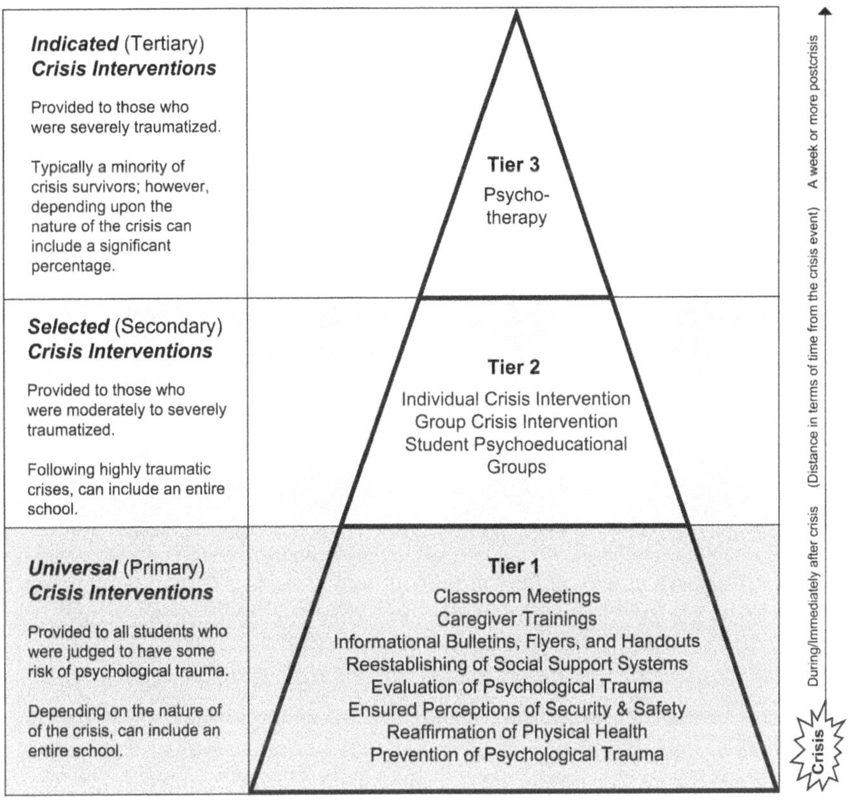

Figure 14.2 Levels of school-based crisis interventions. (Copyright 2016 by the National Association of School Psychologists. Bethesda, MD. Reprinted with permission of the publisher. http://www.nasponline.org)

responses to crisis, effective coping strategies, and resources for individual assistance. Information can be shared through printed handouts, digital media, and/or face-to-face meetings with caregivers and students. School staff can be provided with guidance on conducting classroom meetings with their students (Brock et al., 2016; Reeves et al., 2010). Sharing this information, particularly when used as part of comprehensive crisis intervention, is associated with better coping and reduced mental health symptoms (Gelkopf & Berger, 2009; Pynoos, Goenjian, & Steinberg, 1998).

In the case example, initial interventions involved holding classroom meetings to share the facts of the incident, answer questions, and inform students of supports available. In addition, crisis interveners set up different support locations (e.g., guidance offices for individual crisis intervention, library for reestablishing peer support). Psychoeducation was provided to school staff members through e-mail and by a meeting immediately after school to inform them of the facts of the event, prepare them for expected crisis reactions, and provide guidance in coping for themselves and their students. Parents were provided this information through the school's emergency notification system, the website, and other channels as appropriate (social media, letter home), and an open meeting was scheduled for parents.

Tier 2 group crisis interventions are designed to meet the needs of individuals determined through psychological triage to be at moderate risk of psychological trauma (Brock et al., 2009, 2016). For example, students who witnessed a crisis event or a team or group of friends who were close to a student that died would be at moderate risk of traumatic reactions given their physical or emotional proximity to the crisis. Tier 2 group interventions in the PREPaRE model are the student psychoeducational group and the classroom-based (or group-based) crisis intervention. Both of these interventions involve providing facts about the crisis event, answering questions about the incident, and correcting inaccurate information if needed. These interventions also identify common crisis reactions and teach coping strategies, including talking to a trusted adult or close friend, engaging in pleasant and distracting activities, using deep breathing and other relaxation methods, and other methods that have worked in the past (Brymer et al., 2012; Kronenberg et al., 2010). The primary difference between the two interventions is that the student psychoeducational group is a shorter (approximately one hour) didactic intervention that can be taught similar to an academic or social skills lesson. In contrast, the classroom-based (or group-based) crisis intervention is longer (2–3 hours), more intensive, and utilizes the group process to have students share their common experiences in terms of their experience with the crisis and their reactions. Given the potential for emotional arousal and sensitivity to the traumatic experience (Bisson, 2003; Yule, 2001), this intervention is conducted by a mental health professional with students who share similarities in degree of crisis exposure and experience, crisis impact, and developmental level (and who are secondary, as opposed to primary victims of trauma). An emphasis is placed on empowering individuals to engage in effective coping to help themselves and others; facilitators continue to conduct psychological triage to identify individuals in need of more intensive intervention, and access to more comprehensive treatment is made available as needed (Brock et al., 2009, 2016).

Highly traumatized students (e.g., primary crisis victims, those suffering from more acute reactions) are not recommended to be included in a group intervention; instead, individual crisis intervention consisting of a basic problem-solving model to help reestablish immediate coping is indicated. This Tier 2 intervention, also referred to as psychological first aid, includes establishing rapport, ensuring physical and psychological safety and comfort, providing emotional support, gathering information to identify crisis-generated problems, supporting adaptive coping and problem-solving, connecting the person with social support, providing information on coping, assessing trauma risk, and providing linkages to appropriate assistance resources (Brock et al., 2009, 2016; Brymer et al., 2012).

In the case example, the crisis team identified students and staff who witnessed the incident and those who had close relationships with the victim(s), and made decisions about whom to provide with the psychoeducational group, group crisis intervention, and individual crisis intervention in the coming days based on need, indications (grouping those with similar crisis exposure), parent permission, and availability of crisis responders. Hannah and the two injured students were provided with individual crisis intervention. The students who witnessed the incident were questioned by law enforcement and many reported having trouble concentrating and feeling guilty for not saving Michael. The crisis team conducted group crisis intervention with these students, and a separate group crisis intervention with the close friends of Michael. The team also provided guidance to students, parents, and the school community about funeral arrangement, memorials, and other ways to provide support and empower them to begin to heal.

Although individual crisis intervention may be an immediate first step for more severely traumatized individuals, if the reactions persist or do not remit, more intensive and sustained Tier 3 interventions are needed. Cognitive behavioral therapy interventions in the school setting (e.g., Cognitive-Behavioral Intervention for Trauma in Schools [CBITS]; Jaycox, 2003) have been found to reduce PTSD and co-occurring symptoms (Kataoka et al., 2003; Rolfsnes & Idsoe, 2011). Positive results have been found with cultural modifications (Morsette et al., 2009) and implementing in a curriculum-style format by teachers and counselors (Jaycox et al., 2009).

For students with PTSD or other mental health disorders resulting from or exacerbated by a crisis event, evidence-based treatments such as Trauma-Focused Cognitive Behavioral Therapy (Leenarts, Diehle, Doreleijers, Jansma, & Lindauer, 2013) and Cognitive-Behavioral Therapy for Childhood Traumatic Grief (Cohen & Mannarino, 2004) are warranted. These intensive treatments are usually beyond the role, scope of practice, and competency of school-based practitioners. Therefore, it is critical that schools work within a systems of care model and make referrals to community-based professionals (SAMHSA Now Is The Time Technical Assistance Center, 2016).

In the case example, triage was an ongoing process to determine those who needed more intensive interventions to connect them with the appropriate services. Hannah had ongoing problems with nightmares and flashbacks about the event and refused to attend school. The crisis team worked with the family and outside wraparound providers for Hannah to get the treatment she needed.

Research Findings and Future Directions

PREPaRE has been systematically evaluated through a pre-post program evaluation since its inception. Participants attending the PREPaRE Crisis Prevention and Intervention Training workshops show significant improvements in crisis prevention and intervention attitudes and knowledge, with high participant satisfaction (Brock, Nickerson, Reeves, Savage, & Woitaszewski, 2011; Nickerson et al., 2014). PREPaRE was particularly beneficial for participants with fewer hours of prior crisis training (Nickerson et al., 2014). In a follow-up study, school-based mental health professionals who completed the *PREPaRE* Workshop 2 scored an average of 20% higher on crisis-related content than those who did not complete PREPaRE (Lazzaro, 2013). To date, there are no studies that examine the specific outcomes of crises handled by school staff using PREPaRE training. A randomized controlled trial of PREPaRE and a follow-up study of participants are currently in progress to assess the extent to which the knowledge and skills gained from the training are used in practice and result in improved outcomes in schools.

Conclusion

The Virginia Student Threat Assessment Guidelines and the PREPaRE School Crisis Prevention and Intervention Model, grounded in theory and empirical research, offer guidance and protocols for multidisciplinary team approaches to prevent, respond to, and recover from acts of targeted violence and other crises (Nickerson & Cornell, 2019). Despite the demonstrated success of threat assessment and a multitiered public health model of prevention, policy makers have been slow to embrace violence prevention. A challenge for the prevention field is that the benefits of successful prevention are largely invisible and unrecognized (Nickerson & Gurdineer, 2012), while the occasional but inevitable failures of prevention create a strong impression that prevention efforts are futile. Only controlled studies can show that a prevention effort reduced the level of a problem, but rigorous research in the sensitive area of crisis prevention is difficult to conduct (Nickerson, Pagliocca, & Palladino, 2012).

If violent acts or other crisis impact a school, multidisciplinary crisis teams can use a set of sequential steps to identify and intervene according to a multitiered model designed to help schools and their community partners meet the physical and psychological needs of students, school staff, and their communities. A well-planned and practiced response can mitigate the harm from a crisis event, although the challenge is to make adequate preparations for the wide range of potential crises that could occur and to engage in interagency collaboration so that multiple agencies can provide a coordinated and efficient response under stressful conditions. The process of recovery and restoration is ongoing and can be enhanced by school professionals receiving the training and ongoing guidance on understanding the impact of trauma on students and the school community, how to evaluate level of risk, and implement crisis interventions designed to promote adaptive and healthy recovery as demonstrated by the case examples in this chapter.

Notes

1. The Virginia Student Threat Assessment Guidelines (VSTAG) are described in the 2006 publication, *Guidelines for Responding to Student Threats of Violence* and is distinguished from the 2013 publication, *Threat Assessment in Virginia Public Schools: Model Policies, Procedures, and Guidelines*, by the Virginia Department of Criminal Justice Services, which was intended to be a more generic set of guidelines for schools using different models of threat assessment.

2. Mental health professionals should be familiar with the legal duty to warn or protect requirements in their state. For example, Virginia law (§ 54.1-2400.1) specifies that mental health service providers, including counselors, school psychologists, and social workers, have a duty to take precautions to protect third parties from violence threatened by a client. These precautions are based on the circumstances of the situation, but could include warning potential victims, contacting law enforcement, or providing therapy or counseling that resolves the client's intent.

References

Achilles, G. M., McLaughlin, M. J., & Croninger, R. G. (2007). Sociocultural correlates of disciplinary exclusion among students with emotional, behavioral, and learning disabilities in the SEELS national dataset. *Journal of Emotional and Behavioral Disorders, 15*, 36–45. doi:10.1177/10634266070150010401

Adamson, A. D., & Gimple Peacock, G. (2007). Crisis response in the public schools: A survey of school psychologists' experiences and perceptions. *Psychology in the Schools, 44*, 749–764. doi:10.1002/pits.20263

Allen, K., Cornell, D., Lorek, E., & Sheras, P. (2008). Response of school personnel to student threat assessment training. *School Effectiveness and School Improvement, 19*, 319–332. doi:10.1080/09243450802332184

American Psychiatric Association. (2013). *Diagnostic and statistical manual of mental disorders* (5th ed.). Washington, DC: American Psychiatric Press. doi:10.1108/RR-10-2013-0256

American Psychological Association. (2013). *Gun violence: Prediction, prevention, and policy.* Retrieved from https://www.apa.org/pubs/info/reports/gun-violence-prevention.aspx. doi:10.1037/e647302013-001

American Psychological Association Zero Tolerance Task Force. (2008). Are zero tolerance policies effect in the schools? An evidentiary review and recommendations. *American Psychologist, 63*, 852–862. doi:10.1037/0003-066X.63.9.852

ASIS International and Society for Human Resource Management. (2011). *Workplace violence prevention and intervention: An American standard* (ASIS/SHRM WVP.1-2011). New York: American National Standards Institute. doi:10.4135/9781412952415.n221

Bachman, R., Randolph, A., & Brown, B. L. (2011). Predicting perceptions of fear at school and going to and from school for African American and white students: The effect of school security measures. *Youth & Society, 43*, 705–726. doi:10.1177/0044118X10366674

Banks, D. M., & Weems, C. F. (2014). Family and peer social support and their links to psychological distress among hurricane-exposed minority youth. *American Journal of Orthopsychiatry, 84*, 341–352. doi:10.1037/ort0000006

Barnes, T. N., Leite, W., & Smith, S. W. (2015). A quasi-experimental analysis of school-wide violence prevention programs. *Journal of School Violence*. doi:10.1080/15388220.2015.1112806

Bisson, J. I. (2003). Single-session early psychological interventions following traumatic events. *Clinical Psychology Review, 23*, 481–499. doi:10.1016/S0272-7358(03)00034-5

Borum, R., Cornell, D. G., Modzeleski, W., & Jimerson, S. R. (2010). What can be done about school shootings? A review of the evidence. *Educational Researcher, 39*, 27–37. doi:10.3102/0013189X09357620

Bracy, N. L. (2011). Student perceptions of high-security school environments. *Youth & Society, 43*, 365–395. doi:10.1177/0044118X10365082

Bradshaw, C. P., Reinke, W. M., Brown, L. D., Bevans, K. B., & Leaf, P. J. (2008). Implementation of school-wide positive behavioral interventions and supports (PBIS) in elementary schools: Observations from a randomized trial. *Education and Treatment of Children, 31*, 1–26. doi:10.1353/etc.0.0025

Brock, S. E., Nickerson, A. B., Reeves, M. A., Conolly, C., Jimerson, S. R., Pesce, R. C., & Lazzaro, B. (2016). *School crisis prevention and intervention: The PREPaRE model* (2nd ed.). Bethesda, MD: National Association of School Psychologists.

Brock, S. E., Nickerson, A. B., Reeves, M. A., Jimerson, S. R., Feinberg, T., & Lieberman, R. (2009). *School crisis prevention and intervention: The PREPaRE model*. Bethesda, MD: National Association of School Psychologists.

Brock, S. E., Nickerson, A. B., Reeves, M. A., & Savage, T. A., & Woitaszewski, S. A. (2011). Development, evaluation, and future directions of the PREPaRE School Crisis Prevention and Intervention Training Curriculum. *Journal of School Violence, 10*, 34–52. doi:10.1080/15388220.2010.519268

Brymer, M., Taylor, M., Escudero, P., Jacobs, A., Kronenberg, M., Macy, R., . . . Vogel, J. (2012). *Psychological first aid for schools: Field operations guide* (2nd ed.). Los Angeles: National Child Traumatic Stress Network. Retrieved from http://www.nctsn.org/content/psychological-first-aid-schoolspfa

Centers for Disease Control and Prevention. (2010). Youth risk behavior surveillance—United States, 2009. *Morbidity and Mortality Weekly Report, 59*, SS-5. Retrieved from http://www.cdc.gov/mmwr/pdf/ss/ss5905.pdf

Charuvastra, A., & Cloitre, M. (2008). Social bonds and posttraumatic stress disorder. *Annual Review of Psychology, 59*, 301–328. doi:10.1146/annurev.psych.58.110405.085650

Cohen, J. A., & Mannarino, A. P. (2004). Treatment of childhood traumatic grief. *Journal of Clinical Child & Adolescent Psychology, 33*, 819–831. doi:10.1207/s15374424jccp3304_17

Cornell, D., & Allen, K. (2011). Development, evaluation, and future directions of the Virginia Student Threat Assessment Guidelines. *Journal of School Violence, 10*, 88–106. doi:10.1080/15388220.2010.519432

Cornell, D., Allen, K., & Fan, X. (2012). A randomized controlled study of the Virginia Student Threat Assessment Guidelines in grades K–12. *School Psychology Review, 41*, 100–115.

Cornell, D., Gregory, A., & Fan, X. (2011). Reductions in long-term suspensions following adoption of the Virginia Student Threat Assessment Guidelines. *Bulletin of the National Association of Secondary School Principals, 95*, 175–194. doi:10.1177/0192636511415255

Cornell, D., Maeng, J., Burnette, A. G., Datta, P., Huang, F., & Jia, Y. (2016). *Threat assessment in Virginia schools: Technical report of the Threat Assessment Survey for 2014–2015.* Charlottesville, VA: Curry School of Education, University of Virginia.

Cornell, D., Maeng, J., Huang, F., Shukla, K., & Konold, T. (2018). Racial/ethnic parity in disciplinary consequences using student threat assessment. *School Psychology Review, 47*, 183–195. doi: 0.17105/SPR-2017-0030.V47-2

Cornell, D., & Sheras, P. (2006). *Guidelines for responding to student threats of violence.* Longmont, CO: Sopris West.

Cornell, D., Sheras, P., Gregory, A., & Fan, X. (2009). A retrospective study of school safety conditions in high schools using the Virginia Threat Assessment Guidelines versus alternative approaches. *School Psychology Quarterly, 24*, 119–129. doi:10.1037/a0016182

Cornell, D., Sheras, P., Kaplan, S., McConville, D., Douglass, J., Elkon, A., . . . Cole, J. (2004). Guidelines for student threat assessment: Field-test findings. *School Psychology Review, 33*, 527–546.

De Bellis, M. D., Woolley, D. P., & Hooper, S. R. (2013). Neuropsychological findings in pediatric maltreatment: Relationship of PTSD, dissociative symptoms, and abuse/neglect indices to neurocognitive outcomes. *Child Maltreatment, 18*, 171–183. doi:10.1177/1077559513497420

DeVoe, E. R., Klein, T. P., Bannon, W., Jr., & Miranda-Julian, C. (2011). Young children in the aftermath of the World Trade Center attacks. *Psychological Trauma: Theory, Research, Practice, and Policy, 3*, 1–7. doi:10.1037/a0020567

Durlak, J. A., Weissberg, R. P., & Pachan, M. (2010). A meta-analysis of after-school programs that seek to promote personal and social skills in children and adolescents. *American Journal of Community Psychology, 45*(3–4), 294–309. doi:10.1007/s10464-010-9300-6

Fazel, S., Singh, J. P., Doll, H., & Grann, M. (2012). Use of risk assessment instruments to predict violence and antisocial behavior in 73 samples involving 24,827 people: Systematic review and meta-analysis. *BMJ, 345*, e4692. doi:10.1136/bmj.e4692

Gastic, B. (2011). Metal detectors and feeling safe at school. *Education and Urban Society, 43*, 486–498. doi:10.1177/0013124510380717

Gelkopf, M., & Berger, R. (2009). A school-based, teacher-mediated prevention program (ERASE-Stress) for reducing terror-related traumatic reactions in Israeli youth: A quasi-randomized controlled trial. *Journal of Child Psychology and Psychiatry, 50*, 962–971. doi:10.1111/j.1469-7610.2008.02021.x

Gregory, A., Skiba, R. J., & Noguera P. A. (2010). The achievement gap and the discipline gap: Two sides of the same coin? *Education and Educational Researcher, 39*, 59–68. doi:10.3102/0013189X09357621

Hankin, A., Hertz, M., & Simon, T. (2011). Impacts of metal detector use in schools: Insights from 15 years of research. *Journal of School Health, 81*, 100–106. doi:10.1111/j.1746-1561.2010.00566.x

James, N., & McCallion, G. (2013). School resource officers: Law enforcement officers in schools. *Congressional Research Service, June, 26*(201), 3.

Jaycox, L. (2003). *Cognitive-behavioral intervention for trauma in schools*. Longmont, CO: Sopris West.

Jaycox, L. H., Langley, A. K., Stein, B. D., Wong, M., Sharma, P., Scott, M., & Schonlau, M. (2009). Support for students exposed to trauma: A pilot study. *School Mental Health, 1*, 49–60. doi:10.1007/s12310-009-9007-8

JustChildren, & Cornell, D. (2013). *Prevention v. punishment: Threat assessment, school suspensions, and racial disparities*. University of Virginia, Curry School of Education. Retrieved from http://curry.virginia.edu/uploads/resourceLibrary/UVA_and_JustChildren_Report_-_Prevention_v._Punishment.pdf

Kataoka, S. H., Stein, B. D., Jaycox, L. H., Wong, M., Escudero, P., Tu, W., . . . Fink, A. (2003). A school-based mental health program for traumatized Latino immigrant children. *Journal of the American Academy of Child and Adolescent Psychiatry, 42*, 311–318. doi:10.1097/00004583-200303000-00011

Kolaitis, G., Kotsopoulos, J., Tsiantis, J., Haritaki, S., Rigizou, R., Zacharaki, L., . . . Katerelos, P. (2003). Post-traumatic stress reactions among children following the Athens earthquake of September 1999. *European Child & Adolescent Psychiatry, 12*, 273–280. doi:10.1007/s00787-003-0339-x

Kronenberg, M. E., Hansel, T. C., Brennan, A. M., Osofsky, H. J., Osofsky, J. D., & Lawrason, B. (2010). Children of Katrina: Lesson learned about post-disaster symptoms and recovery patterns. *Child Development, 81*, 1241–1259. doi:10.1111/j.1467-8624.2010.01465.x

Lazzaro, B. R. (2013). A survey study of PREPaRE workshop participants' application of knowledge, confidence levels, and utilization of school crisis response and recovery training curriculum. Dissertations. Paper 674. Retrieved from http://ecommons.luc.edu/luc_diss/674

Leenarts, L. E., Diehle, J., Doreleijers, T. A. H., Jansma, E. P., & Lindauer, R. J. L. (2013). Evidenced-based treatments for children with trauma-related psychopathology as a result of childhood maltreatment: A systematic review. *European Journal of Child and Adolescent Psychiatry, 22*, 269–283. doi:10.1007/s00787-012-0367-5

Lonigan, C. J., Phillips, B. M., & Richey, J. A. (2003). Posttraumatic stress disorder in children: Diagnosis, assessment, and associated features. *Child and Adolescent Psychiatric Clinics of North America, 12*, 171–194. doi:10.1016/S1056-4993(02)00105-0

Ma, X., Liu, X., Hu, X., Qiu, C., Wang, Y., Huang, Y., . . . Li, T. (2011). Risk indicators for post-traumatic stress disorder in adolescents exposed to the 5.12 Wenchuan earthquake in China. *Psychiatry Research, 189*, 385–391. doi:10.1016/j.psychres.2010.12.016

Marsac, M. L., Donlon, K. A., Hildenbrand, A. K., Winston, F. K., & Kassam-Adams, N. (2014). Understanding recovery in children following traffic-related injuries: Exploring acute traumatic stress reactions, child coping, and coping assistance. *Clinical Child Psychology and Psychiatry, 19*, 233–243. doi:10.1177/1359104513487000

McLaughlin, K. A., Koene, K. C., Hill, E. D., Petukhova, M., Sampson, N. A., Zaslavsky, A. M., & Kessler, R. C. (2013). Trauma exposure and posttraumatic stress disorder in a national sample of adolescents. *Journal of the American Academy of Child & Adolescent Psychiatry, 52*, 815–830.e14. doi:10.1016/j.jaac.2013.05.011

Möhlen, H., Parzer, P., Resch, F., & Brunner, R. (2005). Psychosocial support for war-traumatized child and adolescent refugees: Evaluation of a short-term treatment program. *Australian and New Zealand Journal of Psychiatry, 39*, 81–87. doi:10.1111/j.1440-1614.2005.01513.x

Morgan, E., Salomen, N., Plotkin, M., & Cohen, R. (2014). *The school discipline consensus report: Strategies from the field to keep students engaged in school and out of the juvenile justice system.* New York: The Council of State Governments Justice Center. Retrieved from: http://csgjusticecenter.org/wp-content/uploads/2014/06/The_School_Discipline_Consensus_Report.pdf

Morsette, A., Swaney, G., Stolle, D., Schuldberg, D., van den Pol, R., & Young, M. (2009). Cognitive Behavioral Intervention for Trauma in Schools (CBITS): School-based treatment on a rural American Indian reservation. *Journal of Behavior Therapy and Experimental Psychiatry, 40*, 169–178. doi:10.1016/j.jbtep.2008.07.006

Mozaffarian, D., Hemenway, D., & Ludwig, D. S. (2013). Curbing gun violence: Lessons from public health successes. *JAMA: Journal of the American Medical Association, 309*, 551–552. doi:10.1001/jama.2013.38

National Association of School Psychologists. (2016). *School-based mental health services: Improving student learning and well-being.* Retrieved from https://www.nasponline.org/resources-and-publications/resources/mental-health/school-psychology-and-mental-health/school-based-mental-health-services

National Registry of Evidence-Based Programs and Practices. (2013). *Virginia Student Threat Assessment Guidelines.* Retrieved from https://www.samhsa.gov/nrepp

Nekvasil, E., & Cornell, D. (2015). Student threat assessment associated with positive school climate in middle schools. *Journal of Threat Assessment and Management, 2,* 98–113. doi:10.1037/tam0000038

Nekvasil, E., Cornell, D., & Huang, F. (2015). Prevalence and offense characteristics of multiple casualty homicides: Are schools at higher risk than other locations? *Psychology of Violence, 5,* 236–245. doi:10.1037/a0038967

Nickerson, A., & Cornell, D. (2019). School crisis prevention, response, and recovery. In M. Mayer & S. Jimerson (Eds.), *School safety and violence prevention: Science, practice, and policy driving change* (pp. 223-246). Washington, DC: American Psychological Association.

Nickerson, A. B., & Gurdineer, E. E. (2012). Research needs for crisis prevention. In S. E. Brock & S. R. Jimerson (Eds.), *Best practices in crisis prevention and intervention in the schools* (2nd ed., pp. 683–700). Bethesda, MD: National Association of School Psychologists.

Nickerson, A. B., Pagliocca, P. M., & Palladino, S. (2012). Research and evaluation needs for crisis intervention. In S. E. Brock & S. R. Jimerson (Eds.), *Best practices in crisis prevention and intervention in the schools* (2nd ed., pp. 701–730). Bethesda, MD: National Association of School Psychologists.

Nickerson, A. B., Reeves, M. A., Brock, S. E., & Jimerson, S. R. (2009). *Identifying, assessing, and treating posttraumatic stress disorder at school.* New York: Springer.

Nickerson, A. B., Serwacki, M. L., Brock, S. E., Savage, T. A., Woitaszewski, S. A., & Reeves, M. A. (2014). Program evaluation of the PREPaRE School Crisis Prevention and Intervention Training Curriculum. *Psychology in the Schools, 51,* 466–479. doi:10.1002/pits.21757

Nickerson, A. B., & Spears, W. H. (2007). Influences on authoritarian and educational/ therapeutic approaches to school violence prevention. *Journal of School Violence, 6,* 3–31. doi:10.1300/J202v06n04_02

Noltemeyer, A. L., Ward, R. M., & Mcloughlin, C. (2015). Relationship between school suspension and student outcomes: A meta-analysis. *School Psychology Review, 44,* 224–240. doi:10.17105/spr-14-0008.1

Nooner, K. B., Linares, O., Batinjane, J., Kramer, R. A., Silva, R., & Cloitre, M. (2012). Factors related to posttraumatic stress disorder in adolescence. *Trauma Violence Abuse, 13,* 153–166. doi:10.1177/1524838012447698

O'Connell, M. E., Boat, T., & Warner, K. E. (Eds.). (2009). *Preventing mental, emotional, and behavioral disorders among young people: Progress and possibilities.* Washington, DC: National Academies Press.

Olff, M., Langeland, W., & Gersons, B. P. R. (2005). The psychobiology of PTSD: Coping with trauma. *Psychoneuroendocrinology, 30,* 974–982. doi:10.1016/j.psyneuen.2005.04.009

O'Toole, M. E. (2000). *The school shooter: A threat assessment perspective.* Quantico, VA: National Center for the Analysis of Violent Crime, Federal Bureau of Investigation.

Petrosino, A., Guckenburg, S., & Fronius, T. (2012). "Policing schools" strategies: A review of the evaluation evidence. *Journal of Multidisciplinary Evaluation, 8,* 80–101.

Pynoos, R. S., Goenjian, A. K., & Steinberg, A. M. (1998). A public mental health approach to the postdisaster treatment of children and adolescents. *Child and Adolescent Psychiatric Clinics of North America, 7,* 195–210. doi:10.1046/j.1440-1819.1998.0520s5S129.x

Reeves, M. A, Kanan, L. M., & Plog, A. E. (2010). *Comprehensive planning for safe learning environments: A school professional's guide to integrating physical and psychological safety—Prevention through recovery.* New York: Routledge.

Rolfsnes, E. S., & Idsoe, T. (2011). School-based intervention programs for PTSD symptoms: A review and meta-analysis. *Journal of Traumatic Stress, 24,* 155–165. doi:10.1002/jts.20622

Rubin, D. E., Bernsten, D., & Bohni, M. K. (2008). A memory-based model of posttraumatic stress disorder: Evaluating basic assumptions underlying the PTSD diagnosis. *Psychological Review, 115,* 985–1011. doi:10.1037/a0013397

SAMHSA Now Is the Time Technical Assistance Center [Lead contributors Guttman-Lapin, D., Nickerson, A., O'Malley, M., Renshaw, T., Silva, K., & Sockalingam, S.] (2016). *School mental health referral pathways toolkit.* Rockville, MD: SAMHSA.

Saylor, C. F., Belter, R., & Stokes, S. J. (1997). Children and families coping with disaster. In S. A. Wolchik & I. N. Sandler (Eds.), *Handbook of children's coping: Linking theory and intervention* (pp. 361–383). New York: Plenum.

Schneider, T., Walker, H., & Sprague, J. (2000). *Safe school design: A handbook for educational leaders: Applying the principles of crime prevention through environmental design.* Eugene, OR: ERIC Clearinghouse on Educational Management.

Servoss, T. J., & Finn, J. D. (2014). School security: For whom and with what results? *Leadership and Policy in Schools, 13,* 61–92. doi:10.1080/15700763.2014.890734

Skiba, R. J., & Knesting, K. (2001). Zero tolerance, zero evidence: An analysis of school disciplinary practice. *New Directions for Student Leadership, 92,* 17–43. doi:10.1002/yd.23320019204

Strong, K., & Cornell, D. (2008). Student threat assessment in Memphis City Schools: A descriptive report. *Behavioral Disorders, 34,* 42–54.

Trickey, D., Siddaway, A. P., Meiser-Stedman, R., Serpell, L., & Field, A. P. (2012). A meta-analysis for risk factors for post-traumatic stress disorder in children and adolescents. *Clinical Psychology Review, 32*, 122–138. doi:10.1016/j.cpr.2011.12.001

U.S. Department of Education. (2013, June). *Guide for developing high-quality school emergency operations plans*. Washington, DC: Author: Retrieved from http://www2.ed.gov/admins/lead/safety/emergencyplan/index.html

U.S. Department of Homeland Security. (2008, December). *National incident management system*. Washington, DC: Author. Retrieved from https://www.fema.gov/pdf/emergency/nims/NIMS_core.pdf

U.S. Government Accountability Office (GAO). (2007). *Most school districts have developed emergency management plans, but would benefit from additional federal guidance* (Report No. GAO-07-609). Retrieved from http://www.gao.gov/new.items/d07609.pdf

Vossekuil, B., Fein, R. A., Reddy, M., Borum, R., & Modzeleski, W. (2002). *The final report and findings of the Safe School Initiative: Implications for the prevention of school attacks in the United States*. Washington, DC: U.S. Secret Service and U.S. Department of Education.

Wilson, S. J., & Lipsey, M. W. (2007). School-based interventions for aggressive and disruptive behavior: Update of a meta-analysis. *American Journal of Preventive Medicine, 33*, 130–143. doi:10.1016/j.amepre.2007.04.01

World Health Organization. (2014). Mental health: A state of well-being. Retrieved from http://www.who.int/features/factfiles/mental_health/en/

Yule, W. (2001). Posttraumatic stress disorder in the general population and in children. *Journal of Clinical Psychiatry, 62*, 23–28.

Zhang, A., Musu-Gillette, L., & Oudekerk, B. A. (2016). *Indicators of school crime and safety: 2015* (NCES 2016-079/NCJ 249758). Washington, DC: National Center for Education Statistics, U.S. Department of Education, and Bureau of Justice Statistics, Office of Justice Programs, U.S. Department of Justice.

PART 3

Planning, Evaluation, and Policy Development

CHAPTER FIFTEEN

Using Data to Improve Outcomes

Collaborative Planning, Progress Monitoring, and Continuous Improvement

Jason Katz, Abraham Wandersman, Patricia E. Campie, and Manolya Tanyu

Schools are becoming increasingly focused on school climate and safety, mental health supports, and wellness. This shift is influenced in part by increased flexibility that states have under the Every Student Succeeds Act (ESSA) (U.S. Department of Education, 2016). More fundamentally, it is influenced by a recognition that schools have an important role not only in preventing violence but also in promoting students' well-being. The challenge of school violence is complex, so the solutions will take time, involve trial and error, and include many voices and perspectives. We know that progress is incremental, so *getting started* is as important as progress monitoring and improving over time. The following questions will be considered in this chapter: What does it look like for a school to engage in a collaborative problem-solving process to improve school safety and well-being? What are some techniques that stakeholders can use for progress planning, monitoring, and improvement?

Step 1. Developing a Problem-Solving Team

To begin the process toward improving the conditions for learning in a school, school administrators must identify a team to lead the work. An inclusive team may include school staff, students, and families, and a broader array of local stakeholders as appropriate (e.g., community members, staff from municipal or local offices, district education agency leaders) (Campie, Tanyu, & Osher, 2016). An inclusive approach brings more voices and helps the team to better understand the nuances involved in a problem. Having diverse voices also helps the team to explore potential solutions that are socially and culturally acceptable. Parents, students, and community members must have a strong and valued role in partnership with schools to help ensure that progress is comprehensive, inclusive, and relevant to local context and culture. A problem-solving team could be integrated into an existing school team based on the topic (e.g., a school climate team). We suggest that the team develop a charter statement and that all members of the team collaborate in its development. This statement broadly describes the purpose and scope of the problem-solving team; the expected impact, methods, and procedures to be used; and potential challenges the group may face, as well as how the process will be sustained and how results will be communicated with stakeholders. Below we present a fictional example of a charter statement from (an also fictional) high school. In creating an interdisciplinary problem-solving team, Davis High School focused on assessing and improving safety, mental health, and wellness. The charter statement reflects the team's intention to engage in an inclusive and collaborative process and offers a description of the team's purpose and agenda.

Hypothetical Example of a Charter Statement: Davis High School's Safety and Wellness Problem-Solving Team

Project Background

In response to escalating violent behavior on the school campus, including an incident that resulted in an emergency room visit for a student, Davis High School's principal called for the development of an interdisciplinary problem-solving team focused on identifying, prioritizing, and improving school-level needs associated with safety, mental health, and wellness.

Opportunity/Impact Statement

The expected impact of the problem-solving team's work is a safer school environment and increased well-being of all members of the school community. This will be indicated by pro-social behavior and fewer violent incidents on the school campus.

Approach

Individuals represented on the problem-solving team include teachers, guidance counselors, administration staff, parent advocates, student leaders, community partners, and district-level personnel. Primary activities include defining the problem; assessing what may be causing the problem; setting improvement targets; selecting, implementing, and monitoring improvement strategies; making midcourse and strategic improvements as needed; and—if efforts are successful—sustaining the progress. Semi-annual reports describing activities and results will be developed by the team in collaboration with a facilitator (described below) and will be disseminated to administrators, families, and other identified stakeholders.

Potential Limitations

Members of the problem-solving team bring expertise about the school, yet may have somewhat limited experience in participating in a data-informed, collaborative problem-solving process. A facilitator with experience in team-based progress monitoring and improvement will provide support.

Step 2. Defining Safety and Well-Being Needs

What is the need? In the above example, there is an expressed need and a commitment from school leadership to improve schoolwide safety and well-being. This decision may have been influenced by a variety of factors, including input received from families and the community. It is important to complement these pressures for change with a review of data. Extracting administrative data on behavioral incidents is a low-burden, objective measure that can be used later against which to measure progress. User-friendly tools, such as an incident reporting template as part of a larger resource developed by the National Center for Safe and Supportive Learning Environments (https://safesupportivelearning.ed.gov/addressing-root-causes-disparities-school-discipline), are available to help organize administrative data into an actionable format (see Figure 15.1). Data can be reviewed for subgroup differences (e.g., disciplinary incidents by race, ethnicity, poverty, disability, gender, sexual orientation). Readers who are familiar with Positive Behavioral Intervention and Supports may want to look at data that are specific to students who are at risk (i.e., Tier 2), and/or students who require more intensive and individualized support (i.e., Tier 3) (Lever & Freeman, 2015).

If additional data are needed, common collection methods include surveys, observations, interviews, and focus groups. Surveys can be used to gather information about individuals' perceptions of others, themselves, or

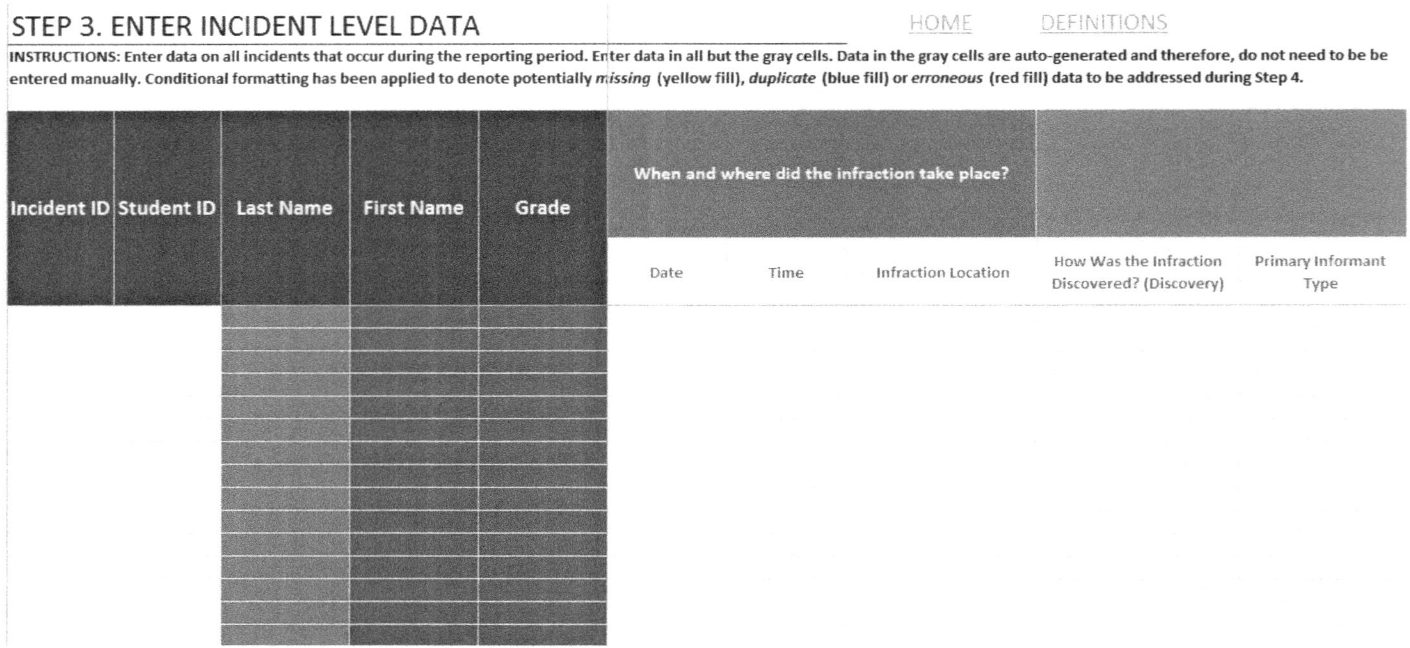

Figure 15.1 Incident reporting database

the environment. This can be useful if you want to learn, for example, about how safe students feel at school. Surveys can also inform the team's understanding of potential contributing factors, to be discussed below. Educators can check to see if there are existing surveys that are publicly available. For example, the Department of Education offers free school climate surveys for middle and high school students, instructional staff, non-instructional staff, and parents or guardians (https://safesupportivelearning.ed.gov/edscls). The surveys measure a school's engagement, safety, and environment, and free tools are available for scoring and reporting that show how a school's results compare to national benchmarks. An observation protocol (e.g., the Comer Visitor Observation instrument: https://files.eric.ed.gov/fulltext/ED420925.pdf) can be used to capture behavior as it occurs (e.g., to assess peer interactions occurring on the playground or in the classroom). Interviews or focus groups with students, staff, or families help to deepen information collected from other data sources. For example, focus groups could be conducted to better understand what is revealed via surveys (e.g., why some students feel physically safe but not emotionally safe in school). Focus groups and some of the other methods described can serve as a source of input to the fishbone diagram activity described in the next section.

Across assessment activities, the team may need to confer or collaborate with internal or external evaluation coaches who bring technical expertise in data collection and analysis. Also, be mindful of the school and district's confidentiality requirements if data are of a sensitive nature and include personally identifiable information.

Step 3. Identifying and Prioritizing Factors Contributing to Safety and Well-Being

What may be contributing to the identified need? Two techniques will be highlighted, one of which is used to identify potential contributing factors, the other of which is to prioritize a subset of these factors. First, a fishbone diagram is used to interactively identify such factors. The diagram in figure 15.2 has a broad outcome area (safe and supportive schools) at the head of the fish (right-hand side). To the left are contributing factors, categorized into themes. The facilitator may provide themes (e.g., safe and respectful climate) up front as prompts, informed by the literature or experience. For illustrative purposes, figure 15.2 provides a simple sketch of what a fishbone diagram could look like for conditions for learning (Osher & Kendziora, 2010).

Second, an evaluation activity called *Taking Stock* (Fetterman, 2002) is a way for stakeholders to prioritize one or more of the options identified through the fishbone diagram. Each stakeholder receives five "dot" stickers and places the dots in the fishbone diagram next to his or her preferred option or option(s) about what to evaluate. The dots can be distributed however the stakeholder wants—from one dot for each of five factors, to all five

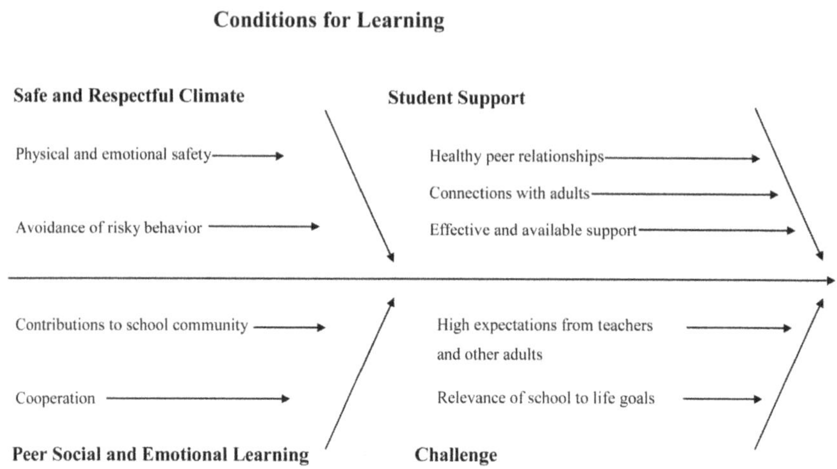

Figure 15.2 Illustration of a fishbone diagram

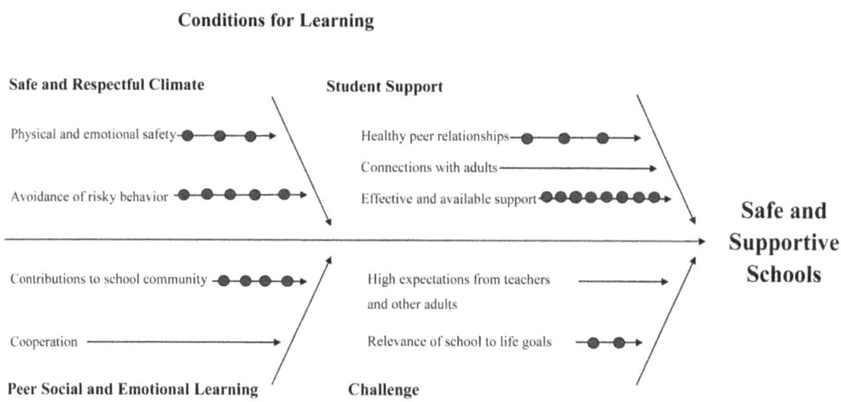

Figure 15.3 Illustration of a nomination process with a fishbone diagram

dots for just one factor. Whichever areas end up with the most dots are then prioritized and used to set the direction for a progress monitoring and improvement project. This activity has been used, for example, as part of a school inventory to identify school-level improvement targets that map onto performance standards related to school culture, community and family support, among other domains (Smith & Goodwin, 2014). In the example provided in figure 15.3, the top priority is "effective and available support."

After *Taking Stock* is completed, taking an additional step to identify or collect relevant data about the prioritized factors can improve precision. In the example above, what type of "effective and available support" is meant? A school safety toolkit developed by the American Institutes for Research is

Table 15.1 Example of a tool to further define a priority

Item[a]	Yes	No	Not Sure
Does the school collaborate with the community to facilitate available supports that enhance student safety and well-being?	✓		
Do community organizations provide the school with access to			
. . . adequate mental health supports for students?		✓	
. . . a health promotion programs for students?			✓
. . . adequate violence and delinquency prevention programs?	✓		
. . . adequate services that can offer an alternative to suspension or expulsion from school?		✓	
. . . adequate family supports for parents and students in need?	✓		
. . . prosocial opportunities and mentoring programs for students?		✓	

[a] The items in table 15.1 were adapted from the California School Safety Toolkit (https://www.air.org/sites/default/files/downloads/report/California-School-Safety-Toolkit-First%20Edition-January-2017.pdf), which includes eight assessment tools, each of which has rubrics to assist with interpretation of the results (Campie et al., 2016).

one example of a resource that synthesizes the evidence-base and includes related needs assessment items, a selection of which is provided in table 15.1 (items that focus on different types of supports provided to students). The results in table 15.1 suggest that students are not currently receiving mentorship as a type of support.

Step 4. Setting Improvement Targets

Schools can set one or more specific, measurable, assignable, realistic, and time-bound (SMART) desired outcomes that correspond to safety and well-being priorities. For example, "By the end of the current academic year, decrease the number of violent incidents occurring on the school campus by 50%." The amount of targeted change could be informed by using state or national averages as a point of comparison. It is important to balance desire and feasibility when selecting a specific and measurable improvement target. For example, a targeted change of 75% could be considered overly ambitious or unrealistic in light of limited capacities to bring to bear to improve the identified problem.

Step 5. Selecting, Implementing, and Monitoring Improvement Strategies

It is a good idea to select an intervention strategy (or best practice) to make progress toward improvement targets. If aligned with the identified improvement targets, existing strategies (either in the school or in partner agencies) should be considered for the sake of feasibility. School staff may conduct a resource assessment to identify existing strategies (e.g., http://csmh.umaryland.edu/media/SOM/Microsites/CSMH/docs/Resource-Mapping-in-Schools-and-School-Districts10.14.14_2-(1).pdf). If there are no existing strategies that you can use, it can be helpful to peruse registries or other types of compilations of evidence-based strategies. Examples include Blueprints for Healthy Youth Development (http://www.colorado.edu/cspv/blueprints), What Works Clearinghouse (http://ies.ed.gov/ncee/wwc/), CASEL program guides (http://www.casel.org/guide/), and CrimeSolutions.gov.

Consider readiness for implementation as part of decision-making about a strategy. There must be adequate ability and willingness (i.e., readiness) among the schools, students, staff, parents, partners, and so on to implement a particular strategy (Scaccia et al., 2015). This includes having the specialized knowledge and skills required for a strategy, an implementation champion (an individual who has charisma or expertise and encourages others to use the strategy), stakeholder buy-in, and implementation partnerships, if needed (e.g., with the YMCA for an after-school program). For additional information about readiness, please refer to this brief on readiness: https://aspe.hhs.gov/system/files/pdf/77076/ib_Readiness.pdf.

Multiple types of data should be collected to provide a comprehensive picture of a strategy's implementation and progress toward improvement targets. This includes monitoring the extent to which the key ingredients of a strategy are put into practice as intended as well as appropriate adaptations (Hall, Dymnicki, Coffey, & Brodowski, 2014). If a strategy is an evidence-based intervention, there will usually be a standardized implementation monitoring tool, included along with the manual, which includes criteria for assessing fidelity. For example, a mentoring strategy may require a structured mentor-mentee matching process, family engagement, and case management (Komosa-Hawkins, 2010). If the strategy is emerging or based on community knowledge, you will need to identify the components to monitor and determine measures and a process for doing so.

Other types of implementation data that you might collect are bulleted below:

- The "output" of implementation (e.g., number of sessions; number or percentage of students participating in sessions, with breakdowns by demographic group)

- The "manner" of implementation (e.g., the teacher delivering the social-emotional learning practices is genuinely excited about it and puts careful thought into making the curriculum interesting and relevant for students)
- Students' perceptions of what is implemented, including their engagement (students may have more positive reactions when implementation quality is higher) (Durlak & DuPre, 2008; Meyers et al., 2012).

For example, the problem-solving team at Davis High School partnered with a community agency to provide mentorship for students identified as being at increased risk for behavioral challenges. Mentors met with students after school in community settings such as coffee shops. Mentors were trained to use a specific protocol and completed a brief fidelity form after each session, which also included questions about the mentee's level of engagement in the sessions. The protocol included guidance about steps for facilitating bonding opportunities, supporting the student's social and emotional needs, and advocating for the student when needed (Banks Amos, Katz, Vriniotis, & Osher, 2016). One of the outputs measured at the group level was the percent of students receiving mentorship out of the total group of students deemed to be at greater risk.

Step 6. Conducting Midcourse and Strategic Improvements

Midcourse improvements occur during implementation. If students struggle to attend mentorship sessions, for example, changes can be made in when and where the sessions take place. If there is adequate implementation of a strategy and desired outcomes are not accomplished (e.g., at the end of the academic year, the number of violent incidents occurring on the school campus did not improve by 50%), this suggests a need for *strategic improvements*. (Note that this is distinct from "improvement strategies" as described earlier; to minimize any confusion, we refer to the latter as an "intervention strategy" in the next two sentences.) Strategic improvements may follow from these questions: Was the intervention strategy sufficiently aligned with the improvement target? If not, the intervention strategy may need to be complemented with, or replaced by, other types of support. Is there a need to revisit the improvement targets (e.g., in the event that they were overly ambitious)? Is it possible that the needs assessment missed something important? For example, the mentorship protocol may have unintentionally overemphasized being a "buddy" to the mentees instead of doing what is needed to guide mentees to a productive future (e.g., college and career planning) (Jarjoura, 2013). If the latter is true, then the protocol can be revised and used in a next iteration of implementation.

Step 7. Sustaining Progress

If improvement targets are accomplished, the improvement strategy may have contributed to success. The problem-solving team can explore the possibility of institutionalizing the strategy (e.g., so that a future cohort of students stands to benefit from mentoring). Also, the team may consider graphing performance to observe trends and patterns over time. A statistical control chart helps to identify and distinguish two kinds of variation that may occur in a process over time: one type of variation is normal and random (technically, this is called "*common cause variation*"). For example, this could be everyday fluctuation in the number of students attending mentoring, such as when a couple of students have a cold or are on a class trip. The other type of variation is contrasted with everyday fluctuation (technically, this is called "*special cause variation*"). For example, this could be a significant shift in the number of students attending mentoring, in either direction, such as when there is a shortage of trained mentors. In this case, innovative policies and procedures are responsive special causes that could improve a process so that it becomes normal again (e.g., addressing the shortage of mentors by training successful mentees to serve in mentor roles) (Ammerman, Putnam, Margolis, & Van Ginkel, 2009). Control charts could also be used as a tool to inform changes even when there isn't a problem or deficiency, in the sense of striving for excellence. A "run chart" is somewhat simpler than a statistical control chart; see this link for a digestible summary of both types of charts http://www.fammed.usouthal.edu/Guides&JobAids/QILandingPage/Run%20Chart%20Control%20Chart.pdf

Conclusion

With growing attention to school safety and students' well-being, schools may increasingly volunteer or be expected to convene a broad-based team to develop improvement plans and to monitor and improve progress toward intended outcomes. This chapter provided an overview of a problem-solving process including specific techniques that school teams can adopt to monitor and improve progress on safety- and well-being-related outcomes. The problem-solving process is intended to be flexible, iterative, and dynamic. We recognize that schools are at different stages and are faced with differing opportunities and challenges. Some schools may elect to adopt or adapt the overall process described in this chapter, while other schools may decide to integrate one or two of the techniques into an existing process. Although we focus primarily on the school-level, many of the techniques could be used at other levels—for example, monitoring and improving a particular mentor-mentee dyad.

References

Ammerman, R. T., Putnam, F. W., Margolis, P. A., & Van Ginkel, J. B. (2009). Quality improvement in child abuse prevention programs. In K. A. Dodge & D. L. Coleman (Eds.), *Preventing child maltreatment: Community approaches* (pp. 63–86). New York: Guilford Press.

Banks Amos, L., Katz, J., Vriniotis, M., & Osher, D. (2016). *Evaluation of the mentoring for REAL program: Final report: Year 3 study.* Washington, DC: American Institutes for Research.

Campie, P., Tanyu, M., & Osher, D. (2016). *The California school safety toolkit* (1st ed.). San Francisco: Zellerbach Family Foundation.

Durlak, J. A., & DuPre, E. P. (2008). Implementation matters: A review of research on the influence of implementation on program outcomes and the factors affecting implementation. *American Journal of Community Psychology, 41*(3–4), 327–350.

Fetterman, D. (2002). Empowerment Evaluation: Building communities of practice and a culture of learning. *American Journal of Community Psychology, 30*(1), 89–102.

Hall, G. E., Dymnicki, A., Coffey, J., & Brodowski, M. (2014). *Using evidence-based constructs to assess extent of implementation of evidence-based interventions* (ASPE Issue Brief). Washington, DC: Office of the Assistant Secretary for Planning and Evaluation, U.S. Department of Health and Human Services.

Jarjoura, G. R. (2013). Effective strategies for mentoring African American boys. American Institutes of Research. Retrieved from https://www.air.org/sites/default/files/downloads/report/Effective%20Strategies%20for%20Mentoring%20African%20American%20Boys.pdf

Komosa-Hawkins, K. (2010). Best practices in school-based mentoring programs for adolescents. *Child & Youth Services, 31*(3–4), 121–137.

Lever, N., & Freeman, E. (2015). *School-based mental health services.* Safe Supportive Learning. Retrieved from https://safesupportivelearning.ed.gov/sites/default/files/School-based%20MH%20Services_final.pdf

Meyers, D. C., Katz, J., Chien, V., Wandersman, A., Scaccia, J. P., & Wright, A. (2012). Practical implementation science: Developing and piloting the quality implementation tool. *American Journal of Community Psychology, 50*(3–4), 481–496.

Osher, D., & Kendziora, K. (2010). Building conditions for learning and healthy adolescent development: Strategic approaches. In B. Doll, W. Pfohl, & J. Yoon (Eds.), *Handbook of youth prevention science* (pp. 121–140). New York: Routledge.

Scaccia, J. P., Cook, B. S., Lamont, A., Wandersman, A., Castellow, J., Katz, J., & Beidas, R. S. (2015). A practical implementation science heuristic for organizational readiness: R= MC2. *Journal of Community Psychology, 43*(4), 484–501.

Smith, C. F., & Goodwin, D. (2014). A guided empowerment self-audit as a school improvement strategy. *Research in Higher Education Journal, 25*. Retrieved from https://files-eric-ed-gov.ezproxy2.library.drexel.edu/fulltext/EJ1055326.pdf

U.S. Department of Education. (2016). Every Student Succeeds Act: Accountability, state plans, and data reporting: Summary of final regulations. Retrieved from https://www2.ed.gov/policy/elsec/leg/essa/essafactsheet170103.pdf

CHAPTER SIXTEEN

The Importance of Child-Guided and Youth-Directed Approaches

Engaging Youth Participatory Action Research Practices

Lawrence T. Winn and Katie E. Richards-Schuster

There is a growing movement among scholars and practitioners within the field of youth development to consider the importance of child-guided and youth-directed approaches within school and community-based programs and youth interventions. Multiple concepts, terminologies, and framings are used to describe these practices, such as youth-directed, child-guided, youth-led, and youth-engaged. Central to these approaches is the voice of young people in development of the issues, design of the programs and interventions, and in some cases implementation, evaluation, and action outcomes of the work.

Youth participatory action research, also known as YPAR, is a popular example of a set of practices that can be used to engage youth in creating and leading school and community changes. At its simplest, youth participatory action research involves young people in identifying issues, asking questions, gathering information, and using that information to inform decisions, develop policy recommendations, or lead social action and community change efforts (Checkoway & Richards-Schuster, 2003; Sabo, 2008). Increasingly youth-directed approaches, and in particular YPAR, are seen as a model for engaging young people in creating changes in schools and communities (Cammarota & Fine, 2008; Ozer, Newlan, Douglas, & Hubbard, 2013). Ozer, Ritterman, and Wanis (2010) argue that participatory research with youth in school is also linked to healthy and positive youth development. They state that participatory action research "most explicitly addresses the dimensions of opportunities for developmentally-appropriate and meaningful youth participation, support for efficacy and mattering, the development of relevant skills; and supportive relationships" (p. 153).

The purpose of this chapter is to explore the importance of child-guided and youth-directed approaches with a focus on YPAR practices. We draw on lessons and examples from our own work with youth to:

1. Explore the core concepts in youth-directed approaches;
2. Provide examples of YPAR and its importance to schools and communities;
3. Discuss the benefits and challenges of YPAR, and lessons for practice; and
4. Suggest future directions—in research, education, and practice—and remaining questions for the field.

1. Basic Definitions and Core Concepts

Definitions and Core Concepts

We define practices as "child-guided" and "youth-directed" in terms of engagement of youth (often ages 12–18) in the active leadership, development, decision-making, and change process of issues that impact their lives. This can include efforts that are completely youth-led, or those that are adult-initiated but youth-informed and/or youth-directed, and those that are intergenerational or a collaboration between youth and adults.

This approach is rooted in a number of key assumptions that include young people as resources and as strengths in their community. This perspective is based on the notion of young people as "competent citizens" and rooted in asset-development frameworks (Checkoway et al., 2003; Finn & Checkoway, 1998).

This approach is also anchored in youth empowerment concepts and positive youth development frameworks. Positive youth development explores the way that engagement and participation support the development of young people. In addition, positive youth development helps guide understanding about the potential for young people to contribute to community (Sabo, 2008).

Finally, many scholars have brought a set of critical theoretical lenses to examine youth-directed approaches. These include examining the rights of young people to participate in civic processes, the power of young people as active agents of change, the power of participation to raise critical socio-political consciousness, the critical engagement of voice, and the ability for young people to see their voice as challenging status quo systems of power (Cammarota & Fine, 2008; Ginwright et al., 2006; Ozer et al., 2013).

The core concepts of youth-directed approaches include:

- Youth as strengths and assets to schools and communities
- Youth as experts in their own lives
- Youth as having agency, with a right and capacity to contribute
- Adults as allies and supporters or partners in youth-directed efforts
- Meaningful and authentic engagement by youth.

Multilevel Benefits

Youth-directed approaches can have multilevel benefits. This includes benefits for the young people but also for organizations and the community. To date, most of the research on these approaches has focused on the impacts on young people who participate. Scholarship suggests that young people who participate develop leadership skills, increase their capacity to work in groups or with others, increase their sense of agency and efficacy, develop social capital, and learn skills (e.g., project planning, critical thinking, public speaking, civic engagement, reading, and writing) (Sabo, 2008; Zimmerman & London, 2003). For example, London and colleagues (2005) describe the benefits to youth in five ways: (1) social competencies, including teamwork, developing empathy for new perspectives, and building a sense of responsibility; (2) civic competencies, including leadership, political consciousness, and advocacy; (3) self-confidence, including public speaking skills and agency; (4) social capital, including building new relationships with peers and adults; and (5) identity exploration, including the ability to see oneself in new roles.

Youth-directed approaches can also have benefits to organizations and communities. When young people are involved directly in the organization they can provide insight and understanding into what makes for effective programs from their perspectives and in turn help advise programs to be more responsive to youth needs. In addition, youth-directed approaches can engage youth through ongoing feedback loops to ensure that the programs are more well-aligned with youth needs and interests (Akiva, Cortina, & Smoth, 2014; Kirshner, O'Donoghue, & McLaughlin, 2002; Sabo, 2008).

According to Sabo (2008), "The activity of engaging youth in the evaluation process is more than a means of improving the quality of data or ensuring that particular constituents are heard; it is a process that mirrors and supports the tenets of positive youth development and leads to stronger and more appropriate programming" (p. 13).

For schools, in particular, research has highlighted the importance of youth voice in creating more vibrant school cultures (physical and social), informing school programs and events, contributing to school-level decision-making, and engaging in broader educational and school policy issues such as educational curriculum, school policies, expectations of youth, and racialized practices within schools (Aldana, Richards-Schuster, & Checkoway, 2015; Duncan-Andrade & Morrell, 2008; Johnston-Goodstar, 2013). Kirshner (2015) talks about the power of young people as partners in decision-making in schools, stating that in contrast to the traditional roles of young people as "recipients of services" that schools should be a "place where student voice is part of the fabric of institutional decision-making" (p. 4).

While there has been less research on the impact of youth-directed approaches on adults, there are some emerging studies to document this impact. These indicate that adults are more willing to listen to youth, are more reflective of their relationships with youth, and are more aware of youth needs as a result of their participation with youth (Zeldin, 2004).

Youth Participatory Action Research

Youth participatory action research (YPAR) is one example of a youth-directed approach that has direct benefits to organizations, schools, and communities. As noted, at its most basic it involves young people in the development of knowledge and the assessment of issues that impact their lives. Other related work is termed youth participatory evaluation (YPE), community-based participatory research with youth (CBPR with youth), and youth participatory action, research, and evaluation (YPARE). For the purposes of this chapter, we will refer to YPAR as the term for youth-directed research and evaluation. In such efforts, youth engage in systematic research and advocate for social change in their schools and community through action (Aldana et al., 2015; Cammarota & Fine, 2008; Morrell, 2006; Ozer et al., 2010). This form of youth-directed inquiry can include the evaluation of programs and organizations, assessment of needs and community issues, mapping or analysis of policy decisions, analysis of existing data, and research on critical issues of importance to young people.

YPAR is a particularly critical approach to youth engagement as it situates young people as being experts in their lives and puts a value on their expertise in the form of knowledge development. For example, Johnston-Goodstar

(2013) describes the power of YPAR approaches for "marginalized, racialized, and othered youth" (p. 318). In writing about indigenous youth, she describes how YPAR can be a tool to challenge stereotypes about who youth can be and offer them opportunities to use their knowledge and way of knowing as a powerful change tool. Ginwright and James (2002) describe YPAR as a way for youth to "contest, challenge, respond to, and negotiate the use and misuse of power in their lives" (p. 35).

Engaging young people in these ways challenges traditional conceptions about who can develop knowledge and how that knowledge is developed. Too often young people are recipients or subjects of research but rarely are they the directors or collaborators on research about young people. Thus, YPAR can be an alternative that opens up questions about power and positions of young people in a way to provide new perspectives, to critique traditional approaches or narratives, and to open up new possibilities for discussion, debate, and shared decision-making.

For young people of color, in particular, YPAR can have powerful developmental impacts on them. Ozer et al. (2010) state:

> PAR's emphasis on engaging marginalized groups in research and action as a means of achieving social justice and equity goals enhances the potential developmental relevance of PAR processes for ethnic minority youth. PAR processes that involve youth of color in analyzing and having an impact on the social, economic, and political conditions that shape their schools and communities provide key developmental opportunities for youth to appraise themselves as leaders with a meaningful sense of purpose. (p. 154)

As an approach, YPAR can build on concepts of empowerment and adds a critical lens that encourages and requires young people to be critical about the world around them. It involves young people asking questions and learning to be active consumers of knowledge. When done well, young people are engaged in the process in a meaningful and authentic way (not tokenized engagement), they learn to work with others, they raise their own awareness about key issues, and they use their learning to lead to collective action and change (Nygreen, Ah Kwon, & Sanchez, 2006).

While there are many positives, YPAR should also be viewed through a critical lens. In particular, YPAR can create negative impacts—potentially even disempowering experiences—when the process is not taken seriously by adults, in particular. YPAR can be tokenizing when young people are not actually given the power to use their voice and can lead to a feeling of frustration, anger, and resentment by young people. Ozer and colleagues (2013) describe the concept of "bounded empowerment" as that when young people's research is dismissed, ignored, or not acted on by adult stakeholders.

This can lead young people to be less engaged, less efficacious, or feel less agency in the future. For these reasons, it is critical that adults be prepared and able to navigate and negotiate power with young people. This is especially important in schools and other settings where there are more traditional adult-youth relationships. In these settings, YPAR and youth-directed approaches can be a challenge because they disrupt traditional norms and require adults to share power to young people.

Exploring the Process of Youth Participatory Action Research: Entering, Ongoing Engagement and Roles, and Exiting

YPAR involves a set of process steps, including asking questions, gathering information, analyzing information, and then using the data for change. The form of youth-direct inquiry is not research for the sake of research but rather it is research for change. Thus, a critical component of YPAR is using the research to lead to action with an eye toward change. For example, research can lead to the development of new programs, to recommendations for new policies, and new opportunities for youth voice and leadership around key issues in the community.

A first necessary step in YPAR and other youth-directed approaches is the explicit attention to relationships building, especially in the earliest stages of YPAR work (Winn & Winn, 2015b). This often occurs in the beginning or entering into a YPAR project, especially for adults or as Green (2013) suggests *adult allies*. Similarly to research projects that require cultivating relationships with participants, the entering and beginnings of YPAR should be done with caution and respect. One reason for such an approach is that some youth participants may be skeptical of adults and hesitant to work with them. For many adults, their relationships and daily interactions with youth are often connected to positions of authority or influence. Examples include teachers instructing students during school; coaches directing youth at practice; or parents deciding if their child should attend a social event. It is important that when beginning or entering a participatory action research project with youth, adults are cognizant of these relationships and willing to relinquish the need for deference, authority, or decision-making.

There are several ways in which adults initially engage in YPAR. Sometimes adults enter into existing youth-led projects. Youth participants of these projects invite adults to lend their expertise or support to help advance the project. There are also examples of when adults initiate collaborative projects with youth. For example, a university professor researching food deserts may collaborate with students to survey a community deprived of healthy food options. A third way adults enter into a YPAR project is when YPAR is co-created out of opportunities and then youth and adults negotiate the process. This is often the case of teachers and students working on a class project. At the conclusion of the class assignment, one solution is for some form of advocacy and the teachers and students begin to map out the process.

The ongoing roles of adults in participatory action research with youth vary throughout the process. Prior to establishing roles, there are a few helpful prerequisites for adults to consider; the list includes but is not limited to the following: a willingness to share decision-making; an openness to new ideas and approaches; refraining from being judgmental; and becoming familiar with the social and political concerns of the youth. All of these principles embody what Winn and Ubiles (2011) call "worthy witnessing." This is the process in which adults earn the trust and respect from students. "Worthy witnessing" is key to the formation of roles for adults.

Due to the collaborative nature of YPAR, there is no specific role that adults perform. The following are a few ways in which adults have participated in YPAR:

- Lead person to reserve and locate space for meetings
- Point person for establishing financial support to sustain the project
- Organizer of readings, trips, and meetings
- Contact lead for relationships with local universities, elected officials, etc.
- Editor and reviewer of final reports or presentations

In addition to the roles listed above, adults can also play important roles in helping to legitimize the work and be the voice of youth with other adults, in helping youth to push and refine their ideas, and helping young people see their voice as political and part of a larger process of creating change (Richards-Schuster & Timmermans, 2017). These roles are ongoing and always evolving.

Exiting a YPAR project often presents challenges. Since YPAR can extend anywhere from six months to over two years, youth and adults develop relationships and spend many hours together. For youth who come from historically marginalized communities and schools, learning that an adult will leave the group can be difficult. Programs, initiatives, and projects in these communities tend to phase out after funding ends or the intended impact or outcomes are either achieved or not met. If youth are engaged in a YPAR project and funding, connections, or resources leave with the adult, it perpetuates and reinforces problems associated with being under-resourced. The second challenge is for adults to transition away from the project and encourage the youth to take over and lead the work (Winn & Winn, 2015b). This is a result of either the youth not realizing their ability to lead the project without adults or the adults—especially researchers—not wanting to let go of the research project. Some adult researchers become very attached to the project, and it becomes more about their research than youth or community development goals.

2. Examples: Youth Participatory Action Research and Its Impact on Schools and Communities

In this section, we draw on our own experiences to provide a few examples of using YPAR as a youth-directed approach to inform program, school, and community changes.

The first example focuses on the work of young people in metropolitan Detroit, Michigan, to use research as a tool for a regional community change initiative. The second example highlights the work of the BOND program in Madison, Wisconsin, and its members' use of YPAR to change the narrative about their lived experiences and to improve their schools and communities. In each of these efforts, respectively, we played critical roles as adult allies to the youth projects, helping to support and guide the work of the youth in various ways.

Metropolitan Youth Policy Fellows

The Metropolitan Youth Policy Fellows (MYPF) was a multi-year project affiliated with the University of Michigan that engaged a diverse group of young people from across metropolitan Detroit in a large-scale assessment of the region on issues of school, community, and social justice across the region. The MYPF began as an outgrowth of a summer program run by the university that engages high school-aged young people in intergroup dialogues on race and ethnicity. A group of the participants continued to want to engage on issues and be part of a communitywide project to understand and assess social justice issues (Richards-Schuster & Brisson, 2016).

The group included 8–10 youth from several city neighborhoods and suburbs of Detroit. The group was diverse across race, ethnicity, SES, and gender. Their differences in social identities enabled them to think about the region through different lenses and different perspectives, which was an overall strength to the project.

With support from a community foundation that was interested in understanding youth issues from the perspective of young people, the group began meeting to discuss a strategy for the community assessment. Working with a set of adult advisors affiliated with the university, the initial meetings involved team building and discussions about the community and the region (Richards-Schuster & Timmermans, 2017). From these discussions, the youth developed a set of ideas to guide their assessment.

The adult advisors provided support to help the youth refine their ideas and developed skills for how to approach an assessment. The youth decided to develop an online survey so that they could reach as many young people in the region as possible. The assessment involved multiple sections on education, safety, access to youth opportunities and activities (local and regional), opportunities to have a voice in decision-making, transportation, and general perceptions about the region. The questions asked youth to reflect on their own experiences in their schools and communities as well as their ideas about the region and their recommendations and ideas for change.

Working through schools, community groups, and various networks, they cast a wide net to get young people involved in taking the survey. Their goal was to survey 500 young people and in the end they reached over 1,100. To help ensure that there was broad participation, the group did a network analysis to think about the voices that they wanted to reach and the best way to reach them. They worked through their own networks, but then also reached out to different groups that had networks (e.g., the community foundation's youth grantees, and regional organizations) to help reach more youth. The adult advisors also helped the youth to brainstorm ideas for outreach so that they could reach as far as possible and, when possible, encouraged other youth organizations to share with their networks.

They found that young people across the region felt that all young people should have an opportunity to have a voice in their communities, high-quality education, safe parks, and opportunities to engage with others from different communities (across racial and ethnic lines). They also heard about the damaging impact of the media on stereotyping young people and how those stereotypes impact young people's opportunities. To help further understand the ideas, the MYPF decided to conduct focus groups across the region on specific components of the survey including issues of education, civic engagement, and the role of the media. In total they conducted 8 focus groups around the region, with a total of approximately 50 youth participating.

The MYPF then met to analyze the findings and develop a way to share their learning and recommendations. The youth created a report and video to highlight their findings. The youth's video was shared with the community and led to a youth discussion about strategies to engage youth and act on youth issues. One of the strategies was to develop a fund to support youth-directed projects aimed at addressing the issues from the assessment.

The MYPF shared their findings at a youth summit attended by young people from across the region. At this summit, the MYPF encouraged the youth attendees to develop their own ideas for projects in their schools and community that would address the issues that emerged from the assessment.

The community foundation then created a special social justice youth grants project to support these youth-directed ideas. Youth teams were encouraged to apply for funding for small grants to support their project ideas. Examples of projects funded included the development of a youth-led assessment in one specific community, a program to support diversity education in the schools, a project to install a new basketball court to promote community recreation and well-being, a project to promote youth leadership in a community organization, and a project to generate a forum for community solutions within a neighborhood. Young people used their ideas to organize for new actions and to generate new solutions for issues in their community.

After the projects were awarded, the MYPF led trainings to support the youth leading change in their local schools and communities. The MYPF also began to share their experiences in the project more broadly. They worked on a book to highlight their own experiences in the region. They collaborated with the local Detroit PBS station on a television town hall to position youth voice in the region. They also created a tool kit to share their insights with others and have presented on their work at local and national conferences (Scrimger & Kumar, 2017). The MYPF also used their experience to leverage policy changes. They used their findings to advocate for youth rights at the state level and to engage with local policy makers around education and community issues.

While a youth project, there were different types of evaluation and documentation to capture the work, the learning, and emerging impacts. The youth grantees were all required to provide reports to document their learning and to respond to a survey about their impacts. In addition, the MYPF youth engaged in ongoing evaluation as part of their meetings, including their own debriefing, their own evaluation of their work, and their own understanding about their impact. The community foundation was also asked for their assessment of the impact of the project on the community and on the foundation. This work was captured in a written report and a video report of the project.

Some of the results of the MYPF's work are the actual activities that emerged as an outgrowth of the project. For example, through the work of the MYPF multiple youth-directed projects emerged. These projects encouraged local youth leadership, youth skill development, and led to (in some instances) long-standing projects that are still going on today. Evaluation of the project outcomes showcases that some of these projects led to change in communities, including in changing perceptions about young people and in changing opportunities for young people to have a voice (Richards-Schuster, 2017).

For the MYPF members, based on individual reflections, the experience of engaging in a regional assessment was transformative. The project not only impacted the youth but also challenged the supporting foundation and many organizations across the region to hear youth ideas and to support youth-directed projects (Richards-Schuster & Brisson, 2016).

The BOND

The BOND is a youth collective of 20 male participants ranging in ages from 14 to 18 years old. The youth are all African Americans who reside in one of the most impoverished communities in the Midwest according to the *Race to Equity Report: A Baseline Report on the State of Racial Disparities in Dane County* (2013). Many of them relocated to Madison, Wisconsin, with their families from larger urban areas like Chicago, Detroit, and Milwaukee. Similar to most people who migrated to this college town, the youth and their families moved for better schools, employment opportunities, and safe communities. However, upon arrival the youth's experiences did not meet their expectations. To their surprise, they encountered low expectations from teachers, lack of employment opportunities, and harassment from the police (Winn & Winn, 2015a).

In 2013, the Wisconsin Council on Children and Families (WCCF) released the *Race to Equity Report*, which confirmed the BOND members' experiences in their schools and communities. The *Report* highlighted profound and entrenched racial inequities in Madison contradicting everything that the liberal college town is known for being: progressive, highly educated, opportunity rich, racial harmony, and equity-centered. According to the *Race to Equity Report*, during the 2010–2011 academic year, only 50% of black high school students in Dane County graduated on time; 21% of black students were suspended from school compared to 2.3% of the county's white students; and black juveniles (ages 10–17) were arrested at a rate of six times that of white juveniles.

Shortly after the release of the *Race to Equity Report*, I (the first author) was introduced to the BOND through one of the local community mothers' groups. These mothers wanted me to discuss my career trajectory with the youth and the importance of work ethic, collaboration, and advocacy. They also wanted me to share the *Race to Equity Report* with the youth, since I was a co-author of the report. After presenting to the group, the youth invited me back to participate in further conversations as well as group activities, field trips, college visits, and sporting competitions. At several of the BOND weekly meetings, the group continued to read and discuss the *Race to Equity Report*. None of the youth were surprised. In fact, they said the numbers were old news. After four weeks of discussing the report and critically analyzing other policy briefs, members of the BOND wanted to change their experience and improve their communities. With the help of three adult advisors, the youth formed a research team to examine racial disparities in their schools and communities.

For two years, the youth conducted participatory action research. At the start of the project, several graduate students from the University of Wisconsin volunteered to teach a series of classes on research methods. The youth learned to write survey questions, conduct interviews, and analyze data. The

BOND narrowed its list of five questions down to two primary questions: (1) Why are there few black teachers in their schools? (2) Why do the police target black youth? These questions stemmed from their concern that the local district had less than 3% African American teachers when the African American student population was 18% and from a death of a high school friend who was fatally shot by the police.

The youth developed their protocol for the survey questions and mapped out a timeline. Each youth had a specific task and was held accountable for completing their assignment. The youth collected data by using participant observations, surveys, interviews, and artifacts. They attended school meetings, town hall forums, community events, and so on. They also collected data through surveys of 200 teachers, students, parents, youth workers, administrators, and police officers. For example, several BOND members met with the mayor of Madison several times to learn about his role in reducing the disparities. They also interviewed three African American police officers, the Director of Human Resources, and Assistant Superintendent for the local school district.

After a year of collecting and analyzing data the youth presented their findings at several conferences and school forums. For example, the youth traveled to Birmingham, Alabama, to present to over 100 mayors from cities such as Philadelphia, Minneapolis, and New Orleans. They also were keynote speakers at University of Wisconsin School of Social Work's annual conference. The youth were also featured in a documentary about their experiences and YPAR project.

Some of the changes that the BOND advocated that came to fruition included: the construction of a community park with a basketball court, free Wi-Fi, and more summer employment opportunities specifically for youth in their neighborhood. Their findings also brought awareness of the challenges of African American males in schools. The youth also realized how difficult it was to change other more politically charged problems. For example, the over-policing of their community continued and school discipline actions continued to disproportionately impact black males.

For many of BOND members who believed that the "system is fixed" (i.e., policies, laws, decisions, programs, and institutions working against black and brown people to benefit white people), YPAR gave them an opportunity to become civically engaged and a platform to make their concerns heard. They went from politically and socially marginalized to engaged change agents improving their community.

3. Benefits and Challenges to this Approach

Similar to other research methodologies, youth participatory action research has its share of benefits and challenges. Value-centered and equity-oriented scholars and practitioners embrace YPAR because it takes into account the histories, skills, and knowledge of both youth and adults collaborating for change (Fine, 2012; Morrell, 2006). One prominent benefit of YPAR is that the ideas and inputs of participants are valued and their experiences are humanized (Fine, 2012; Winn & Winn, 2015b). However, there are complexities and tensions when conducting YPAR. In this section, we highlight several benefits and challenges often identified by YPAR scholars and practitioners.

Benefits

Youth Matter. Central to the success of YPAR is the active role that youth play during the research process. YPAR elevates youth voice as an essential factor in selecting the issue, planning the research process, identifying the solution, and leading the proposed action for change. Unlike many other participatory approaches or events such as town hall forums and community engagement or organizing initiatives, YPAR is only effective when youth participation is equal to or greater than that of the adult allies. YPAR encourages youth participants to become more than students but critical researchers about their daily lives with the goal of identifying realistic solutions for dealing with the problems that they believe need to be addressed (Morrell, 2006). Their input, feedback, and guidance are critical to transforming their lives, community, and society as a whole.

Mutual Learning and Trust. Both youth and adult participants work together sharing and learning from each other. This requires authentic engagement of young people and necessitates a level of trust between youth and adults. For adults, understanding this process is critical and one that requires attention to power dynamics. Youth share their expertise about the latest social trends, issues, and new ways of thinking while adults offer their knowledge of systems, best ways to navigate potential hurdles, or connections to social networks. For example, the MYPF members described the adults as "coffee filters." In this role, adults refined the ideas and helped the ideas developed, but they didn't change their substance. They were the youths' ideas. In this way, adults and youth partner together in ways that encourage youth and adults to depend on and support one another. Throughout the process, participants begin to value each other's opinions and experiences. As a result, participants form relationships and build trust.

New Experiences. There are many new experiences for youth when conducting YPAR. They meet new people, learn about professions and careers, and build their social, cultural, community, and political capital. For example, when the BOND advocated for a new basketball court to provide additional safe and healthy activities, it required the youth participants to meet with the city council and the mayor as well as the city planners. This was the youth participants' first-time meeting at city hall and learning about the role the city council plays in the development of their community. This new experience gave them insights into the inner workings of city hall and local politics and possible career opportunities such as a city planner or accountant.

Honing of Life and Academic Skills. When conducting YPAR, youth learn how to think critically, research a problem, analyze data, and write an action plan. These skills can enhance their academic progress in schools and provide them with valuable tools needed to be successful in their future careers. For example, analyzing data for 3rd grade reading reports helps the youth learn to read charts and graphs. Similarly, the creation of a PowerPoint for a community presentation teaches the youth how to use the software and how to prepare for a presentation. Youth acquire these skills as a team as they work together for change.

Civic Engagement and Participation. Many YPAR projects involve reforming policy or eliminating discriminatory practices. When youth assume full participation in YPAR, they do not operate in isolation rather they work with others. YPAR requires participants to organize, mobilize, and advocate for their desired change. For example, youth participants of the MYPF were a collective of youth from across Detroit and the suburbs working together to reach youth all over the region. Their goal was to create a platform for youth to voice their concerns and solutions. The participants created their own media outlets to engage youth to discuss social issues and to leverage policy changes at the state level.

Collaborative Work. The design of YPAR projects encourages youth and adult participants to work together to brainstorm problems and map out the process. As noted previously, the nature of YPAR discourages individualism and instead promotes team efforts. It also eliminates distinctions between the researcher and researched and ensures that all participants are equitable partners in the work (Akom, Cammarota, & Ginwright, 2008). For example, the BOND participants each had several issues they wanted to examine. However, they all agreed to list the issues on a white board then vote for the top three issues. After they agreed on their top issues, they collectively came up with the interview questions and interviewee list. There were times when the youth disagreed throughout the process. In one case, in particular, they could not agree whether or not to interview the police because of their tenuous relationship with the law enforcement. The adult allies helped the youth think through this dilemma. They ultimately decided to include the police in the interview pool. Throughout this process the youth and adults, as equal partners, worked collectively to complete the task.

Collective Action. Working together as a team on the issue is only half of the process of YPAR. The second part of the process and a key benefit is collective action. After the participants have engaged in outlining the problem, designing the plan, and seeking information, they initiate an activity based on their research evidence. These activities or actions provide opportunities for participants to make the connection of their research to practice. They are able to witness the challenges and barriers and learn what works and what does not work. As a team, they can maximize their efforts and make a greater impact.

Challenges

Tokenized Experiences. One of the biggest challenges in this work is when youth participation projects are really token experiences for youth. Too often, youth-focused projects are led and dominated by adults in organizations and schools. While sometimes well-intentioned, many of these projects are adult-dominated or have prescribed goals and a set agenda leaving little input from the youth. Youth also experience teacher-driven or teacher-focused transactions in their schools depriving some youth of agency and creativity. This leads to a process in which young people cannot truly own or partner in the process. At worst, this leads to experiences where organizations and schools create inauthentic and tokenized youth-directed approaches.

Youth Owning the Process. Based on these experiences, YPAR can be a strange process because youth voice really matters and young people help drive the agenda. However, convincing youth to take ownership of the research project is difficult (Winn & Winn, 2015b). They often see adults as authoritative figures, who possess expertise, power, and decision-making. Overcoming these beliefs takes time, and trust must be cultivated. Youth participants also must learn to share their knowledge and be comfortable taking the lead. Although adult participants may introduce youth to research methods or their social networks, there are many assets that the youth bring to the group. For example, the youth may know how to use social media to conduct surveys; the youth may know the geographical layout of the community needed to create an asset map; or the youth may have direct contacts with possible interviewees. Getting the youth to own the process and to see themselves as equals is rooted in their past experiences but can be overcome by authenticity in the work. The issues, ideas, and action must be collective with no one voice dominating the process.

Little or No Change. After working diligently for months and even years on issues such as better lunches at the local high school, the end of police surveillance in an urban space, or more after school activities for youth, youth are hopeful for change. However, when or if the change they have advocated for is not realized their hopes in the power of civic engagement and advocacy can diminish. The BOND, for example, led to more summer employment opportunities; however, the youth's advocacy for police reform made very little difference. The prospect of no or limited change through YPAR can lead to tension and uneasiness. It is important throughout the process for the YPAR team to manage expectations and discuss the possibilities of the outcome.

Exiting the Project. Not only is it a challenge for the youth to take ownership of the project but also for adult researchers exiting the project becomes difficult. This begs the question: At what point does or can the adult researcher safely move on from the project? There are several concerns with exiting the project. First is the issue of sustainability. Some YPAR projects grow in size and become actual programs. If the researcher or several adults exit the project, a must plan in place to help the youth continue their research. Another issue with exiting is the trust built with the youth. Too often youth—especially youth from marginalized communities—build relationships with adults only to see the adult (in some cases programs or nonprofits) leave them. Just as building relationships is a benefit, leaving YPAR even for legitimate reasons can lead to disappointed youth participants.

4. Future Directions and Remaining Questions

YPAR has evolved from an unconventional and radical research methodology to one that is accepted as effective and culturally responsive. As demonstrated through the experiences of MYPF and the BOND, YPAR not only encourages youth participants and adults to collaborate to transform their communities, but it also creates opportunities that have enormous impact on the lives of the youth. Benefits for youth include new experiences such as meetings with policy makers or the mayor; relationships with adults allies; and acquisition of valuable skills. There are also the challenges such as adult advisors exiting the project, youth owning the research process, and little change happening after months and years of working for change.

As youth-directed approaches, such as YPAR, move beyond grassroots organizational spaces and become seen as a form of practice for large-scale nonprofits, schools, and more traditional youth development organizations, it is necessary for there to be critical discussion about the processes and outcomes.

For example, YPAR is a research method that is embraced now not only by the social activist researchers working to seek justice and humanize communities under siege (Fine, 2012) in grassroots organizations. Comprehensive middle and high schools, youth development nonprofits, and philanthropic organizations have taken interest in student-led participatory projects focused on community change.

In closing, we feel that as these approaches become acceptable practices to more traditional and mainstream groups, the following issues and questions are critical starting points for anyone considering engaging with youth-directed approaches:

1. *What happens when youth-directed projects raise issues or ideas that challenge schools, organizations, or communities?* Youth-directed approaches must center the voices of youth and help youth amplify their ideas. When their voices challenge the status quo, adults need to be prepared to support the youth and to help open spaces for young people's ideas to be listened to by others.
2. *How are youth-directed projects supported financially?* What impact could funding from foundations, government, and schools have on the autonomy of youth-directed and YPAR projects? In our projects the experiences were mixed. MYPF had assistance from a foundation that willingly supported youth voice. In BOND's case, there were attempts to suppress the BOND's research into police harassment. Several police officers threatened the youth that any money given to them by city government would be taken away. More understanding about funding and the impact of funding is needed as youth-directed projects move forward.
3. *What training is needed to support youth-directed approaches to be successful?* Often training focuses on what young people need, but we also know that adults need training to work as allies to young people. Where does this training occur? How do organizations, groups, and schools ensure that adults are able to authentically support youth directed practices?
4. *What additional resources can be leveraged to support youth-directed projects?* For example, what are the ways in which universities, colleges, nonprofits, and philanthropic organizations support youth-directed and YPAR projects? How can universities and/or other community organizations help to support the efforts, provide guidance and training, and amplify the work of youth?
5. *What future resources could and should be leveraged to sustain youth-directed approaches?* How does this work move from one-off projects to multi-year efforts that are embedded into the fabric of the community?
6. *As youth-directed approaches become more mainstream, does this neutralize the impact and power of marginalized youth advocating for racial, economic, and social justice?* How do YPAR and other youth-directed approaches ensure that those young people that most need to be heard have a voice and can advocate for justice in their schools and community? How can YPAR be

maintained as a space for critical consciousness, for building power, and for critiquing the systems of oppression in schools and communities?

References

Akiva, T., Cortina, K., & Smoth, C. (2014). Involving youth in program decision making: How common and what might it do for youth? *Journal of Youth and Adolescence, 43*, 1844–1860.

Akom, A. A., Cammarota, J., & Ginwright, S. (2008). Youthtopias: Towards a new paradigm of critical youth studies. *Youth Media Reporter, 2*(4), 1–30.

Aldana, A., Richards-Schuster, K., & Checkoway, B. (2015). Dialogic pedagogy for participatory action research: Facilitation of an intergroup youth leadership program. *Social Work with Groups, 39*(4), 339–358.

Cammarota, J., & Fine, M. (2008). *Revolutionizing education: Youth participatory action research in motion.* New York: Routledge.

Checkoway, B., & Richards-Schuster, K. (2003). Young people's participation in research and evaluation. *American Journal of Evaluation, 24*(1), 21–33.

Checkoway, B., Richards-Schuster, K., Abdullah, S., Aragon, M., Facio, E., Figueroa, L., . . . Welsh, M. (2003). Young people as competent citizens. *Community Development Journal: An International Forum, 38*(4), 298–309.

Duncan-Andrade, J., & Morrell, E. (2008). *The art of critical pedagogy: Possibilities for moving from theory to practice in urban schools.* New York: Peter Lang.

Fine, M. (2012). Resuscitating critical psychology for "Revolting" times. *Journal of Social Issues, 68*(2), 416–438.

Finn, J. L., & Checkoway, B. (1998). Young people as competent community builders: A challenge to social work. *Social Work, 43*, 335–345.

Ginwright, S., & James, T. (2002). From assets to agents of change: Social justice, organizing, and youth development. *New Directions for Youth Development, 96*, 27–46.

Ginwright, S. A., Noguera, P., & Cammarota, J. (Eds.). (2006). *Beyond resistance!: Youth activism and community change: New democratic possibilities for practice and policy for America's youth.* New York: Routledge.

Green, K. (2013). Doing double Dutch methodology: Playing with the practice of participant observer. In D. Paris & M. T. Winn (Eds.), *Humanizing research, decolonizing qualitative inquiry with youth and communities* (pp. 147–160). Thousand Oaks, CA: SAGE.

Johnston-Goodstar, K. (2013). Indigenous youth participatory action research: Re-visioning social justice for social work with indigenous youths. *Social work, 58*(4), 314–320.

Kirshner, B. (2015). *Youth activism in an era of educational inequality.* New York: New York Press.

Kirshner, B., O'Donoghue, J. L., & McLaughlin, M. W. (Eds.). (2002). *Youth participation: Improving institutions and communities* (No. 96). San Francisco, CA: Jossey-Bass Inc Pub.

London, J. (2000). *Research, evaluation, and planning: The experiences of youth in focus*. Las Vegas: Focal Point.

Morrell, E. (2006). *Youth participatory action research as critical pedagogy: Lessons from practices*. AERA Annual Conference presentation.

Noguera, P., Ginwright, S., & Cammarota, J. (Eds.). (2013). *Beyond resistance: Youth activism and community change: New democratic possibilities for policy and practice for America's youth*. New York: Routledge.

Nygreen, K., Ah Kwon, S., & Sanchez, P. (2006). Urban youth building community. *Journal of Community Practice, 14*(1), 107.

Ozer, E., Newlan, S., Douglas, L., & Hubbard, E. (2013). "Bounded" empowerment: Analyzing tensions in the practice of youth-led participatory research in urban public schools. *American Journal of Community Psychology, 52*, 13–26.

Ozer, E., Ritterman, M. & Wanis, M. (2010). Participatory Action Research (PAR) in middle schools: Opportunities, constraints and key processes. *American Journal of Community Psychology, 46*, 152–166.

Richards-Schuster, K. (2017). *Youth voices for social justice: Final evaluation report*. Ann Arbor, MI: Author.

Richards-Schuster, K., & Brisson, K. (2016). Strengthening youth leadership in a metropolitan region: Examining lessons from a multi-year community foundation initiative. *Foundation Review*. doi:10.9707/1944-5660.1310

Richards-Schuster, K., & Dobbie, D. (2011). Tagging walls and planting seeds: Creating spaces for civic action. *Journal of Community Practice, 19*(3), 234–251.

Richards-Schuster, K., & Timmermans, B. (2017). Conceptualizing the role of adults in youth social justice work: An example from practice. *Children & Youth Service Review, 81*, 284–292.

Sabo, K. (2008). *Youth participatory evaluation: Strategies for engaging young people*. San Francisco: Wiley.

Scrimger, J., & Kumar, A. (2017). Metropolitan Youth Policy Fellows—American Evaluation Association AEA 365 Blog Post.

Winn, L. T., & Winn, M. T. (2015a). Expectations and realities: Education, the discipline gap, and the experiences of black families migrating to small cities. *Race and Social Problems, 7*, 73–83.

Winn, L. T., & Winn, M. T. (2015b). "We want this to be owned by you": The promise and perils of youth participatory action research. In S. Greene (Eds.), *Youth voices, public spaces, and civic engagement*. New York: Routledge.

Winn, M. T., & Ubiles, J. R. (2011). Worthy witnessing: Collaborative research in urban classrooms. In A. Ball & C. Tyson (Eds.), *Studying diversity in teacher education*. New York: Rowman & Littlefield.

Wisconsin Council on Children and Families. (2013). *Race to equity: A baseline report on racial disparities in Dane County*. Retrieved from http://racetoequity.net/dev/wp-content/uploads/WCCF-R2E-Report.pdf

Zeldin, S. (2004). Youth as agents of adult and community development: Mapping the process and outcomes of youth engaged in organizational governance. *Applied Developmental Science, 8*(2), 75–90.

Zimmerman, K., & London, J. (2003). Getting to go: Building organizational capacity to engage in youth-led research, evaluation, and planning. *CYD Journal, 4*(1), 19–25.

CHAPTER SEVENTEEN

Practical Guidance for Policy and Practice

Strategies and Tools for Assessing and Building Readiness and for Launching Local Efforts

Robert V. Mayo and Deborah A. Moroney

The purpose of a policy is to create a set of agreed upon practices, strategies, conditions for implementing high-quality systemic social, emotional, behavioral, and mental supports a priority. A policy is simply the road map or guidance to implementing a practice toward a shared purpose. Policy adoption and implementation occurs at many levels. For example, the federal government enacts a law, like the newly signed education law entitled the Every Student Succeeds Act (ESSA), which has policy ramifications at the federal, state, and local level. Ultimately, it is up to the end user—or implementer in this case—the people in a state or local education agency to define and determine how a big "P" policy will be enacted in a school through local policies. The little "p" policies at the district, community, and school level ultimately define and determine how a school or community will be able to best implement successful practices.

Throughout these volumes, the authors presented a discussion of the history and research base, systems, strategies, and practices that keep students safe and help them thrive. In this chapter, we present practical guidance for policy and practice implementation at the local level, and we provide strategies and tools for assessing and building readiness for launching local efforts. Policy implementation can be tricky because historically, crafting and implementing policies have been top-down, as opposed to bottom-up approaches; this has made successful implementation of a policy challenging at best (Matland, 1995). We have all sat in a room when a new initiative is being launched and the implementers are the last to know. The very actors who are so critical to implementing the policy then view it as yet another thing that will ultimately pass. One can imagine that their commitment to the success of the activity is not as high as it would be had they been asked and included in the decision to adopt the policy, and how it would be enacted. Another challenge to policy implementation is when the people in the school building are included and excited to implement a new policy, but the time or resources are not available to make it a success. This is what is often referred to as an unfunded mandate. Something that is required, but not supported. Typically unfunded mandates are not looked upon favorably and implementation is challenged from the start. These factors of *buy-in* and *readiness* are all key to successful policy implementation. In this chapter, we present a collaborative approach to policy implementation that can help alleviate or even avoid known policy implementation pitfalls.

A bottom line for all of this is to *not* be that town, city, county, or region that has to experience some sort of disconnect or territorial political jockeying-laden tragedy before developing and implementing high-quality systemic social, emotional, behavioral, and mental supports. The following sections are organized around the stages of crafting policies and implementing strategies to address the policy. Those stages are: creating a shared vision, planning via authentic stakeholder engagement, assessing readiness, implementation, scaling for sustainability, and continuous improvement. This chapter focuses on the first five aforementioned stages. Each section addresses an important step in the policy to implementation process and provides related resources, tools, tips, and key questions to consider. Volume 2, Chapter 18, "Getting to Outcomes: Planning, Continuous Improvement, and Evaluation," addresses continuous improvement practices and strategies in greater detail.

Creating Shared Vision

Policy and practice reform is complex work. Embarking upon this work without an authentically shared vision makes it all the more difficult and less likely to be successful.

Recent theories and strategies on creating a shared vision are grounded in the seminal literature on visionary leadership, education reform, and organizational change theory. The need for a shared vision is critically important because interagency collaboration is intrinsic to implementing a new policy. While there are numerous definitions and descriptions of vision and shared vision, the common themes of creating a shared vision include clarity, inclusiveness, cohesion, direction, and projection. Manasse (1986) defines vision as "the force that molds meaning for the people of an organization" (p.150). Seeley (1992) describes vision as a "goal-oriented mental construct that guides people's behavior." Nanus (1992) offers that vision serves as "a signpost pointing the way for all who need to understand what the organization is and where it intends to go" (p.8). Nanus (1992) goes on to describe the "right vision" as possessing the following five key characteristics:

- *Attracts* commitment and energizes people
- *Creates* meaning in workers' lives
- *Establishes* a standard of excellence
- *Bridges* the present to the future
- *Transcends* the status quo

Creating a shared vision is a widely held crucial first step to authentic change. Dedicated leadership plays a critical role in developing and promoting a shared vision, keeping everyone motivated throughout the change process, and advancing systems change (National Technical Assistance and Evaluation Center for Systems of Care, 2016). This imperative goes well beyond a shared vision's symbolic potential. A thoughtful, clearly articulated shared vision helps frame the "why" of the implementation of policy and practice reform for all stakeholders involved. This is a particularly powerful point in customer-driven fields like mental health services, education, child and family welfare, and the like. A collaboratively developed shared vision can also go a long way toward mitigating potential conflict around some of the new and difficult aspects associated with the evolution of policy and practice change over time. Conversely, not doing so can open the door to unnecessary acrimony and general disconnect from the onset. These less than ideal conditions often make an already complex systems change process more difficult—if not far less likely to gain traction in an authentic manner.

A Collaborative Approach to Developing a Shared Vision

Méndez-Morse (1993) synthesized the literature on organizational vision amidst change and offers key leadership steps for developing a shared vision that will be used to help frame how to approach this very important initial phase. These steps include (1) *know each stakeholder*, (2) *involve critical individuals*, (3) *explore the possibilities*, (4) *build shared vision*, and (5) *put it in writing*. The National Technical Assistance and Evaluation Center for Systems of Care (2016) offers a number of leadership strategies and tips that align with the seminal literature on developing shared visions. Let's breakdown what this could and should look like in action.

Know Each Stakeholder

Context is everything, including that of service delivery organizations and the youth, families, and communities they serve. Fully understanding the mission, vision, and overarching purposes and needs of all of the stakeholders involved in collective efforts to ensure that youth are mentally, emotionally, and physically safe is key. The same holds true for authentic assessment of individual and collective strengths and weaknesses. Doing so allows the collective to identify commonalities and potential disconnect early in the change process, including the absence of other important partners. This exercise can also facilitate the identification of overlaps and gaps in policies, procedures, practices, and systemic service delivery. Some initiatives might find it most useful to map resources in this phase. Others could opt to engage in resource mapping during the next phase—planning and stakeholder engagement.

Tips and Key Questions to Consider

Consider utilizing neutral consultants for facilitation of visioning meetings. External parties are in some ways better positioned to engage stakeholder in problem-solving activities that often involve addressing tough questions and confronting assumptions (National Technical Assistance and Evaluation Center for Systems of Care, 2016).

Get to know as much as possible about each service delivery organization and service consumer stakeholder group and the context in which they work, and live in the case of youth and families, from the onset.

- What are the leadership and organizational structures of agencies and community-based partners?
- What is each stakeholder's overarching charge and/or frame of reference?
- How do these purposes align with the working purpose of the collective group?
    - How are they not aligned?
- What is the locus for the desired policy and practice changes?
    - What federal, state, and local laws guide their work?

  - What are their respective political contexts? What are their core functions, outputs and outcomes?
- How is each stakeholder's success and effectiveness measured?
- What are the high level needs of the youth, families, and communities served?
- What are the policy, practice, procedural, and perceptual obstacles to accessing and benefiting services from youths' and families' perspectives?

Assess each stakeholder's buy-in level early and often.

- How did they arrive to the change initiative at hand?
  - Willingly?
  - Under political pressure?
  - Due to a glaring need?
- Are key leaders fully invested in the change at hand?
  - Why or why not?
- Who are the most passionate partners and why?

Assess individual and collective strengths and weaknesses early and often.

- What are each stakeholder's strengths and weaknesses?
- What is the ecology of each stakeholder?
- What makes them tick?
- What keeps leaders up at night?
- Are they well resourced?
- How data-driven are they?

Involve Critical Individuals

Méndez-Morse (1993) offers that the individuals or groups identified as constituencies should include those that are the most critical to the policy and practice changes at hand. Put another way, it is extremely important to strategically ensure that the right people are at the table—ideally inclusive of those with formal decision-making and supervisory authority within their respective organizations (or those closest to those in authority) and frontline service provider representation (National Technical Assistance and Evaluation Center for Systems of Care, 2016).

The youth and family support arena inherently dictates the need for systemic multi-stakeholder collaboration. These key entities include, but are not limited to:

- School districts
- Local schools
- Youth
- Families
- Youth and family support agencies
- Community-based mental health providers
- Other key community members
- Advocates
- Policy makers
- Unions
- Law enforcement
- Juvenile justice.

Addressing the charges, ideals, and competing priorities of several organizations through the shared vision development process and beyond can be very complex. This is especially true when potentially tough topics such as accountability, collaboration, and data sharing are concerned. Who gets credit for the success? Who shares the blame when things don't go as planned? The deeper involvement of critical individuals representing key stakeholders often presents challenges to the development of a shared vision.

Rogus (1990) suggests that one approach is to have representatives from each stakeholder group write ideas before a meeting. Then as a group methodically identify consensus statements first and then work through areas of non-consensus. Consensus being defined as the absence of serious disagreement, not necessarily total agreement among all involved on every aspect of the matter at hand. Some have found it useful to continuously ground this process in what's best for the students and families they serve. Doing so can mitigate potential disagreement and make consensus building a bit easier when things get sticky.

Tips and Key Questions to Consider

Ensure that key partners, including youth and families, are at the table.

- Who are all key partners?
- Are all of them at the table?
- Are decision makers or those closest to them at the table?

- What are the obstacles to any missing key partners' participation?
    - How can these be addressed?
- Are key stakeholders such as youth, family and community members authentically involved on the partnership level?

Collaboratively and constructively assess and address barriers to consensus building by focusing on goals, not issues—facts, not opinions.

- Are there any major obstacles to consensus building?
- How can they be constructively and collaboratively addressed?
- What's "in it" for each organization and the youth they serve beyond the obvious?
- Do the areas of consensus set the group up for success in the way of reaching its common goals?

Explore the Possibilities

This is the point to dream big and think outside existing boxes and silos in the name of what's best for youth and families—even if some may be initially uncomfortable with some changes at hand. This exercise also allows stakeholders to formally acknowledge what is working well and confirm what service delivery could and should look like in the future, taking recent trends into account in this process. Manasse (1986) also advocates for considering future developments and trends that may affect the initiative(s) at-hand and the youth being served. Méndez-Morse (1993) offers that possible major changes in the economic, social, political, and technological arenas that will impact youths and the support structures around them be explored. Analyzing recent demographic and data trends is an important part of exploratory activities as well. Current data can confirm what is going well, validate known emergent needs, and bring other important needs to the forefront.

Tips and Key Questions to Consider

Dream BIG on the behalf of the most important stakeholders—youth, families and communities.

- What are the common, and aspirational, yet attainable win-win goals of the collective?
- What are the ideal major implications for establishing and sustaining a shared vision for change?
- What promising approaches have like-situated regions utilized?
- What were the key ingredients for success?

- What stakeholders are already collaborating and on what level?
- If certain stakeholders should be partnering on a high level but aren't, what are the obstacles preventing this?

Do your research to find the most current and compelling data to back up the problems and solutions, and add real life situations to exemplify both. Be data-driven in articulating collective goals, outputs, outcomes, and measures.

- What are the emergent needs of the youths, families, and communities being served?
- What possible changes in social, economic, political, or technological areas will impact individual and collective service delivery and support?
- What do recent demographic and data trends tell the collective?
- Broaden the pool of information by holding stakeholder focus groups to collect information about the issue (e.g., youth, families, direct service providers, agency leads, site- and district-level leaders)

Revisit or develop logic models that depict how the collective intends to achieve its vision via implementing planned activities, and mark progress through measurable outputs, outcomes, and short- and long-term goals attainment (National Technical Assistance and Evaluation Center for Systems of Care, 2016).

Avoid Avoidance.

- Are there important areas that haven't been considered yet?
- Have any essential topics been avoided thus far?
    - If so, why?
    - How can the sensitive areas be collaboratively and constructively explored even if uncomfortable for some stakeholders?
    - Should an outside facilitator be involved?

Build the Shared Vision and Put It in Writing

Méndez-Morse (1993) posits that a shared vision can be a powerful motivator. At the same time, she cautions that leaders' visions aren't always shared by those below them. Some might add that top-down visions that are developed in isolation without key stakeholder input and handed down are most susceptible to low or limited buy-in from those closest to the work. The same holds true for the youth, families, and communities that stand to benefit from improved service delivery. This last point serves to reiterate the essential nature of including these key stakeholders in an authentic fashion throughout each phase of policy and practice change efforts.

Senge (1990) describes a "shared vision" as what members of an organization want to create or accomplish as part of an organization and offers that creating a shared vision begins with creative tension. Creative tension is defined as emerging from individuals and organizations having an honest awareness of the way things are or how things currently work as opposed to a vision of what could or should be. These can be very tough discussions that require authentic reflection on and ownership of the good, the bad, and the ugly. Some groups have found it effective to have a trained expert facilitator lead these semi-structured discussions in neutral settings. Doing so allows an unaffiliated individual to probe for clarity, specificity, and depth and explore necessary topics that may be otherwise avoided.

According to Senge (1990), creative tension can be resolved in one of two major ways. The first is by ascending the current reality toward the vision. The second is by watering down the vision toward the current reality. Clearly the former is the ideal, albeit potentially more uncomfortable for those involved due to the need for authentic individual and collective ownership for the current state of affairs and subsequent needs of policy, procedural, and practice change.

The capstone of the shared vision development process is the articulation of a clear and concise vision statement. This statement should succinctly capture the essence of what has been discussed, discovered, and decided upon in earlier steps.

Rogus (1990) suggests using the consensus statements from the previous step to:

- Develop a draft of the vision statement
- Gather a final round of key stakeholder reactions
- Collectively decide upon and memorialize the final version

Hopefully most of the consensus has been gained at this point. However, there may be a need for further consensus building around the vision statement's exact language, points of emphasis, and overarching ideals and outcomes as manifested in the emergent logic model.

Tips and Key Questions to Consider

Make it plain. Specifically:

- What is the aspirational, yet attainable vision?
- What are the core values, beliefs, and/or ideals behind it?

- What are the core inputs, outputs and outcomes?
- Who are the specific primary change agents and beneficiaries?

Sample Tools and Resources

National Technical Assistance and Evaluation Center for Systems of Care Resources. https://www.childwelfare.gov/topics/management/reform/soc/communicate/initiative/ntaec/

Community Tool Box: Workgroup for Community Health and Development, University of Kansas. https://ctb.ku.edu/en

Participatory Asset Mapping: A Community Research Lab Toolkit, The Advancement Project (2012). http://www.communityscience.com/knowledge4equity/AssetMappingToolkit.pdf

Planning via Authentic Stakeholder Engagement

Collaboratively developing a shared vision or statement sets the stage for the next important phase—planning through ongoing authentic stakeholder engagement. At times, the mistake of allowing authentic stakeholder engagement to taper off after the creation of shared vision and mission is made. The likelihood of all of the important "nooks and crannies" being identified and addressed up to this point is small. When carried out correctly, the planning phase allows the collective group to develop an overarching implementation plan that:

- Assesses the perceived needs per key stakeholders
- Exploits and builds upon individual and collective strengths
- Acknowledges and addresses identified individual and collective weaknesses and related obstacles
- Acknowledges and addresses overlaps and gaps in systemic high-quality service delivery, and
- Takes all of the above into strong consideration en route to planning for sustainability.

Zaff and colleagues (2015) present a sound argument for the importance of the alignment of perceived needs and a clear example of how stakeholders can have divergent perceptions of the needs that should be high priorities for youth-focused comprehensive community initiatives. The authors posit that the identification of alignments and misalignments of needs perceptions among key comprehensive community initiatives (CCIs) stakeholders is very important to planning and implementing youth-focused community-based efforts. For example, their key findings include notable misalignment between service recipients, direct service providers, and initiative leadership. They also found that direct service providers and families had the most alignment, while the least alignment was between leadership and families.

Green and Aarons (2011) provide another strong case for comparing and contrasting stakeholder perceptions when planning and implementing evidence-based practices. An important foundational note is the recognition that certain priorities may be perceived as more or less important, depending upon one's vantage point (e.g., agency, unit, service recipient vs. provider, proximity to policy and actual practice, etc.). This is a particularly important point given that children and families are at times recipients of services from providers in multiple sectors. They also reiterate the importance of decision-makers' involvement given their potential to affect critical issues such as funding amidst competing priorities.

The researchers assessed differences in policy and practice stakeholder perspectives on what it takes to implement evidence-based practices (EBPs). Factors that rose to the top of this study included concerns about the strength of the evidence base, limited financial and human resources, effects on clinical practice, consumer concerns about quality and stigma, and potential burden associated with new types of services and general approaches to service delivery. Key findings evidenced significant agreement between administrators or policy makers and those involved in direct practice.

Assessing stakeholder perceptions sets the stage for more strategic and informed implementation and sustainability planning. Exploration and adoption are the planning-related terms used within the implementation science literature to describe the early stages. It is highly likely that obstacles to successful implementation come up during these early stages. Addressing previously identified and other predictable obstacles as early as possible can mitigate some stakeholder concerns and at the same time allow stakeholders to strategize on how to address obstacles that are more malleable and controllable.

Addressing Prevalent Obstacles to Successful Implementation Early

There are a number of known obstacles to successful implementation and related strategies that have been noted as showing promise in addressing them early in the planning phase. Rolewski (2008) outlines the following prevalent obstacles to implementing evidence-based practices. While this list is by no means exhaustive, it does capture a number of potentially problematic areas for policy makers, leaders, and direct service providers.

- Funding
- Cost or availability of training for a program
- Insufficient professional development
- Red tape
- Buy-in
- Resistance to change
- Egos
- Time
- Unions
- Contracts

Funding, Training, and Professional Development

Now for a few strategies aimed at addressing these and related barriers to change. Competing priorities are a harsh reality, whether talking about staffing, time, or funding—particularly in the public sector. Moreover, youth and family mental, social, and behavioral health supports are all too often the first to go in tough fiscal times. This reality makes formal advocacy for the shared vision all the more important. This includes making the specific needs being addressed, programs, strategies, benefits, and efficiencies clear to key decision makers, direct service providers, and the constituents they serve.

Rolewski (2008) offers that funding-related barriers often require organizations to revisit existing budgets and make tough decisions around making cuts in other areas to make room for new programming, or the deepening or expansion of initiatives that either have been evidenced to be effective or show great promise. Revisiting budgets also provides organizations the opportunity to reevaluate the effectiveness of programming and eliminate those found to be minimally effective or ineffective. "Such [fiscal] concerns must not be overlooked when implementing EBPs in public sector settings, and may be addressed by higher policy level initiatives that have the power to change factors that appear unalterable at the agency and practitioner levels" (Green & Aarons, 2011, p. 112). The same holds true for securing and protecting professional development funding. All trainings are not created equal, both quality and availability wise. Highly sought-after trainers can be very costly, which at times only limits them to one-offs. Many agencies take the "train the trainer" approach, which has great potential to build internal capacity in key areas of need, decrease costly staff turnover, and set the stage of sustainability. Building internal capacity can also give practitioners opportunities to exhibit leadership skills and inform professional development activities with important local and organizational context.

In an ideal world, all new hires would already possess the knowledge, skill sets, and dispositions that align with the current direction of the hiring agency or organization. Although next to impossible, this elusive ideal does point to the need for targeted and deliberate recruitment, screening, interviewing, hiring, and onboarding policies and procedures. Put another way, in theory the more equipped staff and leaders are, the less "training up" will be needed (completely new undertakings aside, of course). Moreover, why set the organization up for spending unnecessary time and energy trying to convince those who may not possess desirable dispositions for the work in the first place (e.g., client-driven service delivery, child/youth/family/community-centered, belief in individual and collective efficacy, etc.)?

Securing federal or private funding for new initiatives is another route, although sustainability beyond the life of these funding sources will be an issue that requires forethought in planning. Integrating or braiding multiple funding streams has also been found to be an effective funding approach, yet it too requires sustainability planning for similar reasons (i.e., how can efforts be sustained after funding periods?). Monitoring, evaluating, and disseminating information about an initiative's effectiveness can serve a related purpose. Policy makers and decision makers often utilize data to determine what gets funded or cut and on what levels. Sharing individual and collective milestones and achievements go a long way in showing important stakeholders the value added of an initiative or program. For instance, highlighting positive data in conjunction with real-life success stories coming directly from youth and family constituents can be a powerful approach—particularly at formal budget, performance, and accountability oversight hearings.

In tight fiscal times, it is also important to show any cost-savings or organizational efficiencies realized due to the initiative (actual or projected). Doing so can help key decision makers better serve as champions and give them the information they need to advocate in circles that practitioners likely have limited access to at best. Success stories can also turn skeptics into believers when the data and related stories are compelling. An example of this is comparing the *upfront investments* of mental, social, emotional, and behavioral preventions and interventions to the *long-term costs* associated with juvenile justice, adult correctional facilities, probation services, associated legal costs, and so on.

Streamlining red tape tends to be a more high-level organizational issue. Addressing unnecessary red tape requires leaders, decision makers, and public and private funders to revisit the necessity and efficiency of policies and procedures deemed by professionals to serve minimal purpose aside from slowing down collective progress. As noted earlier, it is very important to know each organization's internal policies and procedures that can affect individual and collective progress, positively or negatively.

Resistance to Change, Egos, and Buy-In

Resistance to change and professional egos take on many shapes, forms, and fashions and can manifest in those at any career stage. Although, some would say that while egos and resistance to change don't necessarily go hand-in-hand, they are more likely to manifest with mid- to late-career professionals who have been around long enough to know a lot (or at least think that they do) and become settled-into how things are done (likely because it's how they've "always been done").

Rolewski (2008) suggests that organizations, agencies, and units should operate in a process-based fashion that focuses on the good of the team, not that of any individuals. He further offers that performance goals can still be met in process-based organizations, even in the face of some turnover. Of course, too much turnover is likely to undermine even the most well-resourced initiatives. Tapping internal practitioners to take on leadership roles and responsibilities can also lead to increased buy-in, and perhaps even stem the tide of high turnover (a major fidelity obstacle) among professionals in some situations.

The author also speaks to a "cutting the head of the snake" type approach, in the way of enlisting the active support and authentic effort of naysayers under the auspices of the team notion and the importance of his or her buy-in and leadership to collective success. This sounds very similar to somewhat risky approaches wherein a leader "flips the script" so to speak by giving the skeptic a leadership role in the effort. The theory here is that the team facing leadership opportunity will undermine (if not outweigh) the skepticism. A leader must be very careful in deciding if and when to take these approaches. He or she must have sufficient social capital and decision-making authority should things go awry. Either way, the leader may have to be prepared to part ways with naysayers—even if top performers—should active or passive resistance continue to the point where leadership and the overall group effort are being undermined.

Green and Aarons (2011) suggest that increased communication from the onset may lead to a better understanding of, or perhaps even empathy for, different stakeholders' perspectives and increased buy-in. Deeper understanding across stakeholder groups may in turn lead to better collaboration among different levels of stakeholders, improved service delivery, and result in more positive implementation outcomes.

One of the major points shared by Green and Aarons (2011) is that each factor can be considered a *facilitator* or *barrier* to EBP implementation to the degree that the issues are effectively addressed. Using funding as an example, they offer that funding is a *facilitator* when sufficient to support training, infrastructure, and fidelity monitoring, but would be considered a *barrier* if not sufficient to meet these and other common issues for EBP implementation.

Unions and Contracts

To put it plainly, it is absolutely critical to involve union representatives throughout the change process. Not for its mere symbolic potential, but out of respect for the essential nature of authentic union involvement. This is especially important when planning and implementing policy and practice changes that significantly change what practitioners do, how they do it, when they do it, and why they do it. Improvements in direct service delivery often require memorialization in the form of contract changes, which can easily bleed into tough compensation-related negotiations.

Moreover, those closer to the work often have valuable insights that can enhance the likelihood of successful and scalable implementation of youth support services. Direct service providers are far more likely to be aware of frontline facilitators and obstacles to real change that can be acknowledged, if not exploited or addressed, early in the planning process. These experiential insights may not readily lend themselves to those farther removed from direct service delivery. Conversely, not including direct services providers and their union leaders sends a clear negative message to the masses as to others' low belief in their individual and collective value. Ignoring hardworking professionals also has the great potential to breed additional naysayers and lead to unnecessary turnover in the process. These are serious buy-in killers.

It is important that all key stakeholders know that their voices have been *heard and considered* throughout the change process—even if some decisions are made contrary to their opinions or desires. In cases of the latter, ensuring that key stakeholders understand the rationale behind these decisions and the positive impacts intended for the most important stakeholder—the youth, families, and communities they serve. On a related note, some of the higher-level political and budgetary realities may not be on practitioners' radars. Sensitizing direct service providers to some of these realities can both increase their general awareness of the greater context within which they work, increase buy-in, and allay other unfounded concerns born of a lack of said knowledge.

Green and Aarons (2011) suggest that tailoring messaging to attend to the needs of distinct stakeholders is a strategy to address perceptual obstacles and increase buy-in.

> Tailoring content and delivery method of EBP and related implementation information for particular stakeholders may promote more positive attitudes toward implementation of change in service models. For example, highlighting positive personal experiences along with research results of EBP on clinical practice may be an effective strategy for practitioners, administrative staff, and consumers; however, policy makers may be more

swayed by presentations of long-term cost effectiveness data for EBPs (Green and Aarons, 2011, p. 112).

Tips and Key Questions to Consider

Equip and empower all stakeholders with information and tools necessary for success.

- Create fact sheets and or position papers that describe the issue, background, group's position, and the action required.
- Locate financial resources that could be used for advocacy.
- Provide training for all members of the group (e.g., what is the process for getting a piece of legislation passed, what will effective implementation look like, what specific changes are being sought and why).
- Host public gatherings that create awareness of the group's purpose.

Anticipate and strategically plan for the predictable to the extent possible (i.e., expect success, plan for barriers).

- Have the anticipated major changes in service delivery level policy, procedures, and practices that will come with implementing the new policy been considered and addressed?
    - What are the existing obstacles to improving service delivery?
    - Which of these are within the group or organization's relative control?
    - What steps can be taken to address these barriers?
- Are the decision makers who can address the barriers at the table?
- Are they willing and able to do so?
    - If so, what is the timeline as it pertains to high-quality implementation?
    - If not, what short- and mid-term strategies need to be enacted to address the identified barriers?
- Are there other accessible power brokers that need to be involved?
- Have all stakeholders, including youth and families, been authentically heard and their input genuinely considered?
    - If so, do they know this?
    - If not, when and how will they be made aware?

Revisit and build upon existing synergies and be creative in establishing new ones to address overlaps and gaps in high-quality service delivery.

- Deepen and expand existing collaborations in a data-driven fashion aimed in response to service delivery overlaps and gaps,

- Formally establish inter- and intra-organization collaboration and memorialize new partnerships in a data-driven fashion aimed in response to service delivery overlaps and gaps.

Work to gain the buy-in of skeptics and naysayers via tapping into their potential and professional/ethical responsibilities.

- Focus on goals and facts, not irrelevant issues and opinions.
- Who are the skeptics and what are the sources of their skepticism?
- Is it clear to them how their goals are aligned with those of the policy and practice changes at hand?
- How can they be incentivized to earnestly participate in, if not lead aspects of the change efforts at hand (or made to)?
- Has the initiative been framed in professional and ethical standards or credos?
- How much formal and informal authority do they have on others?

Plan for sustainability by beginning with the end in mind.

- What does sustainability look like and how does the collective get there?
- What new policies, procedures, and practices merit deeper thought and discussion throughout subsequent phases?
- Are the initiative's goals, outputs, and outcomes aligned with those that are most important to key policy and funding decision makers?
- Have integrated or braided funding strategies been explored?
- What specifically have successful jurisdictions done to sustain high quality efforts over time?
  - Which practices can be replicated in your jurisdiction?
  - Which can't and what are other local strategies that can be employed to reach the same goals?

Sample Tools and Resources

Council of Chief State School Officers ESSA Stakeholder Engagement Guide. https://www.ccsso.org/sites/default/files/2017-10/CCSSO%20Stakeholder%20Engagement%20Guide%20FINAL.pdf

Planning for Sustainability.
https://www.samhsa.gov/capt/tools-learning-resources/planning-sustainability

Assessing Readiness

Organizational readiness for change is critical to successful implementation (Dymnicki, Wandersman, Osher, Grigorescu, & Huang, 2014; Scaccia et al., 2015). Scaccia and colleagues have conceptualized organizational readiness to include three components: (1) motivation to implement an innovation; (2) general capacity—broad organizational characteristics applicable to any innovation; and (3) specific capacity—the organization's ability to deliver the specific innovation as designed. In the context of schools and community programs, readiness to implement a policy initiative can be envisioned as a product of how much staff want to do it and believe it will be better than what has been done before (Cooley & Kohl, 2006), how good the staff are at doing anything new, and how good they are at the topic of the new policy specifically. In addition to readiness for change, policy makers and leaders should be prepared for individuals' response to the change process. Hall and Hord (2015) suggest there are three dimensions of the change process, called the Concerned Based Adoption Model. The three dimensions are (1) the *stages of concern* that implementers experience with the change process, (2) the *levels of use* in implementing an innovation, and (3) *innovation configurations*, which are ways practitioners adapt innovations in their unique context. Both the aspects of organizational readiness for change and the Concerned Based Adoption Model in the tools can be referenced later in the chapter.

Tips and Key Questions to Consider

Ensure that the readiness is present among key stakeholders (or as close to it as possible).

- Are key stakeholders ready to implement the policy and practice changes?
- Given what has been learned in earlier phases, what are the specific obstacles related to:
    - Motivation
    - General capacity
    - Specific capacity?
- Are there still major concerns or barriers that have not been adequately addressed?
- Has professional development for key stakeholders been properly planned for and articulated to all, especially direct service providers?
    - Did direct service providers have input on the professional delivery content and delivery approach?
- Have key stakeholders been on message about the policy and practice changes?

Sample Tools and Resources

Concerns-Based Adoption Model (CBAM). http://www.sedl.org/cbam/

Willing, Able, —> Ready: Basics and Policy Implications of Readiness As a Key Component for Implementation of Evidenced-Based Interventions. http://youth.gov/docs/Readiness_IssueBrief_508.pdf

Implementation

Successful implementation of a policy relies heavily on the people (implementers), places (context), and available resources. Even before we get to the qualifications of the people who are to implement the policy or their stake in it, there is much to consider about how the people interpret the policy. In fact, multiple implementers can interpret a policy differently, and this greatly affects the characteristics and sometimes success of the implementation (Spillane, Reiser, & Gomez, 2006). Three common types of misconceptions about policy are (1) when one interprets a policy to be familiar to another action and makes assumptions about it as a result; (2) when one devalues a policy or doesn't see or embrace the value in the same way as other implementers; and (3) when one simply has a different understanding of the language in the policy or action (Spillane, Reiser, & Gomez, 2006). Strategies to create a shared vision and garner stakeholder engagement detailed in the sections prior can alleviate this challenge. To ensure a shared understanding of a policy, we also suggest that throughout the process of implementation that there is an ongoing reiteration of the value of the policy and intended outcomes, to ensure that there is a shared understanding and ultimately successful implementation.

Although there exist wide and varying research on the key ingredients of policy implementation (Matland, 1995); there are specific policy implementation practices taken from school reform efforts that merit consideration. Desimone (2002) suggests that policies that foster successful implementation are specific, consistent, authoritative, powerful, and stable. Let's break that down a bit. *Specific* refers to the level of detail in the policy to help guide implementers. For example, if the crafters of the policy envision that teachers will need to meet with social workers monthly in order for the initiative to be a success, then the policy should specify this in the language. Desimone (2002) suggests that the policy be *consistent* with other school and community policies. This is especially critical when we know there are so many seemingly competing priorities in schools, when we know in fact they may all be intended to meet the same end goal. Authoritative and powerful, on the surface, present a seeming contradiction to our earlier assertions for bottom-up approaches and stakeholder engagement. In fact, Desimone (2002) intends to portray the *authority* of the policy to be in the hands of traditional structures (top-down) or via champions and stakeholders, as we formerly asserted, but that it needs to exist, and there needs to be a champion for the policy and *power* to persuade or influence others to adopt it. This is sometimes done through monetary incentives or through negative consequences, but we posit that the aforementioned activities (shared vision, stakeholder buy-in, readiness) surface both shared authority and finds a place of power for the policy. Finally, *stability*, Desimone (2002) describes stability as not the stability of the policy or implementation of the policy but of the context in which it is being implemented. In chaotic schools or environments, where schools are under great pressure to meet various demands, the stability of the environment to implement a policy may look different than in a school that has basic issues of safety and support met for all students.

Tips and Key Questions to Consider

Anticipate and address potential misunderstanding about the policy and practice changes. Make the connectivity between these changes and existing policy and practice clear from the onset.

- Have fundamental similarities and differences between the new policies and practices, and the rationales and merits thereof, been clearly articulated to all stakeholders?
- Has every attempt been made to acknowledge and address stakeholders' implementation concerns?
    - Are stakeholders aware of these efforts?
- Has the connection between professional development activities and new requirements been made clear to all?

Ensure that the right implementation approach has been chosen (e.g., district wide from the onset vs. targeted phase in and refinement over time)?

- Were key individual and collective readiness indicators properly evaluated prior to choosing the approach?
- Were major contextual factors taken into strong consideration?
- Are the procedures or practices that can be adjusted, while still maintaining the integrity and spirit of the policy and practice initiative, at hand?

Sample Tools and Resources

Hexagon Tool. https://implementation.fpg.unc.edu/sites/implementation.fpg.unc.edu/files/resources/NIRN_HexagonTool_11.2.18.pdf (Blase, Kiser, & Van Dyke, 2013)

Scaling for Sustainability (or Staying Small and Good!)

All of the aforementioned steps (creating a shared vision, getting stakeholder buy-in, assessing readiness, and successful implementation) are critical in creating sustainable implementation of a policy. *Sustainability* is just one of three phases of scaling, which also includes the *depth* of the implementation of the policy (Coburn, 2003). The third component of scaling is *spread*. Some policies are meant to be spread (e.g., one would want a policy to support to be present in all classrooms in a school and all schools in a district), while others may be time-limited or contextually relevant and specific and intended to be limited to a point in time, one classroom, school, or district. For those policies you wish to scale (deepen, spread, and sustain), there are a few things to keep in mind.

The first consideration is that some experts assert that sustainability relies upon continued attention to the fit between the practice and the place (i.e., context) (Chambers, Glasgow & Strange, 2013). In order to respond to this, we must expect that the implementation of a policy may look different over time and places, and that does not mean it is not sustained, only that it has changed to fit the situation and people in the situation.

A second and very real challenge is that the successful implementation of a policy is often a mix of key ingredients of staff character, context, resources, and support networks. This is often difficult to replicate from classroom to classroom and school to school. Does it need to be exactly the same in every place? Probably not. In an article published in the *Harvard Business Review*, the author suggests, "The objective is to reproduce a successful program's results, not to slavishly recreate every one of its features" (Bradach, 2003). So, this is a hard balance, we want to learn from others who have implemented a policy well, but at the same time, we must realize that the implementation has to fit the people and place, and change over time to be responsive to changes in populations and settings.

Third is that once the interest and resources of a policy diminishes, it may be challenging to keep the implementation of that policy going over time (Coburn, 2003). This merits ongoing engagement in allowing staff to reflect on their practice or implementation of the policy and stakeholders to engage in an ongoing dialogue about the relative merit and fit of the policy. Stakeholders and staff can use data (on implementation of the policy, either formal or anecdotal) to inform their reflections and dialogues. This is often formalized as a process known as continuous improvement (Chambers, Glasgow, & Stange, 2013).

Tips and Key Questions to Consider

Document successes and struggles in a data-driven fashion.

- What do the quantitative and qualitative data tell you about the effectiveness of the initiative?

Allow for model adjustments that make sense for a particular context, while requiring adherence to the major tenets of the chosen approach.

- What school community level innovations and adjustments have been necessary and why?

Share successes and efforts to address obstacles with stakeholders and key decision makers—early and often.

- What improvements or efficiencies can be attributed to the initiative?
- How have youth and families been better served? Let them tell their stories.
- How do direct service providers now feel about the initiative—particularly former naysayers?

Sample Tools and Resources

Leading Change Handbook: Concepts and Tools. http://www.wallacefoundation.org/knowledge-center/Documents/leading-change-handbook.pdf

Program Sustainability Assessment Tool. https://sustaintool.org/

Continuous Improvement

Continuous improvement is the ongoing adjustment to practice based upon data and reflection. It is important to reflect on some of the aforementioned challenges to implementation, like the fitness of the practice to the people and place, the quality of the implementation, and the availability of resources to support the implementation of the policy. Stakeholders can engage in formal and informal continuous improvement practices toward the end of improving practice and getting to the intended result of the practice. Where possible, practitioners and researchers or evaluators can partner to support continuous improvement toward the successful and ongoing implementation of a policy. The following chapter outlines a process for getting to outcome through continuous improvement.

References

Blase, K., Kiser, L., & Van Dyke, M. (2013). *The Hexagon Tool: Exploring context.* Chapel Hill: National Implementation Research Network, FPG Child Development Institute, University of North Carolina at Chapel Hill.

Bradach, J. (2003). Going to scale: The challenge of replicating social programs. *Stanford Social Innovation Review*. Retrieved from http://ssir.org/articles/entry/going_to_scale

Chambers, D. A., Glasgow, R. E., & Strange, K. C. (2013). The dynamic sustainability framework: Addressing the paradox of sustainment amid ongoing change. *Implementation Science, 8*, 117.

Coburn, C. E. (2003). Rethinking scale: Moving beyond numbers to deep and lasting change. *Educational Researcher, 32*(6), 3–12.

Cooley, L., & Kohl, R. (2006). *Scaling up—From vision to large-scale change: A management framework for practitioners*. Washington, DC: Management Systems International. Retrieved from http://www.msiworldwide.com/wp-content/uploads/Scaling-Up-Framework.pdf

Desimone, L. (2002). How can comprehensive school reform models be successfully implemented? *Review of Educational Research, 72*(3), 433–479.

Dymnicki, A., Wandersman, A., Osher, D., Grigorescu, V., & Huang, L. (2014, September). *Willing, able, ready: Basics and policy implications of readiness as a key component for implementation of evidence-based interventions* (ASPE Issue Brief). Washington, DC: Office of the Assistant Secretary for Planning and Evaluation, U.S. Department of Health and Human Services. Retrieved from http://youth.gov/docs/Readiness_IssueBrief_508.pdf

Green, A. E., & Aarons, G. A. (2011). A comparison of policy and direct practice stakeholder perceptions of factors impacting evidence-based practice implementation using concept mapping. *Implementation Science, 6*, 104.

Hall, G. E., & Hord, S. M. (2015). *Implementing change: Patterns, principles and potholes* (4th ed.). Upper Saddle River, NJ: Pearson.

Manasse, A. L. (1986). Vision and leadership: Paying attention to intention. *Peabody Journal of Education, 63*(1), 150–173.

Matland, R. E. (1995, April). Synthesizing the implementation literature: The ambiguity-conflict model of policy implementation. *Journal of Public Administration Research and Theory, 5*(2), 145–174.

Méndez-Morse, S. (1993). Vision, leadership, and change. *Issues . . . about Change, 2*(3). Austin, TX: SEDL. Retrieved from http://www.sedl.org/change/issues/issues23.html

Nanus, B. (1992). *Visionary leadership: Creating a compelling sense of direction for your organization*. San Francisco: Jossey-Bass.

National Technical Assistance and Evaluation Center for Systems of Care. (2016, April). *Leadership in systems of care: Creating and communicating a shared vision*. Washington, DC: Children's Bureau. Retrieved from https://www.childwelfare.gov/pubPDFs/CreatingandCommunicatingaSharedVision.pdf

Rogus, J. F. (1990). Developing a vision statement—Some consideration for principals. *NASSP Bulletin, 74*(523), 6–12.

Rolewski, M. (2008). *Overcoming obstacles to adopting and implementing evidence-based practices*. Retrieved from www.bestevidence.org/resources/general/obstacles_brief08sep22.pdf

Scaccia, J. P., Cook, B. S., Lamont, A., Wandersman, A., Castellow, J., Katz, J., & Beidas, R. S. (2015). A practical implementation science heuristic for organizational readiness: R= MC2. *Journal of Community Psychology, 43*, 484–501.

Seeley, D. S. (1992, April). *Visionary leaders for reforming public schools.* Paper presented at the Annual Meeting of the American Educational Research Association, San Francisco, CA.

Senge, P. M. (1990). *The fifth discipline: The art and practice of the learning organization.* New York: Doubleday/Currency.

Spillane, J. P., Reiser, B. J., & Gomez, L. M. (2006). Policy implementation and cognition: The role of human, social, and distribute cognition in framing policy implementation. In M. Honig (Ed.), *New directions in education policy implementation: Confronting complexity* (pp. 47–64). Albany: SUNY Press.

Zaff, J. F., Jones, E. P., Aasland, K., Donlan, A. E., Lin, E. S., Prescott, J. E., & Baker, A. (2015). Alignment of perceived needs across levels of a community. *Journal of Applied Developmental Psychology, 40*, 8–16.

CHAPTER EIGHTEEN

Getting to Outcomes

Planning, Continuous Improvement, and Evaluation

Aaron R. Butler, Jessica Johnson, and Gene E. Hall

There are many challenges to schools and communities adopting, implementing effectively, institutionalizing, scaling up, and sustaining effective practices. These challenges can be addressed by data-informed planning, monitoring, formative assessment, and outcome evaluation that attend to readiness, implementation quality, and the use of data for continuous quality improvement. Also, there are many evidence-based Change Science models, theories, and constructs that can be used to increase change success.

The chapters in this handbook provide information about major programs, practices, and strategies that can be used to increase outcomes. However, just having a research base and practical guidance does not guarantee the achievement of the intended outcomes. The new way(s) have to be selected and used.

Change Is a Process, Not an Event

An important beginning point is to understand that "change is a process, not an event" (Hall & Hord, 2015, p. 10). Further, accomplishing change entails three major phases: (1) creating the change; (2) implementing the change; and (3) sustaining the change. Each of these phases takes time, resources, and expertise. Further, for each phase to be successful different resources and expertise are necessary. In 1999, Hall proposed the metaphor

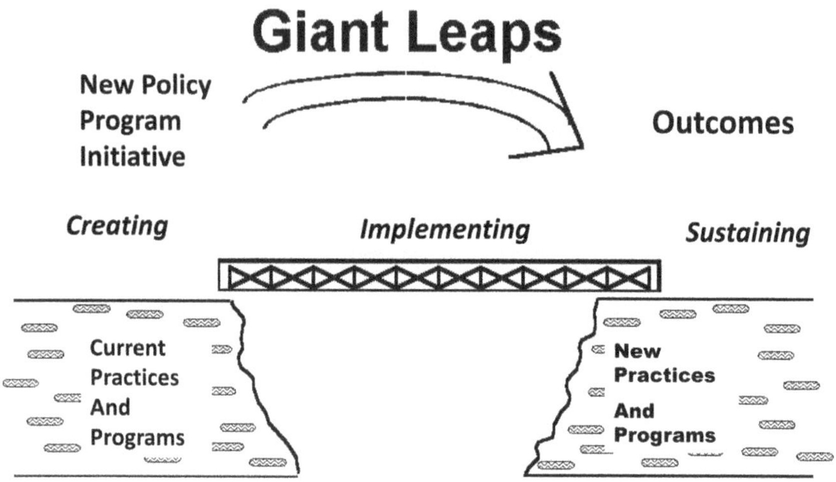

Figure 18.1 Three phases of the change process. (Hall & Hord, forthcoming)

of a bridge for visualizing the change process. The metaphor has continued to be applied and is described in more detail in Hall & Hord (2015) (see figure 18.1).

Additional understanding from change science is represented with the Bridge figure. To begin with, the practices and policies proposed in the many chapters of this handbook represent major changes. They are complex, sophisticated, and entail change in people, organizations, and communities. They are not single innovations. Rather they are *innovation bundles*.

Too often there is an implicit assumption that these changes will be easy to implement. When this assumption is held on to, prospective users are being asked to make a *Giant Leap* across a very wide, and deep, chasm. In most of these cases, the change process fails. There needs to be a *Bridge* that implementers can move across.

Another important symbolism in the Implementation Bridge Metaphor is that just because people or communities move out onto the Bridge, does not mean that they will make it all the way across. Specialized and ongoing support is necessary to achieve the Sustaining Phase.

Although it may seem obvious, it is unlikely that the desired outcomes will be observed before implementers are across the Bridge. In too many change initiatives, summative evaluations are conducted while most are on the Bridge, but not yet across. Unfortunately, the decision is made prematurely that the change is not working and should be abandoned.

The previous chapter addresses several key factors in planning for implementation including creating a shared vision, knowing the organizations, engaging key stakeholders, and assessing readiness. This chapter tackles implementation, continuous improvement, sustainability, and the role of leadership in making them happen. Once you have selected interventions or developed programs or approaches, how do you ensure they are implemented well and modified as needed to reach the desired outcomes? How do you build systems and structures that will outlast individual leaders and become woven into the fabric of the organization?

Implementing Change

Mark, a high school assistant principal, attended a summer workshop on a new positive behavior program. He came back to work the next week excited to start putting this new program into place for the upcoming school year. It had positive results in schools across the state, and he felt it would surely help reduce the number of discipline referrals that he had to deal with each day. Over the next month, he proceeded to put together a plan for implementation that included program goals, strategies for each staff member in the building to utilize, and expectations for how he would monitor success.

The principal allowed him to use one of the August staff development days to share his new program with the staff, provide training on the key strategies, answer questions, and clarify roles, responsibilities, and expectations. Several staff members appeared excited with the practical strategies that they could use in their classrooms and hallways this year. Despite a positive start, Mark noticed that discipline referrals were beginning to increase a month into the school year and staff excitement about the new program was waning. By the end of first semester, there was no evidence of the new program in classrooms or hallways and Mark continued to spend the largest portion of each day dealing with discipline referrals.

Too often, the best laid plans remain just that—plans. Sometimes, as in Mark's case, implementation starts strong but falls apart over time without a careful examination of what's working and thoughtful changes to implementation. Inside this chapter you will find practical approaches and tools to support implementation, continuous improvement, sustainability, and leadership.

Definition of Implementation

Implementation is defined as the process of putting a decision or plan into effect (*Oxford Dictionary*, 2017). Many leaders and their organizations remain true to this definition when implementing new plans or programs. Some organizations leave it to a single leader to examine the plan and attempt to carry out each strategy one by one, checking them off in a sort of compliance exercise. Other organizations put together an implementation team who, theoretically, have greater capacity than a single individual and attempt to implement multiple strategies at once. Too often, examples like these result in implementation of new plans or programs that amounts to just following the recipe of strategies provided in the plan without regard to how what they are attempting to do fits into a larger picture.

Why do so many people and organizations find it so difficult to be consistently successful implementing new programs? The short answer is that, despite the simple definition, implementation in the real world is not as easy as putting a defined plan into action without regard for the complexities and challenges of learning to do things in new ways. There also are outside influences that can hinder attaining the ultimate goal—greater outcomes.

Plan-Do-Study-Act

This chapter focuses on using Plan-Do-Study-Act (PDSA) cycles, which is one model to ensure effective implementation of changes or programs that operate in a complex, real-world context. The following topics will be addressed in order to support implementation efforts:

- Understanding a conceptual framework, stages, and approaches to implementation
- Communicating a plan for successful implementation that includes clear alignment of needs, goals, strategies, and expectations
- Supporting implementation efforts through cycles of continuous improvement
- Increasing the likelihood of sustaining the change.

Framework for Implementation

According to a review of literature from the National Implementation Research Network (NIRN), Fixsen and colleagues (2005) shared the purpose and outcomes of implementation often fall into one of three degrees—paper implementation, process implementation, or performance implementation. First, *paper implementation* refers to creating the appropriate paperwork available in manuals or file cabinets that show new policies or procedures are in place from a compliance perspective. Next, *process implementation* refers to putting workshops, trainings, or other programs in place within an organization that show actions are being taken but the benefits are difficult to observe. Finally, *performance implementation* refers to establishing procedures or processes that lead to actual benefits for the organization and their target audience. Organizations and their leaders should begin their implementation efforts with a shared understanding that not all implementation efforts are the same and a shared agreement as to which degree of implementation they are striving to reach.

Every system is perfectly designed to get the results it gets. That quote, which has been popularized in health care and education improvement work, has been attributed to several people. One of the not so subtle takeaways from that quote includes the interpretation that if an organization makes a change to how they are implementing their processes and procedures, they can get different results—positive or negative.

One way to help ensure that the organization makes changes that result in positive outcomes is by understanding how implementation fits into a larger conceptual framework. Fixsen and colleagues (2005) developed a conceptual framework for implementation that consists of five components:

1. Source—a best practice or model program that other organizations want to replicate or establish
2. Destination—the organization or individual that will implement the new plan or program
3. Communication Link—the leader or team (purveyors)—that actively work to help an organization implement the plan or program strategies with fidelity
4. Feedback—the regular flow of information about progress and performance that can be acted upon by relevant practitioners or purveyors
5. Influence—the social, economic, political, psychological, and other factors that make up the context or environment where implementation efforts are taking place.

Once Fixsen and colleagues (2005) defined degrees of implementation and developed a framework for implementation, they went on to show how implementation is a process, not a single event. The six stages of implementation that they defined provide a roadmap with strategic points along the way where organizations and their leaders can check their current position in the implementation process and prepare to make adjustments to stay or get back on the right course. Table 18.1 shows the six stages of implementation and a brief description of each stage.

During the spring semester, Mark was still searching for answers as to why his new program failed so quickly and easily. Determined to find answers and learn from his mistakes, he began to compare the planning and rollout of his program with the stages of implementation presented by Fixsen. After a short time for review, he believed that he had attempted to move through the stages too quickly and didn't take time to incorporate a single PDSA cycle along the way. He could see how he didn't really establish an active communication link or purveyor to provide ongoing support to staff to implement the ideal program that he learned about in the summer workshop. Armed with this new knowledge on effective implementation, Mark

Table 18.1 Stages of implementation

Stage of Implementation	Description
Exploration and adoption	Initial stage of implementation where the organization assesses needs, examines possible interventions, components, and drivers, and assesses fit.
Program installation	Second stage of implementation focused on acquiring and organizing resources, preparing structural supports within the organization for implementation, and preparing the staff for implementation.
Initial implementation	The awkward and fragile stage of implementation when the new program or intervention is being introduced to the existing culture. The complex work of change implementation meets forces of inertia, fear, and comfort with status quo. This is the stage when many implementation efforts fail.
Full operation	New learning becomes integrated into organizational practices, policies, and procedures. The new program or intervention becomes standard practice within the organization.
Innovation	Opportunities to refine or extend the program or intervention occur. At this stage, organizations must be careful to identify program innovations from program drift.
Sustainability	The goal of implementation is to reach this stage, which is characterized by organizational ability to maintain the program or intervention despite changes and challenges.

was confident that the next program he attempted to establish would follow a much different path.

Key Questions for Consideration

- How will we define successful implementation?
- How does our plan for implementation reflect the five components of effective implementation—source, destination, communication link, feedback, and influence?

- How does our current situation align with the stages of implementation?
- What potential risks do we need to plan for in order to avoid failure during initial implementation?

Approaches to Effective Implementation

Sarah was in her second week as assistant superintendent of the Jackson School District when she was handed an unexpected challenge. Results from a survey completed by students, parents, and staff throughout the district showed that all three groups agreed that schools across the district did not provide a safe, supportive learning environment for students. Following a tumultuous school board meeting, the board and superintendent made addressing this issue a top priority for the upcoming school year. They expected prompt action, positive results, and no excuses.

Fortunately, her predecessor had already been aware of this potential issue and had developed an initial plan, based on a needs assessment, which included root causes, initial goals, and a list of recommended strategies. Sarah felt a sense of urgency to put this plan in place, but still needed to review what had been developed to ensure that she was comfortable and supportive of the strategies and then create a plan for implementation.

Sarah was confident in her abilities and had conducted thorough research on different models for implementation and project management as part of her graduate school program. She knew that addressing this issue of providing a safe, supportive learning environment for all students would not be as simple as setting up a few district-wide trainings or hiring extra security personnel. It would require a concerted effort to connect research to actual practice. As she sat in her office on a Wednesday afternoon, she began to reflect on what she knew about leading implementation efforts from her previous experiences and began looking through her books and other resources to see what ideas she could take from the research.

Making a clear connection between research and practice is always easier said than done. However, when attempting to implement a new plan or program, most organizations find it useful to have a model or approach to follow or at least refer to in order to help guide them through the stages of implementation. Implementation plans that have the best chance for long-term success and sustainability begin with an understanding of the current reality of the situation and the needs of stakeholders. These needs can then be addressed through a series of actions within a cycle of continuous improvement and learning that includes creating the plan, doing the work in the plan, studying the results, and taking action to modify strategies within the plan if goals have not been met. These actions are often referred to as a Plan-Do-Study-Act (PDSA) cycle.

Evidence-Based Change Models

Four models or approaches that have been used extensively in change and improvement efforts across multiple industries—Getting to Outcomes, Six Core Principles for Improvement, Deliverology, and the Concerns-Based Adoption Model—are presented below. These models or approaches are similar in that they all include or support the use of some form of PDSA cycle. Yet their differences show that when it comes to effective implementation, there is no single "right way." As the implementation team examines these models or approaches to inform the implementation efforts, it will be important to consider which, if any, most closely align with the current organizational culture or where it wants to go.

Getting to Outcomes

Getting to Outcomes is an approach to guide implementation teams to plan, implement, and evaluate high-quality, outcomes-based programs. This approach was originally presented in the context of substance abuse prevention programs but has a structure that is generalizable across other fields. The ten steps include:

1. Choose which problems to focus on
2. Identify goals, target population, and desired outcomes
3. Find existing programs and best practices worth copying
4. Modify the program or best practices to fit the organization's needs
5. Assess capacity (staff, financing, etc.) to implement the program
6. Make a plan for getting started: who, what, when, where, and how
7. Evaluate planning and implementation. How did it go?
8. Evaluate program's success in achieving desired results
9. Make a plan for Continuous Quality Improvement
10. Consider how to keep the program going if it is successful.

A key takeaway from this approach to implementing high-quality programs is that it places an emphasis on planning in steps 1–6 and on evaluation and improvement in steps 7–10, with no steps actually dedicated to implementation. However, this apparent oversight remains consistent with the role of the source and feedback presented in the Fixsen and colleagues' (2005) framework for implementation and reinforces that it is a process not a single event.

Six Core Principles for Improvement

The second approach to effective implementation is the Six Core Principles for Improvement model from the Carnegie Foundation for the Advancement of Teaching (Bryk, Gomez, Grunow, & LeMahieu, 2015). This approach has been used primarily to establish networked improvement communities in education, but similar to the other approaches can be generalized across fields. The six principles include:

1. Make the work problem-specific and user-centered
2. Variation in performance is the core problem to address
3. See the system that produces the current outcomes
4. We cannot improve at scale what we cannot measure
5. Anchor practice improvement in disciplined inquiry
6. Accelerate improvements through networked improvement communities.

Key takeaways of this approach are the expectation of variation in degree of implementation and the commitment to continuous improvement throughout the steps to gather feedback consistently and make course corrections.

Deliverology

The third approach to effective implementation is called Deliverology (Barber, Moffit, & Kihn, 2011). This approach was developed through work with the government of the United Kingdom to manage and monitor implementation activities across multiple "delivery units." The key components include:

1. Develop a foundation for delivery
2. Understand the delivery challenge
3. Plan for delivery
4. Drive delivery
5. Create an irreversible delivery culture.

The key takeaways from Deliverology are based on the belief that implementation efforts in the public sector do not often lead to quantifiable results. There are often too many goals and too little real-time data used to monitor progress. Deliverology proposes that developing smaller, focused "delivery units," each focused on delivering a few, specific results, will lead to more timely progress monitoring and course corrections and result in achieving delivery of those intended results.

Concerns Based Adoption Model

The fourth approach to implementation is Concerns Based Adoption Model (CBAM), which is a multivariate and systemic way to understand and address key factors related to change success. The CBAM work provides a number of research-verified tools and techniques for facilitation and assessment of implementation. CBAM began as an undertaking of a team of researchers at the Research and Development Center for Teacher Education at the University of Texas at Austin in the 1970s and 1980s. Since that time the constructs and tools have been applied in many types of organizations and in other countries.

Three of the well-tested and applied constructs are referred to as the Three Diagnostic Dimensions. Each of these has direct application to facilitating and assessing implementation efforts. The Three Diagnostic Dimensions of CBAM are:

- Stages of Concern (SoC) addresses the personal side of change. People move through a series of feelings and perceptions about change.
- Levels of Use (LoU) provides descriptions of eight different behavioral profiles. Each represents a level of proficiency moving from nonuse, to novice, to expert.
- Innovation Configurations (IC) is about Fidelity of Implementation (FoI). Critical components of an innovation are identified with each having a set of "word picture" descriptions that range from traditional practice to ideal use of the innovation.

Each of the Three Diagnostic Dimensions can be used to assess and chart change process progress. In other words, each dimension represents a way to measure how far implementers and their organizations have progressed across the Implementation Bridge that was shared at the beginning of this chapter.

The key takeaway from CBAM is that successful implementation of any initiative requires more than just materials, resources, and training. Human beings are ultimately the key to successful implementation and CBAM prioritizes understanding how each person understands and responds to a new initiative along with the attitudes and beliefs they possess.

Foundation for Sustainability

Laying a foundation for sustainability must begin at the start of a change initiative rather than occur as an afterthought. The ultimate goal of implementation for any new strategy or program should be to create an

Table 18.2 Evidence-based change models

	Getting to Outcomes	Six Core Principles for Improvement	Deliverology	CBAM
Overview				
Steps/ Dimensions	1. Choose which problems to focus on 2. Identify goals, target population, and desired outcomes 3. Find existing programs and best practices worth copying 4. Modify the program or best practices to fit your needs 5. Assess capacity (staff, financing, etc.) to implement the program 6. Make a plan for getting started; who, what, when, where, and how 7. Evaluate planning and implementation. How did it go? 8. Evaluate program's success in achieving desired results 9. Make a plan for Continuous Quality Improvement 10. Consider how to keep the program going if it is successful	1. Make the work problem-specific and user-centered 2. Variation in performance is the core problem to address 3. See the system that produces the current outcomes 4. We cannot improve at scale what we cannot measure 5. Anchor practice improvement in disciplined inquiry (Plan, Do, Study, Act cycles) 6. Accelerate improvements through networked improvement communities	1. Develop a foundation for delivery 2. Understand the delivery challenge 3. Plan for delivery 4. Drive delivery 5. Create an irreversible delivery culture	1. Innovation Configurations 2. Stages of Concern 3. Levels of Use
Organization		Carnegie Foundation for the Advancement of Teaching	US Education Delivery Institute	American Institutes for Research

environment that supports long-term sustainability of the intended results within the organization. This goal is different than just trying to maintain the fidelity of implementation of a specific strategy or program with no latitude for innovation. Chambers and colleagues (2013) clarify that an environment that supports long-term sustainability will prioritize ongoing quality improvement of interventions rather than just quality assurance of those interventions.

An organization that sets an implementation goal focused on creating an environment that sustains results acknowledges, from the beginning, that the people, the immediate context, and the larger environment will likely change over time. This reality of ongoing change highlights the importance of establishing a culture that is committed to ongoing cycles of continuous improvement. This type of organization will be well positioned to constantly monitor results, identify areas of need, and make strategic adjustments to an existing program to give themselves the best chance for sustained success.

The approaches presented in the previous section provide excellent examples of how to organize for continuous improvement and learning while implementing a new process or program. Within each of these approaches, and others not shared here, there are five key considerations that will help an organization set the foundation for sustaining success and integrating new systems into the culture. First, new programs and strategies for improvement should be aligned to the needs of the organization. Second, it is imperative to carefully select the team members who will lead and implement the new program or strategies. Third, all team members, current and future, who will have any role related to implementing the new program should receive standardized training to ensure consistency. Fourth, all team members should receive ongoing coaching to support their implementation efforts and professional growth. Finally, all members of the organization must show a commitment to continuous improvement by consistently monitoring the health of these considerations and overall progress of the new program.

Program Verification

Sarah began her long journey of implementation by comparing the results of her predecessor's needs assessment with the survey. Next, she examined how the priority needs and root causes would be addressed within the strategic plan that was left for her. She found, to her dismay, that the needs assessment that was conducted the previous spring consisted of the previous assistant superintendent asking a group of principals for "2 or 3" areas of concern in their buildings. The strategic plan that was left was a program that members of the district leadership team had learned about earlier in the year at a statewide conference. Obviously, it was a program with a proven record of making students, parents, and teachers feel safer and more supported. However, without being confident that the program would meet the specific needs of the district, Sarah didn't feel comfortable moving forward without revisiting the needs assessment process and getting more input to inform her decisions.

When beginning to develop an implementation plan for a new program or proposed change in practice, it is important to confirm that the new program or change is clearly aligned with identified needs. Seeking answers to a few questions early in the process can help inform decisions to only move forward with programs that will meet the needs of the organization and related stakeholders; thus, saving future time and effort that would be required to deal with yet another failed change effort. Examples of questions include:

- Was a thorough needs assessment conducted prior to selecting the program or strategies?
- Do the goals or objectives of the proposed program or strategies align with the priority needs?
- How will the proposed strategies or program affect the root causes for this issue?

Team Selection and Role Placement

People are the most important ingredient of any change process. A great plan or evidence-based program is important, but without people to implement it, they are just words on a page. Identifying and selecting the right people to lead and support implementation efforts, along with those carrying out the new program or strategy, is essential to success. There is no substitute for talented people who are committed to the hard work that will be required of any implementation effort. When looking for team members to lead or support implementation, seek out those that:

- Have knowledge or experience with the proposed program or strategies
- Have successfully supported previous implementation efforts
- Possess appropriate skills or competencies that are needed to support implementation
- Are relationship builders and good teammates
- Demonstrate commitment to and comfort with giving and receiving feedback regularly from staff in all levels of the organization.

The most successful implementation efforts usually involve some form of initial PDSA cycles that allow a small group to implement the new program, study unforeseen complications to implementation, and inform strategic changes to implementation. These initial PDSA cycles should not focus on making changes to the program or strategies, just processes for initial communication and training on the standard operating procedures that make up the new program. Special consideration should be made for the initial staff that will be asked to carry out these initial cycles to prepare for broader implementation of the new program or strategies. When looking for this group of staff, look for those who:

- Possess the appropriate skills or competencies to implement the new program
- Are seen as influencers in the organization.

Initial Training

Jonathan was given responsibility for planning the initial staff training for the new attendance software in the school. He had spent the entire summer planning this half-day workshop. He was careful to ensure that he shared the rationale for this new system, why it was necessary, and how it would eventually make tracking attendance easier for all teachers and staff. All staff login information was updated and available and there was a computer available for each participant during the session.

The training was developed and presented by the pilot implementation team that had worked with the system over the summer. All staff left the session reporting that they understood how to use the new system and where to go for help, if needed. By all measures, the training was a success! Jonathan was excited to see this new system in action when school began the following week.

All implementation efforts should include some form of initial training for staff members that will be enacting the new program or strategies. The type and intensity of training that is required will depend on several factors including the complexity of the new program or strategies along with the skills and experience of staff who will implement the new program. Regardless of how the initial training is presented, it should be as thorough and timely as possible.

People are more likely to support a change when they understand the need for the new program or strategies and their new roles and responsibilities. An initial training session typically serves as the first time staff get a full picture of the new program, so it is important for implementation leaders to ensure staff members' first exposure to the new program sets a firm foundation. Key takeaways for staff from an initial training should include:

- Why this change is needed
- How the change will address the needs of staff and the organization
- What success will look like for each staff member and the organization

- Who will have new roles and responsibilities
- What is the timeline for implementation
- How the organization will model continuous improvement.

Ongoing Coaching

Jonathan received a call during the third week of school. It was the high school principal. "Jonathan, we have a problem. Half of my staff is completely lost with this new attendance system. I'm trying to help them out as much as I can, but I have a building to run. I'm not sure if we need another training or coaches, but I know we need something, fast!"

Initial training, no matter how thorough, will never provide every staff member with all the information and support necessary for successful implementation. A staff member will lose his notes or forget a step along the way. Someone else may have missed the training altogether. Having a coaching system in place to meet these and other needs that will inevitably come up is essential for successful implementation and sustainability.

A well-planned and executed coaching program can serve multiple purposes in supporting cycles of continuous improvement through implementation. First, ongoing coaching provides staff with real-time feedback and support that is relevant to their needs. Second, effective coaching increases trust—a vital component for sustainability—between and among staff and coaches. Finally, coaching conversations can help quickly identify common issues and provide a mechanism for communicating solutions throughout the organization.

The most effective coaching programs are staffed with effective coaches. While that statement might seem like common sense, it is important to remember the earlier recommendations on team selection and role placement. When recruiting coaches, look for the following characteristics:

- Knowledge of how the program looks when operating effectively
- Optimistic

Continuous Improvement

One Tuesday morning in mid-April, Jonathan was getting prepared to call the high school principal for their monthly progress check. As he was about to pick up the phone, he briefly thought about the journey he had been on, particularly with the high school, this school year. What was originally an introductory training session for a new attendance program turned into a deeper learning experience for him and others across the district on the complexity of implementing a new program.

Jonathan and others across the district learned that perfect implementation does not exist. However, they served as an example that even when implementation efforts appear to be off track, they can be corrected. In late fall, Jonathan collaborated with the high school principal to develop a system of monitoring progress of the new attendance program. They worked with a small team to take the goals of the program and identify interim measures of progress for both building-wide implementation and impact on student attendance. Through their team discussions while identifying these measures, they hypothesized that if all or most of the staff correctly implemented the new attendance program there should be an increase in student attendance and decrease in chronic absenteeism each month. Following this line of thought, they also agreed that if these monthly measures were met at a certain level each month, then the school would meet or exceed its attendance goals for the year. As Jonathan dialed the high school principal's number, he was excited, yet nervous, to see if the positive trend from the past three months would continue.

The difference between successful implementation of a change process and failure often comes down to the organizational commitment to continuous improvement seen through consistently monitoring results and making strategic adjustments. Successful organizations commit to developing a culture that supports ongoing small-scale PDSA cycles during implementation. These PDSA cycles start by developing and aligning interim performance measures with the long-term goals outlined in the original plan. Interim performance measures should be selected based on their correlation to the future performance of the long-term goals. When selecting interim performance measures, consider the following questions:

- How is success being measured for this program?
- What changes need to take place to meet the long-term goals?
- Are any data currently being collected that are related to the long-term goals?
- Does research highlight any potential measures that are related to the long-term goals?
- How confident of success on the long-term goals are we if we meet these interim targets?

Identifying long-term goals and interim performance measures is not enough. In order to complete a PDSA cycle, organizations must do the work, study their progress on these interim measures, and take strategic corrective actions. Organizations that display a commitment to continuous improvement establish an expectation and system for bringing the right people together on a regular basis to review their data and make strategic adjustments. While the logistics of these progress monitoring meetings can and should vary to meet the needs and culture of each organization, each meeting should be focused on the data and include discussion on questions that may include, but not be limited to the following:

- Do our interim progress measures show that we are on track to meet our long-term goals?
- What actions are team members, including leadership, currently responsible for on a daily or weekly basis?
- Are all team members, including leadership, meeting their expected responsibilities?
- If we are on track, are there any potential risks that could affect continued progress?
- If we are not on track, are there any team member responsibilities that need to be added, removed, or modified?

The Role of Leadership

Friday, two o'clock in the afternoon. Weekly Reflection. The calendar reminder popped up on Jamal's screen to signal that it was time to finish what he was doing and prepare for his Friday ritual of reflecting on the current week and then preparing for the next one. He hadn't always followed this practice as a principal, but once he started it two years ago and saw the positive results across the school, now he doesn't feel his week is complete until he does it.

Jamal begins each weekly reflection session by reviewing the goals that he had set for the week. He asks himself, "Did I accomplish my goals for this week? Why or Why not?" Next, he reviews the weekly student attendance and tardies by grade level and whole school, chronic absentees, teacher attendance, discipline referrals, and his record of classroom observations. All the data looked good this week, so he jotted a note to remind himself to send a positive email to the staff and leadership team on Monday morning. Before transitioning to plan out his goals for the next week, Jamal always takes time to answer two important questions, "How have I helped make my team better this week? How have I personally and professionally grown this week?"

The role of a leader during implementation is to create conditions that support a culture of continuous improvement. Although leadership does not have to be isolated to a single individual, it does require individuals to separate themselves from the crowd and take on additional responsibilities. When leading implementation, there are three key responsibilities for a leader to support continuous improvement—communicate, model, and reflect.

Communicate

When it comes to communication, the job of a leader is never finished. Leaders must communicate through multiple formats early, often, and with a consistent and clear message. It is imperative to make sure every member of the team understands, individually and collectively, where they are, where they are going, and how they plan to reach that goal. Examples of information to communicate with team members include:

- Current situation or state of affairs regarding the new program
- Vision for what the organization will look like when the program is fully implemented
- Team member roles, responsibilities, and how progress will be measured
- Expectations for supporting a culture of continuous improvement.

Model

We have all heard the old saying, "actions speak louder than words." That phrase is especially true when it comes to the role of a leader when implementing change. Despite the most effective communication strategy, all eyes will still be on the leader to see if his actions align with the expectations of all team members.

A leader builds credibility when he consistently models the expectations that have been set for all members of the organization. A leader's actions show what he values and, when implementing a change, those values should include people, consistent effort, and results. When a leader models these values and expectations, he clearly shows that he can lead himself, which then gives him the opportunity to lead others. Additional opportunities for a leader to model expectations include:

- Be visible every day
- Take time to get to know your team members, their names, and some personal/family information (as appropriate)
- Promote the accomplishments of team members, not yourself
- Let your team members see your values through your daily actions
- Don't be afraid to show vulnerability
- Tap into the power of storytelling

Reflect

One of the most important actions that a leader can take on a regular basis is also one of the most difficult for a leader to actually take time to do—reflect. Maybe it's because reflection requires you to be still for a few moments and clear your mind of what needs to be done next. Maybe it's due to the lack of a deliverable that contributes to implementation goals. No matter what the reasons or excuses for not taking time to reflect may be for a leader, that doesn't diminish the importance.

The most effective leaders are disciplined with their time for personal and professional reflection. Exactly what effective leaders reflect on and when they take time to reflect may differ, but the disciplined action is the same. Three key areas that a leader can reflect on when leading an organization through a change process include the progress of implementation, team culture, and self-reflection by the leader. Examples of reflective questions that you can ask yourself as a leader include:

- What has been the greatest strength of our implementation efforts so far?
- What is one thing that we could do differently as an organization to improve implementation of this new program?
- How would a team member at each level of the organization explain our culture?
- How would I explain our organizational culture to a leader at another company or school?
- What have I done this week, month, or year to empower team members to become leaders?
- What past struggles or failures have I overcome to help me address a current challenge?

Jamal hit the send button on his latest Monday morning email to his staff. He was happy to share good news from the previous week and highlight the hard work of the teachers and administrators. He grabbed his coffee mug and looked out the window to see Mrs. Martin walking into the building. She was always the first teacher to arrive and he was excited to greet her and hear about her son's basketball game over the weekend. This conversation would be the first of many that he would have with staff and students over the next hour and a half. A new week was about to begin and that meant new challenges and new opportunities to learn and lead.

Key Points on Implementation and Sustainability

- Make time and effort to learn and understand the frameworks and stages of implementation in order to improve at it
- Incorporate cycles of continuous improvement and learning—Plan, Do, Study, Act (PDSA)—into implementation efforts
- Implementation should begin with sustainability in mind
- Change efforts should be continuously monitored to ensure they remain aligned to the needs of the organization
- Ensure that a knowledgeable and committed team is leading implementation

- Establish systems to train all existing and future staff and provide them with ongoing coaching support
- Be disciplined as a leader by taking time to communicate with your team, model expectations, and reflect on the change process, team culture, and yourself

References

Barber, M., Moffit, A., & Kihn, P. (2011). *Deliverology 101: A field guide for educational leaders*. Thousand Oaks, CA: Corwin Press.

Bryk, A. S., Gomez, L. M., Grunow, A., & LeMahieu, P. G. (2015). *Learning to improve: How America's schools can get better at getting better.* Cambridge, MA: Harvard Education Press.

Chambers, D. A., Glasgow, R. E., & Stange, K. C. (2013). The dynamic sustainability framework: Addressing the paradox of sustainment amid ongoing change. *Implementation Science 2013, 8*(117), 1–11.

Fixsen, D. L., Naoom, S. F., Blase, K. A., Friedman, R. M., & Wallace, F. (2005). *Implementation research: A synthesis of the literature.* Tampa: University of Southern Florida. Retrieved from https://nirn.fpg.unc.edu/sites/nirn.fpg.unc.edu/files/resources/NIRN-MonographFull-01-2005.pdf

Hall, G. E. (1999). Using constructs and techniques from research to facilitate and assess implementation of an innovative mathematics curriculum. *Journal of Classroom Interaction, 34*(1), 1–8.

Hall, G. E., & Hord, S. M. (2015). *Implementing change: Patterns, principles and potholes* (4th ed., p. 10). Upper Saddle River, NJ: Pearson Education.

Hall, G. E., & Hord, S. M. (forthcoming). *Implementing change: Patterns, principles and potholes* (5th ed.). Upper Saddle River, NJ: Pearson Education.

Implementation [Def. 1]. *Oxford English Living Dictionary.* Retrieved from https://en.oxforddictionaries.com/definition/implementation

CHAPTER NINETEEN

Updating the National Agenda for Achieving Better Results for Children and Youth with Emotional and Behavioral Disorders

Nicholas A. Gage, Nicolette M. Grasley-Boy, Trina Osher, David Osher, and Mark D. Weist

Children and youth with emotional and behavioral disorders (EBD) continue to experience myriad challenges, as do their families, schools, mental health professionals, and communities. Addressing the needs of these children and youth is clear. Without systematic, targeted, and evidence-based intervention, many will be unable to experience short- and long-term educational success, resulting in life-long consequences. Almost 25 years ago, the U.S. Department of Education's Office of Special Education and Rehabilitative Services' Office of Special Education Programs commissioned the Chesapeake Institute (which became a part of American Institutes for Research) to prepare a national agenda for achieving better results for children and youth with EBD (Chesapeake Institute, 1994). The purpose of this chapter is to revisit and update that agenda for the next 25 years. Although progress has been made, the following data suggest the enormity of the challenges faced by these children and youth remains:

- *School Placement.* Students with EBD are placed in more restrictive settings at higher rates than other students with disabilities. Nearly 18% of students with EBD are not educated in their zoned schools, while only 5.1% of all students with disabilities are placed in these settings. Students with EBD are placed in correctional facilities at exceptionally higher rates (1.5%) than other students with disabilities (0.2%). Among students with EBD educated in their zoned schools, 18.8% are placed in general education settings for less than 40% of the day, compared to 13.7% of all students with disabilities. Forty-six percent of students with EBD spend the majority of the day (>80%) in general education settings; however, this is well below the average among all students with disabilities (62.6%) (McFarland et al., 2017).
- *Academic Outcomes.* Over 77% of secondary students with EBD had failed one or more graded high school courses, compared to 66.4% of all students with disabilities and just 47.3% of the general population. Students with EBD also had lower high school grade point averages (2.0 on a 4.0 scale) than all students with disabilities (2.3) and the general population (2.7). Twenty-two percent of students with EBD had also been retained at least once during elementary or middle school (Newman et al., 2011a).
- *Encounters with the Juvenile/Criminal Justice System.* Among students with disabilities, those with EBD were immensely more likely to have had contact with the juvenile or criminal justice system by the time they were young adults (up to eight years out of high school). Over 60% of young adults with EBD had been arrested at some point, compared to just 32.3% of young adults across all disabilities. Forty-four percent had also been on parole or probation at some point versus 17.8% across disabilities. Young adults with EBD were also more likely to report having been involved in a physical fight in the last year (14.0% compared to 10.5% across disabilities). Nearly a quarter (23.7%) reported carrying a weapon in the last 30 days, compared to 17.0% of young adults with disabilities (Newman et al., 2011b).
- *Graduation Rates.* Students with EBD are less likely than their peers with disabilities to graduate with a regular diploma (54.75% vs. 66.1%). They also earn fewer alternative certificates (9.0%) compared to other students with disabilities (13.5%) (McFarland et al., 2017).
- *Dropout Rates.* Students with EBD have the highest dropout rate (35.2%) among all students with disabilities (18.5% across disabilities) between 14 and 21 years of age (McFarland et al., 2017).
- *Post-School Outcomes.* Young adults with EBD have poorer post-school outcomes than their peers with and without disabilities. Fifty-three percent had enrolled in postsecondary education at some time up to eight years after high school, compared to 60.1% of young adults with disabilities and 67.4%

of their peers without disabilities. Just under half of young adults with EBD were employed when interviewed for the National Longitudinal Transition Study-2 (NLTS-2) in 2009, compared to 60.2% of all young adults with disabilities and 67.4% of their peers without disabilities. Young adults with EBD held the highest average number of jobs (4.6) since high school and spent the least time employed at these jobs (18.8 months on average). Peers with disabilities average 23.5 months employed, while those without disabilities averaged 21.8 months. Young adults with EBD were also more likely to report cigarette, alcohol, or illegal drug use in past 30 days compared to peers in all other disability categories (Newman et al., 2011b).

- *Identification Rates by Ethnicity and Socioeconomic Backgrounds.* Identification of students with EBD across ethnicity, gender, and socioeconomic backgrounds is not representative of the general population. Although white students are identified with EBD at a rate similar to the population (52.5% vs. 50.3% of all students), over a quarter of students with EBD are black, compared to 15.6% of all students. Conversely, Hispanic and Asian students appear to be under-identified. Hispanic students account for 15.5% of students with EBD, compared to 24.8% of all students, while 0.9% of students with EBD are Asian, compared to 4.8% of all students. Males are much more likely to be identified with EBD than females (74% vs. 26% of students with EBD). Students with EBD are also more likely to come from lower income households (McFarland et al., 2017).

Taken together, research has palpably documented dismal short- and long-term outcomes for these students. Perhaps most concerning are the recent estimates that only 57% of students with EBD graduate high school with a regular diploma and only 64% complete high school (regular diploma or alternative certification) (McFarland et al., 2017). Evidence-based policies and practices exist to reverse these negative trends in outcomes students with EBD experience. We contend that maintaining the status quo is untenable.

Legislative Background

A number of federal and state-level legislative and policy actions have developed since the publication of the original national agenda that have a direct and meaningful effect on students with EBD. Below, we highlight a few of those important policies.

Federal Definition of Emotional and Behavioral Disorders

With the passage of the Education for All Handicapped Children (P.L. 94-142) law in 1975, later renamed the Individuals with Disabilities Education Act (IDEA), students experiencing significant EBD in schools became eligible for specialized services under federal law. Those services, deemed special education and necessary related services, continue to be provided to students that meet eligibility criteria defined in the law. The original definition, termed "Serious Emotional Disturbance" and later changed to simply "Emotional Disturbance" in 1997, was based on criteria developed by Eli Bower in 1957. His criteria were developed to assist with identifying students for intervention in California but were modified in ways he did not agree with (Bower, 1982). The criteria qualifying a student for Emotion Disturbance (ED) have not changed since 1975 and are as follows:

(i) Emotional disturbance means a condition exhibiting one or more of the following characteristics over a long period of time and to a marked degree that adversely affects a child's educational performance:
  (A) An inability to learn that cannot be explained by intellectual, sensory, or health factors.
  (B) An inability to build or maintain satisfactory interpersonal relationships with peers and teachers.
  (C) Inappropriate types of behavior or feelings under normal circumstances.
  (D) A general pervasive mood of unhappiness or depression.
  (E) A tendency to develop physical symptoms or fears associated with personal or school problems.

(ii) Emotional disturbance includes schizophrenia. The term does not apply to children who are socially maladjusted, unless it is determined that they have an emotional disturbance under paragraph (c)(4)(i) of this section (IDEA, 34 CFR §300.8(c)(4), 2004).

The criteria qualifying a student for ED has been criticized for a handful of specific concerns. First, there are no objective criteria for determining "over a long period of time" and "to a marked degree." Discretion for determining each of these rests with the school district and the evaluation team, but that discretion has resulted in varying legal interpretations (Dietrich, Snyder, & Villani, 2016). For example, in *R.B. v. Napa Valley Unified Sch. Dist.* (2007), the court ruled that the student was not eligible for special education services because, although she displayed inappropriate behaviors over a long period of time, those behaviors were not severe (i.e., to a marked degree) for a long period of time, but instead were only severe for a trimester and improved following an adjustment to her placement.

Perhaps the most controversial component of the federal definition is part two, which explicitly excludes children who are socially maladjusted. The "social maladjustment clause," as it came to be known, has been routinely criticized (Merrell & Walker, 2004) and is essentially designed to exclude students that "choose" to behave the way they do compared with those whose behavior is a manifestation of their disability. A number of efforts were made in the 1980s and 1990s to change the definition of ED, led by the Council for Children with Behavioral Disorders (CCBD), a division of the Council for Exceptional Children (CEC), in a 1987 white paper wherein they made five specific recommendations: (1) revise the federal definition, (2) eliminate arbitrary exclusions, (3) focus on sources of data collection, (4) provide alternative models of service delivery, and (5) meet the priority needs of children with behavior disorders (pp. 16–17). The impetus for the policy recommendations stemmed from a decade of stagnant national percentages of students receiving special education services, which have remained less than 1% of the total student population from 1976 to today. A few years later, Forness & Knitzer (1992) created a coalition of special education and mental health professionals to go beyond the recommendations forwarded by CCBD and push for a new, more inclusive definition that no longer excluded students determined to be socially maladjusted. Although their efforts resulted in congressional testimony, no change at the federal level ever came to fruition.

Although the federal definition for ED has not changed since the inception of IDEA, a number of significant legislative actions have had a profound legal and practical impact on the education of students with ED. First, and rarely a point of discussion, is the designation of autism as a separate, independent category for receipt of special education services. Prior to this change in 1990, students with high functioning autism would have qualified for special education services under the ED category. Although not causally linked, the percentage of students receiving special education services for ED was approximately 1.0% of the total population of U.S. students, while students with intellectual disability accounted for 1.3% of the total U.S. student population. In 2015–2016, approximately 1.2% of students received special education services for autism, while only 0.7% of students received services for ED and 0.8% received services for intellectual disability (National Center for Educational Statistics, 2017).

The sustained prevalence of less than 1% of students receiving special education services due to ED has also been a point of significant criticism. A report by the National Research Council and Institute of Medicine (2009) found that between 14% and 20% of students have an emotional or behavioral disorder. It's worth noting that their figures also include students with diagnosable disorders (e.g., Conduct Disorder), as well as drug and alcohol abuse, antisocial behavior, and violence. More recently, Forness, Freeman, Pararella, Kauffman, and Walker (2012) conducted a meta-analysis to evaluate the actual prevalence of EBD in schools. They reported a conservative prevalence estimate rate for students with EBD of 12.7% at any single point in time in the K–12 population and a cumulative estimate of 37–39% for any point in their school life.

Taken together, it is apparent that the federal definition, which has remained unchanged for over 40 years, beyond the removal of the term "serious" from its title, has been controversial and contentious. Those criticisms have come from Eli Bower (the source of the definition), senior researchers in special education, and from senior researchers in mental health. When compared with national prevalence estimates both with special education research and beyond, it is clear that the less than 1% of students receiving the specialized instruction entitled to those with the ED label represents only a small proportion of those students that are truly in need of those services.

Functional Behavior Assessment and Behavior Intervention Plans

The 1997 reauthorization of IDEA included an amendment, which was later clarified in the 2004 reauthorization, requiring schools use functional behavior assessments (FBA) to develop behavior intervention plans (BIP) under certain, specific circumstances for students with disabilities. FBA is broadly defined as a set of methods that collect information to identify environmental events, or antecedents and consequences, that predict and maintain problem behaviors. An FBA is designed to identify the "function" of a behavior in order to develop a BIP to reduce the occurrence of the challenging behavior and increase the occurrence of a replacement behavior that results in the same or similar outcomes (O'Neill, Albin, Storey, Horner, & Sprague, 2014). The logic of FBA is based on principles of applied behavior analysis, where operant behavior is defined by the three-term contingency of antecedent-behavior-consequence that specifies the functional relationships between antecedent stimuli, a behavior, and its maintaining consequence. Specifically, FBA is an assessment procedure for identifying both antecedent stimuli and maintaining consequences to develop interventions to reduce or increase the likelihood a target behavior occurs and teaches a new alternative behavior for access to the desired consequence.

Research has confirmed the effectiveness of FBA-based BIP for reducing challenging behaviors in school. Gage, Lewis, and Stichter (2012) conducted a systematic review and meta-analysis on the effect of FBA-based BIP for students with or at-risk for EBD. They found 69 single-case design studies and, on average, FBA-based BIP reduced challenging behavior by 70.5%. Recently, the U.S. Department of Education's What Works Clearinghouse (2016) reviewed FBA and found FBA-based interventions to have potentially positive effects on school engagement and potentially positive effects on problem behavior for children identified with or at risk for an emotional disturbance based on evidence from single-case design studies. Taken together, FBA-based BIP are considered evidence-based practices.

According to IDEA (2004), the need for an FBA is triggered when: (1) there is a child with a disability, (2) who is removed for more than 10 school days,

(3) for misconduct that either (a) is a manifestation of the child's disability, (b) is not a manifestation of the child's disability, or (c) involves weapons, drugs, or serious bodily injury, regardless of the outcome of the manifestation determination review, or (4) for behavior that interferes with the learning environment (34 CFR § 300.530(f) (2004)). It's worth noting that, although an FBA is required for students identified with disabilities according to IDEA, the procedural right to an FBA also extends to a "child who has not [yet] been determined to be eligible for special education and related services under IDEA and who has engaged in behavior that violates a code of student conduct . . . if the local educational agency had knowledge . . . that the child was a child with a disability before the behavior that precipitated the disciplinary action occurred" (20 U.S.C. § 1415(k)(5)(A) (2004)). Critical features of the FBA requirement in IDEA are beyond the scope of this chapter and have been fully discussed in the literature (cf. Collins & Zirkel, 2017).

Restraint and Seclusion

The use of restraints and seclusions for violent and aggressive behavior in U.S. schools has directly resulted in significant injury and death (U.S. Government Accountability Office [U.S. GAO], 2009). The Civil Rights Data Collection (CRDC), a biennial survey required by the U.S. Department of Education's (U.S. DOE) Office of Civil Rights designed to assess access and barriers to educational opportunity in U.S. schools, define restraint and seclusion as follows: (a) a *physical restraint* is a personal restriction that immobilizes or reduces the ability of a student to move his or her torso, arms, legs, or head freely; (b) a *mechanical restraint* is any device or equipment used to restrict a student's freedom of movement (excluding devices prescribed for medical services or vehicle safety restraints); and (c) *seclusion* is the involuntary confinement of a student alone in a room or area from which the student is physically prevented from leaving. Table 19.1 provides the most recent statistics from the CRDC. A total of 92,255 schools provided data on the use of restraint and seclusion during the 2015–2016 school year for all students, students with receiving IEP services under IDEA, and students receiving 504 Plan supports. Overall, students with disabilities are five times more likely to receive mechanical restraints, 48 times more likely to receive a physical restraint, and 28 times more likely to be secluded in school. Research suggests that many of the restraint and seclusion incidents are the result of violent and aggressive behavior, as well as noncompliance and property damage, behaviors very often exhibited by students with EBD (Fogt, George, Kern, White, & George, 2008).

Attempts were made in both 2010 and 2014 to pass The Keeping All Students Safe Act (S. 2036, 113th Cong.), legislation designed to provide federal

Table 19.1 The average restraint and seclusion incident per 100 students during the 2015–2016 school year

Restraint/Seclusion	Student Disability Status	Average Number of Incidents per 100 students
Mechanical Restraint		
	Without Disabilities	0.023
	IDEA	0.124
	504 Plan	0.039
Physical Restraint		
	Without Disabilities	0.065
	IDEA	3.179
	504 Plan	0.138
Seclusion		
	Without Disabilities	0.060
	IDEA	1.723
	504 Plan	0.099

Note: Data from the 2015–2016 Civil Rights Data Collection (https://ocrdata.ed.gov/).

minimum standards for the protection of students against restraint and seclusion based on concerns raised in the GAO report. To date, the bill has not been passed. However, to address concerns about restraints and seclusions in schools, the U.S. DOE developed and released a resource document for states to consider when drafting policies and legislation (2012). The resource document provides 15 principles to guide states, districts, and other stakeholders when developing and implementing policies related to restraint and seclusion. For example, the first principle suggests that "every effort should be made to prevent the need for the use of restraint and seclusion," such as positive behavior interventions and supports (PBIS), while the sixth suggests that restraint and seclusion "should never be used as punishment or discipline."

Marx and Baker (2017) recently examined the influence of the U.S. DOE resource document on state legislation and policies on restraint and seclusion. The authors reviewed the websites for all 50 U.S. states and Washington, DC, to determine how many had developed and passed legislation, defined as adopted regulations or statutes on restraint and seclusion, and policies, defined as any written guidance to districts from the state's DOE on restraint and seclusion. The authors found that 38 states had passed legislation and

45 had developed policies, and, of those, 16 specifically referenced the U.S. DOE resource document. It is noteworthy that 17 states passed legislation and 32 states developed policies focused on prevention efforts, with most focused on PBIS.

Positive Behavior Interventions and Supports

Another important legislative advancement since the publication of the first national agenda for achieving better results for children and youth with EBD is the inclusion of PBIS in IDEA. By the late 1990s, Congress began to recognize the need for schools to use evidence-based approaches to proactively address the behavioral needs of students with disabilities (LeBel, Nunno, Mohr, & O'Halloran, 2012). As a result, the reauthorization of IDEA in both 1997 and 2004 explicitly recognized PBIS as a model and approach for preventing the exclusion of students with disabilities and its potential for improving educational results. Specifically, in 20 U.S.C. § 1401(c)(5)(F), Congress notes that:

> (5) Almost 30 years of research and experience has demonstrated that the education of children with disabilities can be made more effective by—(...)
>
> (F) providing incentives for whole-school approaches, scientifically based early reading programs, *positive behavioral interventions and supports*, and early intervening services to reduce the need to label children as disabled in order to address the learning and behavioral needs of such children. (emphasis added)

To increase implementation of PBIS in schools, Congress recognized that funding would be necessary for professional development opportunities. Thus, IDEA provides additional support for the use of PBIS by authorizing states to use professional development funds to "provide training in methods of . . . positive behavioral interventions and supports to improve student behavior in the classroom" (20 U.S.C. §1454(a)(3)(B)(iii)(I)). Further, Congress provided for competitive grant funds used to:

- Ensure that pre-service and in-service training, to general as well as special educators, include positive behavior interventions and supports (20 U.S.C. §1464 (a)(6)(D) & (f)(2)(A)(iv)(I))
- Develop and disseminate PBIS models for addressing conduct that impedes learning (20 U.S.C. §1464(b)(2)(H))
- Provide training and joint training to the entire spectrum of school personnel in the use of whole school positive behavioral interventions and supports (20 U.S.C. §1483(1)(C & D))

Professional development is a critical component of effective PBIS implementation. The professional development ensures that schools have the local capacity to provide universal, preventative behavior management, as well as the expertise to develop and implement high quality FBAs per 34 CFR § 300.530(f) (2004).

Strategic Targets and Cross-Cutting Themes

Based on current data, there remains an opportunity to continue improving outcomes for students with EBD. Therefore, we propose to update the National Agenda, highlight current practices exemplifying each of the updated strategic targets, and forward recommendations for improving implementation and outcomes across the strategic targets. First, we provide an overview of the original National Agenda and a study of program, policies, and initiatives that exemplified the original strategic targets.

Original National Agenda

The original National Agenda for achieving better results for children and youth with EBD identified seven interdependent strategic targets focused on transforming service systems, reorienting professional attitudes, and emphasizing positive outcomes. The strategic targets were as follows:

1. Expand positive learning opportunities and results
2. Strengthen school and community capacity
3. Value and address diversity
4. Collaborate with families
5. Promote appropriate assessment
6. Provide ongoing skill development and support
7. Create comprehensive and collaborative systems (Chesapeake Institute, 1994).

The fundamental assumption underlying the seven original targets is that students with EBD need a proactive continuum of services that wrap around the student and his or her family. In addition to the seven targets, three cross-cutting themes were identified: (1) collaborative efforts must extend to initiatives that prevent emotional and behavioral problems from developing or escalating; (2) services must be provided in a culturally sensitive and respectful manner; and (3) services must empower all stakeholders and maintain a climate of possibility and accountability. The targets were developed to be implemented in concert with each other, not independently, to increase the likelihood students with EBD are successful.

Osher and Hanley (2001) examined programs that exemplify implementation of the original seven targets of the National Agenda to document their impact and identify similarities and differences. They identified 14 programs, policies, and initiatives using four criteria: (1) consistency with the National Agenda, (2) multiple and consistent nominations from five groups of individuals with knowledge of the National Agenda, (3) face validity regarding claims of accomplishments, and (4) availability of data to support their claims of accomplishment. Although none of the programs, policies, or initiatives implemented all seven targets, one program, the Partner's Project, a county project designed to coordinate public agency services for children and youth with EBD in Oregon, addressed five targets, while two other programs, Grant Middle School Day Treatment Program, a day treatment school for middle school students co-located within a traditional public middle school, and Stark County Family Alliance, a comprehensive public system of care for children and youth with EBD in Ohio, addressed three of the targets. Common characteristics across the programs included embracing diversity and employing culturally competent approaches, assessment and early intervention, and collaborative, unconditional wraparound approaches. The authors also note that the programs, although effective and exemplificative of the National Agenda, experienced five barriers to success: (1) funding, (2) institutional inertia, (3) a lack of effective services, (4) building to scale in an effective manner, and (5) cultural competence. Regardless of these barriers, almost all of the programs found positive outcomes for students with EBD, including increased attendance and academic performance and reduced use of restrictive settings.

Updated Strategic Targets

The original seven strategic targets are still relevant today and continue to epitomize best practice. However, as is clear from the significant legislative and policy changes that have occurred since the original strategic targets were developed, much has changed in education, particularly for children and youth with EBD. Further, research has proliferated in education and special education, with myriad evidence-based practices identified and currently being implemented in schools across the United States. Therefore, we propose to update the National Agenda for the 21st century to guide research, policy, and practice for children and youth with EBD.

We used the original seven strategic targets and only augmented those we felt needed to reflect current policy and practice. The updated National Agenda strategic targets are presented in table 19.2 and are as follows:

1. Expand implementation of evidence-based and high-leverage practices
2. Strengthen school and community capacity

3. Value diversity through culturally responsive practice and address disproportionality
4. Collaborate with families
5. Promote appropriate assessment and data-based decision-making
6. Improve pre-service education and provide ongoing professional development and support
7. Create comprehensive, collaborative, and interconnected systems

Table 19.2 Updated national agenda for achieving better results for children and youth with emotional and behavioral disorders

Target #1: Expand Implementation of Evidence-Based and High-Leverage Practices	
	To ensure the implementation of evidence-based and high-leverage practices for all students with EBD. These practices should meet established and accepted scientific standards of evidence for children and youth with EBD. These practices should acknowledge and respond to the experiences and needs of students with EBD.
Target #2: Strengthen School and Community Capacity	
	To foster initiatives that strengthen the capacity of schools and communities to serve students with EBD in the least restrictive environment as appropriate.
Target #3: Value Diversity through Culturally Responsive Practice and Address Disproportionality	
	To encourage culturally competent and linguistically appropriate exchanges and collaborations among families, professionals, students, and communities. These collaborations should be culturally responsive to issues of race, culture, gender, and socioeconomic status; foster equitable outcomes for all students; and address disproportionality of identification for EBD and behavioral outcomes.
Target #4: Collaborate with Families	
	To foster collaborations that fully include family members on the team of service providers that implements family-focused services to improve educational outcomes. Services should be open, helpful, culturally competent, accessible, and evidence-based.
Target #5: Promote Appropriate Assessment and Data-Based Decision-Making	
	To promote practices ensuring that assessment is integral to the identification, design, and delivery of services for children and youth with EBD. These practices should be culturally appropriate, ethical, functional, and data-based.

(*continued*)

Table 19.2 (continued)

Target #6: Improve Pre-Service Education and Provide Ongoing Professional Development and Support	
	To improve pre-service education programs to ensure all educational professionals are effective implementers of evidence-based universal classroom and behavior management practices. To foster the enhancement of knowledge, understanding, and sensitivity among all who work with children and youth with EBD. Professional development and support should be ongoing and strengthen the capacity of families, service providers, teachers, and other stakeholders to collaborate, persevere, and improve outcomes for children and youth with EBD.
Target #7: Create Comprehensive, Collaborative, and Interconnected Systems	
	To promote systems change resulting in the development of coherent services built around the individual needs of children and youth with EBD. These services should foster collaboration across agencies and expertise to address the mental health, behavioral, academic, and social needs of students with EBD. These interconnected services should be family-centered, community-based, and appropriately funded.

The updated strategic targets are still based on the fundamental assumption that a flexible and proactive continuum of services must be built around the needs of the child. However, we have added to the cross-cutting themes, retaining the original three (*prevention*, *culturally responsive*, and *empowering*) and adding a fourth, *evidence-based*. We contend that achieving successful outcomes for children and youth with EBD depends on continued improvement of legislative and policy-related protections and implementing effective practices for pursuing and attaining all of the updated National Agenda strategic targets.

Strategic Target #1: Expand Implementation of Evidence-Based and High-Leverage Practices

Children and youth with EBD are not experiencing the same level of success as their same age peers without disabilities; therefore, they require educational practices that provide additional services and supports to increase their academic, behavioral, and social performance. Those practices should be evidence-based to increase the likelihood that children and youth with EBD make successful gains. The function of evidence-based practices is to identity and use what works best. However, the determination of "what works best" and what type of evidence confirms or denies how well something works is contentious (Cook, Tankersley, & Landrum, 2009; Odom et al., 2005). Although practices may have face validity and practitioner enthusiasm, educators, specifically special educators, are charged with using practices that increase student achievement, including, but not limited to, academic achievement, social and behavioral performance, and vocational skills to ensure students have the skills to be successful into adulthood. The systematic evaluation of practices using empirical methods is necessary to validate those practices. Achenbach (1975) made this point clear in the early years of the emotional and/or behavioral disorders (E/BD) field: "We need to temper our spirit of reform with an attitude of scientific skepticism and to build into our paradigms fundamental research and development components designed to insure that our enthusiasms are well founded" (p. 14).

The impetus for increased focus on evidence-based practices in education was the passage of the No Child Left Behind Act of 2001 (NCLB), which recommended use of practices based on *scientific evidence* (Lewis, Hudson, Richter, & Johnson, 2004; Slavin, 2008). Although NCLB was the first education act to explicitly legislate the use of evidence-based practices, prior legislation set the stage, including the Government Performance Results Act of 1993, which focused on performance measurement and accountability for government agencies, and a 1998 appropriation of $150 million per year for comprehensive education reform models based on experimental-control and standards-based measures (Slavin, 2002). However, NCLB went further than any previous bill, referencing "scientifically-based research" 110 times, and formally defining it as "rigorous, systematic and objective procedures to obtain valid knowledge" (No Child Left Behind Act, 2001).

NCLB put in motion a set of policy augmentations around evidence-based practice, specifically the creation of Institute of Educational Sciences (IES) with the Education Sciences Reform Act of 2002, which serves as the research arm of the U.S. DOE and whose goal is to transform education into an evidence-based field where decisions are made based on the best available data, and the reauthorization of IDEA in 2004 and its emphasis on the use of scientifically based practices. To increase the use of evidence-based practices in education, including special education, IES developed the What Works Clearinghouse (WWC), a federal center designed to identify and recommend evidence-based practices.

To date, WWC has developed one practice guide, a review of the best available evidence and expertise on a specific topic with recommendations for implementation, focused on reducing behavior problems in elementary school classrooms (Epstein, Atkins, Cullinan, Kutash, & Weaver, 2008). Recommendations include identifying the problem behavior and the conditions that prompt and reinforce it, teach and reinforce new appropriate skills, and adoption of schoolwide behavioral strategies. In addition, the WWC has reviewed the evidence-for 54 behavior-focused interventions, 16 of which are considered evidence-based, including First Step to Success (Walker et al., 2009) and Coping Power (Lochman et al., 2009).

A recent development in special education is high-leverage practices, which, unlike evidence-based practices, are considered essential skills *all* special educators should have to ensure student success. Specifically, high-leverage practices are practices that can be used to leverage student learning across different content areas, grade levels, and student abilities and disabilities (McLeskey et al., 2017). There are currently 22 high-leverage practices, and of those, four are focused on the addressing social, emotional, and behavioral concerns. The four EBD-focused high-leverage practices are as follows: (1) establish a consistent, organized, and respectful learning environment; (2) provide positive and constructive feedback to guide students' learning and behavior; (3) teach social behaviors; and (4) conduct functional behavioral assessments to develop individual student behavior support plans.

To increase positive outcomes for children and youth with EBD, all teachers should have expertise and skill in the high-leverage practices and, when needed, employ evidence-based practices targeting specific skill deficits or behavioral concerns. That being said, children and youth with EBD should also have access to challenging curricula, effective teaching, and robust learning experiences to increase their chances for success. We believe that schools and programs using a continuum of evidence-based and high-leverage practices will have the most success and that policy should reflect the need for these practices in all schools for all children and youth, but particularly those with EBD.

Target #2: Strengthen School and Community Capacity

Children and youth with EBD are excluded from general education and removed from regular schools at rates significantly higher than all other students (McLeskey, Landers, Williamson, & Hoppey, 2012). There are a number of deleterious effects associated with removal from a student's home school, including increased risk for school dropout and sustained low academic performance (Lehr, Tan, & Ysseldyke, 2009). Recently, Wilkerson, Afacan, Perzigian, Justin, and Lequia (2016) examined outcomes for students with EBD attending behavior-focused alternative schools. Using data from a large school district, the authors matched students in the alternative schools to students in traditional public schools using propensity scores and found that students in alternative schools earned fewer credits and had lower attendance rates. However, students in the behavior-focused alternative schools also reported fewer office discipline referrals, suggesting that teachers in the alternative schools may have been better at managing student behavior. Essentially, these data indicate that students in alternative schools are not progressing as they should academically and that the behavior management strategies in the alternative schools should be implemented in traditional public schools to increase credits earned, attendance, and decrease office discipline referrals.

This strategic target, then, calls for increasing access to the general curriculum for children and youth with EBD to ensure that they are being educated in the least restrictive environment. This requires that schools and communities build capacity to prevent and address social and behavioral concerns. To accomplish this goal, schools need to develop and expand initiatives to improve the readiness and capacity to educate and provide the needed services to children and youth with EBD. This target supports early intervention, prevention, and pre-referral initiatives, including early screening, teacher consultation, and mainstream assistance teams. Further, there is a need for active collaborations among regular and special educators, service providers, and families. One evidence-based model that currently exemplifies this target is schoolwide positive behavior interventions and supports (SWPBIS; Gage, Grasley-Boy, George, Childs, & Kincaid, 2018). SWPBIS is a multitiered framework of behavioral supports that increases use of evidence-based prevention and intervention strategies throughout a school (Sugai & Horner, 2009). The SWPBIS framework organizes behavioral supports into three tiers: universal (Tier 1), secondary (Tier 2), and tertiary (Tier 3). All tiers emphasize frequent and accurate data collection and analysis to inform systems- and individual-level decisions, including moving individual students to more intensive supports and systematically removing those supports once the student demonstrates improvement.

Strategic Target #3: Value Diversity through Culturally Responsive Practice and Address Disproportionality

Children and youth with EBD are diverse across myriad characteristics, including ethnicity, culture, English proficiency, gender, and socioeconomic status (Skiba, Middelberg, & McClain, 2014). To avoid misidentification and inappropriate treatment for some students, diversity must be addressed and valued. To value diversity is to acknowledge, understand, and appreciate the characteristics of different cultures and different groups of people. To address diversity is to develop the ability to work successfully with people of diverse backgrounds when designing and implementing interventions, practices, and programs for children with EBD. Doing so ensures that practices are culturally responsive, which is defined as using the cultural characteristics, experiences, and perspectives of ethnically diverse students as conduits for teaching and intervening more effectively (Gay, 2002).

Many students of color experience culturally unresponsive practices (Osher, Cartledge, Oswald, Artiles, & Coutinho, 2004) and cultural responsiveness has been promoted as an effective way of addressing this challenge (Cartledge & Lo, 2006). Although no review of culturally responsive practices for children and youth with EBD has been conducted, a review has been conducted for children and youth with disabilities broadly. Aceves and Orosco (2014) identified eight emerging and recommended evidence-based culturally responsive practices for children and youth with disabilities. Specific practices include: (a) collaborative teaching, which involves joint intellectual effort between students and teachers; (b) responsive feedback, defined as critical, ongoing, and immediate feedback regarding students' responses and participation; (c) modeling, which involves explicit discussion of instructional expectations while providing examples based on students' cultural, linguistic, and lived experiences; (d) instructional scaffolding, which occurs when the teachers control for task difficulty and promote a deeper level of understanding using students' contributions and their cultural and linguistic backgrounds; (e) problem-solving approach, which requires teachers to create opportunities for students to investigate real, open-ended problems, formulate questions, and develop solutions to genuine challenging situations; (f) child-centered instruction, where teachers respond to students' cultural and linguistic backgrounds and learning needs; (g) assessments designed to consider students' linguistic and cultural identities; and (h) materials that integrate research-developed and teacher-selected materials that validate and consider students' cultural, linguistic, and racial identities.

In addition to culturally responsive practice, this strategic target is focused on preventing discrimination by addressing issues of disproportionate representation of diverse children and youth identified for EBD and disproportionate discipline for diverse students (CCBD, 2013). Although dated, a seminal study by Donovan and Cross (2002) found significant disproportionate representation of nonwhite students receiving special education services for EBD and Artiles and colleagues (2010) extended this analysis. However, this conclusion continues to be debated (cf. Sullivan, 2017; Voulgarides, Fergus, & King Thorious, 2017). Nonetheless, disproportionate identification and discipline is a significant concern. The Council for Children with Behavioral Disorders (2013) developed a series of policy recommendations, including interpreting "inappropriate identification" broadly, to include all educational practices that might contribute to disproportionate representation and an increased focus on issues of culture. We contend that the strategic target goes further by recommending culturally responsive approaches that recognize the cultural grounding of teachers' and service providers' views, behaviors, and methods, and that they recognize the power of language and attend to the communicative styles of their students and families. Overall, pre-referral and preventive approaches should be culturally competent and linguistically appropriate to recognize and nurture the strengths—individual and cultural—that students bring to school.

Strategic Target #4: Collaborate with Families

Family-driven practices (Osher & Osher, 2002) and family support services are key factors in successfully addressing the needs of children and youth with EBD. Increased parent involvement is associated with regular school attendance, higher academic performance, higher standardized test scores, improved behavior, and higher homework completion (Dearing, Kreider, Simpkins, & Weiss, 2006). To improve outcomes for these children and youth, educators and service providers should collaborate with families and support the active participation of families in program planning and evaluation.

The object of this strategic target is to reorient family-school interactions to build a partnership that reflects the input of families' goals, knowledge, culture, and, in some cases, need for additional services, while also maintaining the integrity of the intervention. For example, the First Steps to Success program (Walker et al., 2009), highlighted in the Osher and Hanley (2001) review of programs and an evidence-based practice according to the WWC, includes a parent component called homebound. Specifically, the program is designed to increase communication and collaboration between parents and their child's teacher so that the interventions focused on specific behaviors are also addressed consistently at home.

Any collaborative relationship between schools or teachers and parents should be marked by a demonstration of respect and compassion for family members; an understanding and an accommodation of different styles of social interaction; the use of straightforward language; creative outreach efforts; respect for families' cultures and experiences; providing families with crucial information and viable options; and the scheduling of IEP meetings at convenient times and places for families (Minke & Anderson, 2005). In addition, families may need assistance with transportation, translation services, respite care, day care, and help making connections to community resources to meet the needs of their other children and possibly adult family members.

Strategic Target #5: Promote Appropriate Assessment and Data-Based Decision-Making

Appropriate, periodic, and practical assessment is essential to identify, monitor, and make instructional decisions for children and youth with EBD. Screening, monitoring, and intervening early, based on data, may reduce the need for formal identification at a later time, augment planning, and monitor the implementation of comprehensive support services. Research has consistently found intervening early has a positive long-term effect on externalizing (e.g., physical aggression, noncompliance) and internalizing behaviors (e.g., depression, anxiety) and academic success (Duncan et al., 2007; Masten et al., 2005). Therefore, screening children and youth early to identify those in need of intervention and support is a focus of this strategic target.

A number of screening tools have been developed and evaluated over the past 25 years (for a complete review of screening tools, see Lane, Oakes, Menzies, & Germer, 2014). The Systematic Screening for Behavior Disorders (SSBD; Walker & Severson, 1992) is among the oldest, yet most reliable screening measures for EBD. The SSBD uses a three-stage, or gate, model for screening and identifying children and youth with EBD. The first gate involves the ranking of all students by a classroom teacher, taking into account both external and internal behaviors. In the second gate, the teacher completes a more detailed measure of the students who were most at risk for externalizing and internalizing behaviors and the results are compared to a normed sample of students. The third, and last, gate involves an observation of identified students by a trained data collector using a rating scale. Another reliable screening tool is the Student Risk Screening Scale—Internalizing and Externalizing (SRSS-IE; Lane et al., 2015). Students are rated across seven items: (1) steal; (2) lie, cheat, sneak; (3) behavior problem; (4) peer rejection; (5) low academic achievement; (6) negative attitude; and (7) aggressive behavior. At the elementary level, teachers independently rate each student in their classroom on the seven items using a 4-point Likert-type scale, then the items are summed to offer a total score. Students are then identified as low, moderate, or high risk for EBD. Unlike the SSBD, the SSRS is free-access, making it an ideal tool for schoolwide screening.

For classification of students under IDEA, myriad measures and approaches are available (for an overview, see Pierangelo & Giuliani, 2012). That being said, all assessment and evaluation procedures should be culturally competent, linguistically appropriate, and multidisciplinary; involve families; focus on helping teachers build on student strengths; and address the changing developmental needs of children and youth with EBD. During the 1970s and 1980s, research suggested that overrepresentation of certain groups with EBD was linked to test bias, however, that research has been challenged (Valencia & Suzuki, 2000). Nonetheless, some continue to make a strong case for the role of culture, ethnicity, gender, and socioeconomic status on misidentification. For example, Artiles and colleagues (2010) argue that there has been significant undertheorizing with regards to issues of culture and race in identification for EBD. Therefore, this target encourages the development of identification and assessment procedures that meet the needs of all children that are accurate, linguistically appropriate, and culturally fair and capable of generating necessary information to enable educators to provide appropriate educational experiences for all children and youth with EBD. One evidence-based approach that meets both the appropriate and data-based component of the strategic target is FBA. All students exhibiting EBD in schools should receive FBA as necessary in order to develop interventions that target the function of the behavior, increasing the likelihood of success (Gage et al., 2012).

Strategic Target #6: Improve Pre-Service Education and Provide Ongoing Professional Development and Support

Learning to teach is difficult. Effective teachers, particularly special education teachers, have extensive knowledge and skill to increase achievement and manage behavior. Instructional expertise is developed through coursework and careful practice coupled with constructive feedback. Pre-service teachers need high-quality opportunities to practice above and beyond coursework and to receive feedback as they begin to implement the skills learned (Ball & Forzani, 2009). There is convincing evidence that effective teachers are the most important in-school contributors to student learning in classrooms (cf. Glazerman, et al., 2010). Further, research has found that teachers from pre-service programs that provide direct links between knowledge and practice, providing opportunities in real classroom settings, have more of an effect on their students' learning than teachers from programs that do not provide such opportunities (Boyd, Grossman, Lankford, Loeb, & Wyckoff, 2009). Research also suggests that pre-service preparation has a direct and meaningful impact on the achievement of students with disabilities. Feng and Sass (2013) examined differential achievement for students with disabilities in Florida based on their teacher's pre-service certification. Overall, they found that students with disabilities performed statistically significantly higher if their teacher was certified in special education. Taken together, this strategic target is focused on improving teacher preparation to improve outcomes for children and youth with EBD.

An exemplary model for improving pre-service teacher education is the national technical assistance center, the Collaboration for Effective Educator Development, Accountability and Reform (CEEDAR) Center. CEEDAR works directly with states and institutions of higher education to reform their special education teacher and leader preparation programs, revise licensure standards to align with reforms, refine personnel evaluation systems, and realign policy structures and professional learning systems (http://ceedar .education.ufl.edu/). In addition to their "on the ground" technical assistance, they have developed a series of innovation configurations (IC), which are designed to evaluate current teacher preparation and professional development by determining the extent to which evidence-based practices are taught, observed, and applied within teacher preparation and professional development programs. Among the ICs developed, one specifically addresses evidence-based practices for students with EBD (Gage, 2015).

This strategic target also provides for the ongoing support and professional development of teachers and other service providers in order to: (1) increase their capacity to teach and work effectively for children and youth with EBD, (2) reduce their sense of isolation, and (3) enhance their commitment to meeting the needs of children and youth with EBD. Professional development for teachers and other service providers ensures that they can develop new skills, acquire knowledge of promising intervention techniques, and become aware of new innovations and practices. Research has not identified the most salient professional approach (Yoon, Duncan, Lee, Scarloss, & Shapley, 2007), but it is accepted that professional development is ineffective without sustained, ongoing, and significant support and follow-up (Fixsen, Naoom, Blase, Friedman, & Wallace, 2005), defined as 30 or more direct contact hours with each teacher (Yoon et al., 2007). Professional development contact should, at minimum, include didactic skill instruction, coaching, and performance feedback (Simonsen et al., 2014). An exemplary professional development model for improving outcomes for students with EBD is the BEST in CLASS program (Vo, Sutherland, & Conroy, 2012). The BEST in CLASS professional development model consists of seven modules focused on instructional support practices for children with EBD (i.e., rules, precorrection, opportunities to respond, behavior-specific praise, corrective feedback, instructive feedback, and linking and mastery). Teachers are introduced to the model at a BEST in CLASS workshop and then receive support during 14 weeks of practice-based coaching as they master each module.

Strategic Target #7: Create Comprehensive, Collaborative, and Interconnected Systems

Systemic change is necessary to enhance school and community capacity to meet the needs and challenges of children and youth with EBD. This strategic target supports frameworks and initiatives designed to generate comprehensive and seamless systems of appropriate, culturally competent, mutually reinforcing services. This target envisions systems that are more than linkages of initiatives, programs, and agencies. It aims instead at developing new systems, built around the needs of children and youth with EBD, their families, and their communities. In addition to being comprehensive and collaborative, we envision these initiatives as also interconnected, defined as having all constituent parts linked. Systems that are comprehensive, collaborative, and interconnected ensure that all necessary systems are working together, seamlessly, to have sustained positive effects of children and youth with EBD.

One approach characterizing this strategic target is the Interconnected Systems Framework (ISF; Barrett, Eber, & Weist, 2013). The ISF is a comprehensive and collaborative interconnection of positive behavior interventions and supports (PBIS) and school mental health (SMH). As noted above, PBIS is an evidence-based multitiered framework for prevention and intervention of behavior problems in schools (Gage et al., 2018). SMH is the continuum of mental health promotion programs and services in schools, including mental health screening, psychotherapy services, cognitive behavioral interventions, and multi-systemic therapy (Barrett et al., 2013). ISF, then, involves collaborating community and school mental health providers working closely within a multitiered teaming structure, actively reviewing data and coordinating the implementation, and fidelity and progress monitoring of supports delivered at multiple levels of intensity, and collaborating with and engaging families in the design and implementation of interventions.

Another exemplary model is the wraparound process, defined as a team-based collaborative across multiple community agencies for developing and implementing interventions and supports for students with EBD (Bruns, Walker, & National Wraparound Initiative Advisory Group, 2008). Walker and Bruns (2006) outlined 10 principles of the wraparound process: (1) family voice and choice, (2) team-based, (3) natural supports, (4) collaboration, (5) community-based, (6) culturally competent, (7) individualized, (8) strength-based, (9) unconditional, and (10) outcome-based. The evidence for the wraparound process is encouraging. Suter and Burns (2009) conducted a meta-analysis on the effects of the wraparound process on children with EBD. They found seven studies that included 802 children with EBD and, across the studies, the overall effect on behavior was $d = 0.33$ ($p < 0.05$).

Conclusion

Children and youth with emotional and behavioral disorders (EBD) continue to experience and present myriad challenges and the need for addressing those challenges is clear. The goal of this chapter was to update the national agenda for achieving better results for children and youth with EBD (Chesapeake Institute, 1994). We believe that building programs and services that meet the seven strategic targets of the updated national agenda will have the best opportunity to make truly meaningful impacts on the lives of children and youth with EBD. By exemplifying the four cross-cutting themes (prevention, culturally responsive, empowering, and evidence-based), stakeholders can develop, grow, proliferate, and sustain effective programs.

Appendix

IDEA 2004: Functional Behavioral Assessment – Fact Sheet

School districts are required to conduct functional behavioral assessment of problem behaviors, under certain circumstances. Framed by IDEA are several contextual factors which taken together alert school administrators that the need to conduct a functional behavioral assessment has been triggered:

(1) There is a child with a disability

(2) Who is removed for more than ten school days

(3) For misconduct that either:

> (a) is a manifestation of the child's disability,
>
> (b) is not a manifestation of the child's disability,
>
> (c) involves weapons, drugs, or serious bodily injury, regardless of the outcome of the manifestation determination review

(4) For behavior that interferes with the learning environment

In addition, schools are expected to use functional behavioral assessment proactively and to intervene early to prevent serious problem behaviors: The IDEA states that a behavior intervention plan based on a functional behavioral assessment should be considered when developing the IEP if a student's behavior interferes with his or her learning or the learning of classmates (20 U.S.C. § 1414(d)(3)(B)(i) (2004)). To be meaningful, plans need to be reviewed at least annually and revised as often as needed. However, the plan may be reviewed and reevaluated whenever any member of the child's IEP team feels it is necessary.

Administrators continue to have great flexibility with respect to the substance of the functional behavioral assessment, being that they are provided with only contextual guidance respecting their duty to provide the assessment.

The IDEA does not specify any members of a particular profession (or member(s) of the IEP team) who might be qualified to conduct functional behavioral assessments. As a result of the lack of federal direction, states or even districts must determine who conducts the assessments.

IDEA 2004 provisions call for schools to have properly trained professionals available to conduct functional behavioral assessments and develop appropriate behavioral intervention plans. It is the district's responsibility, working with the state department of education, to provide professional development, in-service training, and technical assistance, as needed, for school staff members to be able to conduct FBAs well.

In Closing, schools have a legal responsibility to students with disabilities to provide behavioral support needed for a free, public, appropriate education. Under some circumstances, this includes a functional behavioral assessment and a related positive behavior intervention plan and services. Although IDEA 2004 provided some changes in wording and in requirements related to functional behavioral assessments from IDEA '97, professional judgment remains essential for deciding how to conduct functional behavioral assessments on an individual basis. This is consistent with the basis for special education, which is an individualized education plan.

The follow Q&A was taken from: http://idea.ed.gov/explore/view/p/,root,dynamic,QaCorner,7,

US Department of Ed
Building the Legacy: 2004

Questions and Answers
on Discipline Procedures

Revised June 2009

Functional Behavior Assessments (FBAs) and Behavioral Intervention Plans (BIPs)

Question E-1: Was the requirement for a "positive behavioral intervention plan" removed from the discipline regulations?

Answer: No. Under 34 CFR §300.324(a)(2)(i), the use of positive behavioral interventions and supports must be considered in the case of a child whose behavior impedes his or her learning or that of others. The requirement in 34 CFR §300.530(f) that a child with a disability receive, as appropriate, an FBA and a BIP and modifications designed to address the child's behavior now only applies to students whose behavior is a manifestation of their disability as determined by the LEA, the parent, and the relevant members of the child's IEP Team under 34 CFR §300.530(e). However, FBAs and BIPs must also be used proactively, if the IEP Team determines that they would be appropriate for the child. The regulations in 34 CFR §300.530(d) require that school districts provide FBAs and behavior intervention services (and modifications) "as appropriate" to students when the student's disciplinary change in placement would exceed 10 consecutive school days and the student's behavior was not a manifestation of his or her disability. See 34 CFR §300.530(c) and (d). Please see question E-2 in this section for more information about the use and development of FBAs and BIPs.

(continued)

Question E-2: Under what circumstances must an IEP Team use FBAs and BIPs?

Answer: As noted above, pursuant to 34 CFR §300.530(f), FBAs and BIPs are required when the LEA, the parent, and the relevant members of the child's IEP Team determine that a student's conduct was a manifestation of his or her disability under 34 CFR §300.530(e). If a child's misconduct has been found to have a direct and substantial relationship to his or her disability, the IEP Team will need to conduct an FBA of the child, unless one has already been conducted. Similarly, the IEP Team must write a BIP for this child, unless one already exists. If a BIP already exists, then the IEP Team will need to review the plan and modify it, as necessary, to address the behavior.

An FBA focuses on identifying the function or purpose behind a child's behavior. Typically, the process involves looking closely at a wide range of child-specific factors (e.g., social, affective, environmental). Knowing why a child misbehaves is directly helpful to the IEP Team in developing a BIP that will reduce or eliminate the misbehavior.

For a child with a disability whose behavior impedes his or her learning or that of others, and for whom the IEP Team has decided that a BIP is appropriate, or for a child with a disability whose violation of the code of student conduct is a manifestation of the child's disability, the IEP Team must include a BIP in the child's IEP to address the behavioral needs of the child.

Question E-3: How can an IEP address behavior?

Answer: When a child's behavior impedes the child's learning or that of others, the IEP Team must consider the use of positive behavioral interventions and supports, and other strategies, to address that behavior (34 CFR §300.324(a)(2)(i)). Additionally, the Team may address the behavior through annual goals in the IEP (34 CFR §300.320(a)(2)(i)). The child's IEP may include modifications in his or her program, support for his or her teachers, and any related services necessary to achieve those behavioral goals (34 CFR §300.320(a)(4)). If the child needs a BIP to improve learning and socialization, the BIP can be included in the IEP and aligned with the goals in the IEP.

Question E-4: Is consent required to do an FBA for a child?

Answer: Yes. An FBA is generally understood to be an individualized evaluation of a child in accordance with 34 CFR §§300.301 through 300.311 to assist in determining whether the child is, or continues to be, a child with a disability. The FBA process is frequently used to determine the nature and extent of the special education and related services that the child needs, including the need for a BIP. As with other individualized evaluation procedures, and consistent with 34 CFR §300.300(a) and (c), parental consent is required for an FBA to be conducted as

(continued)

part of the initial evaluation or a reevaluation.

Question E-5: If a parent disagrees with the results of an FBA, may the parent obtain an independent educational evaluation (IEE) at public expense?

Answer: Yes. The parent of a child with a disability has the right to request an IEE of the child, under 34 CFR §300.502, if the parent disagrees with an evaluation obtained by the public agency. However, the parent's right to an IEE at public expense is subject to certain conditions, including the LEA's option to request a due process hearing to show that its evaluation is appropriate. See 34 CFR §300.502(b)(2) through (b)(5). The Department has clarified previously that an FBA that was not identified as an initial evaluation, was not included as part of the required triennial reevaluation, or was not done in response to a disciplinary removal, would nonetheless be considered a reevaluation or part of a reevaluation under Part B because it was an individualized evaluation conducted in order to develop an appropriate IEP for the child. Therefore, a parent who disagrees with an FBA that is conducted in order to develop an appropriate IEP also is entitled to request an IEE. Subject to the conditions in 34 CFR §300.502(b)(2) through (b)(5), the IEE of the child will be at public expense.

References

Aceves, T. C., & Orosco, M. J. (2014). *Culturally responsive teaching* (Document No. IC-2). University of Florida, Collaboration for Effective Educator, Development, Accountability, and Reform Center. Retrieved from http://ceedar.education.ufl.edu/tools/innovation-configurations/

Achenbach, T. M. (1975). The historical context of treatment for delinquent and maladjusted children: Past, present, and future. *Behavioral Disorders*, *1*, 3–64.

Artiles, A. J., Kozleski, E. B., Trent, S. C., Osher, D., & Ortiz, A. (2010). Justifying and explaining disproportionality, 1968–2008: A critique of underlying views of culture. *Exceptional Children, 76*, 279–299.

Ball, D. L., & Forzani, F. M. (2009). The work of teaching and the challenge for teacher education. *Journal of Teacher Education, 60*, 497–511.

Barrett, S., Eber, L., & Weist, M. (2013). *Advancing education effectiveness: Interconnecting school mental health and school-wide positive behavior support.* Retrieved from https://www.pbis.org/school/school-mental-health/interconnected-systems

Blackorby, J., Wagner, M., Cameto, R., Davies, E., Levine, P., Newman, L., . . . Sumi, C. (2005). *Engagement, academics, social adjustment, and independents: The achievements of elementary and middle school students with disabilities* (SRI Project P10656). Menlo Park, CA: SRI International.

Bower, E. M. (1982). Defining emotional disturbance public policy and research. *Psychology in the Schools, 19*, 55–60. doi:10.1002/1520-6807(19820108)19:1<55::AID-PITS2310190112>3.0.CO;2-2

Boyd, D. J., Grossman, P. L., Lankford, H., Loeb, S., & Wyckoff, J. (2009). Teacher preparation and student achievement. *Educational Evaluation and Policy Analysis, 31*, 416–440.

Bruns, E. J., Walker, J. S., & National Wraparound Initiative Advisory Group. (2008). Ten principles of the wraparound process. In E. J. Bruns & J. S. Walker (Eds.), *The resource guide to wraparound*. Portland, OR: National Wraparound Initiative, Research and Training Center for Family Support and Children's Mental Health, Portland State University. Retrieved from http:// www.rtc.pdx.edu/NWI-book

Cartledge, G., & Lo, Y. (2006). *Teaching urban learners: Culturally responsive strategies for developing academic and behavioral competence*. Champaign, IL: Research Press.

Chesapeake Institute (1994). *National agenda for achieving better results for children and youth with serious emotional disturbance*. Washington, DC: U. S. Department of Education, Office of Special Education and Rehabilitative Services.

Collins, L. W., & Zirkel, P. A. (2017). Functional behavior assessments and behavior intervention plans: Legal requirements and professional recommendations. *Journal of Positive Behavior Interventions, 19*, 180–190. doi:10.1177/1098300716682201

Cook, B. G., Tankersley, M., & Landrum, T. J. (2009). Determining evidence-based practices in special education. *Exceptional Children, 75*, 365–383. doi:10.1177/001440290907500306

Council for Children with Behavioral Disorders. (2013). CCBD's position summary on federal policy on disproportionality in special education. *Behavioral Disorders, 38*, 108–120.

Dearing, E., Kreider, H., Simpkins, S., & Weiss, H. B. (2006). Family involvement in school and low-income children's literacy: Longitudinal associations between and within families. *Journal of Educational Psychology, 98*, 653–664.

Dietrich, C. A., Snyder, N. D., & Villani, C. J. (2016). Legal study of children with emotional disturbance and mental health needs and implication for practice. *Journal of Law & Education*, 45, 39–64.

Donovan, S., & Cross, C. T. (2002). *Minority students in special and gifted education*. Washington, DC: National Academies Press. doi:10.17226/10128

Duncan, G. J., Dowsett, C. J., Claessens, A., Magnuson, K., Huston, A. C., Klebanov, P., . . . Sexton, H. (2007). School readiness and later achievement. *Developmental Psychology, 43*, 1428–1446. doi:10.1037/0012-1649.43.6.1428

Epstein, M., Atkins, M., Cullinan, D., Kutash, K., & Weaver, R. (2008). *Reducing behavior problems in the elementary school classroom: A practice guide* (NCEE #2008-012). Washington, DC: National Center for Education Evaluation and Regional Assistance, Institute of Education Sciences, U.S. Department of Education. Retrieved from http://ies.ed.gov/ncee/wwc/publications/practiceguides

Feng, L., & Sass, T. R. (2013). What makes special-education teachers special? Teacher training and achievement of students with disabilities. *Economics of Education Review, 36*, 122–134.

Fixsen, D. L., Naoom, S. F., Blase, K. A., Friedman, R. M., & Wallace, F. (2005). *Implementation research: A synthesis of the literature* (FMHI Publication

#231). Tampa: University of South Florida, Louis de la Parte Florida Mental Health Institute, The National Implementation Research Network.

Fogt, J. B., George, M. P., Kern, L., White, G. P., & George, N. L. (2008). Physical restraint of students with behavior disorders in day treatment and residential settings. *Behavioral Disorders, 34*, 4–13.

Forness, S. R., Freeman, S. F. N., Pararella, T., Kauffman, J. M., & Walker, H. M. (2012). Special education implications of point and cumulative prevalence for children with emotional or behavioral disorders. *Journal of Emotional and Behavioral Disorders, 20*, 4–18. doi:10.1177/1063426611401624

Forness, S. R., & Knitzer, J. (1992). A new proposed definition and terminology to replace "serious emotional disturbance" in Individuals with Disabilities Act. *School Psychology Review, 21*, 12–21.

Gage, N. A. (2015). *Evidence-based practices for classroom and behavior management: Tier 2 and Tier 3 strategies* (Document No. IC-15). University of Florida, Collaboration for Effective Educator, Development, Accountability, and Reform Center. Retrieved from http://ceedar.education.ufl.edu/tools/innovation-configurations/

Gage, N. A., Grasley-Boy, N., George, H. P., Childs, K., & Kincaid, D. (2018). A quasi-experimental design analysis of the effects of school-wide positive behavior interventions and supports on discipline in Florida. *Journal of Positive Behavior Interventions*. doi:10.1177/1098300718768208

Gage, N. A., Lewis, T. J., & Stichter, J. P. (2012). Functional behavioral assessment-based interventions for students with emotional and/or behavioral disorders in school: An HLM-meta-analysis. *Behavioral Disorders, 37*(2), 55–77.

Gay, G. (2002). Preparing for culturally responsive teaching. *Journal of Teacher Education, 53*, 106–116.

Glazerman, S., Loeb, S., Goldhaber, D. D., Raudenbush, S., & Whitehurst, G. J. (2010). *Evaluating teachers: The important role of value-added* (Vol. 201). Washington, DC: Brown Center on Education Policy at Brookings.

Individuals with Disabilities Education Improvement Act of 2004, Pub. L. No. 108-446; 20 U.S.C. §§ 1401 et seq.

Lane, K. L., Oakes, W. P., Menzies, H. M., & Germer, K. A. (2014). Screening and identification approaches for detecting students at risk. In H. M. Walker & F. M. Gresham (Eds.), *Handbook of evidence-based practices for emotional and behavioral disorders: Applications in schools* (pp. 129–151). New York: Guilford Press.

Lane, K. L., Oakes, W. P., Swogger, E. D., Schatschneider, C., Menzies, H., M., & Sanchez, J. (2015). Student risk screening scale for internalizing and externalizing behaviors: Preliminary cut scores to support data-informed decision making. *Behavioral Disorders, 40*, 159–170.

LeBel, J., Nunno, M. A., Mohr, W. K., & O'Halloran, R. (2012). Restraint and seclusion use in U.S. school settings: Recommendations from allied treatment disciplines. *American Journal of Orthopsychiatry, 82*(1), 75–86. doi:10.1111/j.1939-0025.2011.01134.x

Lehr, C. A., Tan, C. S., & Ysseldyke, J. (2009). Alternative schools: A synthesis of state-level policy and research. *Remedial and Special Education, 30*, 19–32. doi:10.1177/0741932508315645

Lewis, T. J., Hudson, S., Richter, M., & Johnson, N. (2004). Scientifically supported practices in emotional and behavioral disorders: A proposed approach and brief review of current practices. *Behavioral Disorders, 29*, 247–259. doi:10.1177/019874290402900306

Lochman, J. E., Boxmeyer, C., Powell, N., Qu, L., Wells, K., & Windle, M. (2009). Dissemination of the Coping Power program: Importance of intensity of counselor training. *Journal of Consulting and Clinical Psychology, 77*, 397–409.

Marx, T. A., & Baker, J. N (2017). Analysis of restraint and seclusion legislation and policy across states: Adherence to recommended principles. *Journal of Disability Policy Studies, 28*, 23–31.

Masten, A. S., Roisman, G. I., Long, J. D., Burt, K. B., Obradović, J., Riley, J. R., . . . Tellegen, A. (2005). Developmental cascades: Linking academic achievement and externalizing and internalizing symptoms over 20 years. *Developmental Psychology, 41*, 733–746. doi:10.1037/0012-1649.41.5.733

McFarland, J., Hussar, B., de Brey, C., Snyder, T., Wang, X., Wilkinson-Flicker, S., . . . Hinz, S. (2017). *The condition of education 2017* (NCES 2017- 144). U.S. Department of Education. Washington, DC: National Center for Education Statistics. Retrieved from https://nces.ed.gov/pubsearch/pubsinfo.asp?pubid=2017144

McLeskey, J., Barringer, M.-D., Billingsley, B., Brownell, M., Jackson, D., Kennedy, M., . . . Ziegler, D. (2017, January). *High-leverage practices in special education*. Arlington, VA: Council for Exceptional Children & CEEDAR Center.

McLeskey, J., Landers, E., Williamson, P., & Hoppey, D. (2012). Are we moving toward educating students with disabilities in less restrictive settings? *Journal of Special Education, 46*, 131–140.

Merrell, K. W., & Walker, H. M. (2004). Deconstructing a definition: Social maladjustment versus emotional disturbance and moving the EBD field forward. *Psychology in the Schools, 41*, 899–910. doi:10.1002/pits.20046

Minke, K. M., & Anderson, K. J. (2005). Family-school collaboration and positive behavior support. *Journal of Positive Behavior Interventions, 7*, 181–185.

National Research Council and Institute of Medicine. (2009). *Preventing mental, emotional, and behavioral disorders among young people: Progress and possibilities*. Washington, DC: National Academies Press.

Newman, L., Wagner, M., Huang, T., Shaver, D., Knokey, A.-M., Yu, J., . . . Cameto, R. (2011a). *Secondary school programs and performance of students with disabilities. A special topic report of findings from the National Longitudinal Transition Study-2 (NLTS2)* (NCSER 2012-3000). U.S. Department of Education. Washington, DC: National Center for Special Education Research.

Newman, L., Wagner, M., Knokey, A.-M., Marder, C., Nagle, K., Shaver, D., . . . Schwarting, M. (2011b). *The post-high school outcomes of young adults with disabilities up to 8 years after high school. A report from the National*

Longitudinal Transition Study-2 (NLTS2) (NCSER 2011-3005). Menlo Park, CA: SRI International.

Odom, S. L., Brantlinger, E., Gersten, R., Horner, R. H., Thompson, B., & Harris, K. R. (2005). Research in special education: Scientific methods and evidence-based practices. *Exceptional children, 71*, 137–148. doi:10.1177/001440290507100201

O'Neill, R. E., Albin, R. W., Storey, K., Horner, R. H., & Sprague, J. R. (2014). *Functional assessment and program development for problem behavior: A practical handbook* (3rd ed.). Stamford, CT: Cengage Learning.

Osher, D., Cartledge, G., Oswald, D., Artiles, A. J., & Coutinho, M. (2004). Issues of cultural and linguistic competency and disproportionate representation. In R. Rutherford, M. Quinn, & S. Mather (Eds.), *Handbook of research in behavioral disorders* (pp. 54–77). New York: Guilford.

Osher, D., & Hanley, T. V. (2001). Implementing the SED national agenda: Promising programs and policies for children and youth with emotional and behavioral problems. *Education and Treatment of Children, 24*, 374–403.

Pierangelo, R., & Giuliani, G. (2012). *Assessment in special education: A practical approach* (4th ed.). Upper Saddle River, NJ: Pearson.

R.B. v. Napa Valley Unified Sch. Dist., 496 F.3d 932, 945–946 (9th Cir. 2007).

Simonsen, B., MacSuga-Gage, A. S., Briere, D. E., Freeman, J., Myers, D., Scott, T. M., & Sugai, G. (2014). Multitiered support framework for teachers' classroom-management practices: Overview and case study of building the triangle for teachers. *Journal of Positive Behavior Interventions, 16*, 179–190. doi:10.1177/1098300713484062

Skiba, R. J., Middelberg, L. V., & McClain, M. B. (2014). Multicultural issues for schools and students with emotional and behavioral disorders: Disproportionality in discipline and special education. In H. M. Walker & F. M. Gresham (Eds.), *Handbook of evidence-based practices for emotional and behavioral disorders: Application in schools* (pp. 54–70). New York: Guilford Press.

Slavin, R. E. (2002). Evidence-based education policies: Transforming educational practice and research. *Educational Researcher, 31*, 15–21. doi:10.3102/0013189X031007015

Slavin, R. E. (2008). Perspectives on evidence-based research in education—What works? Issues in synthesizing educational program evaluations. *Educational Researcher, 37*, 5–14. doi:10.3102/0013189X08314117

Sugai, G., & Horner, R. H. (2009). Responsiveness-to-intervention and school-wide positive behavior supports: Integration of multi-tiered system approaches. *Exceptionality, 17*, 223–237. doi:10.1080/09362830903235375

Sullivan, A. L. (2017). Wading through the quicksand: Making sense of minority disproportionality in identification of emotional disturbance. *Behavioral Disorders, 43*, 244–252.

Suter, J. C., & Bruns, E. J. (2009). Effectiveness of the wraparound process for children with emotional and behavioral disorders: A meta-analysis.

Clinical Child and Family Psychology Review, 12, 336–351. doi:10.1007/s10567-009-0059-y

U.S. Department of Education. (2012). *Restraint and seclusion: Resource document*. Retrieved from http://www2.ed.gov/policy/seclusion/restraints-and-seclusion-resources.pdf

U.S. Government Accountability Office. (2009). *Seclusion and restraints: Selected cases of death and abuse at public and private schools and treatment centers*. Retrieved from http://www.gao.gov/assets/130/122526.pdf

Valencia, R. R., & Suzuki, L. A. (2000). *Intelligence testing and minority students: Foundations, performance factors, and assessment issues* (Vol. 3). Thousand Oaks, CA: Sage Publications.

Vo, A., Sutherland, K., & Conroy, M. A. (2012). BEST in CLASS: A classroom-based model for ameliorating problem behavior in early childhood settings. *Psychology in the Schools, 49*, 402–415.

Voulgarides, C. K., Fergus, E., & King Thorious, K. A. (2017). Pursuing equity: Disproportionality in special education and the reframing of technical solutions to address systemic inequities. *Reviews of Research in Education, 41*, 61–87.

Walker, H. M., Seeley, J. R., Small, J., Severson, H. H., Graham, B. A., Feil, E. G., . . . Forness, S. R. (2009). A randomized controlled trial of the First Step to Success early intervention: Demonstration of program efficacy outcomes in a diverse, urban school district. *Journal of Emotional and Behavioral Disorders, 17*, 197–212.

Walker, H. M., & Severson, H. (1992). *Systematic screening for behavior disorders: Technical manual*. Longmont, CO: Sopris West.

Walker, J. S., & Bruns, E. J. (2006). The wraparound process: Individualized, community-based care for children and adolescents with intensive needs. In J. Rosenberg & S. Rosenberg (Eds.), *Community mental health reader: Challenges for the 21st century* (pp. 47–57). New York: Brunner-Routledge.

What Works Clearinghouse. (2016). *WWC intervention report: Functional behavioral assessment-based interventions*. Retrieved from https://ies.ed.gov/ncee/wwc/Docs/InterventionReports/wwc_fba_011017.pdf

Wilkerson, K., Afacan, K., Perzigian, A., Justin, W., & Lequia, J. (2016). Behavior-focused alternative schools: Impact on student outcomes. *Behavioral Disorders, 41*, 81–94. doi:10.17988/0198-7429-41.2.81

Yoon, K. S., Duncan, T., Lee, S. W., Scarloss, B., & Shapley, K. L. (2007). *Reviewing the evidence on how teacher professional development affects student achievement* (Issues and Answers Report, REL 2007–No. 033). Washington, DC: U.S. Department of Education, Institute of Education Sciences, National Center for Education Evaluation and Regional Assistance, Regional Educational Laboratory Southwest. Retrieved from http://ies.ed.gov/ncee/edlabs

Yu, J., Huang, T., & Newman, L. (2008). *Facts from NLTS-2: Substance use among young adults with disabilities* (NCSER 2008-3009). Menlo Park, CA: SRI International.

About the Editors and Contributors

Editors

Robert J. Jagers, PhD, is the Vice President of Research at the Collaborative for Academic, Social and Emotional Learning (CASEL). He was a faculty member in the Combined Program in Education and Psychology at the University of Michigan, a Co-PI of the Center for the Study of Black Youth in Context (CSBYC) and the founding director of a university-sponsored diversity pipeline program for qualified secondary school students. He now leads CASEL action research efforts to leverage social and emotional learning to promote equitable learning environments and equitable developmental outcomes, especially for students from historically under-served groups.

Kimberly Kendziora, PhD, has worked at the American Institutes for Research for 20 years. In this time, her work has been shaped by her lived experience as a family member of individuals with mental health challenges, her training as a practitioner, and her professional role as a researcher. She is honored to contribute to this project as an editor and author and support the blending of voices in support of better environments and better outcomes for our children.

Matthew J. Mayer, PhD, is an Associate Professor at Rutgers University. His published research includes analyzing national level data, modeling school violence processes, related school safety issues, cognitive-behavioral interventions, and methodological issues and evidence-based standards in social-behavioral research. Mayer has led several trans-disciplinary teams in research journal special issues and book projects addressing school safety. He is on the editorial board of *Behavioral Disorders* and *Journal of School Violence*, and is an associate editor of *School Psychology Quarterly*. He led a Capitol Hill briefing on school safety for AERA and was on the AERA task force on bullying prevention.

David Osher is Vice President and Institute Fellow at the American Institutes for Research, where he has led many national centers and research and consultation projects that that involve School Improvement, Conditions for Learning, Social and Emotional Learning, Mental Health, Student Support, Cultural Competence, Family Engagement, Youth Development, Collaboration, and Implementation Science. Osher has worked in every U.S. state and over 20 other countries. He has authored or coauthored over 450 books, monographs, chapters, articles, and reports and 200 peer-reviewed papers and invitational presentations, and served as Academic Dean of a Liberal Arts College and Dean of two Schools of Human Services. Osher received his AB, AM, and PhD from Columbia University.

Lacy Wood, a Principal Technical Assistance Consultant at the American Institutes for Research has been in working in the field of family and community engagement and supportive learning environments for over 18 years. Her work focuses on education policy consulting and building professional development, and technical assistance programs. She has particular expertise in state education policy; family and stakeholder engagement; expanded learning opportunities; school improvement supports; and supporting State Education Agency (SEA) staff to implement federal initiatives. She currently serves as vice-chair of the National Association of Family, School and Community Engagement (NAFSCE) Policy Committee and is a founding board member of the association. Wood also chairs the Family Engagement State Leaders Network, a cadre of SEA family engagement staff across the United States, focused on providing resources and capacity-building supports for SEA family engagement initiatives.

Contributors

James Alsip, EdS, is a school psychologist with Green Dot Public Schools in Los Angeles, California, and a current doctoral student in Educational Leadership at Chapman University. His interests include systems-level change, developing trauma-informed schools, and consultation and collaboration. He is currently involved in the development of a universal model of collaboration and accompanying measure, as well the initial implementation of School-Wide Positive Behavioral Interventions and Supports in a culturally and linguistically diverse middle school.

Ron Avi Astor is the Stein-Wood Professor of School Behavioral Health in the USC Suzanne Dworak-Peck School of Social Work and USC Rossier School of Education (*by courtesy*). His work examines the role of the physical, social-organizational, and cultural contexts in schools related to different kinds of bullying and school violence (e.g., sexual harassment, cyber bullying, discrimination hate acts, school fights, emotional abuse, weapon use, teacher and child violence). Along with his colleague Rami Benbenishty, Astor has developed a school mapping and monitoring procedure that can be used "at scale" regionally and with local students and teachers to generate "grassroots" solutions to safety problems.

George Bear, PhD, is a professor in the school psychology program at the University of Delaware. Bear's research focuses on school climate, school discipline, and self-discipline. Recent studies include developing measures in those areas and examining cross-cultural differences related to bullying, student engagement, and social-emotional learning.

Rami Benbenishty, PhD, is a professor at the School of Social Work, Bar Ilan University. He is conducting research on children and youth at risk in the community and in out-of-home placements. With Ron Avi Astor, he is studying bullying, school violence, and climate in schools around the world. Together they developed the model "Bullying, School Violence and Climate in Evolving Contexts" and are monitoring as a methodology for school improvement.

Abby A. Bode, MA, is a graduate student at the University of South Carolina. Abby has been working in the field of School Mental Health for seven years. She has particular expertise in service provision in rural schools. She is also involved in assessing student response to mental health interventions and developing individualized educational and mental health plans to increase students' academic success.

Catherine P. Bradshaw, PhD, MEd, is a Professor and the Associate Dean for Research and Faculty Development at the Curry School of Education at the University of Virginia. Her primary research interests focus on the development of aggressive behavior and school-based prevention. She collaborates on research projects examining bullying and school climate; the development of aggressive and problem behaviors; effects of exposure to violence, peer victimization, and environmental stress on children; children with emotional and behavioral disorders and autism; and the design, evaluation, and implementation of evidence-based prevention programs in schools. She was previously the Associate Editor for the *Journal of Research on Adolescence* and is currently the editor of *Prevention Science*. She is a coeditor of the *Handbook of School Mental Health* (2014) and the editor of *Handbook on Bullying: A Life Course Perspective* (2017).

Aaron R. Butler, PhD, is a principal technical assistance consultant at American Institutes for Research (AIR). Aaron has been working in the field of educational leadership for 12 years. He has particular expertise in implementation science, leadership coaching, strategic planning, resource allocation, and developing progress monitoring systems. He is also involved in training school leaders on the effective use of data, curriculum and standards mapping, and district and school improvement planning and budgeting.

Patricia E. Campie, PhD, is a criminologist with more than 20 years of experience leading community-based research, evaluation, and implementation science initiatives across systems and communities where justice involvement is a key concern of populations made vulnerable by economic and social disparities.

Sarah Caverly, PhD, is a principal researcher at the American Institutes for Research. She has been conducting rigorous research for over 15 years. Caverly has experience in early childhood, social and emotional learning interventions, and early literacy. In addition, she leads projects focused on building the capacity of local and state education agencies related to conducting, planning, and implementing rigorous evaluations, and translating science into practice.

Heather J. Clawson, PhD, Executive Vice President of Insights and Innovation for Communities in Schools (CIS), has more than 20 years of experience as a program evaluator for school- and community-based prevention, intervention, and enrichment programs for at-risk children and youth. Clawson oversees the execution of a research agenda designed to improve quality and impact of the CIS Model of Integrated Student Supports. She oversees network-wide data management and utilization, research and evaluations, translation of research into practice, and the identification of innovative solutions that drive greater efficiency and impact across the CIS network. Clawson received her doctorate in social psychology from the University of Nevada-Reno.

Dewey G. Cornell, PhD, holds the Bunker Chair as Professor of Education at the University of Virginia. Trained as a forensic clinical psychologist, Cornell has worked in the field of school safety and violence prevention for more than 30 years. He has conducted studies of authoritative school climate and bullying, and developed the Virginia Student Threat Assessment Guidelines as an evidence-based strategy for school violence prevention.

Dwight Davis, PhD, currently serves as principal at Hugh M. Browne Education Campus. Dwight has been in working in the field of

Education for 15 years. He has particular expertise in childhood trauma and its impact on teaching in learning within the classroom. Dwight is also passionate about curriculum and instruction, specifically the use of culturally and contextually relevant texts and teaching practices.

Elena Liles Diamond, PhD, is an Assistant Professor and Program Director of the School Psychology program in the Graduate School of Education and Counseling at Lewis & Clark College. Diamond has been working in the field of School Psychology for seven years. She has particular expertise in school-based interventions related to students' social and emotional learning and overall well-being. She is also involved in consultation to support student achievement through the evaluation of resiliency factors.

Kevin P. Dwyer, MA, NCSP, is a past president, Distinguished and Life-time Achievement Awardee of the National Association of School Psychologists. He retired from 30 years as a school psychologist in Maryland to serve the profession in supporting public and professional policies using the prevention early and intensive intervention paradigm. In 1998, at the request of U.S. DOE Secretary Riley, Dwyer led the development of *Early Warning Timely Response: A Guide to Safe Schools*, a cornerstone for applied violence prevention science in the schools. In 2000, he received the Tipper Gore "Advocacy award for improving the lives and mental health of America's children" from the National Mental Health Association. He continues to provide consultation on school climate and mental health and systems change.

Dorothy L. Espelage, PhD, is Professor of Psychology at the University of Florida. She is the recipient of the APA Lifetime Achievement Award in Prevention Science and the 2016 APA Award for Distinguished Contributions to Research in Public Policy, and is a Fellow of APS, APA, and AERA. She was just elected to the National Academy of Education. She earned her PhD in Counseling Psychology from Indiana University in 1997. Over the last 22 years, she has authored over 200 peer-reviewed articles, 6 edited books, and 70 chapters on bullying, homophobic teasing, sexual harassment, dating violence, and gang violence. Her research focuses on translating empirical findings into prevention and intervention programming.

Daniel J. Flannery, PhD, is the Dr. Semi J. and Ruth Begun Professor and Director of the Begun Center for Violence Prevention Research and Education at Case Western Reserve University. His primary areas of research are in youth violence prevention, the link between violence and mental health, and community-based program evaluation. He has authored several books including the recently released *Cambridge Handbook of Violent Behavior and Aggression* (2nd ed., 2018).

Michael J. Furlong (UC Santa Barbara) is a Distinguished Professor and Associate Dean for Research in the Gervitz School of Education. He is past Editor of the *Journal of School Violence* (2008–2015), and a coeditor of the *Handbook of School Violence and Safety* (2006, 2012), and a coauthor of the original California Department of Education school safety planning guide (*Safe School: A Planning Guide for Action*, 1989).

Nicholas A. Gage, PhD, is an Assistant Professor of Special Education at the University of Florida and current President of the Council for Children with Behavioral Disorders (CCBD). Specific research interests include identification of policies and practices at the national, state, local, and classroom level to support the academic, social, and behavioral needs of students with or at-risk for emotional and/or behavioral disorders through rigorous and diverse research practices and his expertise is in supporting schools, districts, and states in leveraging their data resources to best develop effective and efficient systems of support for students' academic and behavioral needs. Gage's expertise includes statistical modeling, research design and methodology, direct observation, single-subject research, and Functional Behavioral Assessment.

Denise C. Gottfredson is a Professor at the University of Maryland Department of Criminal Justice and Criminology. She received a PhD in Social Relations from the Johns Hopkins University, where she specialized in Sociology of Education. Gottfredson's research interests include delinquency and delinquency prevention, and particularly the effects of school environments on youth behavior. Gottfredson conducted randomized experiments to test the effectiveness of the Baltimore City Drug Treatment Court, the Strengthening Families Program in Washington, DC, and the effects of after school programs on the development of problem behavior. She is currently implementing a randomized trial of a gang prevention program in Philadelphia and a study of the effects of school resource officers in two states.

Nicolette M. Grasley-Boy, MEd, BCBA, is a doctoral student studying Special Education at the University of Florida. A former special educator and educational consultant, her expertise is in teaching students with disabilities, along with providing professional development and coaching support on implementing effective classroom management strategies and schoolwide positive behavioral interventions and supports (SWPBIS). Her specific research interests include supporting students with and at-risk for emotional and/or behavioral disorders, identifying and implementing effective classroom management strategies, SWPBIS in public schools and alternative settings, as well as research design and methodology.

Ambra L. Green, PhD, is an Assistant Professor of Special Education at the University of Texas at Arlington. Green has been working in the field of special education for eight years and has particular expertise in behavior disorders, positive behavior intervention and supports, and disproportionality in special education identification and exclusionary discipline practices. She also has experience providing professional special education consultation in a number of capacities, including for U.S. Senators, working within the U.S. Department of Education Office for Special Education Programs (OSEP), and serves on the OSEP Center on PBIS disproportionality workgroup.

Jennifer Greif Green, PhD is an Associate Professor in the School of Education at Boston University. Green has been in working in the field of school mental health for 15 years. She has particular expertise in bullying prevention and schoolwide efforts to support student mental health. She is also involved in research on disparities in mental health service access and how school staff, including teachers, can contribute to reducing disparities.

Frank M. Gresham, PhD, is a Professor in the Department of Psychology at Louisiana State University. Gresham's research interests focus on assessment and intervention procedures for social emotional learning (SEL), interventions for children and youth with emotional and behavioral disorders, and expert testimony and writings on Atkins (death penalty) cases for individuals with intellectual disability. He is a fellow of the American Psychological Association (APA), three APA divisions (Quantitative and Qualitative Methods, School Psychology, and Clinical Child and Adolescent Psychology), and the American Association for the Advancement of Science.

Amy-Jane Griffiths, PhD, is an assistant professor in the Attallah College of Educational Studies at Chapman University. She is a licensed psychologist and a nationally certified school psychologist. Her expertise and experiences center around systems change, supporting youth and families from underserved communities, particularly related to youth with emotional and behavioral challenges, and collaborative approaches to academic and mental health intervention.

Kathleen Guarino is a Senior TA Consultant at American Institutes for Research. Guarino has been working in the field of trauma for 17 years. She has particular expertise in developing tools and curricula and providing training and consultation for supporting child-serving systems in adopting a trauma-informed approach. She is also involved in developing frameworks and processes for enhancing the capacity of schools and districts to identify, assess, and serve students exposed to adversity and trauma.

Nancy G. Guerra is the dean of the School of Social Ecology at University of California, Irvine, and internationally known expert on youth development and violence prevention. She has spent decades in violence prevention research, leading numerous large-scale projects. She was recently cochair and administrative director of Know Violence in Childhood, a global initiative to prevent violence in childhood sponsored by the Public Health Foundation of India. More recently, Guerra has also been involved in international programs, as Associate Provost and Senior International Officer at the University of Delaware (2012–2015), and as a consultant for international agencies including The World Bank, the Inter-American Development Bank, and U.S. AID.

Gene E. Hall, PhD, is Professor Emeritus, University of Nevada, Las Vegas, and President, Concerns Based Systems, Inc. Throughout his career, his scholarship has been related to understanding, evaluating, and coaching change processes. He is the lead architect of the Concerns Based Adoption Model (CBAM). He also has had career-long involvement in teacher education, especially program innovation and national accreditation.

Samantha N. Hartley is a doctoral student in clinical-community psychology at the University of South Carolina. Samantha has been working in the field of school mental health for six years. She has particular expertise in research on frameworks for integrating efforts addressing student behavioral and mental health needs, as well as youth suicide prevention. She is also involved in program evaluation and interested in understanding and promoting factors related to successful school mental health implementation.

Kimberly Hills, PhD, is a clinical associate professor and licensed psychologist at the University of South Carolina. Hills has been working in the field of school and clinical psychology for 15 years. She has particular expertise in child/adolescent assessment, applied work in school contexts, and school-based programs and processes related to students' social and emotional development. She is also deeply involved in training graduate and undergraduate students to become effective scholars and practitioners across school and community contexts.

Shanna E. Hirsch is an assistant professor of Special Education at Clemson University. She has been working in the field of education as a special teacher, behavior analyst, and researcher for 14 years. Her research focuses on implementing positive behavior interventions and supports, supporting novice teachers with classroom management, and implementing intensive interventions to support students with and at risk for emotional behavioral disorders.

Scott Huebner, PhD, is professor in the Department of Psychology at the University of South Carolina. He has conducted research in positive psychology for about 30 years, with particular expertise in child and adolescent subjective well-being, including the assessment of subjective well-being.

Shane R. Jimerson, PhD, is a Professor at the University of California, Santa Barbara. He has been working in the field of education, child development, and school psychology for the past 25 years. His scholarly publications and presentations have provided insights regarding developmental pathways of school success and failure, the efficacy of early prevention and intervention programs, school psychology internationally, developmental psychopathology, and school crisis prevention and intervention. He is also has provided leadership as President of the International School Psychology Association and President of Division 16 (school psychology) of the American Psychological Association, and Editor of the *School Psychology Quarterly* journal.

Jessica Johnson is a Senior Vice President for Policy, Practice, and Systems Change at the American Institutes for Research (AIR). Johnson oversees domestic and international capacity-building work across AIR's professional services practice areas including education, health, and workforce. For the past 15 years, she has focused on developing and implementing evidence-based services at the federal, state, and local levels focused on improving outcomes for low-performing districts and schools. Her areas of expertise include statewide systems of support, school and district improvement, and systems change.

Jason Katz, PhD, is a researcher at American Institutes for Research. Katz has been working in the fields of program evaluation and implementation science for over 10 years. He has particular expertise in evaluating training and technical assistance to support implementation of programs and practices in community settings. He is also involved in the measurement of readiness, including school- and district-level readiness for implementing social and emotional learning.

Eui Kyung Kim, PhD, is an assistant professor at North Carolina State University. Her research interests focus on universal mental health screening, early identification, and prevention services for children's emotional and behavioral health. Particularly, she is interested in the use of a dual-factor approach to promote strengths that may serve as protective factors, as well as treating distress. She also conducts research internationally, examining social emotional development of Korean children and adolescents.

Kathleen Lynne Lane is a Professor in the Department of Special Education at the University of Kansas. Lane's research interests focus on school-based interventions (academic and behavioral) with students at risk for emotional and behavioral disorders (EBD), with an emphasis on systematic screenings to detect students with behavioral challenges at the earliest possible juncture. She has designed, implemented, and evaluated comprehensive, integrated, three-tiered (Ci3T) models of prevention in elementary, middle, and high school settings to (a) prevent the development of learning and behavior challenges and (b) respond to existing instances.

Robert V. Mayo, NCC, PhD, is a Senior Technical Assistance Consultant at the American Institutes for Research. Mayo has been in working in the fields of education and student support services for 26 years. He has particular expertise in education leadership, supportive school discipline, and social, emotional, and behavioral student supports. He is also involved in supporting states and school district initiatives aimed at supporting neglected, delinquent, and at-risk students, as well as those exposed to trauma.

Barbara McClung is a mental health clinician whose work with communities over the past 25 years has focused on interrupting the school-to-prison pipeline. She has worked with youth and families in schools in California and Washington and in the juvenile justice system, implementing programs and services designed to heal trauma and promote equity. After completing graduate school in Seattle, Barbara worked for Children's Hospital and Medical Center, Department of Child Psychiatry coordinating school-based and juvenile justice intervention programs. Upon returning home to the Bay Area in 2000, she served as Director of Outpatient Programs for Alameda Family Services. She currently works for the Oakland Unified School District leading the District's Behavioral Health Initiatives, which include school-based mental health, positive behavioral intervention and support (PBIS), restorative justice, trauma-informed practices, and substance abuse and violence prevention programs.

Sara C. McDaniel, PhD, is an associate professor of Special Education in the Department of Special Education and Multiple Abilities at the University of Alabama and is the Director of the Alabama Positive Behavior Support Office (APBSO). The APBSO is a statewide PBIS technical assistance center that focuses on supporting schools and districts in implementing PBIS in Alabama. She conducts research and teaches in the areas of: (a) secondary tier PBIS, (b) classroom management assessment and coaching, (c) PBIS for alternative education settings, and (d) early prevention for diverse populations of children at high risk.

Kent McIntosh, PhD, is a Professor at the University of Oregon and Director of Educational and Community Supports, a research unit in the university's

College of Education. McIntosh has been in working in the field of education and supporting marginalized youth for over 20 years. His research interests include implementation science and systems-level interventions to improve school climate and equity in school discipline. He is Co-Investigator on the OSEP National Technical Assistance Center on PBIS and lead of the Center's Disproportionality Workgroup and has worked as a school psychologist, teacher trainer, and teacher in both general and special education.

Elaine Miller, MAT, is a Research Associate at the University of South Carolina, Department of Psychology. Miller has been working in the field of school mental health research for eight years. Her research interests include evidence-based practices for students with emotional and behavioral disorders, interconnecting PBIS and school mental health services, and improving the quality of Individualized Education Plans.

Deborah A. Moroney, PhD, is a Managing Director at American Institutes for Research and she serves as the practice area director for the Youth Development and Supportive Learning Environments group. Moroney has been working in the field of youth development for over 20 years. She has particular expertise in implementation science and making research relevant to practitioners. Moroney is also involved in numerous national evaluation and technical assistance efforts that support the positive development of young people in partnership with families, schools, and communities.

Brenda E. Morrison, PhD, is an Associate Professor and the Director of the Centre for Restorative Justice at Simon Fraser University. Morrison has been working in the field of restorative justice for 20 years. Her research began in Australia, moved to Philadelphia, and is now based in Canada. She is a social psychologist with teaching, research, and field experience in outdoor education, governance, and justice. She wrote the first international review of restorative justice in education (RJE) and has developed a number of courses for teachers on RJE. With her graduate students, her current research is focusing on community praxis in restorative justice.

Maury Nation, PhD, is Associate Professor of Human and Organizational Development at Vanderbilt University. He has been working in the field of youth violence prevention for the past 20 years. His research is focused on school- and community-based youth violence prevention programs, school climate interventions, and other interventions designed to promote positive development for children and adolescents.

Rhonda N. T. Nese, PhD, is a Research Assistant Professor at the University of Oregon. Nese has been in working in the fields of school psychology and special education for 12 years. She has particular expertise in intervention delivery within a multitiered behavior support framework, with her current research focused on alternatives to exclusionary discipline practices, reducing racial disproportionality in school discipline, and improving professional development tools for educators. She is also involved in the National Technical Assistance Center on PBIS as a technical assistant provider to school, district, and state-level teams.

Amanda B. Nickerson, PhD, is a professor of school psychology and director of the Alberti Center for Bullying Abuse Prevention at the University at Buffalo, the State University of New York. Her research focuses on school violence and bullying, and the critical role of family, peers, and schools in preventing violence and building social-emotional strengths of youth.

Pedro A. Noguera, PhD, is the Distinguished Professor of Education at the Graduate School of Education and Information Studies at UCLA. His research focuses on the ways in which schools are influenced by social and economic conditions, as well as by demographic trends in local, regional, and global contexts. He serves on the boards of numerous national and local organizations and appears as a regular commentator on educational issues in major national and local media outlets. His editorials have appeared in the *NY Times*, *Washington Post*, *Wall Street Journal*, *Huffington Post*, and the *Dallas Morning News*.

Trina Osher is an independent consultant dedicated to promoting the social, emotional, and physical well-being of all children and insuring families have the skills and support to help their children thrive especially when conditions or needs are challenging and complex. Recently, she served as a consultant helping AIR write a comprehensive set of WeChat posts on SEL for families China. She is the principle architect of the definition of family-driven care and primary author of the Ambassador's Guide to promote its practice. Using her expertise and focusing on social and emotional learning and parenting she co-constructs practical strategies and culturally relevant materials with participants that they can easily use to engage and work collaboratively with families. She actively collaborates with researchers bringing her family engagement expertise to studies yielding information that can improve the quality of life for children and their families. She provides consultation to government agencies, family-run organizations, advocacy and policy organizations, and school systems throughout the United States and in Europe, Asia, and South Africa.

Katie E. Richards-Schuster, PhD, is an assistant professor and director of the undergraduate minor programs at the School of Social Work at the

University of Michigan. Her research focuses on youth empowerment and youth participation, with a particular emphasis on examining the factors and contexts that facilitate youth engagement. In addition, she is a leading expert in using youth participatory research and evaluation as a method and practice approach to engage youth in creating change. Over the last 15 years, she has produced multiple publications on youth participation, presented at national and international conferences, and coauthored two workbooks on youth participatory research and evaluation that have been translated into multiple languages. She currently serves as the cochair for the American Evaluation Association's Youth Focused Evaluation Topical Interest Group.

Nancy Riestenberg is the Restorative Practices Specialist at the Minnesota Department of Education. She has over 40 years of experience in the fields of bullying prevention and intervention, crisis recovery in schools, school connectedness and climate, child sexual abuse prevention education, and restorative practices in schools. She is the author of *Circle in the Square: Building Community and Repairing Harm in Schools.*

Terry Salinger, PhD, is an Institute Fellow and Chief Scientist for Reading at the American Institutes for Research. Over her 40 years as a professional, Salinger has been a classroom teacher and university professor, has led development of reading assessments for students and professional knowledge assessments for adults, and has conducted research and led evaluations in the areas of reading and writing across the full life span. Her particular interests are in the factors that motivate or stymie literacy development for individuals for whom usual classroom instruction has not been successful.

Trish Shaffer is the Coordinator for Multi-Tiered System of Supports and Social Emotional Learning for the Washoe County School District. A 2013 recipient of the Mary Utne O'Brien Award for Excellence in Expanding the Evidence-Based Practice of Social and Emotional Learning, Shaffer is a passionate leader of Social and Emotional Learning in the Nevada community. She has experience in special and general education at the university, district, and classroom levels. She has provided professional development and technical assistance for schools pre-kindergarten to grade 12, consulted for school districts across the nation, and presented at numerous events and conferences at the local, state, and national levels.

Cheri J. Shapiro, PhD, is a Research Associate Professor and Interim Director of the Institute for Families in Society in the College of Social Work at the University of South Carolina. Shapiro has been working in the field of child and adolescent psychology for more than 25 years as a clinician, researcher, and administrator. She has particular expertise in implementation of evidence-based interventions and juvenile justice, with a focus on improving practices within community organizations.

Russell J. Skiba, PhD, is a Professor of Counseling and Educational Psychology at Indiana University. He has been working in the field of special education and school psychology for 30 years. His particular areas of expertise are disproportionality in school discipline and special education. He has also published in the area of school violence prevention.

Jeffrey R. Sprague, PhD, is a Professor of Special Education and Director of the University of Oregon Institute on Violence and Destructive Behavior. He directs federal, state, and local research and demonstration projects related to positive behavior interventions and supports, multitiered support systems (MTSS), alternative education, juvenile delinquency prevention and treatment, restorative practices, and school safety. His research activities encompass applied behavior analysis, positive behavior supports, behavioral response to intervention, functional behavioral assessment, implementation science, school safety, youth violence prevention, and juvenile delinquency prevention.

George Sugai is Professor and Carole J. Neag Endowed Chair in the Neag School of Education, Department of Educational Psychology at the University of Connecticut. Over the last 40 years, his research and practice interests have included schoolwide positive behavior support, behavioral disorders, applied behavior analysis, classroom and behavior management, and school discipline. He is research scientist at the Center on Behavioral Education and Research at the University of Connecticut and has been codirector of the OSEP National Technical Assistance Center on Positive Behavioral Interventions and Supports for the past 20 years.

Manolya Tanyu is a Senior Researcher at the American Institutes for Research. Manolya has been in working in the field of educational research and evaluation for more than 15 years. She has particular expertise in evaluating school and community initiatives related to social and emotional learning, positive youth development (e.g., youth mentoring), violence prevention, and effective prevention strategies (e.g., improving school climate and discipline to promote academic achievement).

Deborah A. Temkin, PhD, is a senior director of education research at Child Trends. Temkin has been working in the field of developmental science and education for 15 years. She has particular expertise in bullying prevention and understanding how education policies affect students' social and emotional development. She is also involved in evaluations of school climate initiatives and analyzing and developing policy under the Whole School, Whole Community, Whole Child framework.

John Terry, PhD, is a Captain and Clinical Psychologist in the U.S. Air Force. Terry serves as the Officer in Charge of the Mental Health Element serving approximately 15,000 active duty military service members and as the Suicide Prevention Program Manager serving approximately 22,000 military service members and civilian mission partners. He is a subject matter expert in Motivation Interviewing for adolescents in schools and is involved in research focusing on improving mental health services for Military Connected Youth.

Thomas W. Tramaglini, EdD, is the Superintendent of the Kenilworth Schools (Kenilworth, NJ) and a part-time lecturer at Rutgers University. Tramaglini has 20 years of experience as a practitioner and has been teaching at Rutgers for 10 years, where he completed his doctoral work in Educational Administration. His research interests include organizational change for student achievement through various vehicles such as curriculum development. He also serves on the ASCD Board of Directors.

Abraham Wandersman, PhD, is a Professor of Psychology at the University of South Carolina, Columbia. Wandersman performs research and program evaluation on citizen participation in community organizations and coalitions and on interagency collaboration. He is a coeditor of three books on empowerment evaluation and a coauthor of several Getting To Outcomes accountability books (how-to manuals for planning, implementation, and evaluation to achieve results). Wandersman collaborated with CDC to develop the Interactive Systems Framework for Dissemination and Implementation—the subject of two special issues of a peer-reviewed journal (2008, 2012). In 1998, he received the Myrdal Award for Evaluation Practice from the American Evaluation Association. In 2000, he was elected President of the Society for Community Research and Action (SCRA). In 2005, he was awarded the Distinguished Theory and Research Contributions Award by SCRA. In 2008, Getting To Outcomes won the American Evaluation Association's Outstanding Publication Award. In 2013, he was a Visiting Scholar at the Center for Injury Prevention of the Centers for Disease Control and Prevention. In 2017, he received the 2017 Outstanding Evaluation Award from the American Evaluation Association, and he received Research of the Year from the Healthy Teen Network. Since 2015, Wandersman has been involved in the evaluation of several community health initiatives funded by the Robert Wood Johnson Foundation.

Shannon B. Wanless is an Associate Professor in the School of Education and is the Director of the Office of Child Development at the University of

Pittsburgh. She has expertise in social-emotional learning, early childhood education, and implementation science. Shannon is involved in strengthening the translation of research to practice and in bringing the voices of practitioners to research, with a focus on issues of social justice and equity in those processes.

Daniel W. Webster is Bloomberg Professor of American Health and Director of the Johns Hopkins Center for Gun Policy and Research at the Johns Hopkins Bloomberg School of Public Health. Webster is one of the nation's leading experts on the prevention of gun violence. He has published widely in scientific journals on topics including gun policy, violence prevention, youth violence, intimate partner violence, suicide, substance abuse, and injury prevention. He is the lead editor and a contributor to *Reducing Gun Violence in America: Informing Policy with Evidence and Analysis* (Johns Hopkins University Press, 2013). Over the past 25 years, Webster's research and policy analyses have helped shape local, state, and federal policies on gun violence prevention.

Mark D. Weist, PhD, is a Professor in Clinical-Community and School Psychology in the Department of Psychology at the University of South Carolina. He was on the faculty of the University of Maryland for 19 years where he helped to found and direct the Center for School Mental Health (http://csmh.umaryland.edu), providing leadership to the advancement of school mental health (SMH) policies and programs in the United States. He has edited 10 books and has published and presented widely in SMH and in the areas of trauma, violence and youth, evidence-based practice, cognitive behavioral therapy, positive behavioral interventions and supports (PBIS), and on an interconnected systems framework (ISF) for SMH and PBIS. He is currently coleading a regional conference on school behavioral health (reflecting integrated SMH and PBIS, see https://www.schoolbehavioralhealth.org) and leading a randomized controlled trial on the ISF.

Lawrence T. Winn, PhD (Human Ecology, University of Wisconsin, Madison), is the Cofounder and Executive Director of the Transformative Justice in Education (TJE) Center in the School of Education at the University of California, Davis. His program of research examines race and social capital in out-of-school learning spaces. A trained ethnographer, Winn is interested in the relationship between ethnography and Participatory Action Research. After earning his JD at Vanderbilt School of Law and his M.Div. at Princeton Seminary, Winn worked for an education nonprofit where he also developed leadership programs for high school students as well as a program designed to support incarcerated African American boys in transitioning into school and civic engagement. With over a decade of experience in the nonprofit sector, including work with Casey Family Programs and the Annie E. Casey Foundation, Winn was a member of the Race to Equity Team (R2E), which published the *Race to Equity Report* about racial disparities in education, criminal justice, workforce, and healthcare for black and white families in Dane County, Wisconsin. He is the coauthor of articles that have appeared in *Race and Social Problems* and *Adolescent Research Review.*

Stephanie Wu is City Year's Chief Impact Officer and a founding member of City Year. She leads Whole School, Whole Child services, which are provided by 3,000 AmeriCorps members in more than 300 schools in over 45 districts nationwide. Stephanie has been in working in the field of youth development, national youth service, and education for 30 years. She has particular expertise in the development and scaling of programs, and has been a thought leader to programs in England, Europe, and South Africa.

Index

Page numbers followed by *t* indicate tables and *f* indicate figures.